STATISTICS FOR
THE BEHAVIORAL SCIENCES

STATISTICS *FOR*
THE BEHAVIORAL SCIENCES

WOODROW W. WYATT

University of Tennessee

CHARLES M. BRIDGES, Jr.

University of Florida

D. C. HEATH AND COMPANY BOSTON

ENGLEWOOD   INDIANAPOLIS   SAN FRANCISCO   ATLANTA   DALLAS

Library of Congress Catalog Card
Number 66–28291

Copyright © 1967 by

D. C. HEATH AND COMPANY

No part of the material covered by this
copyright may be reproduced in any
form without written permission of the
publisher.

Printed in the United States of America

PRINTED DECEMBER 1966

PREFACE

The authors of this book have attempted to present the fundamentals of statistics in a manner that should be applicable to a number of fields. Accordingly, emphasis has been placed on sampling distributions, probability, and statistical inference, thus offering investigators and students in the behavioral sciences a reasonably wide range of procedures. Whereas some attention has been given to elementary descriptive statistics, the greater portion of this treatment is devoted to the analysis and interpretation of data.

For most topics, the only mathematical prerequisite is the ability to use the fundamental processes of arithmetic and elementary algebra. For those few topics requiring some understanding of more advanced mathematics, the instructor should determine the best method of presentation. Since one set of observations is used as the illustrative material for numerous treatments, students may minimize the time spent in computation, and thus expedite their learning of basic procedures.

Each concept has been introduced in a systematic manner in order to provide an orderly accumulation of the basic statistical procedures. Concepts of population, sample, and decision making are introduced early in the book in preparation for designing experiments, testing hypotheses, and making inferences. The tests of significance are intended to demonstrate how the student may determine real differences between sets of measures.

The order of topics is based largely upon the experiences of the authors as teachers of statistics courses at university level. Attention given to elementary probability theory is for the purpose of effecting an uninterrupted transition from descriptive statistical procedures to applications of the normal curve. For the instructor using the text in a one-semester course and exercising some freedom of choice in selection of topics, it is likely that Chapters 1 through 12 will be used. However, a judicious choice of topics may include material found in Chapters 13 to 15. Problems and questions found at the close of the chapters offer the student some opportunities for developing skill in application of the various techniques. Answers to problems are given in the back of the book.

The authors are indebted to Professor Sir Ronald A. Fisher, F.R.S., Cambridge, and to Dr. Frank Yates, F.R.S., Rothamsted, also to Messrs. Oliver and Boyd Ltd., Edinburgh, for permission to reprint Table I, "The Normal Probability Integral," Table II, "The t Distribution," Table V, "Values of the Correlation Coefficient for Different Levels of Significance," and Table VI, "Fisher's Transformation of r to ζ," from their book *Statistical Tables for Biological, Agricultural and Medical Research;* to the Iowa State University Press and the authors for their permission to reprint the table of random numbers from George W. Snedecor, *Statistical Methods Applied to Experiments in Agriculture and Biology*, and Table II, "The t Distribution," from Appendix 6, "Percentage Points of the t-Distribution," in Bernard Ostle, *Statistics in Research;* to A. Hald and S. A. Sinkbaek, for permission to reprint Table III, "Percentile Values of the χ^2 Distribution" from *Skandinavisk Aktuarietidskrift*, 1950; to Professor E. S. Pearson and the Biometrika Trustees for Table IV, from Merrington and Thompson, "Tables of Percentage Points of the Inverted Beta (F) Distribution," from *Biometrika*, Vol. 33, pp. 73 88; also to A. Mahalanobis, Editorial Secretary, for Table IV, from Banerjee, "The One-Tenth Per Cent Level of the Ratio of Variances," *Sankhya*, 2:427–428; to Frieda S. Swed and C. Eisenhart, for permission to reprint Table VIIa, "Probability for Total Number of Runs in Sample of Size (N_1, N_2)," from "Tables for Testing Randomness of Grouping in a Sequence of Alternatives," *Annals of Mathematical Statistics*, 14:66–87, 1943, and Table VIIb, "Significance Level of r," from the same source; to the editor, author, and publisher for permission to reprint Table VIII, "Critical Values for the Walsh Test," from J. E. Walsh, "Applications of Some Significance Tests for the Median Which Are Valid under Very General Conditions," *Journal of the American Statistical Association*, 44:343, 1949; to the authors and publishers for permission to reprint Table IXa, "Probabilities Associated with Observed Small Values of U in the Mann-Whitney Test," from H. B. Mann and D. R. Whitney, "On a Test Whether One of Two Random Variables Is Stochastically Larger than the Other," *Annals of Mathematical Statistics*, 18:50–60, 1947; to the author and publisher for permission to reprint Table IXb, "Critical Values of U in the Mann-Whitney Test," from Auble, "Extended Tables for the Mann-Whitney Statistic," *Bulletin of the Institute of Educational Research at Indiana University*, Volume I, Number 2, 1953; to C. W. Dunnett, Head, Statistical Design and Analysis, Lederle Laboratories of American Cyanamid Company, for permission to reprint Table X, "Critical Values of T in the Wilcoxon Test for Paired Data," from Frank Wilcoxon, *Some Rapid Approximate Statistical Procedures;* to fhe editor and publisher for permission to reprint Table XI, "Critical Values tor H (for three samples) for the Kruskal-Wallis Test," from William H.

Kruskal and W. Allen Wallis, "Use of Ranks in One-Criterion Variance Analysis," *Journal of the American Statistical Association*, 48:907–911, December 1953; to the editor and publisher for permission to reprint Table XIIa, "Values of Σd^2 for Spearman Rank Correlation," from E. G. Olds, "Distribution of Sums of Squares of Rank Differences for Small Numbers of Individuals," *Annals of Mathematical Statistics*, 9:133–148, 1938, and E. G. Olds, "The 5% Significance Levels for Sums of Squares of Rank Differences and a Correction," *Annals of Mathematical Statistics*, 20:117–118, 1949; to Paul H. Oehser, Chief, Editorial and Publications Division, Smithsonian Institution, for permission to reprint Table XIII, "Squares, Square Roots, and Reciprocals," from Frederick E. Fowle, Table 9, "Values of Reciprocals, Squares, Cubes, and Square Roots of Natural Numbers," Table XIV, "Values of the Exponential e^{-x} ," from Table 19, "Exponential Functions," and Table XVIII, "Factorials," from Table 12, "Factorials," *Smithsonian Physical Tables*, Ninth Edition, Washington, D.C.; to the editor and publisher for permission to reprint Table XV, "Common Logarithms" and Table XVI, "Natural Logarithms" from Table VII, "Common Logarithms of Numbers from 1 to 10009 to Five Decimal Places," and Table VIII, "Natural Logarithms of Numbers," *Heath's Logarithmic and Trigonometric Tables;* and to Dr. Richard V. Andree and Charles B. Maudlin, University of Oklahoma, for assistance in the preparation of Table XIX.

W. W. WYATT

CHARLES M. BRIDGES, JR.

CONTENTS

Chapter 1   **Introduction**   1

1.1   Need for Reduction of Data   1
1.2   Population and Sample   1
1.3   Counting and Measuring   3
    1.3.1   Methods of Measurement   4
    1.3.2   Exact and Approximate Numbers   4
    1.3.3   Computations   6
1.4   Selecting a Random Sample   7

Chapter 2   **Frequency Distributions and Measures of Central Tendency**   10

2.1   Frequency Distributions   10
    2.1.1   Frequency Tables   10
    2.1.2   Histograms   12
    2.1.3   Frequency Polygons   12
    2.1.4   Cumulative Frequency Polygons   13
2.2   Measures of Central Tendency   14
    2.2.1   The Mode   14
    2.2.2   The Median and the Percentiles   14
    2.2.3   The Arithmetic Mean   16
        2.2.3.1   Summation Notation   16
        2.2.3.2   Calculation of the Mean from Grouped Data   18
        2.2.3.3   Other Methods of Calculation of the Mean   19
    2.2.4   Choice of a Measure of Central Value   21

Chapter 3   **Measures of Variability**   25

3.1   Simple Measures of Variability   25
    3.1.1   The Average Deviation   26
    3.1.2   The Interquartile Range   27
3.2   Variance   28
3.3   The Standard Deviation   30
    3.3.1   The Standard Deviation from Grouped Data   31
    3.3.2   The Charlier Checks   34
    3.3.3   Derivation of the Standard Deviation   34

3.4   Standard Scores   35
   3.4.1 T-Scores   36
   3.4.2   The Stanine Scale   38

Chapter 4   *Elementary Probability and Theoretical Distributions*   42

4.1   Simple Probability Problems   43
4.2   Probability Defined   44
4.3   Relative Frequencies in Extended Trials   44
4.4   Prediction of Frequencies in Repeated Trials   45
4.5   Combinations of Events   46
   4.5.1   The Addition Rules   46
   4.5.2   The Multiplication Rule   46
   4.5.3   Conditional Probability   47
4.6   The Binomial Distribution   47
4.7   Theoretical Binomial Frequencies   49
4.8   Permutations and Combinations   50
   4.8.1   Permutations   50
   4.8.2   Combinations   51
   4.8.3   Values of $C_{n,r}$ as Binomial Coefficients   52
4.9   The Mean and Variance of the Binomial Distribution   53

Chapter 5   *Continuous Sampling Distributions*   60

5.1   The Rectangular Probability Distribution   60
5.2   The Normal Distribution   61
   5.2.1   Normal Distribution of Sample Means   65
   5.2.2   Normal Distribution of Differences Between Sample Means of Two Populations (Independent Data)   68
   5.2.3   Normal Distribution of Differences Between Sample Means of Two Populations (Paired Data)   71
5.3   Student's t Distribution   72
5.4   The Chi-Square (χ^2) Distribution   74
   5.4.1   Distribution of Enumeration Data   75
   5.4.2   Distribution of Sample Variances   77
5.5   The F Distribution   78
5.6   Elementary Data Transformations   81
   5.6.1   The Logarithmic Transformation   81

Chapter 6   *Elements of Statistical Decision Making*   85

6.1   Formation of Statistical Hypotheses   85
6.2   Types of Statistical Errors   87
   6.2.1   Type I Error, Alpha (α)   88
   6.2.2   Type II Error, Beta (β)   91

6.3   Effects of Different Size α and n on Size of β 92
6.4   Power of the Test   97
6.5   Tests of Statistical Hypotheses   100

Chapter 7   ***Tests of Hypotheses about Measures of Central Tendency***   104

7.1   Tests of Hypotheses about Single Population Means   104
7.2   Confidence Interval Estimate of Single Population Means   105
7.3   Tests of Hypotheses Concerning the Differences Between Means of
       Two Populations   106
       7.3.1   Both Standard Deviations Known   108
       7.3.2   Both Population Standard Deviations Unknown (Non-paired
                Data)   108
       7.3.3   Tests for Correlated or Paired Data   112
7.4   Confidence Interval Estimates for True Differences Between Two
       Population Means   113
       7.4.1   Both Variances Known   113
       7.4.2   Both Variances Unknown (Uncorrelated Data)   114
       7.4.3   Both Variances Unknown (Correlated Data)   114

Chapter 8   ***Tests of Hypotheses about Measures of Dispersion***   117

8.1   Tests of Hypotheses about Single Population Variance σ_o^2 117
8.2   Confidence Interval Estimate of the True Population Variance, σ^2 119
8.3   Tests of Hypotheses Concerning Relationship Between Two Population
       Variances   120
8.4   Confidence Interval Estimate of the True Ratio of Two Population
       Variances   122
8.5   Tests of the Equality of More than Two Population Variances (Test
       for Homogeneity of Variances)   123

Chapter 9   ***Test of Hypotheses about Proportions***   128

9.1   Tests for Hypotheses Concerning the Binomial Distribution   128
9.2   Tests of Hypotheses about a Single Proportion   130
9.3   Tests of Hypotheses about Differences Between Two Population Pro-
       portions   131
       9.3.1   Uncorrelated Data   131
       9.3.2   Correlated Data   133
9.4   Tests of Hypotheses for Differences among More than Two Population
       Proportions   134
       9.4.1   Single Classification   137
       9.4.2   Double Classification, Independency of Data   138
       9.4.3   Double Classification, 2×2 Contingency Table   139
9.5   Test for Goodness of Fit   140

Chapter 10 *Analysis of Variance* 144

10.1 Single Classification 144
10.2 Two-Way Classification, Single Value 150
10.3 Two-Way Classification with Replication 156
10.4 Three-Way Classification 163

Chapter 11 *Linear Regression* 172

11.1 Regression 172
11.2 The Regression of Y on X 172
    11.2.1 The Regression Equation 174
    11.2.2 The Concept of Least Squares 175
11.3 The Regression of X on Y 178
11.4 The Sum of Products and Covariance 179
11.5 The Standard Error of Estimate 180
11.6 The Regression Concept 181
11.7 Tests for Basic Assumptions 185
    11.7.1 Test for Linearity of Data 185
    11.7.2 Test for Independence of Variables 188
11.8 Tests of Hypotheses and Confidence Interval Estimates 189
    11.8.1 Discussion of $A_{y.x}$ 189
    11.8.2 Discussion of $B_{y.x}$ 189
    11.8.3 Discussion of $\mu_{y.x}$ 190
    11.8.4 Discussion of Individual Values of Y 190
    11.8.5 Discussion of $\sigma^2_{y.x}$ 190

Chapter 12 *Linear Correlation* 193

12.1 The Meaning of Correlation 193
12.2 Underlying Assumptions 196
12.3 Methods of Calculation of r 199
    12.3.1 The Correlation Table from Grouped Data 199
    12.3.2 Calculation of r from the Deviations from the Means 204
    12.3.3 Machine Calculation of r from Raw Scores 205
    12.3.4 Regression and the Coefficient of Correlation 205
12.4 The Transformation of r into Fisher's ζ 207
12.5 Tests of Hypotheses about the Correlation Coefficient 208
    12.5.1 Test of the Hypothesis $\rho = 0$ 208
    12.5.2 Establishing Confidence Interval for ρ 208
    12.5.3 Test of the Hypothesis $H_o: \rho \neq 0$ 209
    12.5.4 Differences Between Two Correlation Coefficients, a Test of the Hypothesis $\rho_1 = \rho_2 = \rho$ 209

Special Topics

Chapter 13   ***Further Consideration of the Analysis of Variance***   217

13.1   Estimate of Variance   217
13.2   Completely Randomized Block Design   221
13.3   Latin Square Design   224
13.4   Factorial Design   226

Chapter 14   ***Analysis of Covariance***   230

14.1   Basic Assumptions   230
14.2   Completely Randomized Design   231
14.3   Randomized Complete Block Design   234
14.4   Latin Square Design   237
14.5   Two-Factor Factorial Randomized Complete Block   240

Chapter 15   ***Other Statistical Procedures***   244

15.1   Single Sample Techniques   244
15.2   Techniques for Two Samples   248
        15.2.1   Uncorrelated Data   248
        15.2.2   Correlated Data   251
                15.2.2.1   Wilcoxon Signed Rank Test   251
                15.2.2.2   Walsh Test   253
15.3   The Median Test   255
15.4   Correlated Data for $(k > 2)$ Samples   256
        15.4.1   Cochran Q Test   256
15.5   Independent Data for $(k > 2)$ Samples   258
15.6   Spearman's Rank-Difference Correlation, R 261

Appendix A   269

        Tables I–XIX

Appendix B   363

        School and College Ability Test Scores, Verbal (X) and Quantitative (Y), for 995 College Freshmen

Appendix C   369

        Analysis-of-Data Sheet

Answers to Problems   371

Index   381

APPENDIX A

TABLES

TABLE I.	The Normal Probability Integral	270
TABLE II.	The t Distribution	271
TABLE III.	Percentile Values of the X^2 Distribution	272
TABLE IVa.	F Distribution: 50% Points	276
TABLE IVb.	F Distribution: 25% Points	277
TABLE IVc.	F Distribution: 10% Points	278
TABLE IVd.	F Distribution: 5% Points	279
TABLE IVe.	F Distribution: 1% Points	280
TABLE IVf.	F Distribution: 0.5% Points	281
TABLE IVg.	F Distribution: 0.1% Points	282
TABLE V.	Values of the Correlation Coefficient for Different Levels of Significance	283
TABLE VI.	Fisher's Transformation of r to ζ	284
TABLE VIIa.	Probability for Total Number of Runs in Samples of Size (N_1, N_2)	285
TABLE VIIb.	Significance Level of r	294
TABLE VIII.	Critical Values for the Walsh Test	300
TABLE IXa.	Probabilities Associated with Observed Small Values of U in the Mann-Whitney Test	301
TABLE IXb.	Critical Values of U in the Mann-Whitney Test	303
TABLE X.	Critical Values of T in the Wilcoxon Test for Paired Data	306
TABLE XI.	Critical Values of H (for three samples) for the Kruskal-Wallis Test	307
TABLE XIIa.	Values of $\sum d^2$ for Spearman Rank Correlation	308
TABLE XIIb.	Critical Values for the Spearman Rank Coefficient, R	310
TABLE XIII.	Squares, Square Roots, and Reciprocals	311
TABLE XIV.	Values of the Exponential e^{-x}	328
TABLE XV.	Common Logarithms of Numbers (Five Decimal Places)	331
TABLE XVI.	Natural Logarithms of Numbers (Five Decimal Places)	350
TABLE XVII.	Ten Thousand Randomly Assorted Digits	352
TABLE XVIII.	Factorials	356
TABLE XIX.	Logarithms of the Binomial Coefficients	357

STATISTICS FOR
THE BEHAVIORAL SCIENCES

1

INTRODUCTION

The study of statistics involves a variety of matters, including analysis and presentation of data, experimental design, and decision making. Since all statistical conclusions must be based on the analysis and interpretation of accumulated data, it is the purpose of this chapter to describe certain initial steps necessary for the processing of such data.

1.1 *Need for Reduction of Data.* Statistical methods offer means for the classification, organization, and presentation of numerical data in such a manner as to facilitate comprehension and interpretation. While this may suggest to the reader a series of bar charts and tables of numerical data neatly arranged in a publication entitled "Statistical Reports," statistical methods can go well beyond such an elementary phase. For the investigator desiring to present his findings in a systematic, orderly manner, scientific methods of collecting, analyzing, and interpreting data are available.

For example, questions may be raised concerning the achievement of students enrolled in freshman classes within the various divisions of a university, and similarly, questions may be raised concerning how college sophomores compare in achievement with previous classes within the institution. In either instance, further questions may be raised concerning the way in which a program of obtaining data can be planned and also how these data shall be presented and analyzed. To obtain useful results, a mass of raw data must be classified and summarized.

1.2 *Population and Sample.* In general, statistical observations of a quantitative nature arise from a series of numerical measurements made on the objects within a given set of objects. Any set of objects having a common observable characteristic constitutes a *population*, or *universe*, while a selection of objects from this population constitutes a *sample*. We shall use the terms *population* and *universe* synonymously. For such objects, variations in size, weight, or height may be used as a classification scheme, resulting in a quantitative series.

Some examples of *populations* and *samples* are given below:

a. A population may be specified as the workers employed in a given factory during a given year.

b. In a saturation test situation involving a study of the mathematics achievement level of twelfth grade students, tests were administered to all the students of this grade in all the schools of a given city. The population may be defined as all twelfth grade students of that city school system.

c. A survey is made to determine the preference of students within a major university for the quarter or semester system. A sample of 100 is questioned and their preferences are recorded. The population consists of a total enrollment of 14,000 students, while the sample includes the 100 who are questioned.

d. The seeds of a certain variety of wheat are subjected to high level radiation before planting. A sample of 100 seeds is planted so that the yields may be observed. The population consists of all the seeds of this variety of wheat which have been subjected to this level of radiation.

In general, there are two kinds of populations; a population can be *finite* (the undergraduates enrolled in a given university, the licensed fishermen of a given state, or the number of ball-point pens manufactured during a given day); or it can be *infinite* (all points on a line, or the sequence of number of spots obtained by throwing a pair of dice an indefinite number of times). In many cases, a population will be finite but so large that it is treated as though it were infinite (e.g., the heights of all 10-year-old boys in the public schools of the United States). Any investigation of infinite populations must necessarily be limited to samples.

A measure associated with a population is called a *parameter*. Examples of parameters are: the *mean*, the *median* or a *percentile* (discussed in Chapter 2). The corresponding measure derived from the sample is called a *statistic*. In the conduct of a scholarly investigation, the researcher may derive statistics from a series of measurements and from these statistics he may make inferences about the population from which the samples were drawn. Since the investigator wishes to emerge with sound conclusions from a given set of data, his concern is to obtain a reasonably representative sample and to form some estimate of the plausibility of the results. Methods of doing this will be developed as we proceed.

1.3 *Counting and Measuring.* A series of values obtained by *counting* must be expressed by whole numbers; such a series is called *discontinuous* or *discrete;* for example: numbers of rooms occupied, census data, school enrollment, number of affirmative votes in a committee.

A series of values obtained by *measuring* is called *continuous.* For example, physical measures of height and weight, as well as test scores of a group of students, fall into *continuous series.* Through the use of more refined measuring devices it should become practical to obtain achievement test scores which may be thought of as increasing by small increments in a continuous scale.

Measurements in the behavioral sciences may be conveniently carried out through a classification scheme based on four levels, or scales, each having special characteristics. These four levels include *nominal* and *ordinal* arrangements and proceed to the *interval* and *ratio* scales. The following scheme will serve to illustrate both basic operations and examples for each of the four levels.

TABLE 1.1

SCALES OF MEASUREMENTS

Scale	*Basic Operations*	*Examples*
Nominal	Determination of equality	Assignment of sections in university courses Numbering of football players
Ordinal	Determination of greater or less	Intelligence test scores Hardness of minerals Street numbers
Interval	Determination of equality of intervals	Time Temperature Grade scores Age scores Standard scores
Ratio	Determination of equality of ratios	Weight in pounds Time in seconds Length Rate of learning

In the behavioral sciences, we deal largely with ordinal and interval scales. From the examples shown above, we may learn that interval scales have equal steps or differences, but have no true zero point. Thus, a mental test may be scaled so that a gain of 10 points from 30 to 40 is equivalent to a 10-point gain from 60 to 70. However, this does not imply that there is a zero point in mental ability, nor is there a perfect mental ability.

1.3.1 *Methods of Measurement.* Perhaps the simplest sort of measurement with respect to an attribute or performance of individuals is that of *ranking* in a series. Performers in track and field events may be ranked on a scale often ranging from one through five in major competition. In other instances, salesmen may be ranked in volume of sales for a given period, or children may be arranged in an order based upon height or weight. Other than telling us the position within the group, rank order yields little information since this is a relative measurement, rather than an absolute one.

Measurements of properties such as weight, volume, and density may be obtained through the application of some device which compares objects.

In the assignment of *scores* to indicate quality such as that assigned to the quality of a brand of orange juice, there may be an arbitrary assignment of a given number of points for appearance, freedom from after-taste, and flavor. This score lacks the comparability obtainable when individuals have been measured for some attribute such as intelligence. Also, while the scale of test scores does not permit judgment supporting the claim that one student is twice as intelligent as another, it has the advantage of comparing individuals on the basis of the quantity of the particular attribute. From test scores, we have measures answering the question of *how much* the students have achieved at the time of testing.

1.3.2 *Exact and Approximate Numbers.* With certain exceptions, we think of *exact numbers* as those obtained by counting, while *approximate numbers* are those obtained by measurement. Since many of the measurements with which the investigator deals are approximations, he must consider the *degree of precision* with which the original data were obtained. In reporting the length of a room, one may say that it is 22 feet, but it is not implied that this is the exact length. If the measurement is reported to the nearest quarter inch, the length may be 22 feet, $\frac{1}{4}$ inch, or 21 feet, $11\frac{3}{4}$ inches; the reported figure of 22 feet is recognized as an approximate number. On the other hand, we may say that there are 30 children in the room, meaning that this is an exact count.

In reporting measurements, acceptable procedure indicates that the investigator should give some notion of the degree of precision involved. An approximate number is generally considered precise to the nearest *unit of measurement* in which it is reported, with consideration given for reporting no more figures than are warranted by the nature of the objects and the measuring device employed. For example, a measurement of 21.37 inches (to hundredths) is more precise than a measurement of 21.4 inches (to tenths) because the first unit of measurement, 0.01 inch, is smaller than the second, 0.1 inch. Thus, if heights of students are being measured to the nearest tenth of an inch, an investigator should report the average height as 64.4 inches, since reporting an average height of 64.421 inches would imply an unjustified degree of precision.

By reporting a height of 64.4 inches, the figure 64.421 is *rounded* to the nearest tenth. Other examples of rounding are:

386.17	rounded to units is	386.
0.186	rounded to tenths is	0.2
386.17	rounded to three digits is	386.
64.96	rounded to two digits is	65.
0.186	rounded to one digit is	0.2
15.06915	rounded to five digits is	15.069

The basic rules for rounding numbers are:

a. When the right-hand digit of a number is dropped and that digit is less than 5, the digit immediately preceding it is not changed.

b. If the right-hand digit of a number is dropped and that digit is more than 5, the digit immediately preceding it is increased by one.

c. If the first digit to the right of those to be retained is exactly 5, or 5 followed by zeros, we shall follow the rule of rounding to the nearest *even number*. Thus, we would round 64.25 to 64.2, and we would round 64.55 to 64.6. Later experience with elementary probability theory will indicate that we should expect one half of the numbers preceding the 5 to be even numbers and one half of the numbers preceding the 5 to be odd numbers.

Care in rounding numbers should be exercised, since substantial errors may be introduced. Thus the careful worker may carry along two or three extra figures, later cutting the final result back to the number of digits warranted by the data and the computation involved.

In computing with approximate numbers, we shall often need to consider the number of *significant digits* in the measurements, that is, those digits that are needed to express the number of times the implied *unit of measurement* is contained in the measurement. An examination of the following data may serve to clarify the concept:

Given Measurement		Unit Implied		Number of Units of Measurement	Significant Digits
4.601	grams	0.001	gram	4601	4
186,000.	miles	1,000.	miles	186	3
5.35	inches	0.01	inch	535	3
655.	milliliters	1.	milliliter	655	3
0.0069	gram	0.0001	gram	69	2
0.0007	inch	0.0001	inch	7	1
0.260	inch	0.001	inch	260	3

1.3.3 *Computations.* The investigator should have access to calculating machines, since the statistical treatment of large numbers of observations may otherwise be laborious. Since the research worker frequently deals with approximate data, the principles governing computation with approximate numbers are reviewed here.

1.3.3.1 *The sum or difference of a set of measurements which have different degrees of precision can be no more precise than the least precise measurement used.*

For example, if we obtain the algebraic sum of 8.1, 2.25, −15.3, and 22.323, we have:

$$8.1 + 2.25 + (-15.3) + 22.323 = 17.373$$

By reporting the algebraic sum of these four numbers as 17.373, precision to thousandths is claimed without justification. The number of decimal places to be retained in an algebraic sum should be no greater than the number of decimal places in the least precise of the numbers added, in this case 8.1 and −15.3. Thus, we should round the answer to tenths, obtaining 17.4 as the algebraic sum of the four approximate numbers.

For ease in handling numbers, all measurements to be used as a set should be made with the same unit of measurement, thus avoiding any difficulty arising from the use of different units.

1.3.3.2 *In multiplying two or more numbers, one or more of which are approximate, retain in the product the smallest number of significant digits found in the approximate factors multiplied.*

To illustrate: $3.4 \times 1.822 = 6.1948$, which rounded to the allowable number of significant digits is 6.2. However, $2 \times 3.47 = 6.94$ if 2 is exact.

1.3.3.3 *The quotient obtained by dividing two approximate numbers or an approximate and an exact number should contain the smaller number of significant digits found in any approximate number used.*

To illustrate: $\frac{15}{2721}$ should be written 0.0055, not 0.005512, since 15 has only two significant digits.

1.3.3.4 Since the square root of a number is one of two equal factors whose product is the number, finding the square root of a number is the inverse of finding the product of two approximate numbers. Hence, *the square root of an approximate number can contain no more significant digits than there are in the number itself.*

To illustrate: the square root of 21.27 is 4.612. To check this result, square 4.612 and round the product to four digits. (This value may be found by interpolation of Table XIII, Appendix A.)

In general, the investigator wishes to obtain results which give as accurate a representation of the data as possible within the limits of the nature of the data and the reliability of the measuring device. At all times the exercise of good judgment must prevail.

1.4 *Selecting a Random Sample.* In Section 1.2 it was indicated that the process of making inferences about the population involves the projection of findings from samples to the populations from which these samples were drawn. In order to obtain useful results, we must first avoid errors arising from biased sampling. Thus, we need a technique that provides for *randomness* in selection of samples. To accomplish this purpose, we may make use of a table of random digits, as shown in Table XVII in Appendix A. In this table we find 10,000 digits, randomly arranged in groups of five and presented as 100 rows and 100 columns.

To illustrate the use of the table, let us begin with the task of drawing a sample of 26 from a group of 250 measurements. First, we number these measurements consecutively from 001 through 250. Since the digits in Table XVII have been entered in random fashion, we may begin at any point in the table, merely by pointing to one of the groups and reading the first four digits of the group selected. The first two digits may be used to determine the row, and the second two digits to determine the column, for selecting the first member of the sample.

Suppose that the first group we select from the table is 40914, located at row 25, columns 80–84. Now, using the first four digits of 40914, we begin with row 40, column 91, and copy the digits: 96071 05813. Since these two groups terminate the row, we continue with row 41, column 1, finding:

44560	38750	83635	56540	64900	42912
13953	79149	18710	68618	47606	93410

Since the measures of the group from which we wish to draw the sample have been assigned three-digit numbers, the random digits will be grouped into sets of three digits each, yielding:

607	105	813	445	603	875	083	635	565	406	490	042	912
139	537	914	918	710	686	184	760	693	410	163	598	903
389	696	472	316	449	831	776	053	833	990	268	328	833
786	336	971	381	395	640	561	542	451	645	599	750	165
747	526	694	503	096	279	147	095	237	287	832	027	355
080	372	744	882	084	693	938	689	586	250	834	230	459
858	632	078	109	284	263	339	177	716	738	601	590	742
562	369	075	158	272	137	875	711	532	131	500	132	835
448	614	115	707	962	562	306	813	782	(084)	678	946	993
842	553	495	934	811	695	457	511	586	574	739	055	

Underline each set of three digits having any value less than 250 until there are 26 *different* underlined sets. This process ends in this case at row 44, column 77. Arranging these sets in numerical order, we select as our sample of 26 those measurements which were previously designated as 027, 042, 053, 055, 075, 078, 080, 083, 084, 095, 096, 105, 109, 115, 131, 132, 137, 139, 147, 158, 163, 165, 177, 184, 230, 237. It should be observed here that the number 084 appeared a second time in the selection. The second appearance of this number is ignored and the drawing continues until 26 different sample members are drawn.

Variations may be made in reading the digits of the table by proceeding diagonally, up, down, left, or right from the starting point. As another procedure, we may read succeeding rows from left or right, or succeeding columns from top or bottom.

For each sample drawn, record the following data:

(a) initial point (row and number),
(b) direction of reading from the table, and
(c) the sample size.

QUESTIONS

1. Classify the following with respect to *counting* or *measurement* data:
   (a) Achievement scores,
   (b) Words spelled incorrectly in a theme,
   (c) Rooms in a school building,
   (d) Annual income in dollars,
   (e) Height in inches,
   (f) Existing world record in mile run.

2. What is meant by a *unit of measurement?* What relationship is there between the size of a *unit of measurement* and the *degree of precision* in the measurement?

3. How does the placement of the decimal point in a number affect the precision of the number? Which is the most precise number of the following: 98 millimeters, 9.8 millimeters, or 0.98 millimeter?

4. Consider the manufacture of expanding metal bellows for automobile thermostats or "autostats." What is the population of autostats from one factory? Is this a *finite* population or an *infinite* population?

5. How should a water chemist proceed to collect samples from city owned water mains in order to make determinations of bacterial content of treated water in the mains?

6. State whether each of the following series is *continuous* or *discrete:*
   (a) Scores in an achievement test,
   (b) Number of red cards held in 100 bridge hands,
   (c) Mental ages of third grade children in one school,
   (d) Traffic violations at a given intersection during one day,
   (e) Annual rainfall in a given county, expressed in inches.

7. The dean of admissions in a land-grant university attempted to obtain information from 1800 entering freshmen concerning factors affecting their choice of that particular university. How should a sample of 100 be chosen? What is the population sampled?

PROBLEMS

1. Round each of the following numbers to three significant digits: 3357; 29,431; 68,564.07; 19.081.

2. Extract the square root of each of the following numbers and round each result to the appropriate figure: 1608.62, 1783, 91.86.

3. Round each of the following numbers to two decimal places: 3.1416, 26.851, 125.8250, 29.922, 26.0048, 88.195.

4. Give answers for the following, assuming the numbers to be approximate:
   (a) $0.06 \times 3.18 =$
   (b) $0.12 \times 0.0016 =$
   (c) $0.16 \div 0.029 =$
   (d) $1.18 \div 0.161 =$

5. Multiply and round the result to an appropriate value:
   (a) 0.036 mm. $\times$ 0.35 mm. $=$
   (b) 2.28 in. $\times$ 1.62 in. $=$
   (c) 3.25 cm. $\times$ 2.36 cm. $=$

6. All numbers in this exercise are to be considered approximate numbers unless indicated otherwise. Perform the indicated division and round each quotient to give the appropriate answer:
   (a) $16.21 \div 2.24 =$
   (b) $0.687 \div 12$ (exact) $=$
   (c) 668 (exact) $\div 24.6 =$
   (d) $0.0568 \div 0.29 =$

7. Find the square roots of the following numbers, using Table XIII in Appendix A:
   (a) 1225   (c) 345.96   (e) 184.96   (g) 21609   (i) 694
   (b) 0.0169   (d) 61.1524   (f) 835.21   (h) 265.43

8. By the method of Section 1.4, select a random sample of 25 pages from this book. Make a count of the number of pages in the sample having either a table or a figure. Then estimate the number of pages in this book having either tables or figures. (Do not include Appendices.)

REFERENCES

Arkin, Herbert, and Colton, Raymond. *Tables for Statisticians*. New York: Barnes and Noble, Inc., 1950.

DuBois, Philip H. *An Introduction to Psychological Statistics*. New York: Harper and Row, Publishers, 1965. Chapters 1 and 2.

Freeman, Linton C. *Elementary Applied Statistics*. New York: John Wiley and Sons, Inc., 1965. Chapters 1–3.

Freund, John C., and Williams, Frank J. *Elementary Business Statistics: The Modern Approach*. Englewood Cliffs, New Jersey: Prentice-Hall, Inc., 1964. Chapters 1–3.

Guenther, William C. *Concepts of Statistical Inference*. New York: McGraw-Hill Book Company, 1965. Chapter 1.

Guilford, J. P. *Fundamental Statistics in Psychology and Education*. New York: McGraw-Hill Book Company, 1965. Chapter 2.

Peatman, John. *Introduction to Applied Statistics*. New York: Harper and Row Publishers, 1963. Chapter 1.

Tate, Merle W. *Statistics in Education and Psychology: A First Course*. New York: The Macmillan Company, 1965. Chapters 1 and 2.

Yamane, Taro. *Statistics, An Introductory Analysis*. New York: Harper and Row Publishers, 1964. Chapters 1 and 2.

2

FREQUENCY DISTRIBUTIONS AND MEASURES OF CENTRAL TENDENCY

After gathering the data for a statistical investigation, the researcher is interested in presenting these data in some systematic order. This is often done through the use of tables and graphs from which the reader may more readily ascertain what is the highest, the lowest, or the average measurement. While the data presented in Table 2.1 convey a general idea of numerical value, they have little meaning, since no observable order is apparent and no useful interpretations can readily be made.

TABLE 2.1

SCORES OBTAINED ON A PHYSICAL FITNESS TEST

175	213	186	212	183	199	166	171	193	202
201	209	191	188	207	186	203	198	202	184
196	224	175	207	212	183	195	200	172	192
192	216	218	196	195	200	192	198	199	198
193	210	188	197	196	181	205	174	197	203

2.1 Frequency Distributions. In order to obtain a clearer picture of a collection of data such as that in Table 2.1, it is helpful to organize the data into a *frequency distribution*, which may be described by a table or by graphs.

2.1.1 Frequency Tables. The simplest way of organizing the data of Table 2.1 would be to arrange the scores in numerical order, noting the *frequency* (number of occurrences) of each score, thus forming a *frequency table*.

However, we may produce a more condensed and more manageable table by *grouping* the data into equal *class intervals*. A table formed in this way is called a *grouped frequency table*. After the scores have been grouped, we, of course, lose sight of the actual values, knowing only that the scores fall within the stated intervals. Nevertheless, the errors resulting from grouping are usually not of sufficient magnitude to warrant correction.

Notice that even when a variable is continuous, as in the case of the physical fitness scores of Table 2.1, the observations are recorded as discrete values, implying that the recorded value falls within certain limits. These limits are normally defined as one half unit above and one half unit below the reported value. Thus, a score of 210 represents the interval from 209.5 up to 210.5. The mid-point of this *score interval* is 210:

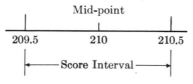

In setting up a grouped frequency table, we usually group the observations so as to have from 10 to 14 class intervals covering the entire range. Thus, to tabulate the scores in Table 2.1, we may use 12 class intervals of 5 units each. The first interval is 165–169 (really 164.5 to 169.5, as indicated above). The frequencies may be counted conveniently by the use of tally marks. The results are shown in columns 1 to 3 of Table 2.2.

TABLE 2.2

GROUPED FREQUENCY TABLE OF 50 TEST SCORES

Class Interval	Tallies	Frequency	Cumulative Frequency
220–224	|	1	50
215–219	||	2	49
210–214	||||	4	47
205–209	||||	4	43
200–204	ЖҬ ||	7	39
195–199	ЖҬ ЖҬ ||	12	32
190–194	ЖҬ |	6	20
185–189	||||	4	14
180–184	||||	4	10
175–179	||	2	6
170–174	|||	3	4
165–169	|	1	1

2.1.2 *Histograms*. A special type of bar graph may be made of the data presented in a grouped frequency table. After placing the class intervals in order along the horizontal axis, and measuring the frequencies along the vertical axis (Figure 2.1), we construct consecutive "bars" such that Figure 2.1 presents graphically the data of Table 2.2. Such a graph is called a *histogram*. The height of each bar measures the frequency for the corresponding interval. Since the area of each rectangle in the histogram is directly proportional to the number of cases within the interval, the histogram is useful for comparing the number of cases in the various intervals.

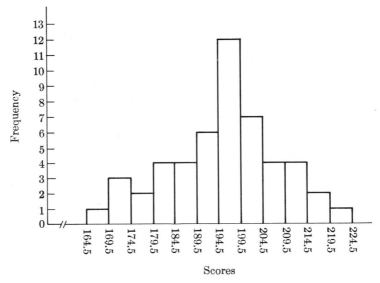

Figure 2.1 *Histogram for the physical fitness test scores of Table 2.2, using five-unit intervals.*

2.1.3 *Frequency Polygons*. A less exact graphic representation of the data shown in Table 2.2 may be made by use of the *frequency polygon* (Figure 2.2), constructed as follows: A point is placed above the mid-point of each interval at a height corresponding to the frequency, and then these points are connected by straight lines. This is equivalent to assuming that all cases in each interval are concentrated at the mid-point.

For the data presented in the histogram in Figure 2.1, the frequency polygon would appear as in Figure 2.2. While the additional intervals shown at the ends of the base line are not found in the grouped frequency table, the practice of showing these intervals is customary in constructing the frequency polygon so that the first and the last frequencies plotted are zero.

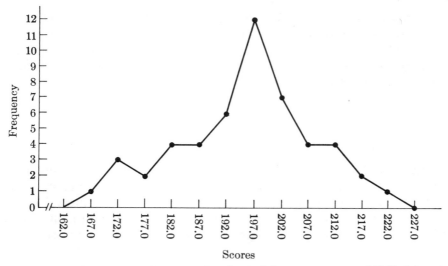

Figure 2.2 *Frequency polygon for the physical fitness test scores of Table 2.2, using mid-points of five-unit intervals.*

2.1.4 Cumulative Frequency Polygons. The *cumulative frequency polygon* (Figure 2.3) may be used also to represent the frequency distribution. The scores of the distribution are added serially, or summed, and plotted above the upper limit of each interval. In Table 2.2, the data are cumulated, or summed, in column 4; in Figure 2.3 we place the cumulative frequency 50 above the upper limit of the interval, that is, above 224.5, and the cumulative frequency 49 above 219.5, at point A.

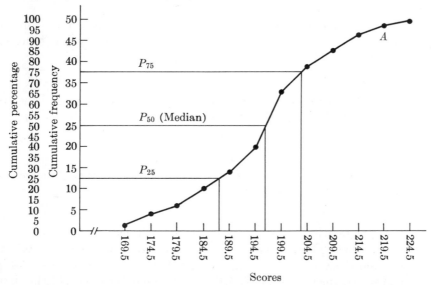

Figure 2.3 *Cumulative frequency polygon (and ogive) for the physical fitness test scores of Table 2.2.* (See also page 15.)

2.2 *Measures of Central Tendency.* After tabulating scores or measures into a frequency distribution, as shown in Table 2.2, the investigator may wish to calculate one or more *measures of central tendency.* This value may be one giving a description of the performance of the entire group, or it may be useful in comparing the performance of two or more groups. The measures of central tendency which are in common usage include the *mode*, the *median*, and the *arithmetic mean.*

2.2.1 *The Mode.* The *mode* is usually the single value which occurs most frequently in a series of measures. In the case of the histogram shown in Figure 2.1, it is the mid-point of the interval 195–199, the interval which contains the largest frequency. However, we may encounter a multi-modal distribution with more than one interval showing a like number of cases.

2.2.2 *The Median and the Percentiles.* The *median* is the *point* on a scale of observations such that one-half of the observations fall above it and the other half fall below it. In short the median is the "middle value" in any set of observations. If the number of observations is small, the median may be found by direct counting to the middle value if the number of observations is odd; if the number of observations is even, the average of the two middle observations is taken as the median.

In the case of the histogram of the 50 scores on the physical fitness test (Figure 2.1), the median is the point on either side of which an equal area under the histogram lies.

If the data is grouped as in Table 2.2, we may determine the point such that one half of the 50 observations fall above this value and the other half fall below by the following computation:

a. Take 50% of the scores, and count into the distribution until the 50% point is reached. In the example referred to above, this is after the 25th case.

b. Find the class interval in which the 25th case lies. The 25th case lies within the interval 194.5–199.5.

c. Interpolate within this interval to locate a value above which and below which 25 cases may be assumed to fall. In order to obtain the five additional scores necessary to make the 25, we take $5[(25-20)/12]$ and add this increment to 194.5, the lower limit of the interval 194.5–199.5. This places the median at 196.58.

The above relationship may be expressed as:

$$\text{Median} = L_o + \left[\frac{\frac{n}{2} - F_o}{F_i}\right] i \qquad (2.1)$$

where

L_o = lower limit of class interval containing the median;
F_o = sum of all frequencies below L_o;
F_i = frequency of cases within interval containing the median;
n = number of cases in sample;
i = number of units in each class interval.

In the example given:

$$\text{Median} = 194.5 + \left[\frac{\frac{50}{2} - 20}{12}\right] 5 = 196.58$$

Similarly, we may compute points below which 75 percent, 60 percent, 27 percent, or any percent of the scores lie. These points are called *percentiles*, and may be designated by P_{75}, P_{60}, P_{27}, P_{50}, and so forth. The 50th percentile is the median, computed above. For example, the method used for calculating P_{75}, the point below which 75 percent of the scores lie, is much like the method used in finding the median, P_{50}:

$$P_{75} = L_o + \left[\frac{\frac{3n}{4} - F_o}{F_i}\right] i$$

where

L_o = lower limit of the class interval containing the 75th percentile,
F_o = sum of all frequencies below L_o,
F_i = frequency of cases within interval containing the 75th percentile,
n = number of cases in the sample,
i = number of units in the class interval.

In the example given:

$$P_{75} = 199.5 + 5\left(\frac{\frac{150}{4} - 32}{7}\right) = 203.43$$

By converting the frequencies of column 4 of Table 2.2 to percentages, we arrive at a *cumulative percentage frequency* for each of the intervals. These frequencies may then be plotted to obtain a cumulative percentage curve, or *ogive*, as shown in Figure 2.3. Then, percentiles may be determined quickly from the ogive. It may be observed that errors in reading at the top and bottom of the distribution are likely to be of greater magnitude than those made in reading from the middle of the distribution.

Approximate values of P_{75}, P_{50}, and P_{25} may be obtained from Figure 2.3. Compare these values with those that we have just computed.

The graph in Figure 2.3 may also be used to estimate the *percentile rank* of a particular score. For example, we may see from the graph that 35% of the scores fall below 192; which means the *percentile rank* of score 192 is 35.

2.2.3 *The Arithmetic Mean.* We may indicate whether the items in a group are large or small by stating something concerning an average, or *arithmetic mean*. By definition, the mean (average) of a set of observations is the sum of all the observations divided by the number of observations. Consider the following numbers: 1, 2, 3, 4, 5, 6, 7, 8, 9, and 10. The sum of these numbers is 55, and the arithmetic mean is 55 divided by 10, or 5.5. To extend this process to the general case, we use symbols, letting X_1 represent the first score, X_2 the second, X_3 the third, X_4 the fourth, X_5 the fifth, etc. If we wish to obtain the arithmetic mean of five observations, then we have:

$$\overline{X} = \frac{X_1 + X_2 + X_3 + X_4 + X_5}{5}$$

The symbol $\overline{X}$, called "X bar," represents the value of the arithmetic mean. If we wish to obtain the mean for 50 observations, then

$$\overline{X} = \frac{X_1 + X_2 + X_3 + \cdots + X_{50}}{50}.$$

2.2.3.1 *Summation Notation.* Since it is often necessary to discuss the addition of several numbers, we shall find it convenient to use the symbol "$\sum$" to represent "the sum of." For example, in the case of the five observations, $X_1, X_2, X_3, X_4,$ and X_5, where $X_1 = 2, X_2 = 3, X_3 = 1, X_4 = -2,$ and $X_5 = 5$, we may write,

$$\sum_{i=1}^{5} X_i = X_1 + X_2 + X_3 + X_4 + X_5 = 2 + 3 + 1 + (-2) + 5 = 9$$

and

$$\overline{X} = \frac{\sum_{i=1}^{5} X_i}{5} = \frac{9}{5} \quad \text{or} \quad 1.8,$$

where $\sum_{i=1}^{5} X_i$ is read: "The sum of X_i from $i = 1$ to $i = 5$." The subscript i attached to the X refers to the ith observation, and X_i is the value of the ith observation.

The sum of all N measures in a population distribution is written

$$\sum_{i=1}^{N} X_i$$

and the mean for all of the population measures is:

$$\mu = \frac{\sum_{i=1}^{N} X_i}{N} \tag{2.2}$$

or when the limits of the summation are clear, simply $\mu = \frac{\sum X_i}{N}$.

The sum of all n measures in a sample is written

$$\sum_{i=1}^{n} X_i$$

and the mean for all of the measures in the sample is:

$$\overline{X} = \frac{\sum_{i=1}^{n} X_i}{n}, \quad \text{or} \quad \overline{X} = \frac{\sum X_i}{n} \tag{2.3}$$

Examples of the notation used in the treatment of statistical data will serve to show application of the Σ symbol and some representative cases in which this convention may be found.

a. The sum of the products of a constant times each of the five numbers is equal to the constant times the sum of the five numbers:

$$\sum_{i=1}^{5} kX_i = kX_1 + kX_2 + kX_3 + kX_4 + kX_5$$

$$= k(X_1 + X_2 + X_3 + X_4 + X_5) = k \sum_{i=1}^{5} X_i$$

In general:

$$\sum_{i=1}^{n} kX_i = k \sum_{i=1}^{n} X_i$$

b. If each value X_i has a frequency f_i, the total number of observations is found as the sum of the products $f_i X_i$. For five values:

$$\sum_{i=1}^{5} f_i X_i = f_1 X_1 + f_2 X_2 + f_3 X_3 + f_4 X_4 + f_5 X_5$$

In general:

$$\overline{X} = \frac{\sum_{i=1}^{n} f_i X_i}{n} \quad \text{or} \quad \overline{X} = \frac{\sum f_i X_i}{n} \tag{2.3'}$$

c. The sum of the five numbers, each number appearing as the deviation of an observation from a constant X_c, is equal to the sum of the five numbers less five times X_c:

$$\sum_{i=1}^{5} (X_i - X_c) = (X_1 - X_c) + (X_2 - X_c) + (X_3 - X_c)$$

$$+ (X_4 - X_c) + (X_5 - X_c)$$

$$= X_1 + X_2 + X_3 + X_4 + X_5 - 5X_c$$

$$= \sum_{i=1}^{5} X_i - 5X_c$$

2.2.3.2 *Calculation of the Mean from Grouped Data.* While the calculation of the mean by the process of summing the observations and dividing by the number of observations is adequate in many situations, this procedure becomes somewhat laborious in handling large samples. Accordingly, large samples may be treated by first placing the data in a grouped frequency distribution. In grouping the 50 physical fitness test scores in the frequency distribution of Table 2.2, the seven observations in the interval 200–204 are assigned a single numerical value corresponding to the mid-point, 202, of the interval. Similarly, the 12 observations in the interval 195–199 are assigned the value of the mid-point, 197.

We rearrange the data of Table 2.2 in a frequency table, Table 2.3, where X_i' denotes the mid-point of each interval.

TABLE 2.3

FREQUENCY TABLE OF 50 PHYSICAL FITNESS TEST SCORES

Mid-Point of Interval X_i'	Frequency f_i	Product $f_i X_i'$
222	1	222
217	2	434
212	4	848
207	4	828
202	7	1414
197	12	2364
192	6	1152
187	4	748
182	4	728
177	2	354
172	3	516
167	1	167
	$\sum f_i = n = 50$	$\sum f_i X_i' = 9775$

We then compute the mean as follows:

$$\overline{X} = \frac{\sum f_i X_i'}{n} = \frac{9775}{50} = 195.5 \tag{2.4}$$

When the scores of the physical fitness test in Table 2.1 are summed and divided by the number 50, the mean is 195.46. The discrepancy between this figure and that calculated from the data in Table 2.3 is attributed to the grouping operation. By decreasing the size of the intervals, the discrepancy may be decreased.

2.2.3.3 *Other Methods of Calculation of the Mean.* Considerable time and labor may be saved in computation of the mean by calculating from a new scale with a different unit and a new origin. In this procedure, the two mathematical principles employed may be stated as follows:

a. *When a constant, X_c, is subtracted from each member of a group of observations, the mean of the original values may be computed by finding the mean of the altered values and adding the constant to this mean.*

For example, in the first column of Table 2.1, let us take the constant $X_c = 190$ from each score. We find the altered values to be $-15, +11, +6, +2,$ and $+3$ respectively. The sum of these values equals 7, and therefore the new mean is $\frac{7}{5}$ or 1.4. The constant 190 must be added to the new mean to reproduce the mean of the original values, 191.4. Check: $\frac{1}{5}(175 + 201 + 196 + 192 + 193) = 191.4$.

From the formulas developed in Section 2.2.3.1, we have:

$$\overline{X} = \frac{\sum\limits_{i=1}^{n} X_i}{n} = \frac{\sum\limits_{i=1}^{n} (X_i - X_c)}{n} + X_c$$

b. *When each member of a group of observations is divided by a constant k, the mean of the original values can be found by multiplying the mean of the altered values by the constant.*

For example, if each of the five numbers, 48, 52, 56, 60, and 64, is divided by 4, the mean of the altered values is 14. If this mean is then multiplied by the constant 4, we reproduce the mean of the original values, which is 56.

If we divide each of the five original observations by a constant k, then the modified observations are:

$$\frac{X_1}{k}, \frac{X_2}{k}, \frac{X_3}{k}, \frac{X_4}{k}, \quad \text{and} \quad \frac{X_5}{k}$$

The mean of these values is, from formula (2.3):

$$\frac{\sum\limits_{i=1}^{5} \dfrac{X_i}{k}}{5} = \frac{\Sigma X_i}{5k} = \frac{1}{k}\,\overline{X}; \quad \text{hence, in general,} \quad \overline{X} = k\left[\frac{\sum\limits_{i=1}^{n} X_i}{kn}\right]$$

Combining both of these principles, a general rule for computing the mean from the altered values, also called *coded* values, u_i, may be expressed symbolically as:

$$\overline{X} = k\left[\frac{\sum\limits_{i=1}^{n} u_i}{n}\right] + X_c, \quad u_i = \frac{(X_i - X_c)}{k} \tag{2.5}$$

Where the number of observations is large, and if the data have been arranged in a frequency distribution, computation time may be reduced by replacing the mid-points of the intervals by the coded values $0, 1, 2, \ldots, n$. This simplified computation of the mean involves changing the measurements to a different scale with a new unit and a new origin. The working origin for grouped data may be chosen at a point near the center of the distribution, or in order to avoid the handling of negative numbers, the mid-point of the lowest interval may be chosen as the working origin, that is, the value for X_c. In the distribution of scores from Table 2.3, we take $X_c = 167$ and $k = 5$, the number of units in the class interval. Thus,

$$u_i = \tfrac{1}{5}(X'_i - 167)$$

The computation of the mean follows:

TABLE 2.4

CALCULATION OF THE MEAN OF 50 SCORES ON A PHYSICAL FITNESS TEST BY THE SIMPLIFIED METHOD

Mid-Point (X'_i)	Frequency (f_i)	u_i	$f_i u_i$
222	1	11	11
217	2	10	20
212	4	9	36
207	4	8	32
202	7	7	49
197	12	6	72
192	6	5	30
187	4	4	16
182	4	3	12
177	2	2	4
172	3	1	3
167	1	0	0
	$n = 50$		$\sum f_i u_i = 285$

As in Equation (2.5), but with $\sum f_i u_i$ instead of $\sum u_i$, we have:

$$\overline{X} = k \left[\frac{\sum\limits_{i=1}^{n} f_i u_i}{n} \right] + X_c$$

$$= 5 \left(\frac{285}{50} \right) + 167 = 195.5$$

It should be noted in connection with calculation of the mean by the simplified method above that no real saving in time or effort is effected unless there are enough observations to justify grouping.

2.2.4 *Choice of a Measure of Central Value.* Before answering a question concerning the best choice of measure of central tendency, it is necessary to know the intended use of the measure and to understand some of the limitations of each. In general, it may be said that the mean is the most *stable* of the measures. Moreover, it is used as a beginning point for subsequent operations, such as calculating the standard deviation, the correlation coefficient, and certain other statistics.

In certain instances, the median may be preferable, especially in a distribution where use of the mean would lead to erroneous ideas about the set of observations. The mean is affected disproportionately by the size of extreme measurements. When unbalanced by extreme measurements at the opposite end of the scale, the median yields a more *representative* value. In addition to this special case, the median is preferred when the distribution involves an interval of unspecified length, either at the top or bottom, as in the case of salary distributions. Since the median is not an algebraic measure, the medians of separate distributions may not be combined to yield a composite value for a number of distributions.

As a measure of central tendency the mode is limited in usefulness, but it does give a quick and easy approximation of the *concentration* of measures in a set.

QUESTIONS

1. The median is the same as what percentile?

   Indicate whether the following are true or false.

2. A high value in a distribution influences the mean to a greater extent than it does the median.

3. All scores tabulated for a given class interval are assumed to lie at the mid-point of that interval.

4. The median score in a distribution may be obtained by adding to the lowest score one-half the difference between the highest and lowest scores.

5. The assumed mean must be considered as being in the interval containing the true mean when computing from a frequency distribution.

PROBLEMS

1. For the following samples or sets of figures calculate the: (1) mean, (2) median and (3) mode (where possible).
   (a) 49, 53, 48, 61
   (b) 23, 29, 26, 21, 25
   (c) 8, 2, 6, 9, 3, 4, 8, 10, 4, 2
   (d) 264, 258, 262, 263, 262, 259, 262, 263, 266, 258
       (Suggestion: Code data by subtracting 260 from each figure before calculations; compare Table 2.4.)

(e) 15.8, 16.5, 16.3, 16.5, 16.2
    (Suggestion: Code data by subtracting 16.0 from each figure and
        multiplying each one by 10.)
(f) 9.3, 8.9, 10.8, 8.6, 10.2, 9.4, 8.7, 9.6
(g) 1,268; 1,274; 1,268; 1,269; 1,262; 1,265; 1,266

2. If $X_1 = 2$, $X_2 = 4$, $X_3 = 3$, $X_4 = 5$ and $X_5 = 7$, $f_1 = 1$, $f_2 = 1$, $f_3 = 3$, $f_4 = 2$, $f_5 = 1$, find the value of the following:

(a) $\displaystyle\sum_{i=1}^{5} X_i$ (b) $\displaystyle\sum_{i=1}^{5} f_i X_i$

(c) $\displaystyle\sum_{i=1}^{5} (X_i - 1)$ (d) $\displaystyle\sum_{i=1}^{5} 7(X_i - 2)$

3. Write in sigma notation:
   (a) $X_1 + X_2 + X_3$
   (b) $3X_1 + 3X_2 + 3X_3 + 3X_4$

4. If we have two or more subgroups, we may wish to find the combined
   mean from the formula:

$$\overline{X} = \frac{n_1 \overline{X}_1 + n_2 \overline{X}_2}{n_1 + n_2}$$

A teacher of second-year algebra found a mean test score of 86 for the
30 students enrolled in section 1, and she found a mean of 73 for the
28 students enrolled in section 2. What was the combined mean for the
two sections?

5. Throw five dice 100 times and record the total number of spots which
   appear on each throw. Make a cumulative frequency polygon of the 100
   sets of observations. Indicate the median from the cumulative polygon,
   or ogive.

6. Find the mean of the following sets of measurements:
   (a) 1, 2, 3, 4, 5, 6
   (b) 1, 4, 9, 16, 25, 36

Square the answer to (a) and compare it with your answer to (b). Under
what circumstances could the square of the mean equal the mean of
the squares?

7. The scores shown below were made by a group of 198 secondary school sophomore boys who took Forms A and B of the *Sequential Test of Educational Progress in Science, Level 2* (Copyright 1957). Arrange these scores in a frequency distribution, with the class intervals equal to 3:
   (a) Find the mean by the simplified method;
   (b) Find the median;
   (c) Prepare a cumulative frequency polygon.

50	48	46	43	33	40	37	35	36	32	28	28	34	35	36	29	27	34
35	40	37	24	32	23	41	27	40	41	39	33	18	33	38	34	38	40
36	38	26	25	39	39	39	26	33	39	28	39	40	39	41	36	30	39
30	35	24	32	39	41	37	27	24	25	34	27	27	34	33	21	38	30
33	40	28	35	41	41	30	40	40	38	27	37	38	39	41	33	35	35
33	33	35	36	37	37	40	39	40	36	36	33	32	36	24	33	38	33
30	35	36	31	26	38	27	39	32	38	38	38	22	30	37	32	41	40
25	41	38	40	39	40	34	29	25	39	25	31	40	21	36	34	33	36
41	34	27	27	36	41	35	24	33	35	35	36	32	41	37	35	38	37
37	36	26	28	29	39	38	41	40	38	41	29	27	40	33	36	39	33
38	29	41	17	32	36	36	40	36	34	33	40	39	38	38	50	52	44

8. Make a graph of diurnal variations in temperature for your city for a given 24-hour period. (a) Find the mean temperature for the period. (b) What was the modal temperature for the period?

9. Throw 10 pennies 30 times, recording the number of heads observed on each throw. Make a cumulative frequency polygon of the results of the 30 throws, determining the median, the 25th percentile and the 75th percentile.

10. A college student having a GPA (grade point average) of 2.3, based on a total of 110.0 semester hours completed, desires to raise his GPA to 2.6 during the completion of the remaining semester hours required for graduation. What minimum GPA must he obtain for these 30 hours in order to have a 2.6 average at graduation?

11. Draw one sample of 100 two-digit numbers from the Table of Random Digits. Enter these numbers in three frequency distributions having:
    (1) three-unit intervals,
    (2) six-unit intervals,
    (3) 10-unit intervals.
    Compute the means and medians and compare the values found from each distribution. Account for the observed differences. Compare the values thus obtained with the true mean obtained from the ungrouped data.

    Prepare an ogive and estimate the median for each of the three groupings.

REFERENCES

Dixon, Wilfrid J., and Massey, Frank J., Jr. *Introduction to Statistical Analysis.* New York: McGraw-Hill Book Company, Inc., 1957. Chapter 2.

DuBois, Philip H. *An Introduction to Psychological Statistics.* New York: Harper and Row, Publishers, 1965. Chapter 4.

Freeman, Linton C. *Elementary Applied Statistics.* New York: John Wiley and Sons, Inc., 1965. Chapters 4–6.

Freund, John C., and Williams, Frank J. *Elementary Business Statistics: The Modern Approach.* Englewood Cliffs, New Jersey: Prentice-Hall, Inc., 1964. Chapter 3.

Guenther, William C. *Concepts of Statistical Inference.* New York: McGraw-Hill Book Company, 1965. Chapter 3.

Guilford, J. P. *Fundamental Statistics in Psychology and Education.* New York: McGraw-Hill Book Company, 1965. Chapters 3 and 4.

Kurtz, Thomas E. *Basic Statistics.* Englewood Cliffs, New Jersey: Prentice-Hall, Inc., 1963. Chapter 3.

Tate, Merle W. *Statistics in Education and Psychology: A First Course.* New York: The Macmillan Company, 1965. Chapters 3 and 5.

3

MEASURES OF VARIABILITY

The mean of a set of observations gives an "average" value, and so it may be said to be the single measure that best represents this set of observations. However, this measure gives no information concerning the scatter, or *dispersion*, of the set of observations or how the shapes of frequency distributions may differ. In this chapter we shall show how the dispersion may be described by several *measures of variability* and how these measures may be computed.

3.1 *Simple Measures of Variability*. In Figure 3.1 we have five sets of observations presented as *dot frequency diagrams* (each observation is plotted as a separate dot). The data were obtained in each case by throwing two unbiased dice five times and recording the appearance of the spots. For example, in diagram (1) one throw showed 4, three throws showed 7 each, and one throw showed 10. Diagrams (2) through (5) were plotted similarly.

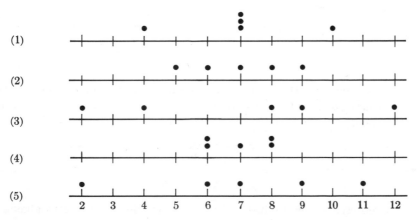

Figure 3.1 *Dot frequency diagrams obtained in five tosses of two dice in each set.*

Each distribution has a mean of 7, and (1), (2), and (4) are symmetrical, and yet the observations in each set are spread, or dispersed, differently over the scale. We seek some effective measures of such dispersion.

The *range* may be defined as the difference between the largest and smallest scores and is often used as a quick means for determining the spread of scores in a distribution. Since the range depends upon the extreme scores, and since other measurements in the series are not considered, the range is generally regarded as an unreliable estimate of dispersion.

If we take the differences between each measurement, X_i, in a series and the mean $\overline{X}$, we have:

$$(X_1 - \overline{X}), (X_2 - \overline{X}), (X_3 - \overline{X}), \ldots, (X_n - \overline{X})$$

Adding these differences, we have

$$\sum_{i=1}^{n} (X_i - \overline{X}) = (X_1 - \overline{X}) + (X_2 - \overline{X}) + (X_3 - \overline{X})$$
$$+ (X_4 - \overline{X}) + \cdots + (X_n - \overline{X})$$
$$= (X_1 + X_2 + X_3 + \cdots + X_n) - n\overline{X}$$
$$= \sum_{i=1}^{n} X_i - n\left[\frac{\sum_{i=1}^{n} X_i}{n}\right] = 0$$

Thus, the sum of the deviations of the observations from the mean is:

$$\sum_{i=1}^{n} (X_i - \overline{X}) = 0$$

Thus, a simple average of the deviations from the mean would give no useful information.

3.1.1 *The Average Deviation.* A useful measure of dispersion is the *average deviation*, defined to be the average of the *absolute* values of deviations from the mean:

$$AD = \frac{\sum |x_i|}{n},$$

where

$$x_i = X_i - \overline{X}$$

Here $|x_i|$ represents the absolute value of x_i, without reference to algebraic sign.

TABLE 3.1

CALCULATION OF THE AVERAGE DEVIATION FROM UNGROUPED DATA

X_i	x_i
7	2
1	−4
7	2
6	1
5	0
3	−2
8	3
9	4
3	−2
1	−4

$\sum X_i = 50 \qquad n = 10 \qquad \sum |x_i| = 24$

$\overline{X} = 5 \qquad\qquad AD = \frac{24}{10} = 2.4$

The average deviation tells us how much, on the average, the measures differ from their mean, and this measure of dispersion is, therefore, an arithmetic mean of the deviations, without reference to size or direction.

3.1.2 *The Interquartile Range*. The 25th percentile (see Section 2.2.2) is often called the *first quartile* and is designated by Q_1; it represents the point below which 25 percent of the cases lie. The 50th and 75th percentiles are called the *second* and *third quartiles*, Q_2 and Q_3, respectively. By taking the difference between the *third quartile* $Q_3 = P_{75}$ and the *first quartile* $Q_1 = P_{25}$, we may obtain a simple measure of dispersion called the *interquartile range*, $Q_3 - Q_1$, within which 50 percent of the cases lie. (The median is the second quartile, Q_2.)

The *semi-interquartile range* Q is half the distance from the first quartile to the third quartile and we have:

$$Q = \frac{Q_3 - Q_1}{2} \qquad (3.1)$$

If the distribution is symmetrical,

$$Q = Q_3 - Q_2 = Q_2 - Q_1.$$

The value of Q as a measure of variability may be seen when we have measures that are either extreme or widely scattered.

If we imagine that the class intervals become smaller and smaller while the number of observations becomes larger and larger, we can imagine that a frequency polygon, such as that in Figure 2.2, would become a continuous *frequency curve*. The area under such a curve would be divided into four equal parts at the quartiles. If such a theoretical distribution were symmetrical, its frequency curve might look something like that in Figure 3.2.

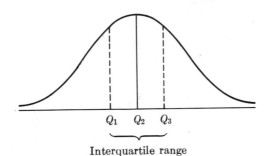

$$Q_1 \quad Q_2 \quad Q_3$$

Interquartile range

Figure 3.2 *Illustration of quartiles and interquartile range.*

3.2 *Variance.* We noted in Section 3.1 that the sum of the deviations from the mean is zero, and so we computed the "average deviation" by taking the average of the absolute values of the deviations. Another approach is to take some sort of average of the *squares* of the deviations. If we square the difference between each measurement and the mean, sum these squares, and divide by one less than the number of observations, we obtain the *variance* of the distribution:

$$\frac{(X_1 - \overline{X})^2 + (X_2 - \overline{X})^2 + (X_3 - \overline{X})^2 + \cdots + (X_n - \overline{X})^2}{n - 1} \tag{3.2}$$

The sigma notation introduced in Section 2.2.3.1 may be used to write the sum of several squares compactly. For example, the sum of the squares of the five measures X_1, X_2, X_3, X_4, and X_5 may be written:

$$\sum_{i=1}^{5} X_i^2 = X_1^2 + X_2^2 + X_3^2 + X_4^2 + X_5^2$$

Using this notation, we may now write the formula for the variance of a sample as:

$$s^2 = \frac{\sum_{i=1}^{n} (X_i - \overline{X})^2}{n - 1} \tag{3.3}$$

The reader will also recall from Section 2.2.3.1 that while the Roman $\overline{X}$ was used as a symbol for the mean of a sample, the Greek letter μ was used as a symbol for the mean of a population. In a similar manner, the Greek symbol σ^2 is used for the variance of a population. In that case, the denominator becomes N.

For computational purposes a more convenient formula for the variance may be obtained by first squaring each term in the numerator of (3.3):

$$\sum_{i=1}^{n} (X_i - \overline{X})^2 = \sum_{i=1}^{n} (X_i^2 - 2X_i\overline{X} + \overline{X}^2)$$

$$= (X_1^2 - 2X_1\overline{X} + \overline{X}^2) + (X_2^2 - 2X_2\overline{X} + \overline{X}^2)$$
$$+ (X_3^2 - 2X_3\overline{X} + \overline{X}^2) + \cdots + (X_n^2 - 2X_n\overline{X} + \overline{X}^2)$$
$$= (X_1^2 + X_2^2 + X_3^2 + \cdots + X_n^2)$$
$$- 2\overline{X}(X_1 + X_2 + X_3 + \cdots + X_n) + n\overline{X}^2$$

$$\sum_{i=1}^{n} (X_i - \overline{X})^2 = \sum_{i=1}^{n} X_i^2 - 2\overline{X}\left[\sum_{i=1}^{n} X_i\right] + n\overline{X}^2$$

Substituting $\dfrac{\sum_{i=1}^{n} X_i}{n}$ for $\overline{X}$, we obtain:

$$\sum_{i=1}^{n} (X_i - \overline{X})^2 = \sum_{i=1}^{n} X_i^2 - 2\left[\frac{\sum_{i=1}^{n} X_i}{n}\right]\left[\sum_{i=1}^{n} X_i\right] + n\left[\frac{\sum_{i=1}^{n} X_i}{n}\right]^2$$

$$= \sum_{i=1}^{n} X_i^2 - 2\frac{\left[\sum_{i=1}^{n} X_i\right]^2}{n} + \frac{\left[\sum_{i=1}^{n} X_i\right]^2}{n}$$

$$= \sum_{i=1}^{n} X_i^2 - \frac{\left[\sum_{i=1}^{n} X_i\right]^2}{n}$$

Thus

$$s^2 = \frac{\sum_{i=1}^{n} X_i^2 - \dfrac{\left[\sum_{i=1}^{n} X_i\right]^2}{n}}{n - 1} \tag{3.4}$$

At this point the reader may inquire as to the reason for using $(n - 1)$ in the Equation (3.4), rather than n. While the number of squares is equal to the number of measures, the *sum of squares* is correctly shown as $(n - 1)$ quantities. If we start with a set of two measurements, X_1 and X_2, the mean $\overline{X} = (X_1 + X_2)/2$, then:

$$\sum_{i=1}^{2} (X_i - \overline{X})^2 = (X_1 - \overline{X})^2 + (X_2 - \overline{X})^2$$

$$= \left[X_1 - \frac{(X_1 + X_2)}{2}\right]^2 + \left[X_2 - \frac{(X_1 + X_2)}{2}\right]^2$$

$$= \left[\frac{X_1 - X_2}{2}\right]^2 + \left[\frac{X_2 - X_1}{2}\right]^2$$

$$= \frac{X_1^2 - 2X_1X_2 + X_2^2}{4} + \frac{X_2^2 - 2X_1X_2 + X_1^2}{4}$$

$$= \frac{X_1^2 - 2X_1X_2 + X_2^2}{2}$$

$$= \left[\frac{X_1 - X_2}{\sqrt{2}}\right]^2$$

Then (3.4) becomes an expression with only one squared term on the right:

$$s^2 = \frac{\left[\dfrac{X_1 - X_2}{\sqrt{2}}\right]^2}{2 - 1} \quad \text{or} \quad (2 - 1)s^2 = \left[\frac{X_1 - X_2}{\sqrt{2}}\right]^2$$

If we have four measures, X_1, X_2, X_3, and X_4, we have:

$$\sum_{i=1}^{4} (X_i - \overline{X})^2 = (X_1 - \overline{X})^2 + (X_2 - \overline{X})^2 + (X_3 - \overline{X})^2 + (X_4 - \overline{X})^2$$

Through the above procedure it may be seen that the sum of the squares of the four deviations yields the sum of three squares. Proof of this exercise is included in the list of problems indicated at the close of this chapter.

3.3 *The Standard Deviation.* The *standard deviation* is defined to be the positive square root of the variance. The advantage of this measure over the variance lies in the fact that the standard deviation can be interpreted as a distance along the original score scale.

To illustrate the computation of the variance and standard deviation of a set of scores, we may use a compilation of errors made in sentence construction in the themes of ten students enrolled in the freshman English class: 7, 6, 7, 1, 9, 8, 3, 3, 1, 5. From Equation (3.4), we have:

$$s^2 = \frac{(7^2 + 6^2 + 7^2 + 1^2 + 9^2 + 8^2 + 3^2 + 3^2 + 1^2 + 5^2)}{10 - 1} - \frac{(7 + 6 + 7 + 1 + 9 + 8 + 3 + 3 + 1 + 5)^2}{10}$$

$$= \frac{324 - (50)^2/10}{9}$$

$$= \frac{324 - 250}{9} = \frac{74}{9}$$

$$= 8.22$$

$$s = \sqrt{s^2} = \sqrt{8.22} = 2.87 \quad \text{(from Table XIII, Appendix A)}$$

3.3.1 *The Standard Deviation from Grouped Data.* The computations necessary for determination of both the mean and the standard deviation of large samples of observations are often facilitated by grouping, particularly under conditions requiring computation by hand. In the computation we begin by using essentially the same procedure employed in finding the mean from grouped data; that is, we arrange the data in a frequency distribution with the scores tabulated according to the mid-point of each interval.

Consider the following set of observations which represent the playing weights of 50 college football players.

TABLE 3.2

CALCULATION OF THE STANDARD DEVIATION FROM GROUPED DATA

Weight (Class Interval)	Mid-Point X_i'	Frequency f_i	$f_i X_i'$	$f_i X_i'^2$
195–199	197	1	197	38809
190–194	192	2	384	73728
185–189	187	3	561	104907
180–184	182	5	910	165620
175–179	177	5	885	156645
170–174	172	7	1204	207088
165–169	167	11	1837	306779
160–164	162	8	1296	209952
155–159	157	4	628	98596
150–154	152	2	304	46208
145–149	147	1	147	21609
140–144	142	1	142	20164
		$n = 50$	$\sum f_i X_i' = 8495$	$\sum f_i X_i'^2 = 1450105$

From Equation (2.3') we have:

$$\overline{X} = \frac{\sum f_i X_i'}{n} = \frac{8495}{50} = 169.9$$

We now modify Equation (3.4) for grouped data. Since we have f_i observations with the value X'_i, $\sum X_i$ is replaced by $\sum f_i X'_i$ and $\sum X_1^2$ is replaced by $\sum f_i X'^2_i$.

$$s^2 = \frac{\sum f_i X'^2_i - \frac{(\sum f_i X'_i)^2}{n}}{n-1} = \frac{1450105 - 1443300}{49} = 138.77$$

$$s = 11.8$$

It was observed in the computation of the mean from coded data in Section 2.2.3.3 that if the mid-points of the intervals are equidistant, a substitute scale may be imposed, by using the numbers $0, 1, 2, \ldots, n$, or we may place the zero of the coded scale near the center of the distribution and arrange the numbers u_i as positive and negative units. The computations for the data of Table 3.2 appear in Table 3.3 when coded with $X_c = 142$ and $k = 5$, the number of units in a class interval.

In coding the observations to obtain u_i shown in Table 3.3 we subtract the coding score 142 from each observation (interval mid-point) and divide the result by a constant k (the number of units in the class interval). Thus $u_i = \frac{1}{5}(X'_i - 142)$. The mean and standard deviation are then computed using the technique discussed in Section 2.2.3.3.

TABLE 3.3

CALCULATION OF THE STANDARD DEVIATION FROM GROUPED DATA BY CODING

Weight (Class Interval)	Mid-Point X'_i	Frequency f_i	u_i	$f_i u_i$	$f_i u_i^2$
195–199	197	1	11	11	121
190–194	192	2	10	20	200
185–189	187	3	9	27	243
180–184	182	5	8	40	320
175–179	177	5	7	35	245
170–174	172	7	6	42	252
165–169	167	11	5	55	275
160–164	162	8	4	32	128
155–159	157	4	3	12	36
150–154	152	2	2	4	8
145–149	147	1	1	1	1
140–144	142	1	0	0	0
		$n = 50$		$\sum f_i u_i = 279$	$\sum f_i u_i^2 = 1829$

$$\overline{X} = k\left[\frac{\sum f_i u_i}{n}\right] + X_c = 5\left[\frac{279}{50}\right] + 142 = 169.9$$

Next we compute the variance and standard deviation of the coded observations,

$$s_u^2 = \frac{\sum f_i u_i^2 - \frac{(\sum f_i u_i)^2}{n}}{n-1} = \frac{1829 - 1556.82}{49} = 5.55 \qquad (3.5)$$

$$s_u = \sqrt{5.55} = 2.36$$

Then we multiply the coded standard deviation by the number of units in a class interval to obtain the actual or uncoded standard deviation:

$$s = 5 \times 2.36 = 11.8$$

As another example, consider the data in Table 2.4, adding the column $f_i u_i^2$.

TABLE 3.4

**STANDARD DEVIATION COMPUTED FROM CODED SCORES
MADE ON PHYSICAL FITNESS TEST**

Mid-Point X_i	Frequency f_i	u_i	$f_i u_i$	$f_i u_i^2$
222	1	11	11	121
217	2	10	20	200
212	4	9	36	324
207	4	8	32	256
202	7	7	49	343
197	12	6	72	432
192	6	5	30	150
187	4	4	16	64
182	4	3	12	36
177	3	2	4	8
172	3	1	3	3
167	1	0	0	0
	$n = 50$		$\sum f_i u_i = 285$	$\sum f_i u_i^2 = 1937$

To obtain the actual standard deviation, s, from the coded data, we use Equation (3.6). This gives the square root of the value found by Equation (3.5) multiplied by k, the number of units in a class interval. Thus we have:

$$s = k \sqrt{\frac{\sum f_i u_i^2 - \frac{(\sum f_i u_i)^2}{n}}{n-1}} \qquad (3.6)$$

$$= 5 \sqrt{\frac{1937 - \frac{285 \times 285}{50}}{49}} = \frac{5}{7} \sqrt{312.5} = 12.6$$

3.3.2 *The Charlier Checks.* The computations for $\sum f_i u_i^2$ may be checked by adding 1 to each u_i and designating the new coded values as y_i, as shown in Table 3.5:

$$f_i y_i = f_i(u_i + 1) = f_i u_i + f_i$$

TABLE 3.5

THE CHARLIER CHECKS

Class Interval	f_i	u_i	$f_i u_i$	$f_i u_i^2$	y_i	$f_i y_i$	$f_i y_i^2$
39–40	1	5	5	25	6	6	36
37–38	3	4	12	48	5	15	75
35–36	8	3	24	72	4	32	128
33–34	14	2	28	56	3	42	126
31–32	6	1	6	6	2	12	24
29–30	3	0	0	0	1	3	3
Totals	$n = 35$		75	207		110	392

If the computations have been made correctly, the following relationships will hold:

$$\sum f_i y_i = \sum f_i u_i + n$$

and

$$\sum f_i y_i^2 = \sum f_i u_i^2 + 2\sum f_i u_i + n$$

Substituting the appropriate values from Table 3.5 we have:

$$\sum f_i y_i^2 = \sum f_i u_i^2 + 2\sum f_i u_i + n = 207 + 2(75) + 35 = 392$$

* 3.3.3 *Derivation of the Standard Deviation.* If we wish to understand the manner in which the standard deviation is derived, we may begin with the set of numbers, $X_1, X_2, X_3, X_4, \ldots, X_n$, with a mean $\overline{X}$, and k, a number from which the deviations are measured. Then, these deviations from k are:

$$X_1 - k, X_2 - k, X_3 - k, X_4 - k, \ldots, X_n - k$$

Obtaining the sum of the squares of these deviations, we have:

$$(X_1 - k)^2 + (X_2 - k)^2 + (X_3 - k)^2 + \cdots + (X_n - k)^2$$

We may then consider the sum of the squares as a function of k:

$$\begin{aligned} f(k) &= (X_1 - k)^2 + (X_2 - k)^2 + (X_3 - k)^2 + (X_4 - k)^2 + \cdots + (X_n - k)^2 \\ &= X_1^2 - 2X_1 k + k^2 + X_2^2 - 2X_2 k + k^2 + \cdots + X_n^2 - 2X_n k + k^2 \\ &= \sum X^2 - 2k\sum X + nk^2 \end{aligned}$$

---

* Knowledge of calculus is required.

Here we wish to find the value of k for which $f(k)$ has a minimum. By differentiating

$$f(k) = \sum X^2 - 2k\sum X + nk^2$$

with respect to k, we find the first derivative to be:

$$f'(k) = 0 - 2\sum X + 2nk$$

or

$$f'(k) = 2nk - 2\sum X$$

Then the second derivative becomes:

$$f''(k) = 2n$$

Since n is positive, the second derivative is also positive. Then the value of k that makes the first derivative equal to zero will make the function $f(k)$ minimum. Then we let:

$$2nk - 2\sum X = 0$$

Solving for k,

$$k = \frac{\sum X}{n} \quad \text{or} \quad k = \overline{X}$$

If we are to obtain a minimum value for the sum of the squares of deviations of a given set of numbers from a constant, the deviations must be taken from the mean.

3.4 Standard Scores. A *score* is the value assigned to a particular observation or measurement. It is often useful to have a means by which various scores can be compared. For each observation X composing any set of sample observations, a *standard score* is defined as:

$$Z = \frac{X - \overline{X}}{s} = \frac{x}{s} \tag{3.7}$$

where
$X =$ an original measurement,
$\overline{X} =$ mean of the distribution,
$s =$ standard deviation of the distribution
$x =$ deviation score $(X - \overline{X})$

Similarly for a population distribution from which the sample is drawn we have:

$$Z = \frac{X - \mu}{\sigma} = \frac{x}{\sigma}$$

where
$\mu =$ mean of the population distribution
$\sigma =$ standard deviation of the population distribution

This will be referred to frequently in the following chapters.
Since $\sum(X - \overline{X}) = 0$, we have

$$\overline{Z} = 0$$

We have defined the variance of a sample to be:

$$s^2 = \frac{\sum(X - \overline{X})^2}{n - 1}$$

Similarly the variance of a set of z-scores derived from such a sample is:

$$s_z^2 = \frac{\sum(z - \bar{z})^2}{n - 1} = \frac{\sum(z - 0)^2}{n - 1} = \frac{\sum \frac{x^2}{s^2}}{n - 1} = \frac{\sum x^2}{(n - 1)s^2}$$

From equation (3.3) we have:

$$(n - 1)s^2 = \sum(X - \overline{X})^2 = \sum x^2$$

Therefore

$$s_z^2 = \frac{\sum x^2}{\sum x^2} = 1$$

Because the variance s_z^2 of the standard score is equal to 1.00, its positive square root s_z, the standard deviation, will also equal 1.00.

Since some of the measures may be smaller than the mean, there may be some z-score values which are negative. To avoid the negative sign, a *transformed standard score* may be used. One such transformation converts all the z-score means to 50 instead of zero, and changes all the z-score standard deviations to 10 instead of 1. The formula for such a transformation is:

$$Z = 50 + 10\left[\frac{X - \overline{X}}{s}\right]$$

Thus a standard z-score originally having a value of 1.5 would have a transformed value of

$$Z = 50 + 10 \times 1.5 = 65$$

3.4.1 *T-Scores*. A *T-score* is a standard score referred to a particular type of distribution, called a *normal distribution*. Normal distributions will be discussed in detail in Chapter 5, but at the present time it is sufficient to know that a normal distribution is symmetrical about the mean and has a bell-shaped curve, which may be something like that in Figure 3.2, page 28, where the quartiles are shown. The area under the curve to the left of the third quartile, for example, is 0.75 of the entire area. This means that 0.25 of the area is to the right of the third quartile. We may find the distance of Q_3 from the mean by using Table I in Appendix A. This table may be used to find the right-hand portion of the area for values of z if the mean is at $z = 0$ and the standard deviation is 1, or vice versa. Since the area beyond the third quartile is 0.25 of the whole, we find 0.25143 in the row opposite $z = 0.6$ in Table I, and read the coordinate of the third quartile as 0.67 to two decimal places. A *T*-score is found by a formula similar to that for the transformed standard score above. Thus:

$$T = 50 + 10z.$$

For the third quartile $T = 50 + 6.7 = 57$ when rounded to two digits.

To illustrate the calculation of T-scores for a general distribution, we begin by entering the data as shown in Table 3.6, where the weights of 50 players are given. The entries in column (5) are computed from columns (3) and (4) by adding one-half the frequency on a given score in column (3) to the cumulative frequency, column (4), shown for the interval below the score. For example, there are no scores below the lowest interval of column (4) and there is a score of one in the lowest interval of column (3); therefore 0 plus one-half of 1 or 0.5 is entered in the lowest interval of column (5). In similar manner for the class interval 165–169, column (3) has a value of 11, while column (4) for the interval 160–164 is 16.0. Adding $\frac{11}{2}$ to 16.0 gives 21.5, the value in column (5) for the 165–169 interval. It should be remembered here that each score is an interval rather than a point on the scale, hence the need for adding one-half the frequency on a given score to the cumulative frequency shown below that score.

TABLE 3.6

ILLUSTRATION OF THE T-SCORE TRANSFORMATION
DATA FROM TABLE 3.2

Class Interval (1)	Mid-Point (2)	Freq. (3)	Cum. Freq. (4)	Cum. Freq. to Mid-Point (5)	Cum. Proportion to Mid-Point (6)	z (7)	T-Score $50 + 10z$ (8)
195–199	197	1	50	49.5	0.99	2.32	73
190–194	192	2	49	48	0.96	1.75	68
185–189	187	3	47	45.5	0.91	1.34	63
180–184	182	5	44	41.5	0.83	0.95	60
175–179	177	5	39	36.5	0.71	0.55	56
170–174	172	7	34	30.5	0.61	0.28	53
165–169	167	11	27	21.5	0.43	−0.18	48
160–164	162	8	16	12	0.24	−0.71	43
155–159	157	4	8	6	0.12	−1.17	38
150–154	152	2	4	3	0.06	−1.55	34
145–149	147	1	2	1.5	0.03	−1.88	31
140–144	142	1	1	0.5	0.01	−2.33	27

The entries in column (6) are proportions, or ratios, of the cumulative frequency entries of column (5) to the total number of cases, 50. For example, $49.5/50 = 0.99$; or 99 percent of the scores lie below the mid-point of the interval, 197. The z values for column (7) are obtained using Table I, Appendix A, as follows: If the cumulative proportion is less than 0.50, this value is found in the body of Table I and the associated z number read directly from the table and indicated as a negative quantity. Thus 0.43, found in the table, has the z value −0.18. If the cumulative proportion is greater than 0.50, its complement must be used and the z value given a positive sign. Thus the table value for the cumulative proportion 0.99 is 1.00 — 0.99 = 0.01 and the z value is +2.32. The z values are then transformed to T-scores in column (8).

A T-score may be said to be a normalized standard score converted to a distribution having a mean equal to 50 and a standard deviation of 10. The horizontal scale of this distribution covers a spread of 10 standard deviations. Thus it extends from -5σ to $+5\sigma$, and places the extremes of the distribution well beyond the limits normally associated with measurements in the social sciences. Their observations are more likely to fall within the range of -3.5σ to $+3.5\sigma$. While the T-scale is frequently used, a number of test and scale makers have used, as theoretical distributions, normal distributions having means and standard deviations other than 50 and 10.

The usefulness of T-scores may be seen when compared with standard scores. The standard score is a linear transformation similar to converting from feet to inches, or from Fahrenheit to Celsius, while the T-scale procedure normalizes the distribution, thereby providing scores that are more nearly comparable. In addition, ordered categories, or ranks, may be normalized by following the procedure shown in connection with Table 3.6.

3.4.2 *The Stanine Scale.* The stanine scale is an approximately normal systematic alteration, or transformation, of a set of scores, using nine categories. The mean of this scale is 5, and the standard deviation is 1.96, with stanines representing intervals of scores on the score scale. Thus, stanine 5 covers the interval from -0.25 to $+0.25$ in standard deviation units, and stanine 6 covers the interval from 0.25 to 0.75 in standard deviation units. This coarse grouping brings about a lack of refinement that sometimes may not be tolerated, particularly in guidance work where the extreme deviates at either end of the distribution should perhaps retain their identity.

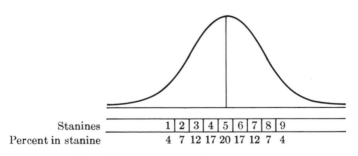

Stanines	1	2	3	4	5	6	7	8	9
Percent in stanine	4	7	12	17	20	17	12	7	4

Figure 3.3   *The stanine scale.*

From Figure 3.3 it may be observed that four percent of the cases have a stanine score equal to 1; seven percent have a score of 2; and 12 percent have a score of 3. One of the ancillary benefits derived from this nine-unit scale is that only one column is necessary on the IBM punched card record that may be used for machine data processing.

PROBLEMS

1. For the following groups of measurements calculate: (1) the mean, (2) the variance, and (3) the standard deviation.
   (a) 5, −3, 2, 1, 8, 3, 4, 4
   (b) 24, 27, 20, 24, 25
   (c) 7, 1, 4, 8, 5, 2, 9, 3, 2, 5

2. A sample of 15 items was drawn from a population. Each of the values was coded by (a) subtracting 41, and (b) dividing each of the resulting differences by 10. The sum of the coded values was 15, and the sum of the coded squared deviations from the sample mean was 150. Find the value of the mean, the variance and the standard deviation.

3. The following data were obtained from test scores established by 17 students in a course of second-year algebra:

Class Interval	Frequency
45–49	1
40–44	3
35–39	4
30–34	5
25–29	2
20–24	2
	$n = 17$

   (a) Calculate the mean and standard deviation,
   (b) Check the result by the Charlier checks.

4. A sample of five 1-pound bags of coffee revealed the following weights when subjected to measurement:

$$16.0, 16.4, 16.3, 16.1, 15.7 \text{ ounces}$$

Code these measurements by subtracting 16.0, and multiply by 10. Find the mean, the variance, and the standard deviation.

5. In five rolls of two dice, the following numbers appeared: 10, 8, 7, 6, 4.
   (a) Calculate the mean and the standard deviation of these five numbers.
   (b) Code the five numbers by subtracting 5 before computing the mean and the standard deviation.
   (c) Multiply each score by 10 before computing the mean and the standard deviation.

6. Prove that $\sum_{i=1}^{4} (X_i - \overline{X})^2$ can be expressed as the sum of three squares.

7. A student in the freshman chemistry class made a score of 31 on one test and a score of 56 in a second test. Distribution of scores for the entire class was essentially the same for both tests. The mean and the standard deviation are:

	$\overline{X}$	s
Test I	28	3
Test II	50	4

Find the z-score for each of the two tests.

8. Express the following measurements in the standard score form: 5, 8, 12, 9, 6, where the mean of the distribution from which these scores derived is 8, and the standard deviation is 2.5.

9. The marks of four students are shown in the table below, along with the mean and the standard deviation for each test. Convert the marks to the standard scores.

Test	$\overline{X}$	s	Student A		B		C	
1	47	8.3	63	——	68	——	40	——
2	49	7.7	49	——	40	——	61	——
3	62	5.5	62	——	65	——	76	——
4	81	9.1	73	——	70	——	60	——

10. A group of 25 applicants for admission to graduate school made the following scores on the quantitative part of an aptitude test:

590	569	425	473	555
410	414	478	513	598
605	614	523	600	434
501	505	606	488	459
549	550	422	589	492

Calculate the mean and the standard deviation by first coding these data.

11. Show that the sum of the squares of a set of z-scores is equal to N:

$$\sum_{i=1}^{N} z_i^2 = N$$

12. When the scores in a distribution are not all equal, show that

$$\sum_{i=1}^{N} x_i^2 \neq (\sum x_i)^2$$

where $x_i = X_i - \mu$.

13. Code the following data and compute the mean, the variance and the standard deviation: 99.997; 100.000; 99.999; 99.997; 99.990; 99.999.

14. Each of the 10 numbers was coded by subtracting 0.999, and the resulting differences were multiplied by 1000. The sum of the coded values was 6, and the sum of the squared deviations from the sample mean was 26.4. What are the mean, the variance, and the standard deviation for the sample in units of the original data? (Adapted from Bridges, Charles M., Jr. "The Application of Elementary Statistics in Analysis of Data by Selected Secondary School Students." Unpublished Doctoral Dissertation, The University of Tennessee, Knoxville, 1959, p. 86.)

15. The following sample values have been coded by subtracting 0.91356 from each value and multiplying the resulting differences by 10^5. Compute the mean, the variance, and the standard deviation for these values: 2, -4, 6, 3, -5, 9, 7, 8, 6, 9. (Bridges, p. 91)

REFERENCES

Alder, Henry L., and Roessler, Edward B. *Introduction to Probability and Statistics*. San Francisco: W. H. Freeman and Company, 1960. Chapter 4.

DuBois, Philip H. *An Introduction to Psychological Statistics*. New York: Harper and Row, Publishers, 1956. Chapter 5.

Freund, John C., and Williams, Frank J. *Elementary Business Statistics: The Modern Approach*. Englewood Cliffs, New Jersey: Prentice-Hall, Inc., 1964. Chapter 3.

Guenther, William C. *Concepts of Statistical Inference*. New York: McGraw-Hill Book Company, 1965. Chapter 3.

Guilford, J. P. *Fundamental Statistics in Psychology and Education*. New York: McGraw-Hill Book Company, 1965. Chapter 5.

Kurtz, Thomas E. *Basic Statistics*. Englewood Cliffs, New Jersey: Prentice-Hall, Inc., 1963. Chapter 3.

McNemar, Quinn. *Psychological Statistics*, Third Edition. New York: John Wiley and Sons, Inc., 1962. Chapter 4.

Tate, Merle W. *Statistics in Education and Psychology: A First Course*. New York: The Macmillan Company, 1965. Chapter 4.

Yamane, Taro. *Statistics, An Introductory Analysis*. New York: Harper and Row, Publishers, 1964. Chapter 4.

4

ELEMENTARY PROBABILITY AND THEORETICAL DISTRIBUTIONS

In describing the characteristics of a given sample, we have used the frequency distribution, the cumulative frequency polygon, the ogive, and the histogram. While these charts and graphs are useful for describing large masses of sample data, our chief interest lies in making inferences about the populations from which the samples came. Consequently, we wish to determine the *probability* that the *statistics* of the sample, such as the sample mean and the standard deviation, are representative of the corresponding population parameters (see page 2). We also wish to determine how the sample and population values can be expected to differ. The inductive process by which the statistician infers population characteristics from those of a single set of observations may be approached through *theoretical sampling laws* or through an *experimental procedure*.

Probability theory first gained status through the efforts of gamblers who sought advice from the mathematicians concerning how to weigh risk against gain in games of chance. This led to the work of Pascal (1623–1662), who with Fermat, arrived at the mathematical analysis of chances in a game played under a set of predetermined rules. Jacob Bernoulli (1713) made use of the ideas associated with "conjecture" and "expectation," but it was the publication of Laplace's probability theory in 1812 which served as the early background work for mathematical statistics.

Theoretical sampling laws, in simple cases, may be approached through the application of *mathematical probability*, a term not similarly defined by members of various disciplines. However, here we accept the classical definition of quantitative probability offered by Laplace — *the ratio of the number of favorable cases to the number of all possible cases*. In using the term *probability* or *chance*, questions concerning the future are discussed and judgments are made which rarely fall into the "yes-or-no," "true-false" categories. Thus we plan for the future, but take into account such descriptive terms as "possible," "extremely likely," and "probable" in dealing with future events which at the moment are uncertainties. In these determinations, it must be remembered that rigorous application of mathematics is in no sense without limitations imposed by conditions. The renowned physicist, Helmholtz, offered a proof that remains correct today showing that man will never be able to fly. His system was developed without accounting for the subsequent high ratio of horsepower to engine weight in heavier-than-air craft. Successful applications of mathematical probability are often restricted through failure of the statistician to realize that the stable situation of the moment may be rapidly approaching instability.

4.1 *Simple Probability Problems.* We begin by confining our discussion to the simplest games of chance. First, we consider the toss of a single coin. Here there are two possible *outcomes* — heads or tails. If we consider these outcomes as *equally likely*, we assign them the same probability, that is, the ratio of one *favorable* outcome to the total number, 2, of possible outcomes, giving $\frac{1}{2}$.

As another illustration, consider the problem of drawing a single marble from a bag containing m red marbles and n white marbles. Here there are $m + n$ possible outcomes. If we consider the *event* of drawing a red marble, there are m outcomes that produce this result; that is, there are m favorable outcomes. If we assume that the drawings of single marbles are equally likely, the *probability of the event* of drawing a red marble is the ratio of m to $(m + n)$; in symbols we have:

$$P(\text{red marble}) = \frac{m}{m + n}$$

Thus, it may be seen that probability is a *ratio* of the number of ways favorable to an event to the total number of possible outcomes, both favorable and unfavorable. The limits of the fraction are 0 and 1, representing certain failure and certain success, respectively.

The probability may be thought of as the theoretical estimate of the *relative frequency* of an event, that is, the ratio of the number of times (*frequency*) an event occurs to the total number of trials. In the example above, if a marble is drawn and replaced in the bag a large number of times, the relative frequency of the occurrence of a red marble may be expected to be close to the probability value $m/(m + n)$.

In one throw of a die there are six possible outcomes; the face appearing may show any one of the number of spots, ranging from 1 to 6. Again, assigning equal probabilities to the six faces of the ideal die, we see one way (m) favorable to the appearance of a six on the top face of the thrown die, and six possible outcomes, $(m + n)$. Hence the probability of the appearance of a six on the die is $\frac{1}{6}$.

4.2 *Probability Defined.* If an event can occur in m ways and fail to occur in n ways, all ways being equally likely, we say that the probability of success p and the probability of failure q are respectively:

$$p = \frac{m}{m + n}$$

$$q = \frac{n}{m + n}$$

Since $p + q = 1$, $q = 1 - p$; that is, the chance of success plus the chance of failure equals 1. By way of illustration, suppose we draw a card from a shuffled deck of playing cards. What is the probability of drawing a spade from the standard 52-card deck?

$$p = \frac{13}{13 + 39} = \frac{13}{52} = \frac{1}{4}$$

Since 13 of the cards in the deck are spades, there are exactly 13 favorable outcomes and 39 unfavorable outcomes.

4.3 *Relative Frequencies in Extended Trials.* We are often interested in *empirical probability* developed from direct observations and interpretations of these observations of measurements on real objects. Under the definition given, the probability of obtaining a head in one toss of a coin is $\frac{1}{2}$. In repeated trials of coin tossing, the percentage of heads appearing is found experimentally to be very near 50 percent, or approximately one-half the coins fall heads. Thus we may think of 500 throws of one coin as a sample of 500 from the population of throws that could be made with that particular coin, or we may make one throw of 500 coins. In either case, repeated trials may yield a series of observations such as 239, 245, 256, or 261 heads. The *relative frequencies* of the number of heads are found near the mean, 250, in a frequency distribution (compare development on page 49). However, a *particular* coin used in an extended series of throws may appear with heads up more often than tails so that heads and tails are not equally likely. In this case we think of the probability of the *particular* coin falling heads as the ratio of the number of heads appearing to the total number of throws of that coin in the series.

From experimental results or from observations made on actual objects or events we can estimate probabilities of future events. Thus we may estimate, from a mortality table, the chance that a person of a given age will live through the next year, or the next five years. A university record system may indicate that 40 of 100 students scoring below a given point K, on ACT tests will fail a mathematics course. From these data we may estimate that an entering freshman who scores above point K has a probability $p = 0.60$ of passing the mathematics course. If we find by inspection an average of 25 defective articles per thousand manufactured in a given process, and one of these 1000 articles is selected at random, we estimate that the probability this article will be defective is $\frac{25}{1000}$, or 2.5 percent.

4.4 *Prediction of Frequencies in Repeated Trials.* By computing the mathematical probability for an experiment, we may estimate what the relative frequency would be if a large number of trials were made.

Let us compute the probability of obtaining two heads in one toss of two coins. The first step is to determine the number of possible outcomes. These are listed below, where H stands for heads and T for tails:

$$HH \qquad HT \qquad TT$$
$$TH$$

The total number of outcomes is four. The number of outcomes that produce the specified event, that of obtaining two heads, is one. Therefore the probability is $\frac{1}{4}$.

If we now ask what is the probability of obtaining exactly two heads in one toss of three coins, we select from the model for this series of outcomes

$$HHH \qquad HHT \qquad HTT \qquad TTT$$
$$HTH \qquad THT$$
$$THH \qquad TTH$$

those combinations which contain exactly two heads. Since the total number of outcomes is eight, and the three combinations containing exactly two heads are observed to be **HHT, HTH, THH**, the probability of this event is $\frac{3}{8}$. Moreover, the sum of the separate probabilities $\sum P(X)$ equals 1.

$$P \text{ (three heads)} = \tfrac{1}{8}$$
$$P \text{ (two heads)} = \tfrac{3}{8}$$
$$P \text{ (one head)} = \tfrac{3}{8}$$
$$P \text{ (no heads)} = \tfrac{1}{8}$$
$$\sum P(X) = 1$$

Similarly, a model may be arranged for all possible outcomes of one throw of two dice, one red (R), the other green (G), as shown below:

R	G	R	G	R	G	R	G	R	G	R	G
1,	1	1,	2	1,	3	1,	4	1,	5	1,	6
2,	1	2,	2	2,	3	2,	4	2,	5	2,	6
3,	1	3,	2	3,	3	3,	4	3,	5	3,	6
4,	1	4,	2	4,	3	4,	4	4,	5	4,	6
5,	1	5,	2	5,	3	5,	4	5,	5	5,	6
6,	1	6,	2	6,	3	6,	4	6,	5	6,	6

For the 36 possible outcomes shown in the combinations above, the number under R refers to the face showing on the red die, while the second number of the pair, under G, refers to the number showing on the green die. Thus the probability of obtaining a total of 6 may be determined by the ratio of the number of ways of making 6, that is, (5, 1), (4, 2), (3, 3), (3, 4), (1, 5), to the 36 possible outcomes, or $\frac{5}{36}$. Again it must be remembered that our mathematical model indicates what may be expected *in the long run.*

4.5 *Combinations of Events*

4.5.1 *The Addition Rules.* Let us suppose that *two events* are *mutually exclusive*, that is, they cannot occur together:

$$P(A \text{ or } B) = P(A) + P(B)$$

Example 1. What is the probability of drawing either a spade or a heart in a single draw from a standard 52-card deck?

$$P \text{ (spade)} = \tfrac{13}{52}, \text{ and } P \text{ (heart)} = \tfrac{13}{52}$$
$$P \text{ (spade or heart)} = \tfrac{13}{52} + \tfrac{13}{52} = \tfrac{26}{52} = \tfrac{1}{2}$$

Example 2. What is the probability of drawing either the ace of spades or a diamond?

$$P \text{ (ace of spades)} = \tfrac{1}{52}$$
$$P \text{ (a diamond)} = \tfrac{13}{52}$$
$$P \text{ (ace of spades or a diamond)} = \tfrac{1}{52} + \tfrac{13}{52} = \tfrac{14}{52}$$

When events A and B are *not* mutually exclusive, the probability that *either* event A or event B will happen is:

$$P(A \text{ or } B) = P(A) + P(B) - P(A \text{ and } B)$$

Example 3. In an advanced mathematics class of 25 students, 15 are mathematics majors, six are seniors, and three of the six seniors are mathematics majors. What is the probability that one student chosen at random is either a mathematics major or a senior?

$P(A) = \tfrac{15}{25}$, that the student is a mathematics major,
$P(B) = \tfrac{6}{25}$, that the student is a senior,
$P(A \text{ and } B) = \tfrac{3}{25}$, that the student is a senior and a mathematics major,
$P(A \text{ or } B) = \tfrac{15}{25} + \tfrac{6}{25} - \tfrac{3}{25} = \tfrac{18}{25}.$

4.5.2 *The Multiplication Rule.* When two events, A and B, are *independent* one of the other, the probability that *both* of the events will occur is the product of the separate probabilities of each event.

$$P(A \text{ and } B) = P(A) \times P(B)$$

For example, when a single coin is tossed twice, the probability of obtaining a head on the first toss is $\tfrac{1}{2}$, and the probability of obtaining a head on the second toss is $\tfrac{1}{2}$; therefore the probability of obtaining two heads is

$$\tfrac{1}{2} \times \tfrac{1}{2} = \tfrac{1}{4}$$

since the two tosses are independent one of the other. If we extend this rule to the throw of a die, we may compute the probability of obtaining a 3 on the first throw and a 5 on the second throw as $\tfrac{1}{6} \times \tfrac{1}{6} = \tfrac{1}{36}.$

Example 1. What is the probability of drawing two aces consecutively, with replacement, from a standard 52-card deck?

$$P(A \text{ and } B) = \tfrac{4}{52} \times \tfrac{4}{52} = \tfrac{1}{169}$$

Example 2. What is the probability of drawing the 2 of spades and the 10 of diamonds, with replacement, from a standard 52-card deck?

$$P(A \text{ and } B) = \tfrac{1}{52} \times \tfrac{1}{52} = \tfrac{1}{2704}$$

4.5.3 *Conditional Probability.* If $P(A)$ indicates the probability of the occurrence of the event (A) and $P(B|A)$ indicates the *conditional probability* of the occurrence of event (B) after (A) is known to have happened, then the probability that both events will occur is:

$$P(A \text{ and } B) = P(A) \times P(B|A)$$

Example 1. What is the probability of drawing two aces consecutively and without replacement from a standard 52-card deck?

$$P(A \text{ and } B) = \tfrac{4}{52} \times \tfrac{3}{51} = \tfrac{1}{221}$$

Example 2. A lot of 100 electrical fuses contains four defectives. A sample of four is drawn from the lot. Compute the probability that the sample contains all four defectives:

$$\frac{4}{100} \times \frac{3}{99} \times \frac{2}{98} \times \frac{1}{97} = \frac{24}{94,109,400} = \frac{1}{3,921,225}$$

4.6 *The Binomial Distribution.* By using mathematical models similar to those in Section 4.4, we can calculate the probabilities for the occurrence of a given number of heads or tails in throwing successively larger numbers of coins. However, this method soon becomes laborious, and we look for another approach.

Compare the array of outcomes for tossing two coins on page 45 with the binomial expansion:

$$(p + q)^2 = p^2 + 2pq + q^2$$

Also, compare the array of outcomes for tossing three coins with the binomial expansion:

$$(p + q)^3 = p^3 + 3p^2q + 3pq^2 + q^3$$

Observe that in each case the sum of the coefficients in the expansion is equal to the number of outcomes and that this sum is equal to 2^n where n is the number of coins tossed. Observe also that the coefficients from left to right are the numerators of the ratios representing the separate probabilities for n, $n - 1, \ldots, 0$ heads. Each denominator is 2^n.

In general, the expansion of $(p + q)^n$ is:

$$(p + q)^n = p^n + np^{n-1}q + \frac{n(n-1)}{2}\,p^{n-2}q^2 + \frac{n(n-1)(n-2)}{2 \cdot 3}\,p^{n-3}q^3$$

$$+ \cdots + \frac{n(n-1)\cdots(n-x+1)}{1 \cdot 2 \cdot 3 \cdots x}\,p^{n-x}q^x + \cdots + q^n$$

Several more observations may be made from the expansion. First, the expansion will contain $(n + 1)$ terms, and will terminate in q^n, if n is any positive whole number. Also, the exponent of p decreases by one from term to term, while the exponent of q increases by one. And if the actual expansions are performed, using exponents beginning with 0, an arrangement called Pascal's triangle develops.

$$(p + q)^0 = \qquad\qquad 1$$
$$(p + q)^1 = \qquad\qquad p + q$$
$$(p + q)^2 = \qquad\quad p^2 + 2pq + q^2$$
$$(p + q)^3 = \qquad p^3 + 3p^2q + 3pq^2 + q^3$$
$$(p + q)^4 = \quad p^4 + 4p^3q + 6p^2q^2 + 4pq^3 + q^4$$
$$(p + q)^5 = p^5 + 5p^4q + 10p^3q^2 + 10p^2q^3 + 5pq^4 + q^5$$

By writing only the numerical coefficients, we obtain the arrangement below:

				1			
1 coin			1		1		
2 coins			1	2	1		
3 coins		1	3		3	1	
4 coins	1	4		6	4	1	
5 coins	1	5	10	10	5	1	

Observe that each of the numbers representing the coefficients is equal to the sum of the two numbers above it, as shown in the small triangle.

For example, we may determine the probabilities of 5, 4, 3, 2, 1, or 0 heads when 5 coins are tossed at once by substituting in the expression $(p + q)^n$, remembering that n is the number of coins rather than the number of tosses.

$$\left(\frac{1}{2} + \frac{1}{2}\right)^5 = \left(\frac{1}{2}\right)^5 + 5\left(\frac{1}{2}\right)^4\left(\frac{1}{2}\right) + \frac{5 \cdot 4}{2}\left(\frac{1}{2}\right)^3\left(\frac{1}{2}\right)^2 + \frac{5 \cdot 4 \cdot 3}{2 \cdot 3}\left(\frac{1}{2}\right)^2\left(\frac{1}{2}\right)^3$$

$$+ \frac{5 \cdot 4 \cdot 3 \cdot 2}{2 \cdot 3 \cdot 4}\left(\frac{1}{2}\right)\left(\frac{1}{2}\right)^4 + \frac{5 \cdot 4 \cdot 3 \cdot 2 \cdot 1}{2 \cdot 3 \cdot 4 \cdot 5}\left(\frac{1}{2}\right)^5$$

The probabilities of tossing a given number of heads are tabulated below:

Number of Heads	5	4	3	2	1	0
Probability	$\frac{1}{32}$	$\frac{5}{32}$	$\frac{10}{32}$	$\frac{10}{32}$	$\frac{5}{32}$	$\frac{1}{32}$

4.7 *Theoretical Binomial Frequencies*. In tossing 10 coins simultaneously, we have an example of the general case $(p + q)^{10}$, and *in the long run*, 10 heads would appear once in 1,024 times, or $P(10) = 0.00098$. In a similar manner $P(9) = \frac{10}{1024} = 0.00977$ for nine heads. The complete frequency distribution for 10 coins is shown in Table 4.1.

TABLE 4.1

FREQUENCY DISTRIBUTION FOR TOSSING 10 COINS

Number of Heads (X)	Frequency (f)	Probability P(X)	XP(X)
10	1	0.00098	0.00980
9	10	0.00977	0.08793
8	45	0.04394	0.35152
7	120	0.11719	0.82033
6	210	0.20508	1.23048
5	252	0.24609	1.23045
4	210	0.20508	0.82032
3	120	0.11719	0.35157
2	45	0.04394	0.08788
1	10	0.00977	0.00977
0	1	0.00098	
Total	1024	1.00001	$\sum XP(X) = 5.00005$

The histogram for this frequency distribution is shown in Figure 4.1. Although any given outcome X is a discrete value, such as 2 or 3, the rectangles are drawn over a range, as from 1.5 to 2.5, centered at the particular value.

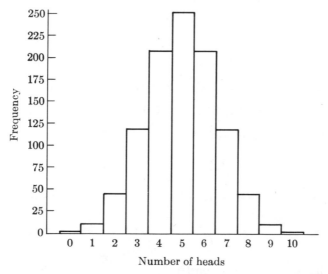

Figure 4.1 *Distribution of probabilities of number of heads in tossing 10 coins.*

Any empirical distribution obtained by tossing 10 coins will yield values which only approximate the values shown in Table 4.1. Let us repeat the coin-tossing process but with the number of coins becoming successively larger (30–50–100). We then plot the histogram by scaling both the ordinate and the abscissa in such a manner that the base line of the histogram will be approximately the same length as in Figure 4.1 and the heights of the more numerous but narrower rectangles will be similar to those of the figure. Then the rectangles of the histogram will approach the contour of a *smooth curve*. Although the binomial distribution deals with a discrete variable, as n becomes larger, the mid-points of the rectangles become closer, so that the figure outline becomes more continuous.

4.8 *Permutations and Combinations*

4.8.1 *Permutations.* It is often useful to enumerate the possible ways events can occur, that is, how many different ways a given number of objects from a set can be *arranged*. Such an *arrangement* designated by $P_{n,r}$, is called a *permutation*, denoting the number of permutations of n objects taken r at a time. A permutation is concerned with the number of members forming a group and the order or arrangement of members within the group.

As a simple example, recall the ways in which three different books may be arranged on a shelf. We have three choices for the first book; then we have two choices for the second book, and finally we have one remaining for the third book. Thus, $3 \times 2 = 6$ arrangements are possible:

$$\text{ABC, ACB; BAC, BCA; CAB, CBA}$$

In general, we have the formula:

$$P_{n,n} = n(n - 1) \cdots 1 = n!$$

If we have four objects, A, B, C, and D, the following pairs may be selected:

$$\text{AB, AC, AD; BA, BC, BD; CA, CB, CD; DA, DB, DC}$$

The number may be computed as:

$$\frac{4 \times 3 \times 2 \times 1}{2 \times 1} = 12$$

In general, the number of permutations of n distinct objects taken r at a time is:

$$P_{n,r} = \frac{n!}{(n - r)!}$$

(Recall that 0! is defined to be 1.)

Example 1. How many *line-ups* are possible for a bowling team of five members to be selected from 10 men?

$$\frac{10 \times 9 \times 8 \times 7 \times 6 \times 5 \times 4 \times 3 \times 2 \times 1}{5 \times 4 \times 3 \times 2 \times 1} = 30{,}240$$

If two of the three books mentioned earlier were alike, the number of distinguishable arrangements would be reduced. If B and C were the same, we would have only:

ABB, BAB, BBA

In general, the number of distinguishable arrangements of n objects, i of which are of one kind, j of another, k of another and so on, is:

$$P_n(i, j, k) = \frac{n!}{i! j! k! \cdots}$$

Example 2. How many different permutations can be obtained from the word *college?* Since there are two l's and two e's, we have:

$$\frac{7!}{1! 1! 2! 2! 1!} = \frac{7!}{2! 2!} = 1{,}260$$

4.8.2 *Combinations*. The total number of possible selections of r objects taken from n objects is referred to as the number of combinations of n objects taken r at a time. Designated as $C_{n,r}$, a combination is concerned with the number of members in a group without regard to the order or arrangement of members within the group.

If order is not to be considered, we have only the following pairs selected from four objects:

AB, AC, AD, BC, BD, CD

In general, the number of combinations of n distinct objects taken r at a time is:

$$C_{n,r} = \frac{n!}{r!(n-r)!} = \frac{P_{n,r}}{r!}$$

Notice that $C_{n,n} = 1$.

Example. How many committees of three members each can be selected from a group of 12 students?

$$\frac{12!}{3! 9!} = 220$$

4.8.3 *Values of $C_{n,r}$ as Binomial Coefficients.* The coefficient of the general term of the binomial expansion on page 48 is:

$$\frac{n(n-1)\cdots(n-r+1)}{1\cdot 2\cdot 3\cdots r}$$

This can be rewritten as:

$$\frac{n(n-1)\cdots(n-r+1)(n-r)\cdots 1}{r!(n-r)!} = \frac{n!}{r!(n-r)!} = C_{n,r}$$

Values of $C_{n,r}$ for $n \le 10$ are shown in Table 4.2 indicating a relationship observed earlier in Pascal's triangle (Section 4.6). Notice that $C_{n,r} = C_{n,n-r}$.

TABLE 4.2

BINOMIAL COEFFICIENTS

n	$C_{n,0}$	$C_{n,1}$	$C_{n,2}$	$C_{n,3}$	$C_{n,4}$	$C_{n,5}$	$C_{n,6}$	$C_{n,7}$	$C_{n,8}$	$C_{n,9}$	$C_{n,10}$	Total
0	1											1
1	1	1										2
2	1	2	1									2^2
3	1	3	3	1								2^3
4	1	4	6	4	1							2^4
5	1	5	10	10	5	1						2^5
6	1	6	15	20	15	6	1					2^6
7	1	7	21	35	35	21	7	1				2^7
8	1	8	28	56	70	56	28	8	1			2^8
9	1	9	36	84	126	126	84	36	9	1		2^9
10	1	10	45	120	210	252	210	120	45	10	1	2^{10}

From the extreme right column, it may be observed that $\sum_{r=0}^{n} C_{n,r} = 2^n$.

If X represents the number of heads appearing on a toss, we see from the development on page 48 that $X = r$. Thus the probability that X heads will appear in one toss of n coins or n tosses of one coin is:

$$P(X) = C_{n,X} \left(\frac{1}{2}\right)^X \left(\frac{1}{2}\right)^{X-r}$$

Example 1. What is the probability of throwing exactly one head in five tosses of a coin?

$$P(1) = 5 \left(\frac{1}{2}\right) \left(\frac{1}{2}\right)^4 = \frac{5}{32}$$

Example 2. What is the probability of throwing either five or six heads in 10 tosses of a coin?

$$P(5 \text{ or } 6) = P(5) + P(6)$$

$$= 252 \left(\frac{1}{2}\right)^5 \left(\frac{1}{2}\right)^5 + 210 \left(\frac{1}{2}\right)^6 \left(\frac{1}{2}\right)^4 = \frac{462}{1024} = \frac{231}{512}$$

4.9 *The Mean and Variance of the Binomial Distribution.* We now consider the general binomial distribution defined by

$$P(X) = \frac{n!}{X!(n-X)!} p^X q^{n-X} = C_{n,X} p^X q^{n-X}$$

where $p + q = 1$. Notice also that:

$$\Sigma P(X) = \Sigma C_{n,X} p^X q^{n-X} = 1$$

In Section 4.7 the separate probabilities for obtaining a given number of heads in one toss of 10 coins were shown in a probability table, where the term $P(X)$ denotes the probability that a given value of X will occur. In Table 4.1 $\Sigma P(X)$ was seen to come out practically 1.

Table 4.3 (pages 54–55) lists the values for a general binomial distribution. We shall now compute formulas for the mean, the variance, and the standard deviation for this distribution. Since the entire population is assumed to be used, we shall use the symbolism μ, σ^2, and σ associated with populations (see pages 16 and 28–29); $N = \Sigma f$.

By definition (pages 16–17) and since $P(X) = f/N$ (page 49):

$$\mu = \frac{\Sigma f X}{N} = \Sigma X P(X)$$

We can find a formula for this by referring to column 3 of Table 4.3. We can factor a common term, np, from each entry in this column. The terms remaining are those of the binomial $(p + q)^{n-1}$. Thus the sum of the terms in column 3 is:

$$\Sigma X P(X) = np(p + q)^{n-1}$$

Since $p + q = 1$, the mean of the binomial distribution is:

$$\mu = np$$

The variance of a population is defined (pages 28–29) as:

$$\sigma^2 = \frac{\Sigma(X - \mu)^2}{N}$$

which can be modified to be:

$$\sigma^2 = \frac{\Sigma X^2}{N} - \mu^2$$

Modifying the definition of variance again to allow for grouped data, we have (compare page 30):

$$\sigma^2 = \frac{\Sigma f X^2}{N} - \mu^2$$

TABLE 4.3

THE MEAN AND VARIANCE OF THE BINOMIAL DISTRIBUTION

X	$P(X)$	$XP(X)$
n	P^n	np^n
$n-1$	$np^{n-1}q$	$n(n-1)p^{n-1}q$
$n-2$	$\dfrac{n(n-1)}{1\cdot 2}p^{n-2}q$	$\dfrac{n(n-1)(n-2)}{1\cdot 2}p^{n-2}q^2$
$n-3$	$\dfrac{n(n-1)(n-2)}{1\cdot 2\cdot 3}p^{n-3}q^2$	$\dfrac{n(n-1)(n-2)(n-3)}{1\cdot 2\cdot 3}p^{n-3}q^3$
$\vdots$	$\vdots$	$\vdots$
3	$\dfrac{n(n-1)(n-2)}{1\cdot 2\cdot 3}p^3 q^{n-3}$	$\dfrac{n(n-1)(n-2)}{1\cdot 2}p^3 q^{n-3}$
2	$\dfrac{n(n-1)}{1\cdot 2}p^2 q^{n-2}$	$(n)(n-1)p^2 q^{n-2}$
1	npq^{n-1}	npq^{n-1}
0	q^n	0

$$\sum XP(X) = np(p+q)^{n-1}$$
$$\mu = np \text{ since } p+q = 1$$

$$X^2 P(X) = (X - 1)XP(X) + XP(X)$$

$$n(n - 1)p^n + np^n = n(n - 1)p^2(p^{n-2}) + np(p^{n-1})$$

$$n(n - 1)(n - 2)p^{n-1}q + n(n - 1)p^{n-1}q$$
$$= n(n - 1)p^2[(n - 2)p^{n-3}q] + np[(n - 1)p^{n-2}q]$$

$$\frac{n(n - 1)(n - 2)(n - 3)}{1 \cdot 2} p^{n-2}q^2 + \frac{n(n - 1)(n - 2)}{1 \cdot 2} p^{n-2}q^2$$
$$= n(n - 1)p^2\left[\frac{(n - 2)(n - 3)}{1 \cdot 2} p^{n-4}q^2\right] + np\left[\frac{(n - 1)(n - 2)}{1 \cdot 2} p^{n-3}q^2\right]$$

$$\frac{n(n - 1)(n - 2)(n - 3)(n - 4)}{1 \cdot 2 \cdot 3} p^{n-3}q^3 + \frac{n(n - 1)(n - 2)(n - 3)}{1 \cdot 2 \cdot 3} p^{n-3}q^3$$
$$= n(n - 1)p^2 \frac{(n - 2)(n - 3)(n - 4)}{1 \cdot 2 \cdot 3} p^{n-5}q^3$$
$$+ np\left[\frac{(n - 1)(n - 2)(n - 3)}{1 \cdot 2 \cdot 3} p^{n-4}q^3\right]$$

$$\vdots$$

$$\frac{n(n - 1)(n - 2)}{1 \cdot 2} p^3 q^{n-3} + \frac{n(n - 1)(n - 2)}{1 \cdot 2} p^3 q^{n-3}$$
$$= n(n - 1)p^2\left[\frac{(n - 2)}{1 \cdot 2} pq^{n-3}\right] + np\left[\frac{(n - 1)(n - 2)}{1 \cdot 2} p^2 q^{n-3}\right]$$

$$n(n - 1)p^2 q^{n-2} + n(n - 1)p^2 q^{n-2}$$
$$= n(n - 1)p^2(q^{n-2}) + np[(n - 1)pq^{n-2}]$$

$$0 + npq^{n-1} = 0 + np(q^{n-1})$$

$$0$$

$$\sum X^2 P(X) = n(n - 1)p^2(p + q)^{n-2} + np(p + q)^{n-1}$$
$$= n(n - 1)p^2 + np$$
$$= n^2 p^2 - np^2 + np$$
$$\sigma^2 = n^2 p^2 - np^2 + np - n^2 p^2 = np(1 - p) = npq$$

In the binomial distribution, $N = \Sigma f$ and $P(X) = f/N$; hence:

$$\sigma^2 = \Sigma X^2 P(X) - \mu^2$$

If we let

$$X^2 = X(X - 1) + X$$

expression $\Sigma X^2 P(X)$ becomes:

$$\Sigma X^2 P(X) = \Sigma[X(X - 1) + X]P(X)$$
$$= \Sigma[X(X - 1)]P(X) + \Sigma XP(X)$$

This sum is computed in column 4 of Table 4.3 on page 55. Notice that each expression has been arranged in two terms. The first term in each case has the factor $n(n - 1)p^2$ and the second has the factor np. When these terms are summed, we find:

$$\Sigma X^2 P(X) = n(n - 1)p^2(p + q)^{n-2} + np(p + q)^{n-1}$$

Since $p + q = 1$, this reduces to:

$$n(n - 1)p^2 + np$$

Therefore we have:

$$\sigma^2 = n(n - 1)p^2 + np - \mu^2$$

Since $\mu = np$ in the binomial distribution, we have:

$$\sigma^2 = n(n - 1)p^2 + np - n^2p^2$$
$$= n^2p^2 - np^2 + np - n^2p^2$$
$$= np - np^2$$
$$= np(1 - p)$$
$$= npq$$

as is shown in Table 4.3.

PROBLEMS

1. What is the probability of:
   (a) Throwing a 3 in one toss of a single die?
   (b) Drawing the ace of spades from a 52-card deck?
   (c) Selecting a male student when choosing one person by lot from a class of 12 men and seven women?
2. What is the probability of the appearance of a number greater than 2 in one throw of an ordinary die?
3. When four coins are tossed, what is the probability that all coins show heads?

4. What is the probability of throwing a total of 8 when two ordinary dice are thrown?

5. A game is played using a die and three coins. The die is rolled and the coins are tossed. Make a table showing all the possible equally likely results. Find the probabilities:
 (a) Of getting a 5 on the die, and two heads and one tail on the coins,
 (b) Of getting at least 3 on the die, and at most one head on the coins.

6. Seven coins are tossed. Make a table of the probabilities of getting $X = 0, 1, 2, 3, 4, 5, 6$, and 7 heads. What is the probability of getting at least two but no more than five heads on one toss?

7. From a set of 19 cards, numbered 1, 2, 3, . . . and 19, one is drawn at random. What is the chance that its number is a multiple of 3 or 7? What is the chance that the number will be a multiple of 3 or 5 or both?

8. If a true die is rolled five times, what is the probability that *exactly* two of the rolls will show 1?

9. What is the probability of *at least* eight heads in 10 tosses of a true coin?

10. What is the probability that, if there are exactly four failures in a class of 50, a random sample of five names will contain all four failures?

11. From six black marbles, and five white marbles, in how many ways can five marbles be selected, with two black and three white?

12. From a group of 10 men students and 20 women students a committee of three is chosen. Find the probability of choosing:
 (a) Three women,
 (b) Three men,
 (c) Two women and one man,
 (d) One woman and two men.

13. From a container holding four red marbles and six white marbles, what is the probability of drawing one of each color when two are drawn at random?

14. In an experiment involving four varieties of corn, four replications are made, with each variety planted in each row and in each column of a block as shown:

a	b	c	d
b	c	d	a
c	d	a	b
d	a	b	c

In how many ways can the four varieties of corn be placed in each row and each column without duplicating row or column arrangement?

15. In taking a true-false test consisting of 10 items, a student responded to each item by tossing a coin. What is the probability that the student answered correctly seven times and incorrectly three times?

16. In taking a 10-item multiple-choice test a student guesses his answer to each question. If each item has five possible responses and his guesses are independent, find the probability that he gets 9 or 10 correct answers.

17. The probability that a freshman student in a given college will enroll in the chemistry class during his first semester is 0.40, and the probability that he will enroll in the German class is 0.25. Assuming independence, what is the probability that a freshman student will enroll in both chemistry and German?

18. If the probability that the freshman student in Problem 17 can pass the semester examination in chemistry is 0.80, and the probability that he can pass the German examination is 0.75, what is the probability that the student passes both examinations, assuming that the two events are independent?

19. A rat is placed in a left-right alley maze and has five choices to make of alternate routes to receive a reward. If the probability of the rat's choosing the correct route is twice that of the probability of choosing the incorrect route, what is the probability that all five choices will be made correctly?

20. In an experiment concerned with art judgment, two color arrangements are compared by the subject. The arrangements are presented in random order and in succession, with the subject expressing a preference for the first or the second. In 10 trials the judgment of the subject agrees eight times with the predetermined answers supplied by the experimenter. Is this result better than chance expectation? How much better?

21. A speech class is divided into Section A with six boys and five girls and Section B with four boys and ten girls. A debater is chosen at random from each of the sections.
    (a) What is the probability that a boy will be chosen from Section A and a girl from Section B?
    (b) What is the probability of choosing a girl from Section A and a boy from Section B?
    (c) What is the probability of a boy and a girl being chosen (without respect to order)?

22. If we assume that boys and girls are equally likely to enroll in a given course, compute the probability that exactly 40 of the first 100 students enrolling in that course will be boys.

23. A coin is tossed until a tail appears, or until the coin has been tossed three times. If a tail does not appear on the first toss, what is the probability that the coin is tossed three times?

24. A student is asked to give the atomic weights of a series of seven chemical elements, ranking these in order from the lightest to the heaviest. If the student is able to arrange these in perfect rank order, how likely is he to be able to do this by guessing? State the probabilities of perfect rank order by chance for the following numbers of elements: 3, 4, 5, 6.

25. A basketball player is able, on the average, to make nine of 10 free throws. Find the probability that he will:
    (a) Make exactly four baskets in 10 throws.
    (b) Make the first five throws and miss the next five in 10 throws.

REFERENCES

Commission on Mathematics. *Introductory Probability and Statistical Inference.* 425 West 117th Street, New York: College Entrance Examination Board, 1957.

DuBois, Philip H. *An Introduction to Psychological Statistics.* New York: Harper and Row, Publishers, 1965. Chapter 11.

Freund, John C., and Williams, Frank J. *Elementary Business Statistics: The Modern Approach.* Englewood Cliffs, New Jersey: Prentice-Hall, Inc., 1964. Chapter 5.

Goldberg, S. *Probability, An Introduction.* Englewood Cliffs, N. J.: Prentice-Hall, Inc., 1960.

Guenther, William C. *Concepts of Statistical Inference.* New York: McGraw-Hill Book Company, 1965. Chapter 2.

McNemar, Quinn. *Psychological Statistics*, Third Edition. New York: John Wiley and Sons, Inc., 1962. Chapter 5.

Mosteller, Frederick, Rourke, Robert E. K. and Thomas, George B., Jr. *Probability, A First Course.* Reading, Massachusetts: Addison-Wesley Publishing Company, Inc., 1961.

Yamane, Taro. *Statistics, An Introductory Analysis.* New York: Harper and Row, Publishers, 1964. Chapter 5.

CONTINUOUS SAMPLING DISTRIBUTIONS

In Section 1.3, attention was directed to measurements made on both *continuous* and *discrete* series of items. In the *continuous* series, measurements are made on items differing by amounts which are infinitely small; in the *discrete* series, the items of the series are expressed by whole numbers. As a result of this nature of the *continuous* series, a single value does not represent a cell of any accountable width within a histogram. For this reason it is not possible to determine the *exact probability* of the value of a given point of a continuous series. Consequently, with continuous data, probability is spoken of in relation to the chances of a value of X occurring within a *range* of values of X, or

$$P(X_a \leq X \leq X_b)$$

Thus, $P(X = X_a) = 0$, and the sum of the probability values, $\sum P(X) = 1$, where 1 corresponds to certainty of occurrence.

In dealing with histograms representing the results of throwing coins, as presented earlier in Section 4.7, we found that as n (the number of coins) becomes successively larger, the rectangles of the histogram approach the contour of a smooth curve. This curve, together with the X-axis, encompasses the area representing all possible values of X. This area is considered to have a value of unity.

5.1 The Rectangular Probability Distribution. The simplest probability distribution function is the *rectangular* or *uniform distribution*.

$$f(X) = \frac{1}{b - a} \qquad (5.1)$$

In this distribution values of X are everywhere zero except between a and b. The $P(X)$ remains constant throughout the entire distribution for all values of X. Graphically this distribution is shown in Figure 5.1. In this distribution, $0 < a < b < 1$.

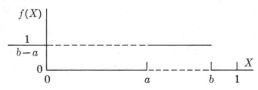

Figure 5.1 *The rectangular or uniform distribution.*

*5.2 The Normal Distribution. The continuous distribution basic to statistics is represented by a bilaterally symmetrical, bell-shaped curve extending over the range $-\infty < X < +\infty$. This distribution is shown in Figure 5.2. The exact description of this *normal distribution* is determined by the parameters μ and σ.

The equation for this distribution is:

$$Y(\mu, \sigma^2) = \frac{1}{\sigma\sqrt{2\pi}} e^{-\frac{1}{2}\left[\frac{(X-\mu)}{\sigma}\right]^2} \tag{5.2}$$

where

$\mu = $ Mean of distribution
$\sigma = $ Standard deviation of distribution
$\sigma^2 = $ Variance of distribution
$\pi = 3.1416$
$e = 2.7183$
$X = $ A measurement along the X-axis or the frequency of the point value X
$Y = $ Ordinate height of the curve at point X and corresponds to the probability of the value at point X.

Previously the statement has been made that in all continuous distribution functions the probability of X is spoken of in terms of a range of values of X within the limits of the particular distribution. Thus for the normal distribution, $P(-\infty < X < +\infty) = 1$. This unit value represents the total area under the curve representing this distribution. To determine

$$P(X_a < X < X_b)$$

we ascertain the relative portion of the area under the curve between $X = X_a$ and $X = X_b$. This may be determined mathematically by integrating the equation for the curve between the two points in question. We have:

$$P(X_a < X < X_b) = \frac{1}{\sigma\sqrt{2\pi}} \int_{X_a}^{X_b} e^{-\frac{1}{2}\left[\frac{X-\mu}{\sigma}\right]^2} dx \tag{5.3}$$

---

* Knowledge of calculus is required.

With such integration we find that

$$P[(\mu - 1\sigma) < X < (\mu + 1\sigma)] = 0.6826$$
$$P[(\mu - 1.282\sigma) < X < (\mu + 1.282\sigma)] = 0.8000$$
$$P[(\mu - 1.645\sigma) < X < (\mu + 1.645\sigma)] = 0.9000$$
$$P[(\mu - 1.96\sigma) < X < (\mu + 1.96\sigma)] = 0.9500$$
$$P[(\mu - 2.326\sigma) < X < (\mu + 2.326\sigma)] = 0.9800$$
$$P[(\mu - 2.576\sigma) < X < (\mu + 2.576\sigma)] = 0.9900$$

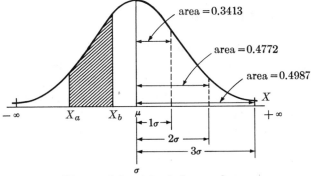

Figure 5.2   *A typical normal curve.*

Since each pair of parametric values for μ and σ describes a different curve, the task of determining $P(X_a < X < X_b)$ would readily become burdensome if it were computed for each use. By converting each normal distribution to a single standard form, the various probability values need be determined only once and can then be used as reference table. Determination of these values involves the conversion of each *value* of X to a standardized variate or standard score. A convenient variate is one which utilizes the two parameters μ and σ and which describes the relative position of the value of X in the distribution with respect to the center or mean of the distribution. (See Figure 5.3.) The value of the standard score, z, then may be computed as

$$z = \frac{X - \mu}{\sigma} \tag{5.4}$$

The area under the corresponding standardized curve is

$$A = P(z_{X_a} < z < z_{X_b}) = \frac{1}{\sqrt{2\pi}} \int_{z_{X_a}}^{z_{X_b}} e^{-\frac{z^2}{2}} \, dz \tag{5.5}$$

As discussed in Chapter 4, the mean, μ_z, of such a set of standard scores equals zero, and the variance, σ_z^2, as well as the standard deviation, σ_z, are each equal to unity.

The value obtained for z is in reality a statement describing the distance from μ to a value of X in units of size σ. Expressing the X values of a normal

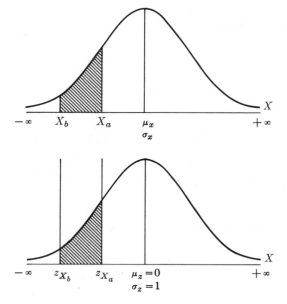

Figure 5.3 *A typical normal distribution of values of X and equivalents in z.*

distribution as standard z values permits this distribution to be compared with any other normal distribution which is similarly treated.

This may be illustrated by the following example.

If a normal distribution has $\mu = 50$ and $\sigma = 10$, a value of $X = 65$ would have a z value of

$$z = \frac{65 - 50}{10} = \frac{15}{10} = 1.5$$

This positions the value of $X = 65$ as 1.5σ units positive with respect to the mean μ.

In another normal distribution with $\mu = 100$ and $\sigma = 16$, a value of $X = 124$ has a z value of

$$z = \frac{124 - 100}{16} = \frac{24}{16} = 1.5$$

and is interpreted similarly.

Thus, if all values of X for any normal distribution that has parameters μ and σ are converted to z values, a standardized normal distribution will be generated. For this distribution of z values, the mean $\mu_z = 0$, and $\sigma_z = 1$.

Such conversion permits the computation of probabilities associated with areas under this standard curve. Table I of Appendix A presents the probabilities of a value of X being within a range of z values. This particular table is presented in such a manner that the probabilities are associated with the area under the curve more distant from μ than is the value of X. As shown in Figure 5.4, this corresponds to that area of the standard curve which is more distant from μ_z than is z.

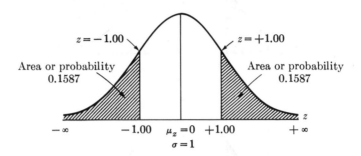

Figure 5.4 *Standardized normal distribution.*

The value of 0.1587 in Table I to be associated with $z = 1.00$ is a statement that $P(z > 1.00) = 0.1587$. Since the normal distribution is bilaterally symmetrical, $P(z < -1.00) = 0.1587$.   Use of Table I, Appendix A is again demonstrated by the following examples:

Example 1. In a normal distribution with $\mu = 25$ and $\sigma = 5$, what proportion of the cases fall between 20 and 30?

$$X_1 = 20, \quad z = \frac{20 - 25}{5} = -1.00$$

$$X_2 = 30, \quad z = \frac{30 - 25}{5} = +1.00$$

By referring to Table I of Appendix A, we observe that the tabulated value for $z = 1.00$ is 0.15866. Because the normal standard curve is symmetrical, the value corresponding to $z = -1.00$ (not shown in the table) is also 0.15866.

The total area under the curve as shown in Figure 5.4 corresponds to all possible cases and therefore is equivalent to certainty, or a probability equal to 1.00. Consequently, the area between $z = -1.00$ and $z = +1.00$, corresponding to the area between X_1 and X_2, must be:

$$1.00000 - (0.15866 + 0.15866) = 0.68268.$$

Example 2. In a normal distribution with $\mu = 12$ and $\sigma = 4$, what proportion of the cases lie above $X = 18$? Below $X = 4$?

$$X_1 = 18, \quad z = \frac{18 - 12}{4} = 1.5$$

From Table I the value corresponding to $z = 1.5$ is 0.066807. Thus the proportion of cases above $X = 18$ is 6.6807%.

$$X_2 = 4, \quad z = \frac{4 - 12}{4} = -2.00$$

From Table I, the value corresponding to $z = 2.00$ is 0.022750. By symmetry the value for $z = -2.00$ is also 0.022750. Hence the proportion of cases below $X = 4$ is 2.275%.

Example 3.   Given a normal distribution with $\mu = 16$ and $\sigma = 4$, what limits will include the middle 75% of the cases? From Table I, 12.507% of the cases lie above the point $z = 1.15\sigma$, and by symmetry, 12.507% of the cases lie below the point $z = -1.15\sigma$.

$$z = \frac{X_i - \mu}{\sigma}$$

Here we have $z = \pm1.15$, $\mu = 16$, and $\sigma = 4$.
Therefore

$$1.15 = \frac{X_1 - 16}{4}, \quad \text{and} \quad -1.15 = \frac{X_2 - 16}{4}$$

Solving for X_1 and X_2 we have:

$$X_1 = 4.60 + 16 = 20.6$$
$$X_2 = -4.60 + 16 = 11.4$$

Therefore, the middle 75% of the distribution lies between the limits $X_1 = 20.6$ and $X_2 = 11.4$.

5.2.1 *Normal Distribution of Sample Means.*   Most frequently in the testing of hypotheses, the researcher is interested in the likelihood of occurrence of a sample mean value within a population of sample means having a given mean ($\mu = \mu_0$), and variance ($\sigma^2 = \sigma_0^2$). (The distribution used is that of the sample mean $\overline{X}$.)

This distribution is predicated upon the following statement: When all possible random samples of size n have been drawn from a normal and independently distributed population having the parameters mean μ_0 and variance σ_0^2, their computed sample means will generate a normally distributed population having a mean $\mu_{\overline{X}}$ and a variance $\sigma_{\overline{X}}^2$.

Table 5.1 presents an example of this solution. Ten values of X (92, 80, 86, 77, 59, 88, 81, 68, 82, 87) represent a hypothetical population having $\mu_X = 80.0$ and $\sigma_X^2 = 99.1111$. Using the combinatorial concept, $C_{n,r}$, introduced in Section 4.8, the sample mean $\overline{X}$ and sample variances s_X^2 are computed for each of the 45 possible samples of size $n = 8$.

The mean $\mu_{\overline{X}}$ of this distribution of $\overline{X}$'s was found to be 80.00, and the mean of the 45 values of s_X^2 was 99.1175. Thus $\mu_X = \mu_{\overline{X}} = 80.00$ and

$$\sigma_X^2 = \frac{s_1^2 + s_2^2 + \cdots + s_{45}^2}{45} \qquad (5.6)$$

When the variance of the distribution of sample means $\sigma_{\overline{X}}^2$ is computed, it is found to be 2.4787, and may be rounded to 2.48. The variation of this value from the theoretical relationship of

$$\sigma_{\overline{X}}^2 = \frac{\sigma_X^2}{n} \qquad (5.7)$$

may be attributed to the small size of the original population. This relationship may be shown more precisely by using the concept of maximum likelihood functions.

It is of interest to note that the range of values for the distribution of $\overline{X}$'s extends from 77.5 to 84.1, and that for the original 10 values it was 59 to 92. This may be attributed to the fact that as $n \to N$, the estimator $\overline{X} \to \mu$, and the *standard error of estimate of the mean* $\sigma_{\overline{X}} \to 0$.

Where both parameters, μ and σ_X^2, are known, the various distributions of $\overline{X}$ may be reduced to the standardized normal distribution by the relationship:

$$z = \frac{\overline{X} - \mu}{\frac{\sigma_X}{\sqrt{n}}}$$

The value of z obtained from this expression is a statement of the number of standard error units the sample mean deviates from the population mean. The size of this standard error unit has been previously presented as a function of the size of the sample. This may be seen in the following examples.

Example 1. What is the probability of a sample of size 16 having a mean of at most 82 when it is drawn from a population with $\mu = 82.5$ and $\sigma_X = 4$?

$$z = \frac{\overline{X} - \mu}{\frac{\sigma_X}{\sqrt{n}}} = \frac{82 - 82.5}{\frac{4}{\sqrt{16}}}$$

$$= -0.500$$

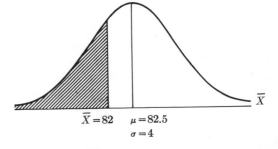

Thus $P(\overline{X} \leq 82) = 0.3085$
(Table I of Appendix A),
$\mu = 82.5$, $\sigma = 4$, $n = 16$.

TABLE 5.1

A DISTRIBUTION OF ALL POSSIBLE SAMPLE MEANS ($\overline{X}$) AND SAMPLE VARIANCES (s^2) FOR A HYPOTHETICAL POPULATION OF 10 VARIABLES ($\mu_X = 80.0$, $\sigma_X^2 = 99.11$); $n = 8$

Sample Number	Variable Values 92	80	86	77	59	88	81	68	82	87	$\overline{X}$	s^2
1			X	X	X	X	X	X	X	X	78.5	104.2857
2	X			X	X	X	X	X	X	X	79.2	121.9286
3	X	X			X	X	X	X	X	X	79.6	120.8393
4	X	X	X			X	X	X	X	X	83.0	52.8571
5	X	X	X	X			X	X	X	X	81.6	52.2679
6	X	X	X	X	X			X	X	X	78.9	116.6964
7	X	X	X	X	X	X			X	X	81.4	104.5536
8	X	X	X	X	X	X	X			X	81.2	104.5000
9	X	X	X	X	X	X	X	X			78.9	118.4107
10		X	X	X	X	X	X	X	X		77.6	93.4107
11	X		X	X	X	X	X	X	X		79.1	119.5536
12	X	X		X	X	X	X	X	X		78.4	112.2679
13	X	X	X		X	X	X	X	X		79.5	118.8571
14	X	X	X	X		X	X	X	X		81.8	53.9286
15	X	X	X	X	X		X	X	X		78.1	107.2679
16	X	X	X	X	X	X		X	X		79.0	119.1429
17	X	X	X	X	X	X	X		X		80.6	99.4107
18		X	X	X	X	X	X	X		X	78.2	102.7857
19	X		X	X	X	X	X	X		X	79.8	126.7857
20	X	X		X	X	X	X	X		X	79.0	120.5714
21	X	X	X		X	X	X	X		X	80.1	125.5536
22	X	X	X	X		X	X	X		X	82.4	57.4107
23	X	X	X	X	X		X	X		X	78.8	115.9286
24	X	X	X	X	X	X		X		X	79.6	126.5536
25		X	X	X	X	X	X		X	X	80.0	86.2857
26	X		X	X	X	X	X		X	X	81.5	104.2857
27	X	X		X	X	X	X		X	X	80.8	101.0714
28	X	X	X		X	X	X		X	X	81.9	101.5536
29	X	X	X	X		X	X		X	X	84.1	24.4107
30	X	X	X	X	X		X		X	X	80.5	97.4286
31		X	X	X	X	X		X	X	X	78.4	103.6964
32	X		X	X	X	X		X	X	X	79.9	127.2679
33	X	X		X	X	X		X	X	X	79.1	121.2679
34	X	X	X		X	X		X	X	X	80.2	125.9286
35	X	X	X	X		X		X	X	X	82.5	57.1429
36		X	X	X	X		X	X	X	X	77.5	90.5714
37	X		X	X	X		X	X	X	X	79.0	117.1429
38	X	X	X	X	X		X	X	X	X	78.2	109.6429
39	X	X	X		X		X	X	X	X	79.4	116.5536
40		X	X	X		X	X	X	X	X	81.1	42.4107
41	X		X	X		X	X	X	X	X	82.6	56.5536
42	X	X		X		X	X	X	X	X	81.9	55.2679
43		X	X		X	X	X	X	X	X	78.9	104.1250
44	X		X		X	X	X	X	X	X	80.4	125.9821
45			X	X	X	X	X	X	X	X	77.8	95.9286

Example 2. What would the probability of the first example be if the sample size were increased to $n = 25$?

$$z = \frac{82 - 82.5}{\dfrac{4}{\sqrt{25}}} = \frac{(-0.5)(5)}{4} = \frac{-2.5}{4} = -0.625$$

$$P(\overline{X} \le 82 | \mu = 82.5, \sigma = 4, n = 25) = 0.2660$$

Therefore, the increase in size of the sample from 16 to 25 increases the number of values of $\overline{X}$ between 82.0 and 82.5 since the standard error, $\sigma_{\overline{X}} = \sigma_X/\sqrt{n}$, has been reduced from 1.00 to 0.80. This is illustrated by the fact that 1,915 sample values of $\overline{X}$ would on the average fall between the two point values in Example 1, whereas 2,340 sample values of $\overline{X}$ would on the average fall between these same two points in Example 2.

5.2.2 *Normal Distribution of Differences between Sample Means of Two Populations (Independent Data).*

Often there is need to know something about the probability associated with the difference between two sample means, $\overline{X}_1$ and $\overline{X}_2$, which have been drawn from two independent populations having means μ_1 and μ_2 and variances σ_1^2 and σ_2^2. To work with the data in this situation and to be able to determine the probabilities, it is necessary to establish a single population. This single population is formed by determining *all* of the differences between all possible pairs of sample means of $\overline{X}$ values taking one from each of the two populations, we have:

$$\overline{X}_{11} - \overline{X}_{12}, \overline{X}_{11} - \overline{X}_{22}, \overline{X}_{11} - \overline{X}_{32}, \overline{X}_{11} - \overline{X}_{42}, \dots, \overline{X}_{11} - \overline{X}_{n_2 2},$$
$$\overline{X}_{21} - \overline{X}_{12}, \overline{X}_{21} - \overline{X}_{22}, \overline{X}_{21} - \overline{X}_{32}, \overline{X}_{21} - \overline{X}_{42}, \dots, \overline{X}_{21} - \overline{X}_{n_2 2},$$
$$\overline{X}_{31} - \overline{X}_{12}, \overline{X}_{31} - \overline{X}_{22}, \overline{X}_{31} - \overline{X}_{32}, \overline{X}_{31} - \overline{X}_{42}, \dots, \overline{X}_{31} - \overline{X}_{n_2 2},$$
$$\overline{X}_{41} - \overline{X}_{12}, \overline{X}_{41} - \overline{X}_{22}, \overline{X}_{41} - \overline{X}_{32}, \overline{X}_{41} - \overline{X}_{42}, \dots, \overline{X}_{41} - \overline{X}_{n_2 2},$$
$$\cdots\cdots\cdots\cdots\cdots\cdots\cdots\cdots\cdots\cdots\cdots\cdots\cdots ,$$
$$\overline{X}_{n_1 1} - \overline{X}_{12}, \overline{X}_{n_1 1} - \overline{X}_{22}, \overline{X}_{n_1 1} - \overline{X}_{32}, \overline{X}_{n_1 1} - \overline{X}_{42}, \dots, \overline{X}_{n_1 1} - \overline{X}_{n_2 2}.$$

The mean of this distribution is $\mu_d = \mu_1 - \mu_2$; the variance is:

$$\sigma_{(\overline{X}_1 - \overline{X}_2)}^2 = \frac{\sigma_1^2}{n_1} + \frac{\sigma_2^2}{n_2} \tag{5.8}$$

and the standardized deviate value, z, obtained by the expression is:

$$z = \frac{(\overline{X}_1 - \overline{X}_2) - (\mu_1 - \mu_2)}{\sqrt{\dfrac{\sigma_1^2}{n_1} + \dfrac{\sigma_2^2}{n_2}}} \tag{5.9}$$

Table 5.2 presents the $\overline{X}$ and s^2 values obtained from another distribution similar to that in Table 5.1. The parameters for the 10 original variable values are $\mu = 79.6$, and $\sigma^2 = 130.4889$. The mean of the sample means is 79.59 or 79.6 when rounded; the mean of the sample variances is 130.4889; and the variance of the distribution of $\overline{X}$'s is 3.2491, or 3.25 when rounded.

TABLE 5.2

A DISTRIBUTION OF ALL POSSIBLE SAMPLE MEANS ($\overline{X}$) AND SAMPLE VARIANCES (s^2) FOR A HYPOTHETICAL POPULATION OF 10 VARIABLES ($\mu_X = 79.6$, $\sigma_X^2 = 130.4889$); $n = 8$

Sample Number	Variable Values										$\overline{X}$	s^2
	83	64	63	85	91	87	93	75	88	67		
1			X	X	X	X	X	X	X	X	81.1	128.6964
2	X			X	X	X	X	X	X	X	83.6	75.1250
3	X	X			X	X	X	X	X	X	81.0	122.0000
4	X	X	X			X	X	X	X	X	77.5	140.0000
5	X	X	X	X			X	X	X	X	77.2	135.0714
6	X	X	X	X	X			X	X	X	77.0	126.5714
7	X	X	X	X	X	X			X	X	78.5	137.7143
8	X	X	X	X	X	X	X			X	79.1	154.4107
9	X	X	X	X	X	X	X	X			80.1	134.6964
10		X	X	X	X	X	X	X	X		80.8	141.9286
11	X		X	X	X	X	X	X	X		83.1	96.1250
12	X	X		X	X	X	X	X	X		83.2	90.5000
13	X	X	X		X	X	X	X	X		80.5	140.0000
14	X	X	X	X		X	X	X	X		79.8	126.5000
15	X	X	X	X	X		X	X	X		80.2	136.7857
16	X	X	X	X	X	X		X	X		79.5	119.4286
17	X	X	X	X	X	X	X		X		81.8	136.7857
18		X	X	X	X	X	X	X		X	78.1	153.5536
19	X		X	X	X	X	X	X		X	80.5	122.0000
20	X	X		X	X	X	X	X		X	80.6	117.1250
21	X	X	X		X	X	X	X		X	77.9	150.1250
22	X	X	X	X		X	X	X		X	77.1	132.1250
23	X	X	X	X	X		X	X		X	77.6	145.4107
24	X	X	X	X	X	X		X		X	76.9	123.5536
25		X	X	X	X	X	X		X	X	79.8	163.0714
26	X		X	X	X	X	X		X	X	82.1	122.6964
27	X	X		X	X	X	X		X	X	82.2	117.3571
28	X	X	X		X	X	X		X	X	79.5	160.5714
29	X	X	X	X		X	X		X	X	78.8	145.3571
30	X	X	X	X	X		X		X	X	79.2	156.7857
31		X	X	X	X	X		X	X	X	77.5	135.4286
32	X		X	X	X	X		X	X	X	79.9	107.2679
33	X	X		X	X	X		X	X	X	80.0	102.5714
34	X	X	X		X	X		X	X	X	77.2	131.6429
35	X	X	X	X		X		X	X	X	76.5	112.5714
36		X	X	X	X		X	X	X	X	78.2	156.2143
37	X		X	X	X		X	X	X	X	80.6	123.9821
38	X	X		X	X		X	X	X	X	80.8	119.0714
39	X	X	X		X		X	X	X	X	78.0	152.8571
40		X	X	X		X	X	X	X	X	77.8	143.6429
41	X		X	X		X	X	X	X	X	80.1	114.1250
42	X	X		X		X	X	X	X	X	80.2	109.3571
43		X	X		X	X	X	X	X	X	78.5	160.5714
44	X		X		X	X	X	X	X	X	80.9	126.9821
45		X		X	X	X	X	X	X	X	81.2	123.6429

TABLE 5.3

FREQUENCY (f) DISTRIBUTION OF 2025 DIFFERENCES BETWEEN VALUES OF TWO DISTRIBUTIONS OF SAMPLE MEANS
$$n_1 = n_2 = 8$$

x	f	x	f	x	f	x	f	x	f
−6.1	1	−3.3	11	−.5	23	2.3	24	5.1	4
−6.0	1	−3.2	12	−.4	30	2.4	30	5.2	3
−5.9	0	−3.1	12	−.3	32	2.5	19	5.3	5
−5.8	1	−3.0	16	−.2	26	2.6	24	5.4	7
−5.7	1	−2.9	10	−.1	27	2.7	21	5.5	5
−5.6	2	−2.8	13	.0	33	2.8	14	5.6	4
−5.5	2	−2.7	17	.1	25	2.9	19	5.7	1
−5.4	3	−2.6	17	.2	22	3.0	19	5.8	2
−5.3	1	−2.5	12	.3	34	3.1	17	5.9	3
−5.2	2	−2.4	20	.4	34	3.2	12	6.0	3
−5.1	2	−2.3	19	.5	27	3.3	17	6.1	3
−5.0	3	−2.2	19	.6	36	3.4	15	6.2	1
−4.9	2	−2.1	22	.7	32	3.5	13	6.3	1
−4.8	3	−2.0	29	.8	26	3.6	13	6.4	
−4.7	7	−1.9	22	.9	35	3.7	10	6.5	2
−4.6	6	−1.8	24	1.0	39	3.8	8	6.6	2
−4.5	3	−1.7	35	1.1	30	3.9	14	6.7	
−4.4	3	−1.6	33	1.2	25	4.0	15	6.8	
−4.3	6	−1.5	20	1.3	39	4.1	10	6.9	2
−4.2	8	−1.4	25	1.4	36	4.2	8	7.0	
−4.1	7	−1.3	29	1.5	25	4.3	13	7.1	1
−4.0	9	−1.2	27	1.6	30	4.4	11	7.2	1
−3.9	3	−1.1	29	1.7	34	4.5	8	7.3	
−3.8	4	−1.0	38	1.8	28	4.6	10	7.4	
−3.7	8	−.9	27	1.9	34	4.7	9	7.5	
−3.6	9	−.8	22	2.0	38	4.8	6	7.6	1
−3.5	5	−.7	33	2.1	26	4.9	9		
−3.4	8	−.6	34	2.2	15	5.0	8		

Table 5.3 shows the values which may be obtained by taking the differences of all possible pairs of values from Tables 5.1 and 5.2. The mean of this distribution of differences between the pairs of sample means was found to be 0.4 and the variance to be 4.69.

Data from Tables 5.1 and 5.2 may be used for examples utilizing Equation (5.9).

Example 1. $\overline{X}_{11} = 78.5$, $\overline{X}_{12} = 81.1$, $n_1 = n_2 = 8$

$$z = \frac{(78.5 - 81.1) - (80.0 - 79.6)}{\sqrt{\frac{99.1111}{8} + \frac{130.4889}{8}}} = -0.560$$

Using Table I, $P[(X_1 - X_2) \leq -2.6] = 0.28774$.

Example 2. $\overline{X}_{21} = 79.2$ and $\overline{X}_{22} = 83.6$

$$z = \frac{(79.2 - 83.6) - 0.4}{\sqrt{\frac{229.6}{8}}} = \frac{-4.4 - 0.4}{\sqrt{\frac{229.6}{8}}}$$

$$= \frac{-4.8}{5.4} = -0.889$$

Again referring to Table I, $P[(\overline{X}_1 - \overline{X}_2) \leq -4.4] = 0.18682$.

5.2.3 *Normal Distribution of Differences between Sample Means of Two Populations (Paired Data).* In certain instances it is unwise to utilize two different populations. An example of this may be in the determination of the effect of certain drugs on reaction times of the various subjects. At first glance it might seem appropriate to use two different groups, one receiving the drug and one receiving a *placebo* dosage. The restrictive feature of this design is that the variation between individuals may produce the observed differences (if they do exist). To eliminate this factor (as nearly as possible) the same subjects may be used to obtain both sets of observations. Then we may work with the *differences* between the individual pairs of values. This distribution of values of d_i represents the differences: $X_{11} - X_{12} = d_1$, $X_{21} - X_{12} = d_2, \ldots, X_{n1} - X_{n2} = d_n$. The mean of the differences is $\mu_d = \mu_1 - \mu_2$, and the variance, σ_d^2, may be computed in a manner similar to that for a distribution of X's.

$$\sigma_d^2 = \frac{\Sigma(d - \mu_d)^2}{N} \tag{5.10}$$

The sample statistic value for the mean is computed by:

$$\bar{d} = \frac{\Sigma d}{n} \tag{5.11}$$

and the sample variance of the differences by:

$$s_d^2 = \frac{\Sigma d^2 - \frac{(\Sigma d)^2}{n}}{n - 1} \tag{5.12}$$

The standardized deviate z is:

$$z = \frac{\bar{d} - \mu_d}{\frac{\sigma_d}{\sqrt{n}}} \qquad (5.13)$$

Further interpretation of problematic results using this distribution is presented in Section 7.3.1.

5.3 *Student's t Distribution.* It is necessary to know the parameter values of both μ and σ^2 to use the z statistic when working with normal distributions of X's, $\bar{X}$'s, $(\bar{X}_1 - \bar{X}_2)$'s or d's. In the majority of cases, however, the population variance, σ^2, is unknown. The only statistic available as an estimator of this parameter is the sample value for s^2. This value does not remain constant from one sample to the next and thus complicates the matter of determining the probability of occurrence of sample values. As was indicated in Chapter 3, the values of s^2 do approximate the value of σ^2. The closeness of approximation narrows rapidly as the sample size increases, or $s^2 \to \sigma^2$ as $n \to N$. This would indicate that the distribution of the sample mean estimators would approach the normal distribution as the sample size increases. This is shown in the set of tables edited by Smirnov. With the infinite number of distributions possible, it is not feasible to use the z statistic any longer. It was proposed by Student that another statistic be used which he called the t statistic. Student showed in his work that if the sample statistic is computed as the mean of the squared deviations of the single sample values from the sample mean, $[\sum(X - \bar{X})^2/n]$, a biased value occurs. He further demonstrated that a correction factor of $[n/(n - 1)]$ should be used with this biased estimator as:

$$s^2 = \frac{\sum(X - \bar{X})^2}{n} \cdot \frac{n}{n - 1}$$

This implies that there is a loss in the freedom of one member of the sample in determining the sample's dispersion. The remaining $(n - 1)$ members of the sample exert their total effect or represent the total *degrees of freedom* affecting the dispersion statistic and the associated distribution. Table II, Appendix A, gives values of t for various values of α (where $\alpha/2$ probability is in the end of each tail of the curve). Each value of α has many values of t. Each value of t is for a different number of degrees of freedom. In the case of distributions resulting from such statistics as $(\bar{X}_1 - \bar{X}_2)$, the degrees of freedom may be determined by subtracting one degree of freedom from the total sample members for each sample statistic used in computing the sample statistic, s^2.

As such, when the sample statistic, s, is used as the estimator of σ in computing the standardized deviate score t, the following formulas are used:

$$t = \frac{\overline{X} - \mu}{\dfrac{s}{\sqrt{n}}}, \quad \text{d.f.} = n - 1 \tag{5.14}$$

$$t = -\frac{(\overline{X}_1 - \overline{X}_2) - (\mu_1 - \mu_2)}{\sqrt{s_p^2\left[\dfrac{1}{n_1} + \dfrac{1}{n_2}\right]}}, \quad \text{d.f.} = n_1 + n_2 - 2 \tag{5.15}$$

(The derivation and nature of s_p^2 will be discussed in Section 7.3.2.)

$$t = \frac{\overline{d} - \mu_d}{\dfrac{s_d}{\sqrt{n}}}, \quad \text{d.f.} = n - 1 \tag{5.16}$$

This distribution has been worked out extensively giving the various values of t corresponding to given probabilities as related to sample size with the corresponding degrees of freedom. (See Table II, Appendix A.)

Three typical curves of the t distribution are presented in Figure 5.5. Inspection of the figure shows that as the number of degrees of freedom increases, the curve more closely approximates that of the normal distribution.

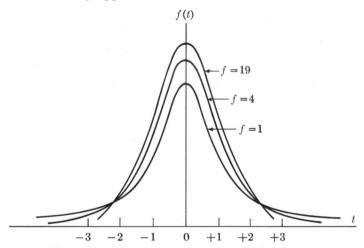

Figure 5.5 *Typical Student's t distribution curves.*

Table II is set up to include the values of t for specified probability levels and degrees of freedom. The value of α given at the top of each column represents the combined probability of a value of X or $\overline{X}$ falling further from the mean than the specified number of standard deviations or standard error units. In other words, if you were to go plus and minus the number of units indicated in the table, the combined areas in the two tails of the curve equals the value of the probability α shown at the head of the column. For example, looking into the column headed by $\alpha = 0.05$, at the level of d.f. $= 10$, the value read is 2.228. This means that the combined chance or probability of a value of X or $\overline{X}$ being either $(\mu - 2.228s_{\overline{X}})$ or $(\mu + 2.228s_{\overline{X}})$ is 0.05, or:

$$P(|\overline{X} - \mu| < -2.228s_{\overline{X}}) + P(|\overline{X} - \mu| > +2.228s_{\overline{X}}) = 0.05$$

This may also be read as

$$t_{0.025,10} = -2.228 \quad \text{and} \quad t_{0.975,10} = 2.228$$

As further practice, using a sample of $n = 12$, the d.f. $= n - 1 = 11$, the values of t read from the table are:

$t_{0.95,11} = 1.796$	$t_{0.975,11} = 2.201$	$t_{0.995,11} = 3.106$
$t_{0.05,11} = -1.796$	$t_{0.025,11} = -2.201$	$t_{0.005,11} = -3.106$

5.4 The Chi-Square (χ^2) Distribution. The normal distribution has been described as a bilaterally symmetrical distribution extending from $(-\infty)$ to $(+\infty)$. This normal distribution may be converted to a standardized distribution in terms of values of z. The mean of this distribution is $\mu = 0$ with $\sigma = 1$. The sum of the values of z for the total distribution is appropriately zero.

If it were desired to formulate a cumulative distribution function from the normal distribution, this would not be possible in terms of the conventional values of z, in that the z's are equally divided between positive and negative values. This troublesome point may be overcome by the process of squaring all of the values of z and then summing these over the range of separate values of z^2 for all members of the various possible samples of size n which may be drawn from any normal distribution:

$$z = \frac{X - \mu}{\sigma}$$

$$z^2 = \frac{(X - \mu)^2}{\sigma^2}$$

$$\Sigma z^2 = \Sigma \frac{(X - \mu)^2}{\sigma^2}$$

Since σ^2 is the same in all cases it may be factored out yielding:

$$\Sigma z^2 = \frac{1}{\sigma^2} [\Sigma (X - \mu)^2]$$

This cumulative distribution of values for Σz^2 for all k possible samples is known as the *Chi-Square distribution*, or more commonly, χ^2 *distribution*. Accordingly the χ^2 distribution is not the same in all cases, but is a function of the sample size, since all values of z are standardized.

Figure 5.6 presents several typical x^2 curves for varying degrees of freedom. It can be seen that for the lower degrees of freedom curves an exponential trait is exhibited, but as the degrees of freedom increase, the curve appears

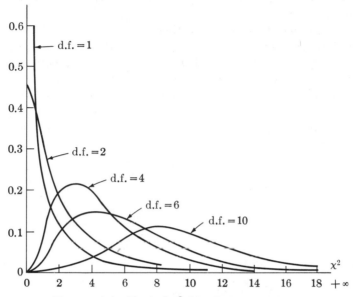

Figure 5.6   *Typical x^2 distribution curves.*

to assume the shape of the normal distribution. The limits of this distribution extend from 0 to $+\infty$. The mean of the distribution is equal to the degrees of freedom.

A further point of discussion may be presented in the consideration where the sample mean is used in place of the population parameter, μ. In this instance the degrees of freedom and, therefore, the mean of the x^2 distribution becomes $(n - 1)$.

5.4.1 *Distribution of Enumeration Data.*

A variation which closely approximates the x^2 distribution is the variation for discrete data. For large values of n, it will be shown in Chapter 9 that a normal approximation to the binomial may be used:

$$z = \frac{X - np}{\sqrt{npq}} \tag{5.17}$$

where

$X =$ the discrete number of times a specific event happens,
$n =$ total number of times the event may or may not happen,
$p =$ probability the specific event will occur in any one trial,
and $q =$ probability the event will not occur in any one trial.

The variation of the χ^2 distribution is predicated upon the amount of devia-tion of *observed frequencies* F_o from the *expected frequencies* F_E. As has been discussed earlier, the *expected value* of any distribution is generally the *mean value*. These two concepts may be used to demonstrate algebraically the χ^2 distribution.

We will consider the case where there are n possible events. The total number of these discrete events X exhibiting the trait of concern will be shown as $\sum X$ and the total number of those discrete events not exhibiting the trait of concern would then be $n - \sum X$. The *expected* number of events *having* the trait would be np and the *expected* number *not having* the trait would be nq, or $n(1 - p)$. Thus we are interested in the combined deviations of $(\sum X - np)$ and $[(n - \sum X) - n(1 - p)]$. Previously the χ^2 distribu-tion was defined as:

$$\chi^2 = \sum z^2$$

where z^2 for discrete data is:

$$z^2 = \left[\frac{\sum X - np}{\sqrt{np(1 - p)}} \right]^2$$

Proceeding with the proof:

$$z^2 = \frac{[\sum X - np]^2}{np(1 - p)} = [\sum X - np]^2 \left[\frac{1}{np(1 - p)} \right]$$

$$= [\sum X - np]^2 \left[\frac{p + q}{np(1 - p)} \right]$$

$$= [\sum X - np]^2 \left[\frac{p}{np(1 - p)} + \frac{(1 - p)}{np(1 - p)} \right]$$

$$= [\sum X - np]^2 \left[\frac{1}{n(1 - p)} + \frac{1}{np} \right]$$

$$= \frac{[\sum X - np]^2}{n(1 - p)} + \frac{[\sum X - np]^2}{np}$$

$$= \frac{[(-1)(-\sum X + np)]^2}{n(1 - p)} + \frac{[\sum X - np]^2}{np}$$

$$= \frac{[-\sum X + np]^2}{n(1 - p)} + \frac{[\sum X - np]^2}{np}$$

$$= \frac{[n - \sum X - n + np]^2}{n(1 - p)} + \frac{[\sum X - np]^2}{np}$$

$$= \frac{[(n - \sum X) - n(1 - p)]^2}{n(1 - p)} + \frac{[\sum X - np]^2}{np}$$

Since

$(n - \Sigma X) =$ *observed frequency* (F_o) of the times the event *did not* exhibit the trait,

$\Sigma X =$ *observed frequency* (F_o) of the times the event *did* exhibit the trait,

$n(1 - p) =$ *expected frequency* (F_E) of the times the event *would not* exhibit the trait, and,

$np =$ *expected frequency* (F_E) of the times the event *should* exhibit the trait,

$$z^2 = \frac{(F_o - F_E)^2}{F_E} + \frac{(F_o - F_E)^2}{F_E}$$

or,

$$\chi^2 = \Sigma z^2 = \Sigma \frac{(F_o - F_E)^2}{F_E} \tag{5.18}$$

In Chapter 4 the concept of expectation was presented. In this discussion, as well as in the earlier discussion of the mean, it was shown that the mean value is the expected value E and "X" is an expression of the number of times the discrete event actually happens. Since $np = \mu$ in the binomial distribution, this value then represents the number of times the event may be expected to happen on the average.

Replacing the "X" by the symbol "O" to represent the number of times the event is actually observed, and with "E" replacing the expected value "np," the relationship approximating the χ^2 distribution for large n's used with discrete data is:

$$\chi^2 = \Sigma \frac{(O - E)^2}{E} \tag{5.19}$$

5.4.2 *Distribution of Sample Variances.* If the sample mean $\overline{X}$ is used to replace the population mean μ, the expression for the χ^2 distribution becomes

$$\chi^2 = \frac{\Sigma(X - \overline{X})^2}{\sigma^2}$$

Both sides of this expression may be divided by $(n - 1)$, yielding

$$\frac{\chi^2}{n - 1} = \frac{\Sigma(X - \overline{X})^2}{(n - 1)\sigma^2} = \frac{\frac{\Sigma(X - \overline{X})^2}{(n - 1)}}{\sigma^2}$$

The expression $\Sigma(X - \overline{X})^2/(n - 1)$ may be recognized from Chapter 3 as the theoretical expression for the sample variance s^2. Thus,

$$\frac{\chi^2}{n - 1} = \frac{\chi^2}{\text{d.f.}} = \frac{s^2}{\sigma^2} \tag{5.20}$$

where the degrees of freedom (d.f.) are those associated with the particular s^2 in question. This is the distribution used in testing hypotheses concerning a single population variance value σ^2.

5.5 *The F Distribution.*   The last of the major sampling distributions to be discussed is formed by the ratios of two $\chi^2/\text{d.f.}$ distributions. As in the case of the previously discussed distributions, the presence of a normally independently distributed population is a basic requirement.

Many times the researcher desires to test hypotheses concerning the presence or absence of equality of two population variances (i.e., $\sigma_1^2 = \sigma_2^2$, $\sigma_1^2 \leq \sigma_2^2, \sigma_1^2 \geq \sigma_2^2$).

The ratio of the values of the two population variances is one if they are equal (i.e., $\sigma_1^2/\sigma_2^2 = 1$). In working with samples, the values of s^2 are generally the only data available. From earlier discussion it may be recalled that the value s^2 estimates the σ^2 for the population from which the sample was drawn. From the previous section, it was shown that the ratio s^2/σ^2 is a $\chi^2/\text{d.f.}$ distribution.

Using this information, a further ratio of these $\chi^2/\text{d.f.}$ values for the two values of s^2 may be made and labeled as a value of F.

$$F = \frac{\dfrac{s_1^2}{\sigma_1^2}}{\dfrac{s_2^2}{\sigma_2^2}} = \frac{\dfrac{\chi_1^2}{\text{d.f.}}}{\dfrac{\chi_2^2}{\text{d.f.}}} \quad (0 \leq F \leq \infty) \tag{5.21}$$

If $\sigma_1^2 = \sigma_2^2$ the above expression becomes:

$$F = \frac{s_1^2}{s_2^2} \tag{5.22}$$

Table 5.4 presents the distribution of ratios of s_1^2/s_2^2 for the sample data of Tables 5.1 and 5.2. Figure 5.7 presents these data in a histogram and graphically presents the form of the distribution.

TABLE 5.4

A FREQUENCY DISTRIBUTION OF 2025 RATIOS OF SAMPLE VARIANCES s_1^2/s_2^2

Interval	f	Interval	f
0.1400–0.1599	8	0.9200–0.9399	63
0.1600–0.1799	11	0.9400–0.9599	60
0.1800–0.1999	11	0.9600–0.9799	52
0.2000–0.2199	9	0.9800–0.9999	51
0.2200–0.2399	3	1.0000–1.0199	41
0.2400–0.2599	1	1.0200–1.0399	47
0.2600–0.2799	9	1.0400–1.0599	26
0.2800–0.2999	6	1.0600–1.0799	28
0.3000–0.3199	8	1.0800–1.0999	21
0.3200–0.3399	20	1.1000–1.1199	19
0.3400–0.3599	40	1.1200–1.1399	12
0.3600–0.3799	38	1.1400–1.1599	16
0.3800–0.3999	45	1.1600–1.1799	10
0.4000–0.4199	39	1.1800–1.1999	5
0.4200–0.4399	37	1.2000–1.2199	6
0.4400–0.4599	29	1.2200–1.2399	8
0.4600–0.4799	33	1.2400–1.2599	6
0.4800–0.4999	15	1.2600–1.2799	3
0.5000–0.5199	11	1.2800–1.2999	5
0.5200–0.5399	10	1.3000–1.3199	8
0.5400–0.5599	9	1.3200–1.3399	5
0.5600–0.5799	12	1.3400–1.3599	4
0.5800–0.5999	19	1.3600–1.3799	1
0.6000–0.6199	17	1.3800–1.3999	10
0.6200–0.6399	35	1.4000–1.4199	2
0.6400–0.6599	42	1.4200–1.4399	1
0.6600–0.6799	53	1.4400–1.4599	1
0.6800–0.6999	50	1.4600–1.4799	
0.7000–0.7199	57	1.4800–1.4999	1
0.7200–0.7399	71	1.5000–1.5199	
0.7400–0.7599	89	1.5200–1.5399	
0.7600–0.7799	93	1.5400–1.5599	4
0.7800–0.7999	80	1.5600–1.5799	1
0.8000–0.8199	82	1.5800–1.5999	3
0.8200–0.8399	92	1.6000–1.6199	3
0.8400–0.8599	86	1.6200–1.6399	1
0.8600–0.8799	91	1.6400–1.6599	
0.8800–0.8999	80	1.6600–1.6799	3
0.9000–0.9199	54	1.6800–1.6999	3

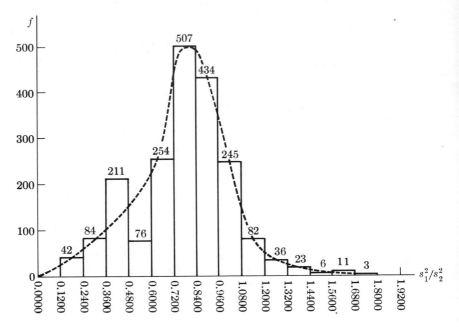

Figure 5.7 *A histogram of* 2025 *ratios of two sample variances shown with an approximating curve* (– – –).

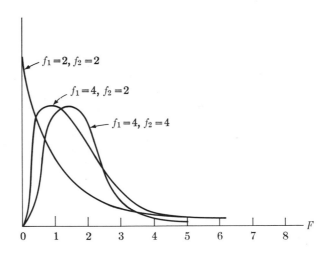

Figure 5.8 *Typical F distribution curves.*

Figure 5.8 presents three typical F distribution curves. These curves demonstrate the fact that as the pairs of degrees of freedom increase the modal value for the ratio of s_1^2/s_2^2 shifts away from zero. The idea that the F distribution is in fact a variation of the χ^2 distributional curve is borne out.

In this case each of the values of s^2 has associated degrees of freedom. Thus the distribution of F is affected by the degrees of freedom associated with the s^2 of the numerator of the ratio and also the degrees of freedom associated with the denominator. It becomes apparent that it is not necessary to have samples where $n_1 = n_2$ to compute the separate values for s_1^2 and s_2^2.

This distribution was developed by R. A. Fisher and as such is named in his honor. The various values of F for varying pairs of degrees of freedom are presented in Table IV, Appendix A.

Inspection of Table IV shows subtables, a, b, c, d, e, f, and g for varying levels of α. All of the values of F contained in these tables are for the cumulative area $(1 - \alpha)$.

The selected value of α will determine which of the tables will be utilized in selecting the critical value of F. The table must be entered with two values, the number of degrees of freedom associated with the s^2 of the numerator (which is denoted as f_1, and read across the top of the table), and the number of degrees of freedom associated with the s^2 of the denominator (which is denoted as f_2, and read down the left side of the table).

5.6 Elementary Data Transformations. It has been stated several times that the previously discussed continuous distributions are generally contingent upon the presence of a normal population distribution for sampling purposes. If the distribution is radically non-normal the investigator has two alternatives, the use of non-parametric technique, or the transformation of the skewed distributional data into a normal distribution. This is accomplished by mathematically treating the raw data in one of several ways, or by combining two or more of these ways. Caution should always be the case to prevent an equally bad situation by over-correction. One of the most commonly used means of transforming skew data is the logarithmic transformation, which we now discuss.

5.6.1 The Logarithmic Transformation. Continuous data may be transformed from a skewed distribution to a normal distribution by applying a function $g(x) = \log x$. If the standardized variate z is computed by:

$$z = \frac{\log x - \log \mu}{\sigma} \qquad (5.23)$$

such that the mean of the z values has $\mu = 0$ and $\sigma^2 = 1$, the logarithmic transformation is appropriate. In working with the "t" distribution it becomes necessary to use the function $g(x)$ in computing both the sample mean and variance. Therefore, where $g(x) = \log x$, the sample mean is:

$$\overline{g(x)} = \frac{\Sigma g(x)}{n} \qquad (5.24)$$

and the sample variance by definition is:

$$s^2 = \frac{\Sigma[g(x) - \overline{g(x)}]^2}{n - 1}$$

(5.25)

$$= \frac{\Sigma g(x)^2 - \frac{[\Sigma g(x)]^2}{n}}{n - 1}$$

The equation for the normal curve changes from

$$P(x) = \frac{1}{\sigma\sqrt{2\pi}} \int_{-\infty}^{X} e^{\frac{-(X-\mu)^2}{2\sigma^2}} dx$$

to

$$P(x) = \frac{1}{\sigma\sqrt{2\pi}} \int_{-\infty}^{\log x} e^{\frac{-(\log x - \log\mu)^2}{2\sigma^2}} d\log x$$

where $\log \mu$ = mean of $\log x$ and not μ of X.

Thus the three measures of central tendency may be computed as:

the mean — $\log x = \log \mu + 1.1513\sigma^2$ (5.26)

the median — $\log x = \log \mu$ (which is the 50th percentile)   (5.27)

the mode — $\log x = \log \mu - 2.3026\sigma^2$ (5.28)

The relationship between the three is the

$$\text{mode} < \text{median} < \text{mean}$$

and the difference is directly proportional to the size of the standard deviation.

PROBLEMS

1. Given a normal distribution of values of X with $\mu = 15$ and $\sigma = 4$. What is the probability of a randomly drawn value of X being at least 17? 21? At most 14? Either at most 13 or at least 17? Deviating from the mean by at most 3 units? Being at least six units greater than the mean?

2. A normal distribution of sample means $\overline{X}$ for $n = 25$ has $\mu = 21$ and $\sigma^2 = 16$. What is the probability of drawing a sample whose mean is at least 22? 19? At least 1.5 units different from the population mean? At most two units greater than the population mean? What would be the values of $\overline{X}$ which would include 95% of all sample means? 99.5%?

3. Population I has $\mu_1 = 18$ and $\sigma_1 = 5$. Population II has $\mu_2 = 24$ and $\sigma_2 = 6$. Using the concept of a distribution of differences of sample means, what is the probability of drawing two samples $n_1 = n_2 = 25$

and the difference between their means being at most 4? At least 3? Within two units of the mean of the distribution? What interval would include the middle 80% of the differences?

4. Using the paired-data distribution where $\mu_d = 2$ and $\sigma_d^2 = 9$, what would be the probability of $\bar{d}$ for a sample of $n = 36$ being one unit less than the mean? Two units greater than the mean? Within one standard error of the mean? What interval would include the middle 99.99% of the values of d?

5. Using the appropriate distribution compute the values enclosing: (a) 90% of all values in the distribution, (b) 95% of all values, (c) 99% of all values. Use sample sizes of $n = 25$ and $n = 100$.
   (a) For s^2, given $\sigma^2 = 20$.
   (b) For $\bar{X}$, given $\mu = 18$, $\sigma^2 = 20$.
   (c) For $(\bar{X}_1 - \bar{X}_2)$, given $\mu_1 = \mu_2$, $\sigma_1^2 = \sigma_2^2$, $s_1^2 = s_2^2 = 9$.
   (d) For $\bar{d}$, given $\mu_d = 1$, $s_d = 0.5$.
   (e) For X, given $p = \frac{1}{2}$.

6. Assume that the average weight of American males is 160 pounds, and that $\sigma = 16$.
   (a) Find the probability that an American male selected at random has a weight equal to or greater than 188 pounds.
   (b) Find the probability that an American male selected at random has a weight less than 145 pounds.
   (c) Find the probability that a group of American males will have an average weight at least six pounds different from the mean weight (let $n = 25$).
   (d) Draw random samples of size $n = 16$, 36, and 49 from the values in Appendix B. Compute the interval limit values which include the middle 90%, 95%, and 99.9% of the values of $\bar{X}$.
   (e) Draw three other samples of size $n = 16$, 36, and 49 respectively from Appendix B. Use these samples and those drawn for problem (d) to compute the same interval limit values for the true difference of population means.

7. If it is known that a certain breed of snake averages 68.2 inches in length when full grown, with a variance of 196, what is the chance of a group of 49 of these snakes having an average length between 69.2 inches and 70.0 inches?

8. The average take-home pay at the Hard-Up Corporation is $66 with a standard deviation of $24. If you are to take a sample of 64 men at the plant and compute their average take-home pay, what is the chance that this mean will be between $73.40 and $73.00?

9. A northern university has found the average score on its English placement test to be 84.5 with a variance of 16. What, then, is the chance that James Knob will score at least 93.5 on this placement test?

10. A power company supplies, on the average, 8800 kw of electricity monthly, to the one-family dwellings of Podunk. The variance is 640,000 kw. What is the probability that the one-family dwelling at 1400 Sputnik Ave. will use less than 7900 kw this month?

11. The average airline trip between Springfield, Massachusetts and Reykjavik, Iceland, has been found to be 2880 miles with a variance of 400 miles. What is the chance that the next trip will cover more than 2917.4 miles?

12. A producer of breathing oxygen has found the average purity of his Type 2-A cylinders to be 99.9% with a standard deviation of 0.13%. Of his semi-annual run of 10,000 cylinders, how many would you expect to find with a purity level between 99.5% and 99.6%?

REFERENCES

Dixon, Wilfrid J., and Massey, Frank J., Jr. *Introduction to Statistical Analysis.* Second Edition. New York: McGraw-Hill Book Company, Inc., 1959. Chapter 5.

DuBois, Philip H. *An Introduction to Psychological Statistics.* New York: Harper and Row, Publishers, 1965. Chapters 11 and 12.

Freund, John C., and Williams, Frank J. *Elementary Business Statistics: The Modern Approach.* Englewood Cliffs, N. J.: Prentice-Hall, Inc., 1964. Chapter 9.

Guenther, William C. *Concepts of Statistical Inference.* New York: McGraw-Hill Book Company, 1965. Chapter 3.

Hoel, Paul G. *Elementary Statistics.* New York: John Wiley and Sons, Inc., 1960. Chapters 4 and 5.

McNemar, Quinn. *Psychological Statistics.* Third Edition. New York: John Wiley and Sons, Inc., 1962. Chapter 4.

Tate, Merle W. *Statistics in Education and Psychology: A First Course.* New York: The Macmillan Company, 1965. Chapters 6 and 11.

Walker, Helen, and Lev, Joseph. *Statistical Inference.* New York: Holt, Rinehart, and Company, Inc., 1953. Chapters 2 and 6.

Yamane, Taro. *Statistics, An Introductory Analysis.* New York: Harper and Row, Publishers, 1964. Chapters 6 and 7.

6

ELEMENTS OF
STATISTICAL DECISION MAKING

In Chapter 1 it was pointed out that in many instances the investigator finds it impractical or impossible to work with all the items within a given class. In such instances he may work with samples, but the results of any analyses must be of such nature that they may be projected to the parent population from which the sample was initially drawn. This process of extending the sample findings is referred to as *statistical inference*.

In an earlier discussion, examples were shown relating to the type of sampling techniques utilized in experimental situations. It was observed that in working with samples it is possible to draw a sample from anywhere within a distribution. It was further demonstrated that the mean of the sample would more than likely be near the mean of the population. This was also amplified in the discussion of the normal curve distribution of sample mean values (Chapter 5).

6.1 *Formation of Statistical Hypotheses.* In the definition of the term *statistical inference*, it was stated that the major concern of the statistical analyst was that of being able to project the results of work with samples back to the parent population from which the sample was drawn. There are certain factors which must be considered long before attention may be directed toward the drawing of the sample or the performing of any type of statistical analysis. The first step in this process is that of adequately stating the problem in a concise and carefully delineated manner. The statement of the problem determines the type and form of hypothesis or hypotheses which shall be tested, and the resulting type of sample which must be drawn. For the statistical process, *the problem is usually stated in the form of a question which may be answered after analysis has been completed.*

The next act is that of formulating statistical test hypotheses. At a glance it appears appropriate to state as a hypothesis, a plausible answer to the question statement of the problem. In very simple terms, this hypothesis is in reality an educated guess as to the answer to the problem question. This "educated guess" is not made *in vacuo* but is based upon all available information previously gathered or known by the investigator or other persons. This positive plausible answer to the problem question may be identified as a *positive hypothesis*. This form is not normally used in statistical analysis, however. Instead, a negative form of the hypothesis is used in its place and is called the *null hypothesis*. This null hypothesis is used with the hope that it will be *rejected* by the data at a defined level of probability. Note should be taken that the null hypothesis is rejected and not disproved since it is not possible to *prove* or *disprove* any statistical hypothesis based upon sample data statistics. It should be remembered that no finite amount of experimentation can ever prove the null hypothesis. Experimentation and testing may lead to the rejection of a null hypothesis, and in hypothesis testing the terms "accept" and "does not reject" do not imply that the null hypothesis is proved.

The utilization of the hypothesis in the process of statistical analysis is predicated upon the assumption that there is some order in nature which, in turn, would imply some form of order operating in any distributional system of values. The statement of the hypothesis may be very general in nature although ideally this should not be the case. This form of an "educated guess" would not operate in an analysis of the type which characterizes statistical operation. Instead hypotheses are formed which will state some positive relationship between one or more of the parameters and a specific value.

For further discussion of this point, the following hypothetical problem will be used for illustrative purposes throughout the remainder of the chapter. In a particular school the students in senior year English are given a standardized proficiency examination at the termination of their year's work. Over a period of years the results of this examination have been found to be normally distributed with parametric values of $\mu = 78.4$ and $\sigma = 7.4$. During the current year, students enrolled in the senior English class have consistently scored higher on all examinations than their predecessors. This condition has aroused the interest of the administration and teachers of this school to such an extent that they want to know if there is any possibility that this group of students may be representative of a "higher calibre" of students to come. If this is the case they desire to modify the curricular program to better suit the future student body.

The problem under inquiry here is the determination of the validity of their suspicions. Stating the problem in question form:

Is it reasonable to suppose that the current group of English students in the senior class are members of a population of students whose English proficiency scores have a $\mu > 78.4$?

On the basis of prior knowledge concerning these students it might be possible to hypothesize that $\mu > 78.4$. This is an indeterminate statement in that an infinite number of values of $\mu > 78.4$ exist and only one is the correct value. It would be better, then, to hypothesize that the mean is not greater than 78.4, but rather that it is still equal to 78.4. For the purpose of including all possible values of μ from 78.4 to negative infinity (the lower limit of the normal distribution), the *null hypothesis*, written H_o, is:

$$H_o : \mu \leq 78.4$$

Next we perform some type of statistical analysis and make decisions as to the adequacy of the hypothesis. Before pursuing this idea it would be well to scrutinize the possible consequences of the decision resulting from the analysis. Suppose a decision is made that if the analysis does permit the investigator to answer the question statement of the problem in the affirmative, the content of the senior English course will be "upgraded." (Let us also assume before pursuing the discussion, that the hypothesis is *FALSE* and the answer to the problem is *in reality YES*, i.e., $\mu > 78.4$.)

If we accept the hypothesis as the answer to the question we will in fact be saying that the mean is not greater than the value 78.4 and will as a result be accepting as an answer to the question something which is *in reality FALSE*. On the other hand, it is also possible that the sample we might draw may be such that its analysis would result in the rejection of the hypothesis. In simple terms, this means that if the *TRUE* value of μ is in reality greater than 78.4, the rejection of the hypothesis ($H_o : \mu \leq 78.4$) is desirable, whereas the acceptance of the hypothesis is undesirable. The consequences of accepting the hypothesis as *TRUE* may be that the senior English course content will not be changed, or, if changed, made easier, thus not offering the appropriate challenge to the students to follow.

If we assume that in reality the hypothesis is *TRUE* and that the answer to the problem question is *NO*, then the acceptance of the hypothesis is not a mistake. The rejection of the hypothesis is then an error having certain possible detrimental effects. If the hypothesis is erroneously rejected, the course content will be upgraded, thus possibly presenting material beyond the level of comprehension and understanding of future students.

6.2 *Types of Statistical Errors.* There are certain errors which may occur in the process of statistical analysis which are for the most part impossible to prevent totally. The commission of these types of errors may result in actions which produce certain undesirable effects. There is only one way that the researcher can make an errorless decision and that would be to use the entire population as the sample. If this were done in our problem there would not be any students left for which the curriculum may be changed. Using the entire population may be considered equivalent to an industrial application of statistical analysis wherein the testing program is based upon destructive sampling (e.g., determining the mean life expectancy of electrical fuses).

To further explain the conditions under which the errors may occur, the following diagram is presented.

The hypothesis being tested may in reality be:

TRUE	*FALSE*

and the inference to be drawn as a result of the testing and sampling process may indicate that the test hypothesis be:

Case A.	*Case B.*	*Case C.*	*Case D.*
ACCEPTED	*REJECTED*	*ACCEPTED*	*REJECTED*
i.e., saying the	*i.e., saying the*	*i.e., saying the*	*i.e., saying the*
hypothesis is	*hypothesis is*	*hypothesis is*	*hypothesis is*
TRUE when it	*FALSE when it*	*TRUE when it*	*FALSE when it*
really is TRUE.	*really is TRUE.*	*really is FALSE.*	*really is FALSE.*

It is obvious that Cases A and D are correct decisions and that errors are committed in the instances of Cases B and C. The error in Case B—*rejecting a TRUE* hypothesis—is classified as a Type I or α error. The error in Case C—*accepting* a *FALSE* hypothesis—is classified as a Type II or β error. This diagram implies that when working with samples in the testing of a hypothesis, it is possible to answer the question in any one of four ways, only two of which are correct.

6.2.1 *Type I Error, Alpha* (α). This particular error is associated with the rejection of a hypothesis when in fact the hypothesis is *TRUE*. This decision regarding the hypothesis is based directly on certain assumptions made about the location of the sample mean with respect to the population mean being tested. The reader will remember the discussion given in Chapter 4 on probability and that in Chapter 5 on the normal distribution, it was stated that the probability of an event happening decreases rapidly as its difference from the population mean increases. For statistical analysis of a problem the researcher selects the size of the α risk and then places this portion either totally in one tail or divides it between both tails of the area under the normal curve. The area corresponding to this α risk represents that portion of the distribution of sample means where the probability of occurrence of such a mean by chance is low if the sample actually does arise from the hypothesized population.

The probability of committing this particular type of error is entirely within the control of the experimenter. If he should desire *never* to commit this type of error, he would *never* reject a hypothesis. This corresponds to the β risk at every possible opportunity, or $\beta \rightarrow \infty$. In any case, the experimenter will usually choose a probability which is low (0.05 or less) as the risk (also known as *level of significance*) he is willing to accept in committing this α error. The size of this risk is also controlled by the accuracy of the measurements used, the financial and time implications, sampling difficulties, and the associated effects of the commission of this type of error. The most commonly used *level of significance* for an α *risk* is 0.05. This is to say that, on the average, the chance of rejecting a *TRUE* hypothesis strictly by chance is one in twenty.

In the case of the proposed problem and its population where $\mu = 78.4$ and $\sigma = 7.4$, the chance of drawing at random a value from the separate distributed scores of at least 90.57 $(\mu + 1.645\sigma)$ is one in twenty, a risk of 0.05. In Table I, Appendix A, a value of 0.05 corresponds closely to $z = 1.645$ in the left hand column. From the equation $z = X - \mu/\sigma$ where $\mu = 78.4$ and $\sigma = 7.4$, we have $X = 90.57$. Similarly, a value of at least 95.62 $(\mu + 2.327\sigma)$ corresponds to one chance in a hundred, a risk of 0.01. The chance of drawing a sample of 25 (Figure 6.1) and of it having a mean of at least 80.83 $(\mu + 1.645\sigma_{\overline{X}})$ is one in twenty, or having a mean of at least 81.84 $(\mu + 2.327\sigma_{\overline{X}})$ is one in a hundred (using the principle of standard error of estimate $[\sigma_{\overline{X}}]$ which would be $7.4/\sqrt{25}$ or 1.48). Here

$$z = \frac{\overline{X} - \mu}{\sigma_{\overline{X}}}$$

Thus, in the statistical test of a hypothesis, the researcher will select a region of the curve of such size that there is little chance a random sample

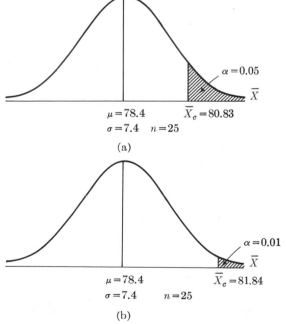

$\alpha = 0.05$

$\mu = 78.4$ $\overline{X}_c = 80.83$
$\sigma = 7.4$ $n = 25$

(a)

$\alpha = 0.01$

$\mu = 78.4$ $\overline{X}_c = 81.84$
$\sigma = 7.4$ $n = 25$

(b)

Figure 6.1 *Diagrammatic representation of the proposed normal population with (a) 0.05 and (b) 0.01 levels of significance. Critical values for sample means $(\overline{X}_c)$ are indicated $(n = 25)$.*

drawn from the hypothesized population has a mean falling by chance within this area. A *decision rule* is formulated stating that if the sample mean is within this specified range of values, the hypothesized value of the population mean shall be rejected.

The placement of this critical region is also of great importance. For example, if there is some information which would tend to suggest that the sample being tested arises from a population having a mean greater than that of the hypothesized population, the entire region should be placed in the right tail of the normal curve (see Figure 6.2, test a). This will generate a greater area representing sample means, thus permitting the rejection of the test hypothesis more often when the $TRUE$ mean of the sampled population *is* greater. Such placement of the critical region will be referred to hereafter as *test a*. The placement of the total region in the left tail for similar reasoning shall hereafter be designated as *test b* (see Figure 6.2, test b). In those cases where there is no indication as to whether the population mean for the sample being tested is greater than or less than the hypothesized population, it would be proper to split the total region α equally and place

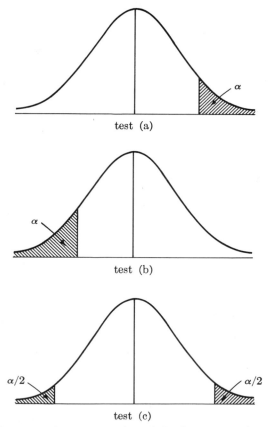

test (a)

test (b)

test (c)

Figure 6.2 *Diagrammatic representation of the three types of statistical tests as to placement of the critical region (α).*

$\alpha/2$ in each of the two tails. Placement of the critical region in this fashion will be referred to as *test c* (see Figure 6.2, test c). The prudence of the placement of the critical regions in this fashion will be demonstrated later in Section 6.4.

The placement of the α region controls, in turn, the likelihood of the commission of the Type II or β error which is discussed in the following section.

6.2.2 *Type II Error, Beta* (β).
To reduce the probability of committing the Type I error, the experimenter would reduce the chance of rejecting the *TRUE* hypothesis. To reduce this probability to zero requires the acceptance of *all* hypotheses. If and when this is done, the probability of accepting a *FALSE* hypothesis is maximized and will occur at every possible opportunity, or $\beta \to \infty$.

Let us consider a situation associated with our proposed problem. Suppose that the sample of 25 students drawn is actually from a population having a mean senior English proficiency score of 81.0. If the selected level of significance, α, is 0.01, what would be the chance of drawing a sample and finding its mean to be such that we would accept the hypothesis $(\mu \le 78.4)$, thus committing the β error? At the chosen level of significance the test hypothesis would be rejected if the sample mean is 81.84 or greater. The hypothesized population is shown in Figure 6.3(a) and the proposed alternate population is shown in Figure 6.3(b).

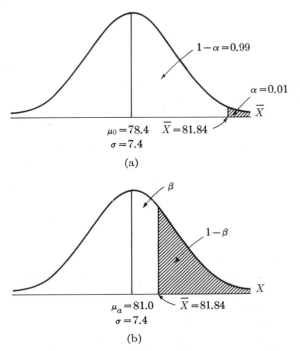

(a)

(b)

Figure 6.3 *Diagrammatic representation of (a) the hypothesized population under test conditions, and (b) the proposed alternate population indicating the β error.*

The area of the curve in (b) indicating sample means having values less than the critical value of 81.84 is to the left of that particular value. If $\overline{X} = 81.84$ for a sample of 25 in a population with $\mu = 81.0$ and $\sigma = 7.4$, we find z to be 0.568. Remember $z = \overline{X} - \mu/\sigma_{\overline{X}}$ where $\sigma_{\overline{X}} = \sigma/\sqrt{n}$. By referring to Table I, Appendix A, we find that there is an area of 0.2851 remaining in the right tail of the distribution. This value indicates that $P(\overline{X} > 81.84) = 0.2851$. This is the probability that the sample will yield a mean value such that the hypothesis $\mu \leq 78.4$ will be rejected. The probability of accepting this $FALSE$ hypothesis (β error) then is:

$$P(\overline{X} < 81.84) = 1 - P(\overline{X} > 81.84) = 1 - 0.2851 = 0.7149$$

This says that on the average the $FALSE$ hypothesis will be accepted, using a sample of $n = 25$ and an $\alpha = 0.01$, 7,149 times in 10,000.

6.3 Effects of Different Size α and n on Size of β. It was stated earlier in this chapter that the only way a positive statement could be made concerning the truth or falsity of the hypothesis would be that of testing the entire population. It was further shown that this action would be highly impractical, if not impossible. A problem was then posed and an analysis was carried out. Using a 5-percent level of significance, it was shown that it would be necessary for the sample mean to equal or exceed 1.645 standard error units before the test hypothesis could be rejected. An interesting fact to note is that the size of the standard error unit is directly dependent on the size of the sample involved ($\sigma_{\overline{X}} = \sigma/\sqrt{n}$).

In the case of the problem posed, a sample of 25 students was used and thus the standard error unit was 1.48 or ($7.4/\sqrt{25}$). This meant that before rejecting the test hypothesis the sample mean would have to equal or exceed 1.645 times 1.48 units above the hypothesized population mean value of 78.4. In Table 6.1 the change in the critical value of $\overline{X}$ due to sample size variation may be observed. This table demonstrates that as the sample size n approaches the size of the population N, the critical value approaches the value of the hypothesized mean. This may be explained by observing that as the sample size grows larger, the size of the standard error decreases. Thus it may be said that as $n \to N$, $\overline{X} \to \mu$, for the population sampled.

Another interesting phenomenon is the effect of this variation in sample size upon the probability of the commission of the Type II or β error. This variation is demonstrated in Table 6.2 for the 0.10, 0.05, and 0.01 levels of significance for a population whose mean is actually 81.0, rather than the hypothesized value of $\mu = 78.4$.

From Table 6.2 it may be observed that as the value of α is decreased the value of β increases. The choice of α is made by the researcher and the decision is based upon the degree of necessity for preventing the rejection of possibly true hypotheses. The choice of α then will affect the chance that the researcher wishes to take in accepting a false hypothesis and accepting

TABLE 6.1

VARIATION IN STANDARD ERROR SIZE AND CRITICAL VALUES AS INFLUENCED BY VARIOUS SAMPLE SIZES, $\sigma_{\overline{X}} = 7.4/\sqrt{n}$, $\mu = 78.4$.

| Sample Size | Standard Error | Critical Values for α | |
| | | 0.05 | 0.01 |
		$(\mu + 1.645\sigma_{\overline{X}})$	$(\mu + 2.327\sigma_{\overline{X}})$
2	5.23	87.01	90.58
3	4.27	85.43	88.34
4	3.70	84.49	87.01
6	3.02	83.37	85.43
8	2.62	82.70	84.49
9	2.47	82.45	84.14
25	1.48	80.84	81.84
36	1.25	80.46	81.31
49	1.06	80.14	80.86
64	0.94	79.94	80.58
81	0.82	79.75	80.31
100	0.74	79.62	80.12
256	0.46	79.16	79.84
500	0.33	78.94	79.17
1000	0.23	78.78	78.94

TABLE 6.2

VALUES OF β FOR VARYING SAMPLE SIZES FOR $\alpha = 0.10$, 0.05, AND 0.01 WHERE $\mu_o = 78.4$, $\sigma = 7.4$, AND $\mu_a = 81.0$, USING TEST (a), FIGURE 6.2

| Sample Size | α | | |
	0.10	0.05	0.01
2	0.78380	0.87450	0.96647
3	0.74984	0.85011	0.95712
4	0.71834	0.82715	0.94780
6	0.66280	0.78346	0.91102
8	0.61296	0.74220	0.90888
9	0.58983	0.72306	0.89851
25	0.31812	0.45420	0.71502
36	0.20414	0.32208	0.58671
49	0.12040	0.20784	0.44750
64	0.06378	0.12140	0.31350
81	0.02975	0.06430	0.20078
100	0.01290	0.03105	0.11720
256	0.00000	0.00036	0.00051
500	0.00000	0.00000	0.00000
1000	0.00000	0.00000	0.00000

the consequences of such an event. The size of β may be controlled, however, by the size of the sample used in the study.

It is possible to determine the size of the sample which would allow for a preselected set of values for α and β. In the case of the normal distribution where both the hypothesized values of μ and σ are known, the formula may be easily determined. The procedure is to utilize the equation for the standardized deviate value z when using sample means and solve it for n. That is:

$$z = \frac{\overline{X} - \mu}{\dfrac{\sigma}{\sqrt{n}}} \quad \text{or} \quad \sqrt{n} = \frac{z\sigma}{(\overline{X} - \mu)}$$

Squaring both sides, we then have the equation:

$$n = \left[\frac{z\sigma}{|(\overline{X} - \mu)|} \right]^2 \tag{6.1}$$

Equation (6.1) permits one to determine the size of the sample which will meet the specifications for a given α for a population having a mean μ_o and standard deviation σ, providing certain other qualifications are established. The denominator of the equation, $|(\overline{X} - \mu)|$, is an expression of the desired accuracy or maximum error which will be acceptable as stated in terms of an absolute number; it shows how far the researcher is willing to permit the sample mean to deviate from the true population mean. To arrive at the formula for determining the appropriate sample size for specified values of both α and β, it is necessary to consider the manner by which the values for Table 6.2 were determined.

For the sake of an example let us use the first value in Table 6.2, namely $\alpha = 0.7838$. This value was determined in the following manner. A normal curve was drawn as may be seen in Figure 6.4(a) noting the value of $\mu = 78.4$ and $\sigma = 7.4$. The value of $\overline{X}$ for the lower limit of the critical region ($\alpha = 0.10$) was determined in the following manner:

The standardized deviate score z for the area of $(1 - \alpha) = 0.90$ is 1.282, commonly expressed, $z_{(1-\alpha)} = z_{0.90} = 1.282$. (See Table I, Appendix A.) When this value is placed in the equation for the normal distribution of sample means, after substitution of the known values for μ and σ, and with a given value for n, the appropriate value for $\overline{X}$ may be computed. The actual computation is as follows:

$$z = \frac{(\overline{X} - \mu)}{\dfrac{\sigma}{\sqrt{n}}}$$

$$1.282 = \frac{(\overline{X} - 78.4)}{\dfrac{7.4}{\sqrt{n}}}$$

For $n = 2$:

$$1.282 \left(\frac{7.4}{\sqrt{2}} \right) = \overline{X} - 78.4$$

$$\frac{9.4868}{1.414} = \overline{X} - 78.4$$

$$6.7091 = \overline{X} - 78.4$$

$$\overline{X} = 78.4 + 6.71 = 85.11$$

Then, to determine the β error using $\mu_a = 81.00$, $\sigma = 7.4$ (Figure 6.4(b)),

$$z = \frac{85.11 - 81.00}{\dfrac{7.4}{\sqrt{2}}} = \frac{(4.11)(1.414)}{7.4} = \frac{5.81154}{7.4} = 0.785$$

Table I shows that for $z = 0.785$, an area of 0.2162 lies in the right tail of the curve. This is the probability that the $\overline{X}$ will fall in the critical region and that the hypothesis $\mu \le 78.4$ will be rejected. To ascertain the β error, or the probability that the hypothesis will be accepted, this value is subtracted from 1.0000. This yields the value, $1 - 0.2162 = 0.7838$.

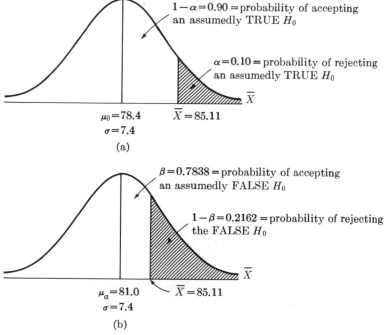

(a)

(b)

Figure 6.4 *Diagrammatic solution of Type II error for populations with*
$\mu_o = 78.4$, $\sigma = 7.4$, $\mu_a = 81.0$, $\sigma = 7.4$, $\alpha = 0.10$.

Using the ideas involved in this computation we may arrive at the formula for determining the appropriate sample size for specified values of α and β. Let us consider simultaneously the equations for computing z in both Figure 6.4(a) and Figure 6.4(b).

In Figure 6.4(a):

$$z_{(1-\alpha)} = \frac{(\overline{X} - \mu_o)}{\dfrac{\sigma}{\sqrt{n}}}$$

then

$$z_{(1-\alpha)}\left[\frac{\sigma}{\sqrt{n}}\right] = (X - \mu_o)$$

In Figure 6.4(b):

$$z_\beta = \frac{(\overline{X} - \mu_a)}{\dfrac{\sigma}{\sqrt{n}}}$$

$$z_\beta\left[\frac{\sigma}{\sqrt{n}}\right] = (\overline{X} - \mu_a)$$

Solving both equations for $\overline{X}$:

$$\frac{z_{(1-\alpha)}\sigma}{\sqrt{n}} + \mu_o = \overline{X}, \quad \text{and} \quad \frac{z_\beta\sigma}{\sqrt{n}} + \mu_a = \overline{X}$$

thus

$$\frac{z_{(1-\alpha)}\sigma}{\sqrt{n}} + \mu_o = \frac{z_\beta\sigma}{\sqrt{n}} + \mu_a$$

or

$$\frac{z_{(1-\alpha)}\sigma}{\sqrt{n}} - \frac{z_\beta\sigma}{\sqrt{n}} = \mu_a - \mu_o$$

By factoring out $\sigma/\sqrt{n}$ we have:

$$\frac{\sigma}{\sqrt{n}}(z_{(1-\alpha)} - z_\beta) = \mu_a - \mu_o$$

$$\frac{\sigma}{\sqrt{n}} = \frac{\mu_a - \mu_o}{z_{(1-\alpha)} - z_\beta}$$

$$\sqrt{n} = \frac{\sigma(z_{(1-\alpha)} - z_\beta)}{(\mu_a - \mu_o)}$$

$$n = \left[\frac{\sigma(z_{(1-\alpha)} - z_\beta)}{\mu_a - \mu_o}\right]^2 \tag{6.2}$$

Equation (6.2) permits the determination of the sample size necessary for a selected pair of values for α and β but is appropriate only for test (a) and test (b) of Figure 6.2. For test (c) it is necessary to use $\alpha/2$ in place of α.

In the case of the original problem posed at the beginning of this chapter, let us compute the sample sizes which might be appropriate, using both Equations (6.1) and (6.2). For Equation (6.1), let us use a value of $\alpha = 0.10$. Also we desire that the mean of the sample we shall draw will be at most 0.5 units in error in estimating the mean for a test (a) situation. If we substitute the proper values in Equation (6.1) we have,

$$n = \left[\frac{(1.282)(7.4)}{0.5}\right]^2$$

$$= (18.97)^2$$

$$= 359.86$$

meaning that we should use a sample of 360 students for this desired accuracy. Now modify these conditions slightly to hold the β error to a maximum of 0.15, and to enable our sample to distinguish between the hypothesized mean and any other population having a mean at least with 0.5 unit difference. Then from Equation 6.2 the required sample size becomes:

$$n = \left[\frac{7.4(1.282 - [-1.036])}{0.5}\right]^2$$

$$= \left[\frac{(7.4)(2.318)}{0.5}\right]^2$$

$$= (34.31)^2$$

$$= 1177.18$$

or a sample size of 1177 is now required. (-1.036 corresponds to the value 0.1500 found in Table I, Appendix A.) This is only one example of the ways that the two types of statistical errors, α and β, and sample size are related to each other.

6.4 Power of the Test. Another element involved in the process of statistical decision making is that which is called the *power of the test*. This term may be defined as the probability of rejecting the hypothesis, whether true or false. To illustrate this point let us re-examine Table 6.2. If β is the probability of accepting an assumedly *FALSE* hypothesis, then the quantity $(1 - \beta)$ is the probability of rejecting that hypothesis. Note that it was not specified whether that hypothesis was in reality *TRUE* or *FALSE*.

TABLE 6.3

POWER OF THE TEST FOR VALUES OF α = 0.10, 0.05, 0.01 USING $\mu_o = 78.4$, $\sigma = 7.4$, $n = 25$

						μ_a					
	71.00	72.48	73.96	75.44	76.92	78.40	79.88	81.36	82.84	84.32	85.80
Test						α = 0.10					
a	0.00000	0.00000	0.00000	0.00051	0.01112	0.10000	0.38826	0.82091	0.94303	0.99666	0.99999
b	0.99999	0.99666	0.94303	0.82091	0.38826	0.10000	0.01112	0.00051	0.00000	0.00000	0.00000
c	0.99960	0.99086	0.91280	0.63974	0.26464	0.10000	0.26464	0.63974	0.91280	0.99086	0.99960
Test						α = 0.05					
a	0.00000	0.00000	0.00000	0.00014	0.00416	0.05000	0.26047	0.63988	0.91280	0.99086	0.99960
b	0.99960	0.99086	0.91280	0.63988	0.26047	0.05000	0.00416	0.00014	0.00000	0.00000	0.00000
c	0.99880	0.97932	0.85092	0.51620	0.16913	0.05000	0.16913	0.51620	0.85092	0.97932	0.99880
Test						α = 0.01					
a	0.00000	0.00000	0.00000	0.00000	0.00045	0.01000	0.09271	0.37287	0.75037	0.95307	0.99626
b	0.99626	0.95307	0.75037	0.37287	0.09271	0.01000	0.00045	0.00000	0.00000	0.00000	0.00000
c	0.99769	0.92300	0.66485	0.28288	0.05790	0.01000	0.05790	0.28288	0.66485	0.92300	0.99769

The data presented in this Table are graphically displayed in Figures 6.5, 6.6, and 6.7, and Tests (a), (b), and (c) refer to Figure 6.2.

As indicated in Table 6.3, and in Figures 6.5, 6.6, and 6.7, as the mean value of the population being sampled moves away from the mean of the hypothesized population, the probability of rejecting the hypothesis increases, depending upon the type of test used.

Power-of-the-test values for our example are shown in Table 6.3. Using the hypothesized population, originally proposed in the beginning of this chapter, $\mu = 78.4$ and $\sigma = 7.4$, β errors were computed using various values for μ_a. After β was computed, the power of each of the tests was then determined by taking the complementary value of β, thus yielding $(1 - \beta)$. These values are listed in Table 6.3. They were then plotted in Figures 6.5,

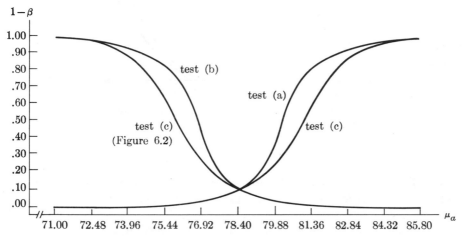

Figure 6.5 *Power-of-the-test curve for hypothesized population having $\mu_o = 78.4$, $\sigma = 7.4$, using alternate values for μ_a as indicated, $\alpha = 0.10$.*

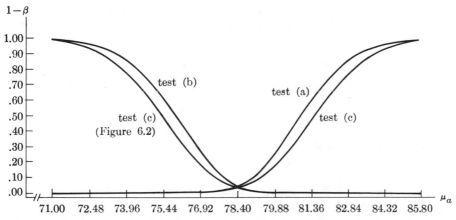

Figure 6.6 *Power-of-the-test curve for hypothesized population having $\mu_o = 78.4$, $\sigma = 7.4$, using alternate values for μ_a as indicated, $\alpha = 0.05$.*

6.6, and 6.7, at the respective α values of 0.10, 0.05, and 0.01. For this particular situation a sample of 25 was used. Needless to say, these values would vary as in Table 6.3 if the sample size were increased or decreased.

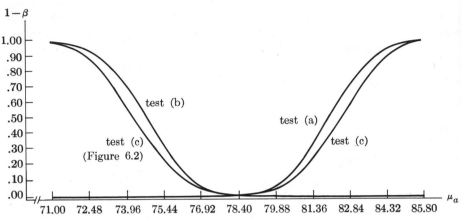

Figure 6.7 *Power-of-the-test curve for hypothesized population having $\mu_o = 78.4$, $\sigma = 7.4$, using alternate values for μ_a as indicated, $\alpha = 0.01$.*

6.5 *Tests of Statistical Hypotheses.* From our prior discussion the following general format has been established for the testing of hypotheses:

1. Statement of the problem in the form of a question.

2. Statement of the null hypothesis to be tested.

3. Specification of the α and β risks should, ideally, be presented. In many instances only the α error will be given. There should also be some statement of the placement of this risk in relation to the three forms of tests as given in Figure 6.2.

4. Statement of the decision rules. Since the standardized deviate value z may be computed for any value of $\overline{X}$ in a distribution of $\overline{X}$'s, the rule is more frequently stated in terms of z.

5. Computation of the test statistic from sample data.

6. Interpretation of the hypothesis in terms of its rejection or acceptance as dictated by the decision rule.

Let us now consider our proposed problem of the population having a value of $\mu = 78.4$ with $\sigma = 7.4$. A sample of 25 students is selected by use of a random process from the incoming class of freshman English students, and after a period of instruction they are given the standardized achievement examination. The results are shown in Table 6.4. This problem stated in the format proposed would be:

1. Is it reasonable to suppose that $\mu > 78.4$?

2. $H_0 : \mu \leq 78.4$.

3. $\alpha = 0.05$, test (a) (Figure 6.2).

4. Reject the H_o if $z > z_{1-\alpha} = z_{0.95} = 1.645$.

5. $z = \dfrac{79.72 - 78.4}{\dfrac{7.4}{\sqrt{25}}} = 0.89$

6. Accept the H_o since the obtained value of $0.89 < 1.645$.

TABLE 6.4

SCORES OF 25 FRESHMAN ENGLISH STUDENTS ON BLANK ACHIEVEMENT TEST

Student Number	Test Score	Student Number	Test Score	Student Number	Test Score
1	79	10	82	18	82
2	76	11	81	19	81
3	85	12	85	20	80
4	82	13	80	21	81
5	83	14	79	22	83
6	78	15	81	23	77
7	70	16	80	24	76
8	75	17	78	25	80
9	79			$\overline{X} = 79.72, s^2 = 10.79, s = 3.3$		

QUESTIONS

1. Define the following terms:
   a. Level of significance
   b. Power of test
   c. Null hypothesis
   d. Statistical error
   e. Statistical inference.
2. Describe a situation where it is of greatest importance to control
   a. The Type I error more than the Type II error.
   b. The Type II error more than the Type I error.

3. Why do few behavioral science researchers rarely consider the Type II error in the formation of their experimental designs?

4. Why does the sample size increase greatly when the β factor is considered?

PROBLEMS

1. Given: $\mu_0 = 100$, $\sigma = 16$, $n = 64$.   Compute $(1 - \beta)$ for values of $\mu_a = 96$, 97, 98, 99, 100, 101, 102, 103, 104, using $\alpha = 0.10$, 0.05, 0.02, 0.01.

2. What size sample would be needed to reject the hypothesis that $\mu_0 > 80$ when $\alpha = 4$, if the population being sampled is *at least* 0.02 units greater? (Use $\alpha = 0.10$, $\beta = 0.20$; $\alpha = 0.05$, $\beta = 0.10$; $\alpha = 0.01$, $\beta = 0.05$.)

3. What is the probability that the hypothesis will be accepted if
    (a) $\mu_0 \leq 25$ given $\sigma = 2$, $n = 25$, $\alpha = 0.05$, if in fact μ_a is 2 units different?
    (b) $\mu_0 = 30$ given $\sigma = 5$, $n = 36$, $\alpha = 0.01$, if in fact μ_a is 2 units different?

4. How will your answer to Problem 3a change if: (a) $\alpha = 0.01$? (b) $n = 50$? (c) $\alpha = 0.01$ and $n = 50$?

5. What size sample will be needed if it is desired to have a level of acceptance, or $(1 - \alpha)$ confidence, of 95% of rejecting the test hypothesis if $\overline{X}$ is at most 0.5 units greater than μ_0 in a population having $\sigma = 10$?

6. What would your answer to Problem 5 be if $(1 - \alpha) = 0.90$, 0.98, 0.99?

7. What would be the change in sample size if a power value $(1 - \beta)$ of 90% is also taken into consideration in Problem 5.

8. What would be the answers to Problem 6 if values of $(1 - \beta) = 0.80$, 0.95, 0.98, respectively, are used?

REFERENCES

Dixon, Wilfrid J., and Massey, Frank J., Jr. *Introduction to Statistical Analysis.* Second Edition. New York: McGraw Hill Book Company, Inc., 1959. Chapter 7.

Freund, John C., and Williams, Frank J. *Elementary Business Statistics: The Modern Approach.* Englewood Cliffs, N. J.: Prentice-Hall, Inc., 1964. Chapter 8.

Guenther, William C. *Concepts of Statistical Inference.* New York: McGraw-Hill Book Company, 1965. Chapter 4.

Li, Jerome C. R. *Introduction to Statistical Inference.* Ann Arbor, Michigan: Edwards Brothers, Inc., 1957. Chapters 6, 13, and 23.

Lindquist, E. F. *Design and Analysis of Experiments in Psychology and Education.* Boston: Houghton Mifflin Company, 1953. Chapter 1.

McNemar, Quinn. *Psychological Statistics.* Third Edition. New York: John Wiley and Sons, Inc., 1962. Chapter 6.

Ostle, Bernard. *Statistics in Research.* Ames, Iowa: The Iowa State University Press, 1954. Chapter 15.

Tate, Merle W. *Statistics in Education and Psychology: A First Course.* New York: The Macmillan Company, 1965. Chapter 9.

Wolf, Frank L. *Elements of Probability and Statistics.* New York: McGraw-Hill Book Company, Inc., 1962. Chapter 8.

Yamane, Taro. *Statistics, An Introductory Analysis.* New York: Harper and Row, Publishers, 1964. Chapter 8.

TESTS OF HYPOTHESES ABOUT MEASURES OF CENTRAL TENDENCY

During analysis of sampling statistics, it is necessary to decide whether the population being sampled has the same parametric mean value as that of the hypothesized population.

7.1 Tests of Hypotheses about Single Population Means. The problem presented in Chapter 6 was developed around a hypothesized population where both the population mean and standard deviation were known. Usually the value of the population standard deviation, σ, is not known. More commonly it is necessary to use the statistic, s, a sample standard deviation which estimates the population parameter, σ. To work with this factor in the testing process, it is necessary to utilize the Student's t distribution.

For the purpose of a sample problem, assume that the problem given in Chapter 6 is modified to state that the σ (7.4) for the senior English proficiency examination is unknown. The testing of the hypothesis (H_o) is modified only in that the t distribution is used to ascertain the critical values and the t statistic is used in the computation of the test statistic.

1. Is it reasonable to suppose that $\mu > 78.4$?
2. $H_o\!:\!\mu \leq 78.4$
3. $\alpha = 0.05$, test (a) (Figure 6.2.)
4. Reject H_o if $t > t_{1-a, \text{ d.f.}} = t_{0.95,\ 24} = 1.711$ (d.f. $= n - 1$).
   (The critical value, 1.711, may be seen by referring to Table II of Appendix A and reading the value in the column headed $\alpha = 0.10$ and having d.f. $= 24$.)
5. From Table 6.4,

$$t = \frac{\overline{X} - \mu}{\dfrac{s}{\sqrt{n}}} = \frac{79.72 - 78.4}{\dfrac{3.3}{\sqrt{25}}} = \frac{(1.32)(5)}{3.3} = 2.00$$

6. Reject the H_o.

The results of this test imply that the "new" students may be expected to be more capable than the "old" students.

7.2 Confidence Interval Estimate of Single Population Means.

Suppose that the results of the two tests of the hypotheses in Chapter 6 and in the preceding section had resulted in the rejection of the hypothesized mean value of 78.4. There arises the justifiable question of "what is a plausible estimate of the mean of the population being sampled?"

One value which may be offered is that of the sample mean which would act as the *point estimate of the mean*. This value would be 79.72. This would be a better estimate if a range of values were given with a stated degree of confidence that this range of values does include the value of the true mean of the population being sampled. The rationale for this assumption of inclusion is that if all values in a distribution of sample means were converted to z scores, then

$$P(-1.96 < z < 1.96) = 0.95$$

since

$$-1.96 = z_{0.025} = z_{\frac{\alpha}{2}}$$

and

$$1.96 = z_{0.975} = z_{(1-\frac{\alpha}{2})}$$

The general expression is:

$$P\left(z_{\frac{\alpha}{2}} < z < z_{(1-\frac{\alpha}{2})}\right) = 1 - \alpha$$

Substituting into the expression the computational equivalent for z, the expression becomes:

$$P\left[z_{\frac{\alpha}{2}} < \frac{\overline{X} - \mu}{\frac{\sigma}{\sqrt{n}}} < z_{(1-\frac{\alpha}{2})}\right] = 1 - \alpha$$

Multiplying the portion of the equation within the brackets by $\sigma/\sqrt{n}$:

$$P\left[z_{\frac{\alpha}{2}} \frac{\sigma}{\sqrt{n}} < (\overline{X} - \mu) < z_{(1-\frac{\alpha}{2})} \frac{\sigma}{\sqrt{n}}\right] = 1 - \alpha$$

Subtracting $\overline{X}$ and then multiplying by (-1) within the brackets:

$$P\left[\left(\overline{X} - z_{\frac{\alpha}{2}} \frac{\sigma}{\sqrt{n}}\right) > \mu > \left(\overline{X} - z_{(1-\frac{\alpha}{2})} \frac{\sigma}{\sqrt{n}}\right)\right] = 1 - \alpha$$

Using the easily demonstrated identity that $-z_{\frac{\alpha}{2}} = z_{(1-\frac{\alpha}{2})}$ and its converse, the equation now becomes:

$$P\left[\left(\overline{X} + z_{(1-\frac{\alpha}{2})} \frac{\sigma}{\sqrt{n}}\right) > \mu > \left(\overline{X} + z_{\frac{\alpha}{2}} \frac{\sigma}{\sqrt{n}}\right)\right] = 1 - \alpha$$

Reversing the relationship so that the inequality progresses from small to large, the equation becomes:

$$P\left[\left(\overline{X} + z_{\frac{\alpha}{2}} \frac{\sigma}{\sqrt{n}}\right) < \mu < \left(\overline{X} + z_{(1-\frac{\alpha}{2})} \frac{\sigma}{\sqrt{n}}\right)\right] = 1 - \alpha \qquad (7.1)$$

Equation (7.1) then is the relationship which may be used to compute an interval estimate of the true mean being sampled with $(1 - \alpha)$ level of confidence. Where the population standard deviation (σ) is unknown, the equation is modified using the statistic s in place of σ and the standardized deviate t rather than z. The resulting probability statement is

$$P\left[\left(\overline{X} + t_{\frac{\alpha}{2},\text{d.f.}} \frac{s}{\sqrt{n}}\right) < \mu < \left(\overline{X} + t_{1-\frac{\alpha}{2},\text{d.f.}} \frac{s}{\sqrt{n}}\right)\right] = 1 - \alpha \qquad (7.2)$$

where d.f. $= n - 1$.

Using the data from Table 6.4, the estimate of the mean of the sampled population using the z statistic and Equation (7.1) is:

$$P\left\{\left[79.72 + (-1.96) \frac{(7.4)}{\sqrt{25}}\right] < \mu < \left[79.72 + (1.96) \frac{(7.4)}{\sqrt{25}}\right]\right\} = 0.95$$

$$P\{[79.72 - 2.90] < \mu < [79.72 + 2.90]\} = 0.95$$

$$P\{76.82 < \mu < 82.62\} = 0.95$$

Using equation (7.2) it is:

$$P\left\{\left[79.72 + (-2.064) \frac{(3.3)}{\sqrt{25}}\right] < \mu < \left[79.72 + (2.064) \frac{3.3}{\sqrt{25}}\right]\right\} = 0.95$$

$$P\{[79.72 - 1.36] < \mu < [79.72 + 1.36]\} = 0.95$$

$$P\{78.36 < \mu < 81.08\} = 0.95$$

Each final statement of the two groups of equations says that the probability is 0.95 that the interval computed may include the value of the true mean.

7.3 Tests of Hypotheses Concerning the Differences between Means of Two Populations.

In many instances the investigator is interested in comparing two different samples. An instance of this is illustrated by the following case. A mathematics teacher desires to compare the effectiveness of two methods of instruction upon achievement. In the following example the two samples used are said to be *independent*. This means that each sample is representative of a different population and the values obtained in one sample do not predetermine the values obtained in the other sample. One group of 20 students will be taught by a teaching machine program and the second group of 20 students by conventional classroom procedures. Students registering for the mathematics course in question are placed in one of the two groups in a random fashion. A valid standardized test is given to both groups at the beginning of the school term to establish the base level of competence. The achievement is to be determined by using the difference between pre-test score and an equivalent form post-test score. Data for this problem are presented in Table 7.1.

TABLE 7.1

PRE-TEST AND POST-TEST ACHIEVEMENT SCORES FOR STUDENTS TAUGHT BY TEACHING-MACHINE PROGRAM AND STUDENTS TAUGHT BY CONVENTIONAL PROCEDURE

	Teaching Machine			Conventional			
Student Number	Pre-test	Post-test	d_{1i}	Pre-test	Post-test	d_{2i}	Student Number
1	46	47	1	42	57	15	21
2	44	47	3	43	45	2	22
3	34	41	7	54	60	6	23
4	47	49	2	35	36	1	24
5	59	56	−3	44	58	14	25
6	52	55	3	44	52	8	26
7	37	51	14	46	53	7	27
8	47	50	3	49	59	10	26
9	41	42	1	51	62	11	29
10	39	45	6	48	56	8	30
11	50	60	10	48	55	7	31
12	45	51	6	48	42	−6	32
13	40	34	−6	34	38	4	33
14	46	51	5	37	43	6	34
15	41	41	0	45	55	10	35
16	36	32	−4	49	44	−5	36
17	51	52	1	38	47	9	37
18	32	34	2	44	49	5	38
19	39	49	10	31	38	7	39
20	45	50	5	55	62	7	40
$\sum d_{ij}$			66			126	
$\sum d_{ij}^2$			666			1326	
$\overline{d}$			3.3			6.3	
s_d^2			23.59			28.01	
s_d			4.8			5.3	

The teacher is not primarily concerned with the exact value of the mean achievement of either group. The major area of concern may be expressed as follows: Is it reasonable to suppose that the mean achievement of those students taught by the teaching machines (μ_1) is not the same as the mean achievement of those students taught by the conventional procedure (μ_2)? (Are the two samples to be used both representative of two populations having a common mean, μ?) Both populations have a $\sigma = \sigma_1 = \sigma_2 = 4.9$.

7.3.1 Both Standard Deviations Known.

Using the format presented in Chapter 6, the problem would be set up as follows:

1. Is it reasonable to suppose that $\mu_1 \neq \mu_2$?
2. $H_o : \mu_1 = \mu_2$ (i.e., $\mu_1 - \mu_2 = 0$)
3. $\alpha = 0.05$, test (c).
4. Reject H_o if $z < z_{0.025} = -1.96$ (From Table I, Appendix A) or if $z > z_{0.975} = 1.96$.

5. $$z = \frac{(\overline{X}_1 - \overline{X}_2) - (\mu_1 - \mu_2)}{\sqrt{\dfrac{\sigma_1^2}{n_1} + \dfrac{\sigma_2^2}{n_2}}}$$

$$= \frac{(3.3 - 6.3) - (0)}{\sqrt{\dfrac{24.01}{20} + \dfrac{24.01}{20}}} = -\frac{3.0}{\sqrt{\dfrac{48.02}{20}}}$$

$$= -\frac{3.0}{1.55} = -1.937$$

6. Accept H_o. This would be interpreted as saying that the evidence indicates that the achievement levels of the two groups are the same and gives indication that no real difference exists between the gains of the two groups.

7.3.2 Both Population Standard Deviations Unknown (Non-paired Data).

Previously it has been pointed out that the researcher may not be aware of the true values of the parameter σ^2. In the case where the true values of σ_1^2 and σ_2^2 are unknown, the Student's t distribution is used in place of the z statistic. At this point the question of concern is whether the values of σ_1^2 and σ_2^2 are equal or may be assumed to be equal. If it can be validly assumed that $\sigma_1^2 = \sigma_2^2 = \sigma^2$, one form of the t statistic for two population means is used. If the assumption cannot be assumed to be valid, another form should be used. The actual test to validate this assumption will be presented in Chapter 8.

If this assumption can be accepted, certain variations may be made in the expression of the standard error of estimate for the distribution of differences in sample means, $(\overline{X}_{1i} - \overline{X}_{2i})$.

Where both variances, σ_1^2 and σ_2^2, are known, the standard error of estimate is expressed as:

$$\sqrt{\frac{\sigma_1^2}{n_1} + \frac{\sigma_2^2}{n_2}}$$

Using the assumption, the common variance value (σ^2) may be substituted for the separate values of σ_1^2 and σ_2^2 giving

$$\sqrt{\frac{\sigma^2}{n_1} + \frac{\sigma^2}{n_2}}$$

which may be factored giving

$$\sqrt{\sigma^2\left[\frac{1}{n_1} + \frac{1}{n_2}\right]}$$

Since the true value of σ^2 is unknown, the sample statistic s^2 is used as the maximum likelihood estimator. In the case of the problem under consideration, with the assumption being made about the variance, both s_1^2 and s_2^2 have the same value. In this instance it would be proper to pool these two estimators, thus securing a single value which is called a *pooled variance* statistic, and which is represented by the symbol s_p^2.

Using the idea of pooling the two separate sample statistics, s_p^2 then becomes:

$$s_p^2 = \frac{\sum_{i=1}^{n_1}(X_{1i} - \overline{X}_1)^2 + \sum_{i=1}^{n_2}(X_{2i} - \overline{X}_2)^2}{(n_1 - 1) + (n_2 - 1)}$$

or

$$s_p^2 = \frac{\sum_{i=1}^{n_1}(X_{1i} - \overline{X}_1)^2 + \sum_{i=1}^{n_2}(X_{2i} - \overline{X}_2)^2}{n_1 + n_2 - 2}$$

This expression may be extended to include any number (k) sample statistic variances to yield:

$$s_p^2 = \frac{\sum_{i=1}^{n_1}(X_{1i} - \overline{X}_1)^2 + \sum_{i=1}^{n_2}(X_{2i} - \overline{X}_2)^2 + \cdots + \sum_{i=1}^{n_k}(X_{ki} - \overline{X}_k)^2}{n_1 + n_2 + \cdots + n_k - k}$$

This general form may be expanded in the same manner as that presented in Chapter 3 for the case of the single sample variance, permitting the derivation of a computational formula:

$$s_p^2 = \frac{\sum_{i=1}^{n_1}X_{1i}^2 - \dfrac{\left[\sum_{i=1}^{n_1}X_{1i}\right]^2}{n_1} + \sum_{i=1}^{n_2}X_{2i}^2 - \dfrac{\left[\sum_{i=1}^{n_2}X_{2i}\right]^2}{n_2} + \cdots + \sum_{i=1}^{n_k}X_{ki}^2 - \dfrac{\left[\sum_{i=1}^{n_k}X_{ki}\right]^2}{n_k}}{n_1 + n_2 + \cdots + n_k - k}$$

If we may substitute the symbol $T._j$ for $\sum X_{ij}$ (since this value is actually the total of the values of X_{ij} for the jth column) and collect the sums of squares as well as the sums of the ratios, the formula now becomes:

$$s_p^2 = \frac{\sum\limits_{i=1}^{n_1} X_{1i}^2 + \sum\limits_{i=1}^{n_2} X_{2i}^2 + \cdots + \sum\limits_{i=1}^{n_k} X_{ki}^2 - \dfrac{T._1^2}{n_1} - \dfrac{T._2^2}{n_2} - \cdots - \dfrac{T._k^2}{n_k}}{\sum\limits_{j=1}^{k} n_j - k}$$

Collecting the terms, the general computational equation for the pooled variance of any (k) number of sample variances is:

$$s_p^2 = \frac{\sum\limits_{j=1}^{k} \sum\limits_{i=1}^{n_j} X_{ij}^2 - \sum\limits_{j=1}^{k} \left[\dfrac{T._j^2}{n_j}\right]}{\sum\limits_{j=1}^{k} n_j - k} \tag{7.3}$$

where $j = 1, 2, \ldots, k$ is the number of the sampled population, and $i = 1, 2, \ldots, n_j$ is the respective member of the jth sample.

Using this estimator of the value of the common variance, the standard error of estimate becomes:

$$s_{(\overline{X}_1 - \overline{X}_2)} = \sqrt{s_p^2 \left[\frac{1}{n_1} + \frac{1}{n_2}\right]} \tag{7.4}$$

where the value for s_p^2 may be computed by use of (7.3) or by another formula (7.5) to be given. Going back to the original expression of the theoretical aspect of the pooled variance estimator, another substitution may be made using the following rationals.

By definition:

$$s_1^2 = \frac{\sum\limits_{i=1}^{n_1} (X_{1i} - X_1)^2}{n_1 - 1}$$

Or

$$s_1^2(n_1 - 1) = \sum\limits_{i=1}^{n_1} (X_{1i} - \overline{X}_1)^2$$

Then

$$s_j^2(n_j - 1) = \sum\limits_{i=1}^{n_j} (X_{ij} - \overline{X}_j)^2$$

which permits the following substitution:

$$s_p^2 = -\frac{s_1^2(n_1 - 1) + s_2^2(n_2 - 1) + \cdots + s_k^2(n_k - 1)}{n_1 + n_2 + \cdots + n_k - k} \tag{7.5}$$

Whether Equation (7.3) or Equation (7.5) shall be used in Equation (7.4) is dependent upon whether the individual sample variance values are known or must be computed.

Using Equation (7.4), the standard error of estimate, the test statistic for the Student's t test becomes

$$t = \frac{(\overline{X}_1 - \overline{X}_2) - (\mu_1 - \mu_2)}{\sqrt{s_p^2 \left(\frac{1}{n_1} + \frac{1}{n_2}\right)}}, \quad \text{d.f.} = n_1 + n_2 - 2 \qquad (7.6)$$

Using Equation (7.6), our proposed problem as presented in Section 7.3 may be modified to the extent that a common variance is assumed, but the value is unknown.

1. Is it reasonable to suppose that $\mu_1 \neq \mu_2$?
2. $H_o: \mu_1 = \mu_2$ (i.e., $\mu_1 - \mu_2 = 0$)
3. $\alpha = 0.05$, test (c)
4. Reject H_o if $t < t_{0.025,38} = -2.0246$ (since $n_1 = n_2 = 20$; therefore d.f. $= n_1 - 1 + n_2 - 1 = 38$), or if $t > t_{0.975,38} = 2.0246$.

5. $t = \dfrac{(3.3 - 6.3) - (0)}{\sqrt{\left[\dfrac{(23.59)(19) + (28.01)(19)}{20 + 20 - 2}\right]\left[\dfrac{1}{20} + \dfrac{1}{20}\right]}} = -1.868$

6. Accept the H_o. This would be interpreted as evidence that a real difference apparently does not exist between the achievement scores of the two groups.

Where the common variance ($\sigma_1^2 = \sigma_2^2 = \sigma^2$) assumption cannot be made, the t statistic, Equation (7.6), cannot be utilized directly as presented. The reasoning for this lies in the fact that under the conditions of $\sigma_1^2 \neq \sigma_2^2$, the sample estimators (s_1^2 and s_2^2) cannot be pooled. It has been proposed by Welch, and Aspin, that the following modification be made. A pseudo t statistic is now computed by directly substituting the respective sample statistic values of s^2 for their respective σ^2 values in the standard error of estimate so that

$$t' = \frac{(\overline{X}_1 - \overline{X}_2) - (\mu_1 - \mu_2)}{\sqrt{\frac{s_1^2}{n_1} + \frac{s_2^2}{n_2}}} \qquad (7.7)$$

with the degrees of freedom changing from $(n_1 + n_2 - 2)$ and being computed by

$$\frac{1}{\text{d.f.}} = \frac{c^2}{\text{d.f.}_1} + \frac{(1 - c)^2}{\text{d.f.}_2} \qquad (7.8)$$

where

$$c = \frac{\frac{s_1^2}{n_1}}{\frac{s_1^2}{n_1} + \frac{s_2^2}{n_2}} \qquad (7.9)$$

7.3.3 *Tests for Correlated or Paired Data*. Rather than use the procedure of "matched" pairs, it is more appropriate to utilize the individual as his own control. The reason for this is the lack of techniques to fully evaluate and control the variables which make each individual unique and which may affect the outcome of the experiment. The "within person" variation is such that only by using the individual as his own control can maximum inference be made.

Suppose a researcher desires to know the effect of a particular antihistamine on the recall ability of students. One way this particular problem may be attacked is through the use of two random samples of students, one group to be given *placebo* application and the other to be given the actual drug. After administration of the respective treatments, the two groups could be assigned a selection to memorize and, after a predetermined series of time lapses, have their recall abilities assessed by some standardized process.

This method for attacking the problem appears appropriate at first glance. Upon closer examination, the factors of individual differences with respect to drug reaction and mental ability arise as areas which may obscure the interpretation of the results. Considerating these two variables, it would be well to consider some means by which these students may be compared with themselves, thus removing this intrapersonal and interpersonal effect. Considering this aspect, the problem may be redesigned as follows. A random sample of students is selected and, after a *placebo* administration, the subjects are asked to memorize a passage of poetry. After a prescribed time lapse, recall ability is measured on a standardized instrument. This first measurement will now act as a basis for comparison. The same group of students are now administered the drug. They are then asked to memorize a comparable selection of poetry and, after an equal time lapse, their recall ability is again ascertained. The effect of the drug may now be tested by comparing the students with themselves, using as the index of effect, the difference between their two scores. Data presented in Table 7.2 illustrate a hypothetical problem of this nature.

In this problem the question now concerns the mean of the differences (μ_d) between the *before* and *after* test scores. This will necessitate the use of the standard error of estimate of the differences ($s_{\bar{d}}$) which is ($s_d/\sqrt{n}$) where

$$s_d^2 = \frac{\sum_{i=1}^{n} d_i^2 - \frac{\left[\sum_{i=1}^{n} d_i\right]^2}{n}}{n-1}, \quad \text{d.f.} = n-1 \tag{7.10}$$

With this in mind the problem would be set up and tested as follows:

1. Is it reasonable to suppose that $\mu_d \neq 0$?
2. $H_o: \mu_d = 0$
3. $\alpha = 0.05$, test (c)

4. Reject H_o if $t < t_{0.025,24} = -2.064$ or if $t > t_{0.975,24} = 2.064$.

5. $$t = \frac{\bar{d} - \mu_d}{\frac{s_d}{\sqrt{n}}} = \frac{6.40 - 0}{\frac{5.02}{\sqrt{25}}} \tag{7.11}$$

$$= 6.37$$

6. Reject H_o.

TABLE 7.2

SCORES ON A TEST OF RECALLED INFORMATION BEFORE AND AFTER ADMINISTRATION OF AN ANTIHISTAMINE

Student Number	Test Scores			Student Number	Test Scores		
	Before	After	d		Before	After	d
1	45	38	7	16	38	35	3
2	41	40	1	17	44	43	1
3	65	56	9	18	48	38	10
4	58	53	5	19	50	39	11
5	59	56	3	20	45	34	11
6	41	31	10	21	40	34	6
7	48	31	17	22	43	35	8
8	60	56	4	23	50	50	0
9	42	33	9	24	50	50	0
10	58	47	11	25	53	44	9
11	33	35	2		$\sum d$	160	
12	43	43	0		$\bar{d}$	6.40	
13	61	59	2		$\sum d^2$	1630	
14	56	42	14		s_d^2	25.25	
15	58	47	11		s_d	5.02	

7.4 Confidence Interval Estimates for True Differences between Two Population Means. Using the proof presented in Section 7.2, the equations for determining the confidence interval estimates of the true differences between population means are given below:

7.4.1 Both Variances Known

$$P\left[\left((\bar{X}_1 - \bar{X}_2) + z_{\frac{\alpha}{2}}\sqrt{\frac{\sigma_1^2}{n_1} + \frac{\sigma_2^2}{n_2}}\right) < (\mu_1 - \mu_2)\right.$$
$$\left. < \left((\bar{X}_1 - \bar{X}_2) + z_{(1-\frac{\alpha}{2})}\sqrt{\frac{\sigma_1^2}{n_1} + \frac{\sigma_2^2}{n_2}}\right)\right] = 1 - \alpha \tag{7.12}$$

7.4.2 *Both Variances Unknown (Uncorrelated Data)*

$$P\left[\left((\bar{X}_1 - \bar{X}_2) + t_{\frac{\alpha}{2}, \text{d.f.}} \sqrt{s_p^2\left[\frac{1}{n_1} + \frac{1}{n_2}\right]}\right) < (\mu_1 - \mu_2)\right.$$

$$\left. < \left((\bar{X}_1 - \bar{X}_2) + t_{(1-\frac{\alpha}{2}), \text{d.f.}} \sqrt{s_p^2\left[\frac{1}{n_1} + \frac{1}{n_2}\right]}\right)\right] = 1 - \alpha \qquad (7.13)$$

7.4.3 *Both Variances Unknown (Correlated Data)*

$$P\left[\left(\bar{d} + t_{\frac{\alpha}{2}, \text{d.f.}} \frac{s_d}{\sqrt{n}}\right) < \mu_d < \left(\bar{d} + t_{(1-\frac{\alpha}{2}), \text{d.f.}} \frac{s_d}{\sqrt{n}}\right)\right] = 1 - \alpha \qquad (7.14)$$

PROBLEMS

1. It was desired to know if a significant difference existed between two samples drawn from two populations having standard deviations of 7.73 and 4.35 respectively. Samples of 37 were drawn from each of the two populations and found to have means of 49.57 and 49.97 respectively. Use $\alpha = 0.01$.

2. Is it reasonable to suppose that the first sample drawn in Problem 1 came from a population having a mean of 51.00? What would be the probability of committing the Type II error if, in fact, the sample was drawn from a population having a mean of 51.5? What size sample would be necessary to detect any population having a mean at least 0.05 units different (power = 99.5%)?

3. Samples of size 37 were drawn from two populations. The question arose as to whether the means of the populations sampled were the same. For sample No. 1, the mean was 46.79 and the sum of squared deviations was 1350.81; for sample No. 2 the mean was 49.57, and the sum of squared deviations was 1829.08. Test the hypothesis appropriate for test (c) and for test (b). Use $\alpha = 0.05$.

4. The following data were obtained and represent the differences between pre-test and post-test scores for 37 individuals on equivalent forms of a standardized test.

8	15	1	7	6	5
3	11	14	8	16	3
12	13	9	0	8	10
15	11	11	7	3	9
14	5	−5	17	9	2
6	2	9	10	9	4
					12

Is it reasonable to suppose that the mean gain in achievement is at least 6.5 points?

5. Determine the 90% confidence interval estimates appropriate for Problems 1–4.

6. The You-Know-Better Chewing Tobacco Company makes a plug that is supposed to have an average nicotine content of 20 milligrams. Nine plugs are tested and the average nicotine content is found to be 21.2 milligrams with a standard deviation of 1.8 milligrams. At the 5% significance level, has the tobacco's nicotine content increased?

7. For several years a college professor has noticed the class average at the end of the term and has found this average score to be 80 with a variance of 225. This term, however, the average term grade of four sections was computed to be 75. Are these sections less capable, if you use a 1% level of significance?

8. The average height of the men on a campus is 70 inches with a variance of 4 inches. A group of 100 men are measured and found to have an average height of 69.5 inches. Is the sample indicative of a population having a shorter mean? Use the 0.01 level of significance.

9. The coffee-break hour at the Silk-E-Shirt Factory has been 10 a.m. for several years. The average number of shirts produced on a particular assembly line is known to have been 32.4. After the new production supervisor was hired, he changed the coffee-break to 9:30 a.m. The mean production on the above assembly line was computed to be 30.7 shirts from a tabulation of 16-hourly readings, as was the standard deviation of 3.2 shirts. If you use a 5% level of significance, can you conclude that the hourly production on this line is not the same?

10. The Foreword Grocery Store has sold an average of $2.40 per person in meat for a long time. The standard deviation is known to be 0.35. Last week the manager fired the good looking clerk at the meat counter. Yesterday meat sales to 25 people averaged $2.18. At the 5% level of significance, has the per capita sale of meat decreased?

11. On a certain test, the following results were obtained:

$$\text{Women: } \overline{X}_1 = 60 \quad s_1^2 = 9 \quad n_1 = 32$$
$$\text{Men: } \overline{X}_2 = 66 \quad s_1^2 = 9 \quad n_2 = 40$$

Is there evidence that the two groups were not equally well prepared? State carefully the assumptions required for your test. Find the 95% confidence limits for the difference between the two means.

REFERENCES

Dixon, Wilfrid J., and Massey, Frank J., Jr. *Introduction to Statistical Analysis.* Second Edition. New York: McGraw-Hill Book Company, Inc., 1959. Chapters 6 and 9.

DuBois, Philip H. *An Introduction to Psychological Statistics.* New York: Harper and Row, Publishers, 1965. Chapter 13.

Edwards, Allen L. *Statistical Methods for Behavioral Sciences.* New York: Holt, Rinehart and Company, Inc., 1954. Pp. 239–245, 248–255, 278–288.

Freund, John C., and Williams, Frank J. *Elementary Business Statistics: The Modern Approach.* Englewood Cliffs, New Jersey: Prentice-Hall, Inc., 1964. Chapter 8.

Guenther, William C. *Concepts of Statistical Inference.* New York: McGraw-Hill Book Company, Inc., 1965. Chapter 5.

Li, Jerome C. R. *Introduction to Statistical Inference.* Ann Arbor, Michigan: Edwards Brothers, Inc., 1957. Chapters 8, 10, and 11.

McNemar, Quinn. *Psychological Statistics.* Third Edition. New York: John Wiley and Sons, Inc., 1962. Chapter 7.

Mode, Elmer B. *Elements of Statistics.* Third Edition. Englewood Cliffs, New Jersey: Prentice-Hall, Inc., 1961. Chapters 8 and 10.

Ostle, Bernard. *Statistics in Research.* Second Edition. Ames, Iowa: The Iowa State University Press, 1963. Chapters 6 and 7.

Steel, Robert G. D., and Torrie, James H. *Principles and Procedures of Statistics.* New York: McGraw-Hill Book Company, Inc., 1960. Chapters 4 and 5.

Tate, Merle W. *Statistics in Education and Psychology: A First Course.* New York: The Macmillan Company, 1965. Chapters 10 and 11.

Weinberg, George H., and Schumaker, John A. *Statistics: An Intuitive Approach.* Belmont, California: Wadsworth Publishing Company, Inc., 1962. Chapter 13.

Wolf, Frank L. *Elements of Probability and Statistics.* New York: McGraw-Hill Book Company, Inc., 1962. Chapters 8, 10, and 13.

TESTS OF HYPOTHESES ABOUT MEASURES OF DISPERSION

Tests of hypotheses concerning the mean μ as one of the basic population parameters were presented in Chapter 7. In this chapter we shall be concerned with tests of hypotheses about the other major population parameters — variance σ^2 and standard deviation σ.

In hypothesizing about the feasibility of the assumption that a sample comes from a given population, the sample must be tested for its relationship to known variance and mean values.

In Section 5.4 it was shown that a $\chi^2/\text{d.f.}$ distribution is generated when variance statistics for all possible samples of size n drawn from a population are placed in ratio with the value σ_o^2. This distribution may be used as the testing agency for the hypotheses about an hypothesized value of σ_o^2. The format to be followed is the same as that used in Chapters 6 and 7.

8.1 *Tests of Hypotheses about Single Population Variance, σ_o^2.* To demonstrate this procedure, we will use the population presented in the example in Chapter 6 having a variance value of $\sigma^2 = \sigma_o^2 = 54.76$ ($\sigma = 7.4$). A sample of 25 items was randomly drawn (data given in Table 8.1) to test the hypothesis that $\sigma^2 = \sigma_o^2 = 54.76$ against the alternate possibility that $\sigma^2 \neq \sigma_o^2 = 54.76$.

1. Is it reasonable to suppose that $\sigma^2 \neq \sigma_o^2 = 54.76$?
2. $H_o : \sigma^2 = \sigma_o^2 = 54.76$
3. $\alpha = 0.05$, test (c) (It is necessary in this testing procedure to again select the appropriate test — (a), (b), or (c) of Figure 6.2.)
4. Reject H_o if $s^2/\sigma^2 < \chi^2_{\alpha/2,\text{d.f.}}/\text{d.f.} = \chi^2_{0.025,24}/24 = 12.4/24 = 0.517$ or if $s^2/\sigma^2 > \chi^2_{1-\alpha/2,\text{ d.f.}}/\text{d.f.} = \chi^2_{0.975,24}/24 = 1.64$.

(By referring to Table III, Appendix A, the value of $\chi^2_{\alpha/2,\text{d.f.}} = \chi^2_{0.025,24} = 12$ [d.f. $= f$ in table] and $\chi^2_{1-\alpha/2,\text{ d.f.}} = \chi^2_{0.975,24} = 39.4$ will be found. By dividing these table values of χ^2 by the d.f. value of 24, the critical test statistic values are determined.)

5. $s^2/\sigma^2 = 94.00/54.76 = 1.717$
6. Reject H_o. This may be interpreted as indication that the sample came from a population with an actual variance $\sigma_a^2 > 54.76$.

TABLE 8.1

DATA FOR A SAMPLE OF $n = 25$

Item Number	Score $(X_i)^*$	X_i^2
1	6	36
2	−11	121
3	−2	4
4	8	64
5	−4	16
6	5	25
7	16	256
8	3	9
9	12	144
10	0	0
11	5	25
12	6	36
13	4	16
14	−14	196
15	1	1
16	−16	256
17	−3	9
18	−17	289
19	17	289
20	13	169
21	4	16
22	7	49
23	16	256
24	1	1
25	13	169
	$\sum X_i = 70$	$\sum X_i^2 = 2452$

* Coded scores (X_i) were obtained by subtracting 82.0 from the original scores.

$$s_1^2 = \frac{2452 - \dfrac{(70)^2}{25}}{24} = 94.00$$

8.2 *Confidence Interval Estimate of the True Population Variance,* σ^2. In rejection of the hypothesis, the plausible question arises as to the true value of σ^2. Again, it is possible to use the point estimate, but for the reasons given in an earlier discussion, the confidence interval estimate is much more valid and useful.

If the s^2/σ^2 distribution is the same as $\chi^2/\text{d.f.}$, then it is permissible to say that $(1 - \alpha)$ proportion of all of the ratios of s^2/σ^2 occur between $\chi^2_{\alpha/2}/\text{d.f.}$ and $\chi^2_{1-\alpha/2}/\text{d.f.}$, or

$$P\left[\frac{\chi^2_{\frac{\alpha}{2}}}{\text{d.f.}} < \frac{s^2}{\sigma^2} < \frac{\chi^2_{(1-\frac{\alpha}{2})}}{\text{d.f.}}\right] = 1 - \alpha$$

From this relationship, an expression for the confidence interval estimate of the true population variance may be derived. If the inequality is multiplied throughout by the reciprocal of s^2, the expression becomes:

$$P\left[\frac{\frac{\chi^2_{\frac{\alpha}{2}}}{\text{d.f.}}}{s^2} < \frac{1}{\sigma^2} < \frac{\frac{\chi^2_{(1-\frac{\alpha}{2})}}{\text{d.f.}}}{s^2}\right] = 1 - \alpha$$

By taking the reciprocal of the inequality expression,

$$P\left[\frac{s^2}{\frac{\chi^2_{\frac{\alpha}{2}}}{\text{d.f.}}} > \sigma^2 > \frac{s^2}{\frac{\chi^2_{(1-\frac{\alpha}{2})}}{\text{d.f.}}}\right] = 1 - \alpha$$

Rearranging the expression in the form of proceeding from the smaller value to the larger value, the expression for the $(1 - \alpha)$ level of confidence interval estimate of the true population variance is derived:

$$P\left[\frac{s^2}{\frac{\chi^2_{(1-\frac{\alpha}{2})}}{\text{d.f.}}} < \sigma^2 < \frac{s^2}{\frac{\chi^2_{\frac{\alpha}{2}}}{\text{d.f.}}}\right] = 1 - \alpha \tag{8.1}$$

Using this expression with the sample value of 94.00 obtained in Table 8.1, the 0.95 level of confidence interval estimate of the true variance σ^2 is:

$$P\left[\frac{94.00}{1.64} < \sigma^2 < \frac{94.00}{0.517}\right] = 0.95$$

or

$$P[57.32 < \sigma^2 < 181.82] = 0.95$$

8.3 Tests of Hypotheses concerning Relationship between Two Population Variances. The structure of the F distribution was discussed in Section 5.5. It was shown there that this distribution is predicated on the concept that:

$$F = \frac{\frac{s_1^2}{\sigma_1^2}}{\frac{s_2^2}{\sigma_2^2}} = \frac{\frac{\chi_1^2}{(\text{d.f.})_1}}{\frac{\chi_2^2}{(\text{d.f.})_2}}$$

and thus involves two sets of degrees of freedom. Therefore, to test the hypothesis concerning the equality of two population variances, the expression for F was resolved to:

$$F = \frac{\frac{s_1^2}{\sigma^2}}{\frac{s_2^2}{\sigma^2}} = \frac{s_1^2}{s_2^2} \tag{8.2}$$

if $\sigma_1^2 = \sigma_2^2 = \sigma^2$, by replacing the separate values of σ_1^2 and σ_2^2 with the common variance value of σ^2.

This F statistic then may be used to test the following hypotheses:

1. $\sigma_1^2 \leq \sigma_2^2$ against the alternate $\sigma_1^2 > \sigma_2^2$ (test (a)).
2. $\sigma_1^2 \geq \sigma_2^2$ against the alternate $\sigma_1^2 < \sigma_2^2$ (test (b)).
3. $\sigma_1^2 = \sigma_2^2$ against the alternate $\sigma_1^2 \neq \sigma_2^2$ (test (c)).

Using the data presented in Table 8.2 (which is an extension of Table 8.1), test the hypothesis that $\sigma^2 = \sigma_1^2 = \sigma_2^2$.

1. Is it reasonable to suppose that $\sigma_1^2 \neq \sigma_2^2$?
2. $H_o: \sigma_1^2 = \sigma_2^2$
3. $\alpha = 0.10$, test (c)

The critical value of F for this problem may be found in Table IVd of Appendix A. The area indicated in that table is that portion of the F distribution curve remaining in the right tail of the curve beyond the selected critical value. It should be noted also that f_1 and f_2 are shortened notations for $(\text{d.f.})_1$ and $(\text{d.f.})_2$. With this in mind the critical value for the *right* tail may be read as:

$$F_{(1-\frac{\alpha}{2}) \cdot (f_1, f_2)} = F_{0.95,(24,24)} = 1.9838$$

If the larger mean square or sample variance is always placed in the numerator, the resultant value of F will always be equal to or greater than unity. This will eliminate the cumbersome computation of the *left* tail critical value of F found by:

$$F_{\frac{\alpha}{2} \cdot (f_1, f_2)} = \frac{1}{F_{(1-\frac{\alpha}{2}) \cdot (f_2, f_1)}} \tag{8.3}$$

which for our problem would be:

$$F_{0.05,(24,24)} = \frac{1}{F_{0.95,(24,24)}} = \frac{1}{1.9838} = 0.5041$$

TABLE 8.2

DATA FOR TWO SAMPLES WHERE $n_1 = n_2 = 25$

Item Number	X_{1i}*	X_{2i}*
1	6	12
2	−11	−8
3	−2	−16
4	8	−13
5	−4	−2
6	5	−4
7	16	−16
8	3	12
9	12	−2
10	0	10
11	5	−5
12	6	2
13	4	−16
14	−14	−10
15	1	13
16	−16	7
17	−3	6
18	−17	−8
19	17	12
20	13	12
21	4	−6
22	7	5
23	16	−9
24	1	−13
25	13	−2

$$\sum X_{2i} = -39$$
$$\sum X_{2i}^2 = 2463$$

* Coded values obtained by subtracting 82.0 from original scores.

$$s_1^2 = 94.00$$

$$s_2^2 = \frac{2463 - \frac{(-39)^2}{25}}{24}$$

$$= 100.09$$

Graphically, the acceptance and rejection regions for our problem may be shown as:

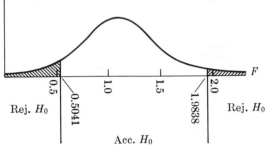

4. Reject H_o if $F < F_{\alpha/2(f_1,f_2)} = F_{0.05(24,24)} = 0.5041$
   or if $F > F_{(1-\alpha/2)(f_1,f_2)} = F_{0.95(24,24)} = 1.9838$.

5. $F = \dfrac{s_1^2}{s_2^2} = \dfrac{94.00}{100.09} = 0.939$

6. Accept H_o. (Interpreted, this would indicate that both samples come from populations having a common variance.)

The use of this test eliminates the necessity for making the assumption of a common variance as was mentioned in Section 7.3.2. With the use of the "F" test, it may be determined which of the two Formulas, (7.6) or (7.7), for testing the equality of two means should be used.

In the example just completed (where the hypothesis was accepted) the two sample variances may be pooled, obtaining s_p^2, and this value used in computing the confidence interval estimate of the common variance value, σ^2.

$$P\left[\dfrac{s_p^2}{\dfrac{\chi_{(1-\frac{\alpha}{2}),\text{d.f.}}^2}{\text{d.f.}}} < \sigma^2 < \dfrac{s_p^2}{\dfrac{\chi_{\frac{\alpha}{2},\text{d.f.}}^2}{\text{d.f.}}}\right] = 1 - \alpha \qquad (8.4)$$

By taking the positive root of the expressions in Equations (8.1) and/or (8.4), a confidence interval estimate of the standard deviation (σ) may be ascertained.

8.4 Confidence Interval Estimate of the True Ratio of Two Population Variances. The "F" ratio is found by:

$$F = \dfrac{\dfrac{s_1^2}{\sigma_1^2}}{\dfrac{s_2^2}{\sigma_2^2}}$$

and there is a probability equal to $(1 - \alpha)$ that the value of this ratio lies between $F_{\alpha/2(f_1,f_2)}$ and $F_{1-\alpha/2(f_1,f_2)}$,

$$P\left[F_{\frac{\alpha}{2}(f_1,f_2)} < \frac{\frac{s_1^2}{\sigma_1^2}}{\frac{s_2^2}{\sigma_2^2}} < F_{(1-\frac{\alpha}{2})(f_1,f_2)}\right] = 1 - \alpha$$

which may be simplified to:

$$P\left[F_{\frac{\alpha}{2}(f_1,f_2)} < \frac{s_1^2\sigma_2^2}{s_2^2\sigma_1^2} < F_{(1-\frac{\alpha}{2})(f_1,f_2)}\right] = 1 - \alpha$$

The reciprocal is:

$$P\left[\frac{1}{F_{\frac{\alpha}{2}(f_1,f_2)}} > \frac{s_2^2\sigma_1^2}{s_1^2\sigma_2^2} > \frac{1}{F_{(1-\frac{\alpha}{2})(f_1,f_2)}}\right] = 1 - \alpha$$

Multiplying the inequality by s_1^2/s_2^2:

$$P\left[\frac{\frac{s_1^2}{s_2^2}}{F_{\frac{\alpha}{2}(f_1,f_2)}} > \frac{\sigma_1^2}{\sigma_2^2} > \frac{\frac{s_1^2}{s_2^2}}{F_{(1-\frac{\alpha}{2})(f_1,f_2)}}\right] = 1 - \alpha$$

Rearranging the relationship to progress from smaller values to larger values:

$$P\left[\frac{\frac{s_1^2}{s_2^2}}{F_{(1-\frac{\alpha}{2})(f_1,f_2)}} < \frac{\sigma_1^2}{\sigma_2^2} < \frac{\frac{s_1^2}{s_2^2}}{F_{\frac{\alpha}{2}(f_1,f_2)}}\right] = 1 - \alpha \tag{8.5}$$

8.5 Tests of the Equality of More than Two Population Variances (Test for Homogeneity of Variances). The Analysis of Variance technique (Chapter 10) is predicated upon the general homogeneity or equality of the variances of the populations involved. This property of commonality is known as that of *homoscedasticity*. The technique most commonly used to assess the validity of this assumption of equality (i.e., $\sigma^2 = \sigma_2^2 = \cdots = \sigma_k^2$) in the case of suspicious data is *Bartlett's Test of Homogeneity for k Variances*. This test is based upon the relationship of the ratio of Q/h approximating the χ^2 distribution with $(k-1)$ degrees of freedom where k is the number of populations involved. The test statistic for the homogeneity of variances is:

$$\chi^2_{(k-1)} = \frac{Q \log_e 10}{h}$$

where

$$Q = f_o \log_{10} s_p^2 - \sum_{j=1}^{k} f_j \log_{10} s_j^2, \quad h = 1 + \frac{1}{3(k-1)}\left[\sum_{j=1}^{k}(1/f_j) - (1/f_o)\right],$$

$$f_o = \Sigma f_j \text{ when } f_j = n_j - 1.$$

To illustrate this technique, Table 8.2 was expanded to include a third and fourth sample as shown in Table 8.3.

Example:

1. Is it reasonable to suppose that $\sigma_1^2 \neq \sigma_2^2 \neq \sigma_3^2 \neq \sigma_4^2$?
2. $H_o: \sigma_1^2 = \sigma_2^2 = \sigma_3^2 = \sigma_4^2$
3. $\alpha = 0.05$ (This statistic uses the right tail (test (a), Figure 6.2) for the critical region.)
4. Reject H_o if $\chi^2 > \chi_{1-\alpha,k-1}^2 = \chi_{0.95,3}^2 = 7.81$ (Table III, Appendix A).
5. $s_p^2 = \dfrac{(24)(94.00) + (24)(100.09) + (24)(90.32) + (24)(93.27)}{96} = 94.42$

$$\sum_{j=1}^{4} f_j \log_{10} s_j^2 = (24)(\log_{10} 94.00) + (24)(\log_{10} 100.09)$$
$$+ (24)(\log_{10} 90.32) + (24)(\log_{10} 93.27)$$
$$= (24)(1.97313 + 2.0003907 + 1.95578 + 1.96974)$$
$$= 189.5769768$$

$$f_o \log_{10} s_p^2 = (96)(\log_{10} 94.42)$$
$$= (96)(1.97506)$$
$$= 189.60576$$

$$\sum_{j=1}^{4}\left(\frac{1}{f_j}\right) = \left[\left(\frac{1}{24}\right) + \left(\frac{1}{24}\right) + \left(\frac{1}{24}\right) + \left(\frac{1}{24}\right)\right]$$
$$= \left(\frac{4}{24}\right)$$
$$= \left(\frac{1}{6}\right)$$

$$\chi^2 = \frac{[189.60576 - 189.5769768][2.3026]}{1 + \dfrac{1}{3(4-1)}\left[\left(\frac{1}{6}\right) - \left(\frac{1}{96}\right)\right]}$$
$$= 0.0651$$

6. Accept H_o.

In an instance such as the example just completed, the evidence supporting the hypothesis of a common variance permits the pooling of these sample statistics for a more powerful estimate of the common parameter. Where the Bartlett's test results in a rejection of the hypothesis, it is then necessary to test the involved sample variances by pairs using the F technique to determine the ratios or relationships.

TABLE 8.3

DATA FOR FOUR SAMPLES WHERE $n_1 = n_2 = n_3 = n_4 = 25$

Item Number	X_{1i}*	X_{2i}*	X_{3i}*	X_{4i}*
1	6	12	−4	−8
2	−11	−8	9	−11
3	−2	−16	−10	13
4	8	−13	−2	−7
5	−4	−2	−5	13
6	5	−4	16	−2
7	16	−16	−4	9
8	3	12	12	1
9	12	−2	16	−6
10	0	10	−15	11
11	5	−5	1	8
12	6	2	−13	10
13	4	−16	−9	−5
14	−14	−10	−15	16
15	1	13	−2	3
16	−16	7	−4	−3
17	−3	6	2	−9
18	−17	−8	−12	−12
19	17	12	−8	−7
20	13	12	−8	5
21	4	−6	2	−17
22	7	5	2	9
23	16	−9	6	−1
24	1	−13	−10	16
25	13	−2	14	−7

$$\sum X_{3i} = -41, \sum X_{4i} = 19$$

* Coded scores obtained by subtracting 82.0 from original scores.

$$s_1^2 = 94.00 \qquad\qquad s_2^2 = 100.09$$

$$s_3^2 = \frac{2235 - \dfrac{(-41)^2}{25}}{24} \qquad s_4^2 = \frac{2253 - \dfrac{(19)^2}{25}}{24}$$

$$= 90.32 \qquad\qquad = 93.27$$

PROBLEMS

1. Given: $s^2 = 3.59$, $n = 25$. Test $H_o: \sigma^2 = 7.4$ using tests (b) and (c).
2. Given: $s_1^2 = 4.8$, $n_1 = 20$, $s_2^2 = 5.3$, $n_2 = 20$. Compute the 0.99 level of confidence interval estimate of the common population variance.
3. Analyze the following data utilizing the appropriate technique(s). $s_1^2 = 27.42$, $s_2^2 = 36.78$, $s_3^2 = 17.19$, $s_4^2 = 39.79$, $s_5^2 = 43.57$, where the common sample size is 16.
4. Determine the validity of the assumption of a common variance for the problems in Chapter 7 involving the testing for equality between two population means.
5. A standard examination has been given for a number of years with a variability of 25. A class of 25 students is tested and their scores exhibit a standard deviation of 6. Does this indicate a difference in population variability?
6. The scores on a standard examination have a value of $\sigma = 18$. A new form of the examination is to be issued if its scores have a standard deviation of not more than 18. If a group of 18 students are used in the try-out, what is the maximum sample standard deviation which would be acceptable if the 0.05 level of significance is used?
7. It is desired to test the hypothesis that $\sigma_1^2 \leq \sigma_2^2$ against the alternative of $\sigma_1^2 > \sigma_2^2$ using a sample of 25 and a 1% risk. What is the critical region for the test?
8. From tests conducted on the number of learning trials for two groups of subjects of sample sizes $n_1 = 13$ and $n_2 = 15$, it was found that the sample variances were 10 and 24, respectively. At the 5% level, can it be concluded that the two represented populations have equal variances?
9. If a sample of 25 observations has $s^2 = 15$, would you accept or reject the hypothesis that the variance of the population is no more than 13, using a significance level of 1%?

REFERENCES

Dixon, Wilfrid J., and Massey, Frank J., Jr. *Introduction to Statistical Analysis.* Second Edition. New York: McGraw-Hill Book Company, Inc., 1959. Chapters 6 and 8.

Ferguson, George A. *Statistical Analysis in Psychology and Education.* New York: McGraw-Hill Book Company, Inc., 1966. Chapter 18.

Freund, John C., and Williams, Frank J. *Elementary Business Statistics: The Modern Approach.* Englewood Cliffs, N. J.: Prentice-Hall, Inc., 1964. Chapter 9.

Guenther, William C. *Concepts of Statistical Inference.* New York: McGraw-Hill Book Company, Inc., 1965. Chapter 5.

Kurtz, Thomas E. *Basic Statistics*. Englewood Cliffs, N. J.: Prentice-Hall, Inc., 1963. Chapters 6 and 8.

Ostle, Bernard. *Statistics in Research*. Ames, Iowa: The Iowa State University Press, 1963. Chapter 7.

Peatman, John. *Introduction to Applied Statistics*. New York: Harper and Row Publishers, 1963. Chapter 8.

Yamane, Taro. *Statistics, An Introductory Analysis*. New York: Harper and Row, Publishers, 1964. Chapter 21.

TEST OF
HYPOTHESES ABOUT PROPORTIONS

The binomial distribution as discussed in Chapter 4 is used when the following conditions are met:

1. The probability of any single event within the set of events is constant and greater than 0.05;
2. The sampling is that involving replacement sampling;
3. The population size N is large enough such that $Np > 5$;
4. The parameters have the values of $\mu = Np$ and $\sigma^2 = Npq$.

9.1 Tests for Hypotheses Concerning the Binomial Distribution. Where the population size, as well as the number of possible events, is very large, the computation of the separate probabilities of each of the cells of the binomial distribution would be extremely tedious. Rather than utilizing the conventional probability statement for the binomial,

$$f(x) = C_{n,x} p^x q^{n-x} \tag{9.1}$$

an approximation formula utilizing the concept of the normal distribution may be used,

$$z = \frac{X - \mu}{\sqrt{\sigma^2}}$$

or

$$z = \frac{X - Np}{\sqrt{Npq}} \qquad (9.2)$$

where

$X =$ the total number of possible events,

$p =$ the probability favorable to the occurrence of the event, and

$q =$ the probability unfavorable to the occurrence of the event.

Using this formula, hypotheses concerning the probability of the occurrence of a range of specified events may be made. An example might be the likelihood of a student making a score of at least 60 on a true-false test of 100 items. The probability of answering correctly any item on a true-false test is $p = \frac{1}{2}$. As such, the mean score to be expected by chance is $\mu = Np = (100)(\frac{1}{2}) = 50$. If the stated events are unusual, then, quite appropriately, the value has a greater probability of coming from a population with $\mu > 50$.

1. Is it reasonable to suppose that $\mu > 50$?

2. $H_o : \mu \le 50$

3. $\alpha = 0.05$, test (a)

4. Reject H_o if $z > z_{0.95} = 1.645$. (From $\alpha = 0.05$ in Table I)

5. $z = \dfrac{60 - 50}{\sqrt{(100)(\frac{1}{2})(\frac{1}{2})}} = \dfrac{10}{\sqrt{25}} = \dfrac{10}{5} = 2.00$

6. Reject H_o and accept the alternate H_a that $\mu > 50$.

Another example might be related to deciding whether a score of at most 20 may be expected by a student on a 4-distractor, 100-item, multiple choice examination. Each item has four answer choices. In a test of this type, the probability of getting any item right by chance is $p = \frac{1}{4}$. For this test the mean expected chance score would be $\mu = Np = (100)(\frac{1}{4}) = 25$.

1. Is it reasonable to suppose that $\mu < 25$?

2. $H_o : \mu \ge 25$

3. $\alpha = 0.05$, test (b)

4. Reject H_o if $z < z_{0.05} = -1.645$.

5. $z = \dfrac{20 - 25}{\sqrt{(100)(\frac{1}{4})(\frac{3}{4})}} = \dfrac{-5}{\sqrt{\frac{300}{16}}} = \dfrac{(-5)(4)}{10\sqrt{3}} = \dfrac{-2}{\sqrt{3}}$

$= \dfrac{-2}{1.732} = -1.1$

6. Accept H_o.

9.2 Test of Hypotheses about a Single Proportion. When divided through by n the expression for the normal approximation (Equation 9.2) may be converted to a normalized expression for a continuous distribution of proportions.

$$z = \frac{\dfrac{(X - np')}{n}}{\sqrt{\dfrac{np'q'}{n^2}}}$$

$$z = \frac{\dfrac{X}{n} - \dfrac{np'}{n}}{\sqrt{\dfrac{np'q'}{n^2}}}$$

$$z = \frac{\dfrac{X}{n} - p'}{\sqrt{\dfrac{p'q'}{n}}}$$

$$z = \frac{p - p'}{\sqrt{\dfrac{p'q'}{n}}} \tag{9.3}$$

where

$p =$ the proportion expressing the ratio of the number of times the specified event occurs out of n total events,

$p' =$ the mean proportion or ratio expected by chance, and

$\sqrt{p'q'/n} =$ the standard error of the distribution of proportions.

Here p' is the expression of a continuous variable, the value X is discrete and in reality is the statement of a range of values extending $\pm\frac{1}{2}$ unit from the point in question. To compensate for this, a correction factor of $\pm\frac{1}{2}n$ is added to the expression, yielding:

$$z = \frac{p \pm \dfrac{1}{2n} - p'}{\sqrt{\dfrac{p'q'}{n}}} \tag{9.4}$$

The sign for the correction factor $\frac{1}{2}n$ placing the sample value p closest to p' is used.

Using the first problem completed in Section 9.1, the test for the single proportion value of $\frac{1}{2}$ may be made.

1. Is it reasonable to suppose that $p' > \frac{1}{2}$ (i.e., $H_a : p' > \frac{1}{2}$)?
2. $H_o : p' \leq \frac{1}{2}$
3. $\alpha = 0.05$, test (a)
4. Reject H_o if $z > z_{0.95} = 1.645$.

5. $z = \dfrac{\frac{6}{10} - \frac{1}{200} - \frac{5}{10}}{\sqrt{\dfrac{(0.5)(0.5)}{100}}} = \dfrac{\frac{120}{200} - \frac{1}{200} - \frac{100}{200}}{\sqrt{\dfrac{(0.5)^2}{10^2}}}$

$= \dfrac{\frac{19}{200}}{\frac{5}{10}} = \dfrac{\frac{19}{200}}{\frac{5}{100}} = \dfrac{0.095}{0.05} = 1.90$

6. Reject H_o.

Using the *approximation* Equation (9.2), a value of $z = 2.00$ was obtained. It should be remembered that in this format the total value of X is concentrated at a point, whereas Equation (9.4) has the factor $\frac{1}{2}n$ to compensate in part for this approximation. Thus the smaller value of $z = 1.90$ was obtained with Equation (9.4).

As in the case of other statistics previously discussed, a statement of the confidence interval estimate of p' is:

$$P\left[p + z_{\frac{\alpha}{2}}\sqrt{\frac{pq}{n}} < p' < p + z_{(1-\frac{\alpha}{2})}\sqrt{\frac{pq}{n}}\right] = 1 - \alpha \qquad (9.5)$$

Since the problem hypothesis presented in this section was rejected, the 0.95 confidence interval estimate of p' would be:

$$P\left[0.6 + (-1.96)\sqrt{\frac{(0.6)(0.4)}{100}} < p' < 0.6 + (1.96)\sqrt{\frac{(0.6)(0.4)}{100}}\right] = 0.95$$

$$P[0.6 - 0.096 < p' < 0.6 + 0.096] = 0.95$$

$$P[0.504 < p' < 0.696] = 0.95$$

9.3 Tests of Hypotheses about Differences Between Two Population Proportions.

An extension of the test about a single population proportion is that of comparing two population proportional values for equality, or $H_o:p_1 = p_2$. This comparison (as in the case of the sample means) must be considered for both uncorrelated and correlated data.

9.3.1 Uncorrelated Data.

Using successive *independent* samples of size n_1 and n_2, drawn from two dichotomous populations, a distribution of $(p_1 - p_2)$ may be formed by comparing all possible pairs of these samples. The assumption basic to this concept is that the resulting distribution is approximately normal *if* the binomial distribution for *each* of the parent populations may be normally approximated with parameters $\mu = Np$ and $\sigma^2 = Npq$.

The mean of this newly formed distribution of $(p_1 - p_2)$ is $\mu_{(p_1-p_2)} = p_1' - p_2'$. The variates are distributed by a variance:

$$\sigma^2_{(p_1-p_2)} = \sigma^2_{p_1} + \sigma^2_{p_2} = \left[\frac{p_1'q_1'}{n_1}\right] + \left[\frac{p_2'q_2'}{n_2}\right]$$

Generally the test hypothesis is $H_o : p_1' = p_2'$ or $p_1' - p_2' = 0$. This means that the two separate distribution mean proportions p_1' and p_2' are equal to a common value p_c'.

If this is the case, the best estimate of p_c' then would be the weighted mean of the two separate sample proportions p_1 and p_2, or:

$$\bar{p}_c = \frac{n_1 p_1 + n_2 p_2}{n_1 + n_2} \tag{9.6}$$

and the value of $\sigma^2_{(p_1 - p_2)}$ would be estimated by:

$$\sigma^2_{(p_1 - p_2)} = \frac{\bar{p}_c \bar{q}_c}{n_1} + \frac{\bar{p}_c \bar{q}_c}{n_2} = \bar{p}_c \bar{q}_c \left(\frac{1}{n_1} + \frac{1}{n_2} \right) \tag{9.7}$$

With these two statistics the test for determining the significance of difference between the two population proportions would be:

$$z = \frac{(p_1 - p_2) - (p_1' - p_2')}{\sqrt{\bar{p}_c \bar{q}_c \left[\dfrac{1}{n_1} + \dfrac{1}{n_2} \right]}} \tag{9.8}$$

For purposes of illustration, suppose it was desired to know whether two classifications of students were different as exhibited by the number of students having mathematics aptitude scores above 125. High school A was found to have 30 students out of 400 and school B had 28 out of 324 in the category.

1. Is it reasonable to suppose that $p_a \neq p_b$?
2. $H_o : p_a = p_b$
3. $\alpha = 0.05$, test (c)
4. Reject H_o if $z < z_{0.025} = -1.96$ or if $z > z_{0.975} = 1.96$.
5. $\bar{p}_c = \dfrac{(400)(\frac{30}{400}) + (324)(\frac{28}{324})}{400 + 324} = \dfrac{58}{724}$

$$z = \frac{\frac{30}{400} - \frac{28}{324}}{\sqrt{(\frac{58}{724})(\frac{666}{724})(\frac{1}{400} + \frac{1}{324})}} = \frac{0.0750 - 0.0864}{\sqrt{(0.0801)(0.9199)(0.0025 + 0.003)}}$$

$$= \frac{-0.0114}{\sqrt{(0.0737)(0.0056)}} = \frac{-0.0114}{\sqrt{0.0004}} = \frac{-0.0114}{0.0203} = -0.563$$

6. Accept H_o.

The confidence interval estimate for the true difference between p_1' and p_2' or $(p_1' - p_2')$ is:

$$P\left[(p_1 - p_2) + z_{\frac{\alpha}{2}} \sqrt{\bar{p}_c \bar{q}_c \left[\frac{1}{n_1} + \frac{1}{n_2} \right]} < (p_1' - p_2') < (p_1 - p_2) \right.$$

$$\left. + z_{(1 - \frac{\alpha}{2})} \sqrt{\bar{p}_c \bar{q}_c \left[\frac{1}{n_1} + \frac{1}{n_2} \right]} \right] = 1 - \alpha \tag{9.9}$$

9.3.2 Correlated Data. When the two sample values, p_1 and p_2, are computed from two measurements or enumerations on the same group, the assumption of independence is no longer valid. Suppose it is desired to compare a group's response to the same test on two occasions. On a particular test taken by 300 students, 158 missed Item 1 the first time and 139 missed the same item the second time. It is desired to know if the observed difference may be attributed to some factor other than chance. The two values p_1 and p_2 are measurements on the same group of students and, as such, are not independent.

The added factor of dependency will require a change in the Equation (9.7). This has been developed by McNemar* and is:

$$\sigma^2_{(p_1-p_2)} = \sigma^2_{p_1'} + \sigma^2_{p_2'} - 2r_{p'}\sigma_{p_1'}\sigma_{p_2'} \qquad (9.10)$$

where $r_{p'}$ is a *point biserial coefficient of correlation*. Using sample data obtained from a 2×2 *contingency table* like Table 9.1, the estimate becomes:

$$\sigma^2_{(p_1-p_2)} = \frac{(a+d) - (a-d)^2}{N} \qquad (9.11)$$

where a and d are the observed frequencies X_{11} and X_{22} (first and fourth cells). When the hypothesis to be tested is $H_o:p_1' = p_2'$, Equation (9.11) becomes:

$$\sigma^2_{(p_1'-p_2')} = \left(\frac{a+d}{N}\right)^2 \qquad (9.12)$$

TABLE 9.1

A THEORETICAL 2 $\times$ 2 CONTINGENCY TABLE

		Factor I		
		I	II	$T_{i.}$
F	I	$X_{11}^{(a)}$	$X_{12}^{(b)}$	$(a+b)$
a c t o r II	II	$X_{21}^{(c)}$	$X_{22}^{(d)}$	$(c+d)$
	$T_{.j}$	$(a+c)$	$(b+d)$	N

Table 9.1 presents the 2×2 contingency table for the hypothetical problem. In this table, the value in cell (a) represents those students under discussion.

---

* See reference at end of this chapter.

TABLE 9.2

NUMBER OF CORRECT AND INCORRECT RESPONSES TO A TEST ITEM ON TWO DIFFERENT PERIODS OF EXAMINATION

		1st Usage		
		Correct	Incorrect	$T_i.$
2nd	Correct	116(a)	145(b)	161
U s a g e	Incorrect	26(c)	113(d)	139
	$T._j$	142	158	300

$$p_1 = \tfrac{142}{300} = 0.473$$
$$p_2 = \tfrac{161}{300} = 0.537$$

The value of $\sigma^2_{(p_1-p_2)}$ for the data of Table 9.2 is:

$$\sigma^2_{(p_1-p_2)} = \left[\frac{116 + 113}{300}\right]^2 = 0.582678$$

With this factor computed, the test of the H_o would become:

1. Is it reasonable to suppose that $p_1' \neq p_2'$?
2. $H_o : p_1' = p_2'$
3. $\alpha = 0.10$, test (a)
4. Reject H_o if $z < z_{0.05} = -1.645$ or if $z > z_{0.095} = 1.645$.

5. $z = \dfrac{0.473 - 0.537}{\sqrt{0.582678}} = 0.084$

6. Accept H_o. The evidence may be interpreted then as supporting the idea of consistent difficulty and that the difference in the number getting the item right in the two tests is due to chance.

9.4 Tests of Hypotheses for Differences among More than Two Population Proportions. The technique utilized in this case is actually a determination of whether k groups of observations are representative of the same population. The data of Table 9.3(a) illustrate, in general, this consideration with X_{ij} observed values of categories $i = 1, 2, \ldots, n = \Sigma n._j$ and $j = 1, 2, \ldots, k$. The totals for each of the categories $T_i.$ and $T._j$ represent the totals for each of the rows and columns, respectively. The grand total for all observations is

$$T.. = \Sigma\Sigma X_{ij} = \Sigma T_i. = \Sigma T._j$$

TABLE 9.3(a)

**THEORETICAL CONTINGENCY TABLE FOR
COMPARISON OF OBSERVATIONS REPRESENTING n AND k POPULATIONS**

	1	2	3	...	k	$T_{i.}$
1	X_{11}	X_{12}	X_{13}	...	X_{1k}	$T_{1.}$
2	X_{21}	X_{22}	X_{23}	...	X_{2k}	$T_{2.}$
3	X_{31}	X_{32}	X_{33}	...	X_{3k}	$T_{3.}$
.	.	.	.	...	.	.
.	.	.	.	...	.	.
.	.	.	.	...	.	.
n	X_{n1}	X_{n2}	X_{n3}	...	X_{nk}	$T_{n.}$
$T_{.j}$	$T_{.1}$	$T_{.2}$	$T_{.3}$	...	$T_{.k}$	$T_{..}$

To further clarify this idea, let us consider a set of fictitious data as is presented in Table 9.3(b) for a contingency table of 6×5 dimensions.

TABLE 9.3(b)

HYPOTHETICAL DATA TO ILLUSTRATE A 6 × 5 CONTINGENCY TABLE

	I	II	III	IV	V	$T_{i.}$
A	12	19	11	17	27	86
B	20	25	13	12	19	89
C	18	16	16	22	13	85
D	28	29	26	28	17	128
E	15	23	21	13	25	97
F	21	19	29	21	29	119
$T_{.j}$	114	131	116	113	130	604

The data of Table 9.3(b) are illustrative of the theoretical situation shown in Table 9.3(a), or:

$X_{11} = X_{AI} = 12, X_{21} = X_{BI} = 20, \ldots, X_{61} = X_{FI} = 21,$

$X_{12} = X_{AII} = 19, X_{22} = X_{BII} = 25, \ldots, X_{62} = X_{FII} = 19, \ldots,$

$$\vdots \qquad\qquad \vdots \qquad\qquad \vdots$$

$X_{15} = X_{AV} = 27, X_{25} = X_{BV} = 19, \ldots, X_{65} = X_{FV} = 29.$

These values are the *observed* frequencies.

The various ratios $T_{1.}/T_{..}, T_{2.}/T_{..}, \ldots, T_{n.}/T_{..}, T_{.1}/T_{..}, T_{.2}/T_{..}, \ldots,$ $T_{.k}/T_{..}$ are actually expressions of the proportions of the various n and k categories of the total observations. Using the *marginal probabilities* or *marginal proportions*, the expected number of observations may be projected for each *cell* of the *contingency table*. The test implied then would be to determine whether the observed values deviate significantly from the theoretically expected values. These expected values X'_{ij} may be determined as:

$$X'_{ij} = (p_{i.})(T_{.j})$$

where $p_{i.} = T_{.j}/T_{...}$.

As such, the *expected* frequencies would be computed as follows:

$$p_A. = \tfrac{86}{604} = 0.142, \quad p_B. = \tfrac{89}{604} = 0.147, \quad p_C. = \tfrac{85}{604} = 0.141,$$

$$p_D. = \tfrac{128}{604} = 0.212, \quad p_E. = \tfrac{97}{604} = 0.161, \quad p_F. = \tfrac{119}{604} = 0.197;$$

$$X'_{AI} = (114)(0.142) = 16.2, \quad X'_{AII} = (131)(0.147) = 18.6, \ldots,$$
$$X'_{DV} = (130)(0.212) = 27.6.$$

Table 9.3(c) presents the *expected* frequencies for the *observed* frequency data of Table 9.3(b).

TABLE 9.3(c)

COMPUTED EXPECTED FREQUENCIES FOR THE DATA OF TABLE 9.3(b)

	I	II	III	IV	V	$T'_{i.}$
A	16.2	18.6	16.5	16.1	18.5	85.9
B	16.8	19.3	17.0	16.6	19.1	88.8
C	16.1	18.5	16.4	15.9	18.3	85.2
D	24.2	27.8	24.6	24.0	27.6	128.2
E	18.4	21.1	18.7	18.2	20.9	97.3
F	22.5	25.8	22.8	22.3	25.6	119.0
$T'_{.j}$	114.2	131.1	116.0	113.1	130.0	604.4

The discrepancies between the values of $T_{.j}$ and $T'_{.j}$ and $T_{i.}$ and $T'_{i.}$ may be attributed to the rounding error.

We now use the χ^2 distribution which was discussed earlier in Chapter 5. The statistic for this distribution is

$$\chi^2 = \sum \frac{(X_{ij} - X'_{ij})^2}{X'_{ij}} \quad \text{with d.f.} = (k-1)(n-1) \qquad (9.13)$$

Using Equation (9.12), the χ^2 statistic for the data of Tables 9.3(b) and 9.3(c) is

$$\chi^2 = \frac{(12 - 16.2)^2}{16.2} + \frac{(19 - 18.7)^2}{18.7} + \frac{(11 - 16.5)^2}{16.5} + \frac{(17 - 16.1)^2}{16.1}$$

$$+ \frac{(27 - 18.5)^2}{18.5} + \frac{(20 - 16.8)^2}{16.8}$$

$$+ \cdots + \frac{(21 - 22.3)^2}{22.3} + \frac{(29 - 25.6)^2}{25.6} = 28.7254$$

9.4.1 Single Classification. One type of analysis involves determining whether data are consistent with a prescribed ratio of proportions. Examples of this form may be seen in genetic problems where inheritance is transmitted according to a mathematical ratio. Another case is that found in test item analysis. In the case of the single classification format, the degrees of freedom are $(k - 1)$ where k is the number of possible categories. An instance of the single classification analysis is described below.

Multiple choice test items should have distractors of such caliber that all responses are equally attractive to the uninformed student. As such the choice should follow the laws of probability (i.e., a five-choice item should have the responses equally distributed among those offered when the selection process is random).

On a particular item (having five choices) students marked the choices as indicated in Table 9.4.

TABLE 9.4

RESPONSES OF 100 STUDENTS TO A FIVE-CHOICE MULTIPLE CHOICE ITEM

Choice	Frequency
A	15
B	26
C	18
D	28
E	13
Total	100

The probability of choice is the same for all distractors ($\frac{1}{5}$). The test of the hypothesis would be as follows.

1. $H_o:p_a = p_b = p_c = p_d = p_e$
2. $\alpha = 0.05$
3. Reject H_o if $\chi^2 < \chi^2_{0.025,4} = 0.484$
   or if $\chi^2 > \chi^2_{0.975,4} = 11.1$.

4.

Choice	Frequency Observed	Frequency Expected	$(X_{ij} - X'_{ij})^2/X'_{ij}$
A	15	20	1.25
B	26	20	1.80
C	18	20	0.20
D	28	20	3.20
E	13	20	2.45
Total	100	100	8.90

5. Accept H_o (i.e., the frequency of choices is randomly distributed).

9.4.2 Double Classification, Independency of Data. Many times it is desirable to know if the occurrence of a classification category of one variable affects the probability of occurrence of a classification category of a second variable. In short, the question is, does the distribution of one variable predict the distribution of a second variable (i.e., is one variable's occurrence *dependent* upon a second variable)?

In working with this type of data, the marginal probabilities, like those presented in Table 9.4, are utilized for analysis of the null hypothesis of *independency of data*. Examples of this type of problem may be the analysis of the effect of pre-test scores on post-test scores, intelligence on achievement, or eye color on hair color.

The following example concerns the independency of pre-test and post-test scores. Table 9.5 presents data for 164 students utilized in an experiment. The data represents a quartile distribution of the ratios of pre-test to post-test scores.

TABLE 9.5

RATIO PRE-TEST TO POST-TEST SCORES FOR 164 STUDENTS QUARTILE DISTRIBUTION

Post-test	Pre-test				
	1	2	3	4	$T_{i.}$
1	29	10	2	0	41
2	9	22	8	2	41
3	2	5	24	10	41
4	1	4	7	29	41
$T_{.j}$	41	41	41	41	164

1. H_o: The two tests are independent.

2. $\alpha = 0.05$

3. Reject H_o if $x^2 < x^2_{0.025,9} = 2.70$
     or if $x^2 > x^2_{0.975,9} = 19.0$.

$$X_{ij} = \frac{T_i.T_{.j}}{T_{..}}$$

$$= 10.25$$

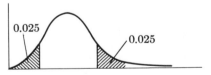

4. $\chi^2 = \dfrac{(29 - 10.25)^2}{10.25}$

$+ \dfrac{(10 - 10.25)^2}{10.25} + \dfrac{(2 - 10.25)^2}{10.25} + \dfrac{(0 - 10.25)^2}{10.25}$

$+ \dfrac{(9 - 10.25)^2}{10.25} + \dfrac{(22 - 10.25)^2}{10.25} + \dfrac{(8 - 10.25)^2}{10.25}$

$+ \dfrac{(2 - 10.25)^2}{10.25} + \dfrac{(2 - 10.25)^2}{10.25} + \dfrac{(5 - 10.25)^2}{10.25}$

$+ \dfrac{(24 - 10.25)^2}{10.25} + \dfrac{(10 - 10.25)^2}{10.25} + \dfrac{(1 - 10.25)^2}{10.25}$

$+ \dfrac{(4 - 10.25)^2}{10.25} + \dfrac{(7 - 10.25)^2}{10.25} + \dfrac{(29 - 10.25)^2}{10.25}$

$= \dfrac{1509.0000}{10.25} = 147.22.$

5. Reject H_o.

9.4.3 Double Classification, 2×2 Contingency Table. When the χ^2 test is based upon one degree of freedom or the contingency table is 2×2, a correction for continuity called the *Yates correction factor* is used. This involves the subtraction of 0.5 from each of the differences between the observed and expected values, or

$$\chi^2 = \Sigma \frac{[(X_{ij} - X'_{ij}) - 0.5]^2}{X'_{ij}} \qquad (9.14)$$

Where the X_{ij} for any cell is less than 5 in a 2×2 table, a technique called *Fisher's exact probability* would be used. Where the order of the table is greater than 2×2, categories may be combined to get a cell frequency greater than 5.

TABLE 9.6

A 2×2 CONTINGENCY TABLE FOR DICHOTOMOUS DATA

	1	2	T_i.
1	a	b	$(a + b)$
2	c	d	$(c + d)$
T_j	$(a + c)$	$(b + d)$	$(a + b + c + d) = n$

In the instance where the data are dichotomous, a variation in the computation is used. The value of χ^2 for the 2×2 table is equal to the square of the *phi coefficient* (r_ϕ).

$$\chi^2 = \frac{n(|ad - bc|)^2}{(a + c)(b + d)(a + b)(c + d)} \qquad (9.15)$$

or with the correction for continuity

$$\chi^2 = \frac{n\left(|ad - bc| - \frac{n}{2}\right)^2}{(a + c)(b + d)(a + b)(c + d)} \tag{9.16}$$

(The two parallel vertical lines surrounding $(ad - bc)$ indicate an absolute value.)

9.5 Test for Goodness of Fit. The various parametric techniques are predicated upon the assumption that the sample utilized is drawn from a normal distribution. In reality the appropriate procedure would be to determine if this assumption is plausible. The data are arranged in a frequency distribution. The probabilities of scores falling within each of the frequency intervals by chance are determined by the use of the z-statistic and the table of probabilities for the normal curve. Then probabilities are used to predict the expected interval frequencies. The remainder of the computation is that of obtaining a χ^2 value.

The data in Table 9.7 represent the *Cooperative School and College Ability Test, Verbal Section* normalized T-scores for 164 students in intervals of 1.0 sample standard deviations.

TABLE 9.7

FREQUENCY DISTRIBUTION OF 164 CODED SCAT-VERBAL SCORES WITH THEORETICAL FREQUENCIES ($\overline{X}$ = 52.04, s = 2.65)

Interval	Observed	Expected
Over $(\mu + 3s)$	15	0.2132
$(\mu + 2s)$ to $(\mu + 3s)$	3	3.5260
$(\mu + 1s)$ to $(\mu + 2s)$	17	22.2876
μ to $(\mu + 1s)$	13	55.9732
$(\mu - 1s)$ to μ	26	55.9732
$(\mu - 2s)$ to $(\mu - 1s)$	22	22.2876
$(\mu - 3s)$ to $(\mu - 2s)$	14	3.5260
Less than $(\mu - 3s)$	54	0.2132
N	164	164.0000

The hypothesis being tested is that the population being sampled is normally distributed. Using the data in Table 9.7, a χ^2 value will be found and is significant at the 0.05 level ($\chi^2_{0.95,5} = 11.1$). Five degrees of freedom are used. Two estimators $(\overline{X}, s)$ were used to establish intervals for the data and, consequently, two more degrees of freedom are lost in addition to the $(k - 1)$ normally found for the χ^2 distribution, thus d.f. $= k - 3$.

PROBLEMS

Compute the 95% confidence interval estimate of the parameter whenever the test hypothesis is rejected.

1. A group of students are taking a 100 item multiple-choice examination. Each item has four choices. One student claimed that he possessed ESP and could get a score greater than chance without looking at the examination. This student marked an answer sheet and when graded was found to have a score of 30. What would you conclude about the event?

2. A coin is tossed 100 times and is found to turn heads $\frac{2}{3}$ of the time. Could you say that the coin was unbiased?

3. School A has 325 graduates out of 600 entering freshmen. School B has 400 out of 750. Can it be concluded that one school has a higher percentage graduating than the other?

4. According to mathematical prediction, a sequence of events should occur in a 1:4:6:4:1 pattern or ratio. When tested 120 times, the over-all ratio was 20:36:36:13:15. Do the data support the theoretical prediction?

5. It was desired to know if achievement in reading was associated with achievement in social studies. Achievement tests were given in both subjects. The students were grouped according to the following:

	Group	Reading	Social Studies
Upper 7%	A	5	8
Next 23%	B	18	15
Next 40%	C	55	47
Next 23%	D	14	16
Last 7%	E	8	14

What would you conclude?

6. In test analyses a "good" item discriminates between the upper and lower level students. On a given item in statistics, the following data were obtained regarding the number who marked the correct answer.

	Correct	Incorrect
Upper 27%	63	37
Lower 27%	48	52

Is there evidence that a dependent relationship exists?

7. It is hypothesized that when given an odd number of choices, a subject will randomly select the middle value more frequently than any other. It is also postulated that over a great number of trials, the number of times each choice is selected deviates from chance expectation. A class of 60 students was asked to choose a number between 1 and 5. Following is a record of their selections. What conclusions would you draw?

Number	Number of Students Selecting
1	3
2	10
3	38
4	12
5	2

8. From a 6 × 3 contingency table, a Chi-Square value of 9.30 was computed. The experimenter concluded that the result was significant. What could you say about his conclusion?

9. In tossing four coins 32 times the following results were obtained. Do these results differ significantly from those expected on the basis of randomness in the tossing?

No. of Heads	f
0	2
1	10
2	10
3	4
4	6

10. A question was asked of two classes of students. The "yes," "no" responses of the two groups are given below. Does a significant difference exist between the two groups based upon the frequency of their responses?

	No	Yes
Class I	50	50
Class II	70	130

REFERENCES

DuBois, Philip H. *An Introduction to Psychological Statistics*. New York: Harper and Row, Publishers, 1965. Chapter 3.

Ferguson, George A. *Statistical Analysis in Psychology and Education*. New York: McGraw-Hill Book Company, Inc., 1966. Chapter 12.

Freund, John C., and Williams, Frank J. *Elementary Business Statistics: The Modern Approach*. Englewood Cliffs, N. J.: Prentice-Hall, Inc., 1964. Chapter 9.

Guenther, William C. *Concepts of Statistical Inference*. New York: McGraw-Hill Book Company, 1965. Chapter 6.

Kurtz, Thomas E. *Basic Statistics*. Englewood Cliffs, N. J.: Prentice-Hall, Inc., 1963. Chapter 5.

McNemar, Quinn. *Psychological Statistics*. Third Edition. New York: John Wiley and Sons, Inc., 1962. Chapter 5.

Tate, Merle W. *Statistics in Education and Psychology: A First Course*. New York: The Macmillan Company, 1965. Chapter 12.

Yamane, Taro. *Statistics, An Introductory Analysis*. New York: Harper and Row, Publishers, 1964. Chapter 20.

10

ANALYSIS OF VARIANCE

The discussion in Chapter 7 involved the concepts associated with the testing of hypotheses about single population means and about the differences between two population means. In many instances it is important to know something about the relationship of more than two means. This implies that it is desired to test hypotheses about the equality of several means; and it would be well if the entire system of population means could be tested simultaneously rather than two at a time. The definite advantage in this single procedure is that the size of the Type I risk is maintained at the desired level. One would think that the risk would be the same regardless of whether the means are tested in pairs or some method of testing the whole system is used. This misconception will be readily refuted when one considers the basic combinatorial laws of probability. In addition to the greatly increased chance of committing the Type I risk, a second prohibitive factor of loss of sensitivity appears.

The procedure whereby an entire system of population means may be tested for equality simultaneously is referred to as the *analysis of variance* technique. As will be shown in the remainder of the chapter, the technique is predicated upon the partitioning of the total variance of all of the sample observations into portions, each of which arises from some specific affecting factor. This means that the total variation is subdivided into the estimator based on the variation *within* each of the several samples involved, and the estimator or estimators computed from the deviation *among* or *between* the several sample means and the overall mean.

10.1 *Single Classification.* The most elementary form of the analysis of variance technique is that of testing the hypothesis about the equality of several means, $\mu_1, \mu_2, \ldots, \mu_k$, each representing one of the k populations.

Each of the separate values of X involved may be a member of one and only one of the k populations.

The assumption is made that the populations being sampled are approximately normal or at least common in distribution, the samples randomly drawn, the population member values independently determined, the population means linearly related, and that a common variance among the populations exists. This last property has been previously referred to in Chapter 8 as *homoscedasticity*. Each of these assumptions should be validated before proceeding with further analysis. Techniques for testing randomness, similarity of distribution, and homoscedasticity are presented elsewhere in this text.

Random samples of size n are drawn from each of the k populations. Ideally the sample sizes should be equal ($n_1 = n_2 = \cdots = n_k$), but this is not a necessity in the case of the single classification. A hypothetical sampling is presented in Table 10.1. In this table the various scores or values within a sample are designated as X_{ij} where $i = 1, 2, \ldots, n_j$, and the specific sample designated by $j = 1, 2, \ldots, k$.

TABLE 10.1

ILLUSTRATION OF SAMPLES FROM k POPULATIONS

			Sample Number			
	X_{11}	X_{12}	X_{13}	...	X_{1k}	
	X_{21}	X_{22}	X_{23}	...	X_{2k}	
	X_{31}	X_{32}	X_{33}	...	X_{3k}	
	.	.	.	...	.	
	.	.	.	...	.	
	.	.	.	...	.	
	X_{n1}	X_{n2}	X_{n3}	...	X_{nk}	
Total	$T_{.1}$	$T_{.2}$	$T_{.3}$	...	$T_{.k}$	$T_{..}$
Mean	$\overline{X}_{.1}$	$\overline{X}_{.2}$	$\overline{X}_{.3}$	...	$\overline{X}_{.k}$	$\overline{\overline{X}}_{..}$

The basic mathematical model for the type of data involved is:

$$X_{ij} = \mu_{..} + \mu_{.j} + e_{ij} \tag{10.1}$$

where

$\mu_{..}$ = total mean of all populations
$\mu_{.j}$ = mean effect of the jth population
e_{ij} = random sampling effect from a population.
    (When all error terms e_{ij} are plotted, a normal distribution with mean $\mu_e = 0$ and variance σ_e^2 will be generated.)

Our problem, then, is to test the hypothesis that all values of $\mu_{.j}$ have a common value μ_o, or $\mu_1 = \mu_2 = \cdots = \mu_k = \mu_o$ where $j = 1, 2, \ldots, k$.

Each sample value X_{ij} may be expressed as:

$$X_{ij} = (X_{ij} - \overline{X}_{.j}) + (\overline{X}_{.j} - \overline{\overline{X}}_{..}) + \overline{\overline{X}}_{..} \qquad (10.2)$$

where $\overline{X}_{.j} = $ mean of the sample drawn from the jth population
and $\overline{\overline{X}}_{..} = $ the best estimate of the common mean μ_o.

It should be noted that this expression is an algebraic identity where both sides of the equation are equal to X_{ij}. This equation may be transformed into a statement of deviation expressed as:

$$(X_{ij} - \overline{\overline{X}}_{..}) = (X_{ij} - \overline{X}_{.j}) + (\overline{X}_{.j} - \overline{\overline{X}}_{..}) \qquad (10.3)$$

Equation (10.3) illustrates the concept basic to the analysis of variance technique that the deviation of the sample member from the common mean may be expressed as the sum of two deviations. These deviations are: (1) the deviation of the sample member X_{ij} from the specific sample mean $\overline{X}_{.j}$, and (2) the deviation of the several sample means $\overline{X}_{.j}$ from the common mean estimator $\overline{\overline{X}}_{..}$.

Following the idea presented in Chapter 3, the various variance components may be determined. By definition, a variance estimator is the mean squared deviation of the item from its mean. Equation (10.3) then results in:

$$\Sigma\Sigma(X_{ij} - \overline{\overline{X}}_{..})^2 = \Sigma\Sigma[(X_{ij} - \overline{X}_{.j}) + (\overline{X}_{.j} - \overline{\overline{X}}_{..})]^2$$

For a single value of X_{ij} this squared deviation form would be:

$$
\begin{aligned}
(X_{ij} - \overline{\overline{X}}_{..})^2 &= [(X_{ij} - \overline{X}_{.j}) + (\overline{X}_{.j} - \overline{\overline{X}}_{..})]^2 \\
&= (X_{ij} - \overline{X}_{.j})^2 + 2(X_{ij} - \overline{X}_{.j})(\overline{X}_{.j} - \overline{\overline{X}}_{..}) + (\overline{X}_{.j} - \overline{\overline{X}}_{..})^2
\end{aligned}
$$

Summing for all $n_{.j}$ values in any column, we would have:

$$\sum_{i=1}^{n_{.j}} (X_{ij} - \overline{\overline{X}}_{..})^2$$

$$= \sum_{i=1}^{n_{.j}} (X_{ij} - \overline{X}_{.j})^2 + 2(\overline{X}_{.j} - \overline{\overline{X}}_{..}) \sum_{i=1}^{n_{.j}} (X_{ij} - \overline{X}_{.j}) + n_{.j}(\overline{X}_{.j} - \overline{\overline{X}}_{..})^2$$

Since the sum of deviations of $(X_{ij} - \overline{X}_{.j})$ for any sample is

$$\sum_{i=1}^{n_{.j}} (X_{ij} - \overline{X}_{.j}) = 0$$

the middle term disappears leaving:

$$\sum_{i=1}^{n_{.j}} (X_{ij} - \overline{\overline{X}}_{..})^2 = \sum_{i=1}^{n_{.j}} (X_{ij} - \overline{X}_{.j})^2 + n_{.j}(\overline{X}_{.j} - \overline{\overline{X}}_{..})^2$$

Summing across all k columns, we have:

$$\sum_{j=1}^{k} \sum_{i=1}^{n_{.j}} (X_{ij} - \overline{\overline{X}}_{..})^2 = \sum_{j=1}^{k} \sum_{i=1}^{n_{.j}} (X_{ij} - \overline{X}_{.j})^2 + \sum_{j=1}^{k} n_{.j}(\overline{X}_{.j} - \overline{\overline{X}}_{..})^2 \quad (10.4)$$

The first member on the right of the Equation (10.4) is the total sums of all squared deviations of the scores from their respective sample means. This member may be expressed as a pooled variance estimator by dividing it by the appropriate number of degrees of freedom $[\sum(n_j - 1)]$, or $(\sum n_j - k)$. This pooled variance estimator is:

$$s_w^2 = \frac{\sum\sum(X_{ij} - \overline{X}_{.j})^2}{\sum n_j - k} \tag{10.5}$$

This is an estimator of the variance value σ^2 which is common *within* all of the populations sampled. The second member on the right of Equation (10.4) is a statement of the summation of the squared deviations of the various sample means $\overline{X}_{.j}$ from the common mean estimator $\overline{X}_{..}$. Dividing this by its appropriate degrees of freedom $(k - 1)$, where k is the number of samples or populations involved, another estimator of this common variance is generated.

$$s_b^2 = \frac{\sum\sum(\overline{X}_{.j} - \overline{X}_{..})^2}{k - 1} \tag{10.6}$$

This variance estimator expresses the variation of the sample means or the variation *between* sample means.

Following the procedure outlined earlier in Chapter 3, these theoretical formulae may be transformed into computational formulae by substitution of

$$\sum_{i=1}^{n_j} X_{ij} = T_{.j} \qquad \frac{T_{.j}}{n_j} = \overline{X}_{.j} \quad \text{and} \quad N = \sum n_j = nk.$$

After expansion, Equation (10.5) becomes

$$s_w^2 = \frac{\sum\sum X_{ij}^2 - \sum\left[\dfrac{T_{.j}^2}{n_j}\right]}{N - k} \tag{10.7}$$

The value of the numerator results from the following expansion:

$$\sum\sum(X_{ij} - \overline{X}_{.j})^2 = \sum(X_{i1} - \overline{X}_{.1})^2 + \sum(X_{i2} - \overline{X}_{.2})^2$$
$$+ \cdots + \sum(X_{ik} - \overline{X}_{.k})^2$$
$$= \sum X_{i1}^2 - \frac{(\sum X_{i1})^2}{n_1} + \sum X_{i2}^2 - \frac{(\sum X_{i2})^2}{n_2}$$
$$+ \cdots + \sum X_{ik}^2 - \frac{(\sum X_{ik})^2}{n_k}$$
$$= \sum X_{i1}^2 + \sum X_{i2}^2$$
$$+ \cdots + \sum X_{ik}^2 - \frac{T_{.1}^2}{n_1} - \frac{T_{.2}^2}{n_2} - \cdots - \frac{T_{.k}^2}{n_k}$$
$$= \sum\sum X_{ij}^2 - \left[\frac{T_{.1}^2}{n_1} + \frac{T_{.2}^2}{n_2} + \cdots + \frac{T_{.k}^2}{n_k}\right]$$
$$= \sum\sum X_{ij}^2 - \sum\left[\frac{T_{.j}^2}{n_j}\right]$$

In a similar manner the computational equivalent for Equation (10.6) may be obtained.

$$\sum_{j=1}^{k} n_{.j}(\overline{X}_{.j} - \overline{\overline{X}}_{..})^2 = n_{.1}(\overline{X}_{.1} - \overline{\overline{X}}_{..})^2 + n_{.2}(\overline{X}_{.2} - \overline{\overline{X}}_{..})^2$$

$$+ \cdots + n_{.k}(\overline{X}_{.k} - \overline{\overline{X}}_{..})^2$$

$$= n_{.1}(\overline{X}_{.1} - 2\overline{\overline{X}}_{..}\overline{X}_{.1} + \overline{\overline{X}}_{..})$$

$$+ n_{.2}(\overline{X}_{.2} - 2\overline{\overline{X}}_{..}\overline{X}_{.2} + \overline{\overline{X}}_{..})$$

$$+ \cdots + n_{.k}(\overline{X}_{.k} - 2\overline{\overline{X}}_{..}\overline{X}_{.k} + \overline{\overline{X}}_{..})$$

Where $\overline{X}_{.j} = \sum_{i=1}^{n_{.j}} X_{ij}/n_{.j} = T_{.j}/n_{.j}$ when $T_{.j} = \sum_{i=1}^{n_{.j}} X_{ij}$, and $\overline{\overline{X}}_{..} = T_{..}/N$ when $T_{..} = \sum T_{.j}$ and $N = \sum n_{.j}$, the expression becomes:

$$\sum_{j=1}^{k} (\overline{X}_{.j} - \overline{\overline{X}}_{..})^2$$

$$= n_{.1}[(T_{.1}/n_{.1})^2 - 2(T_{..}/N)(T_{.1}/n_{.1}) + (T_{..}/N)^2]$$

$$+ n_{.2}[(T_{.2}/n_{.2})^2 - 2(T_{..}/N)(T_{.2}/n_{.2}) + (T_{..}/N)^2]$$

$$+ \cdots + n_{.k}[(T_{.k}/n_{.k})^2 - 2(T_{..}/N)(T_{.k}/n_{.k}) + (T_{..}/N)^2]$$

$$= (T_{.1}^2/n_{.1}) - 2(T_{..}/N)(T_{.1}) + (n_{.1}T_{..}^2/N^2)$$

$$+ (T_{.2}^2/n_{.2}) - 2(T_{..}/N)(T_{.2}) + (n_{.2}T_{..}^2/N^2)$$

$$+ \cdots + (T_{.k}^2/n_{.k}) - 2(T_{..}/N)(T_{.k}) + (n_{.k}T_{..}^2/N^2)$$

$$= (T_{.1}^2/n_{.1}) + (T_{.2}^2/n_{.2}) + \cdots + T_{.k}^2/n_{.k})$$

$$-2(T_{..}/N)(T_{.1}) - 2(T_{..}/N)(T_{.2}) - \cdots - 2(T_{..}/N)(T_{.k})$$

$$+ (n_{.1}T_{..}^2/N^2) + (n_{.2}T_{..}^2/N^2) + \cdots + (n_{.k}T_{..}^2/N^2)$$

$$= \sum(T_{.j}^2/n_{.j}) - 2(T_{..}/N)(T_{.1} + T_{.2} + \cdots + T_{.k})$$

$$+ (T_{..}^2/N^2)(n_{.1} + n_{.2} + \cdots + n_{.k})$$

$$= \sum(T_{.j}^2/n_{.j}) - 2(T_{..}/N)(T_{..}) + (T_{..}^2/N^2)(N)$$

$$= \sum(T_{.j}^2/n_{.j}) - 2(T_{..}^2/N) + (T_{..}^2/N)$$

$$= \sum(T_{.j}^2/n_{.j}) - (T_{..}^2/N)$$

Dividing this numerator equivalent by the $(k - 1)$ degrees of freedom, we have the computational form for Equation (10.6), or

$$s_b^2 = [\sum(T_{.j}^2/n_{.j}) - (T_{..}^2/N)]/(k - 1) \qquad (10.8)$$

The factors for computing the analysis of variance may be classified as in Table 10.2.

The last column of Table 10.2 is the ratio of the two variance estimators. By placing the larger of the two values in the numerator, the tedious computations associated with the critical value of $F_{\alpha(f_1, f_2)}$ may be avoided. In any case, the critical value of the F distribution should have the same ratio of degrees of freedom as the sample F ratio.

TABLE 10.2

COMPUTATION TABLE FOR
SINGLE CLASSIFICATION ANALYSIS OF VARIANCE

Source of Variability	Sum of Squared Deviations	Degrees of Freedom	Variance Estimator or Mean Square	F Ratio
Between Sample Means	$\sum \dfrac{T_{.j}^2}{n_j} - \dfrac{T_{..}^2}{N}$	$k - 1$	s_b^2	
Within Sample	$\sum\sum X_{ij}^2 - \sum \dfrac{T_{.j}^2}{n_j}$	$N - k$	s_w^2	s_b^2/s_w^2
Total	$\sum\sum X_{ij}^2 - \dfrac{T_{..}^2}{N}$	$E - 1$		

A computed F ratio which is not significant indicates that the two variance estimators, s_b^2 and s_w^2, are estimators of a common value of σ^2; the individual variations are attributed to differences between samples due to the sampling process. If the F ratio is significant, there is evidence that the two values are not estimates of a common σ^2, the significance may be attributed to a difference between the means of the populations being sampled.

To illustrate the single classification of the analysis of variance technique, the following hypothetical data (Table 10.3) will be used to test the indicated hypothesis.

TABLE 10.3

HYPOTHETICAL DATA FOR SAMPLES FROM FOUR POPULATIONS

		Sample Number			
		1	2	3	4
		6	4	5	5
		3	6	2	1
		7	2	6	3
		9	8	8	7
Totals		25	20	21	16	82

$$\frac{T_{..}^2}{N} = \frac{82^2}{16} = 420.250$$

$$\sum\sum X_{ij}^2 = 6^2 + 3^2 + \cdots + 2^2 + 8^2 + \cdots + 7^2 = 508$$

$$\sum(T_{.j}^2/n_j) = \frac{25^2}{4} + \frac{20^2}{4} + \frac{21^2}{4} + \frac{16^2}{4} = 430.500$$

1. $H_o: \mu_1 = \mu_2 = \mu_3 = \mu_4$
2. $\alpha = 0.05$

3. Reject the H_o if $F > F_{0.05(12,3)} = 8.74$ (Table IVd, Appendix A). (By referring to Tables IVa–g, various values of the F statistic may be read. The f_1 notation refers to the degrees of freedom (d.f.) associated with the numerator variance estimator of the F ratio and the f_2 notation is associated with the degrees of freedom of the denominator variance estimator. In our problem, the numerator variance estimator has 12 degrees of freedom, or $f_1 = 12$. The denominator variance estimator has 3 degrees of freedom, or $f_2 = 3$. In Table IVd for the $\alpha = 0.05$ level, the intersection of "column 12" [$f_1 = 12$] and "row 3" [$f_2 = 3$] gives us our critical value of F.)

4.

Source of Variability	Sum of Squared Deviations	Degrees of Freedom	Mean Square	F Ratio
Between Sample Means	10.250	3	3.417	$\dfrac{6.458}{3.417} = 1.890$
Within Sample Means	77.500	12	6.458	
Total	87.750	15		

5. Accept H_o.

10.2 Two-Way Classification, Single Value. Frequently, the values are influenced by a combination of two or more factors rather than the single factor just discussed. This section will present the simplest case involving two variables. For this preliminary discussion only one observation per cell will be considered.

TABLE 10.4

CATEGORICAL DATA FOR TWO-VARIABLE ANALYSIS OF VARIANCE

Category I

		1	2	3	4		m	$T_{i.}$	$\mu_{i.}$
C	1	μ_{11}	μ_{12}	μ_{13}	μ_{14}	...	μ_{1m}	$T_1.$	$\mu_1.$
a	2	μ_{21}	μ_{22}	μ_{23}	μ_{24}	...	μ_{2m}	$T_2.$	$\mu_2.$
t	3	μ_{31}	μ_{32}	μ_{33}	μ_{34}	...	μ_{3m}	$T_3.$	$\mu_3.$
e	4	μ_{41}	μ_{42}	μ_{43}	μ_{44}	...	μ_{4m}	$T_4.$	$\mu_4.$
g	.	.	.	.	.	...	.	.	.
o	.	.	.	.	.	...	.	.	.
r	.	.	.	.	.	...	.	.	.
y	n	μ_{n1}	μ_{n2}	μ_{n3}	μ_{n4}	...	μ_{nm}	$T_{n.}$	$\mu_{n.}$
	$T_{.j}$	$T_{.1}$	$T_{.2}$	$T_{.3}$	$T_{.4}$	...	$T_{.m}$	$T_{..}$	$\mu_{..}$
II	$\mu_{.j}$	$\mu_{.1}$	$\mu_{.2}$	$\mu_{.3}$	$\mu_{.4}$	...	$\mu_{.m}$		

As shown in Table 10.4, Category I has m different populations and Category II has n different populations. When considering each observation being influenced by one trait from each of the two categories, it is apparent that instead of work with $(m + n)$ populations, we actually have mn populations. For example, the cell occupying the first position in row and column represents the population having mean μ_{11} and represents population I for both categories. Thus, any mean μ_{ij} actually represents

$$\mu_{ij} = \mu_{..} + \mu_{i.} + \mu_{.j}$$

where

$\mu_{..}$ = the Grand Mean,

$\mu_{i.}$ = mean of *all* Category I populations,

$\mu_{.j}$ = mean of *all* Category II populations.

Thus each individual observation is actually a composite value,

$$X_{ij} = \mu_{..} + \mu_{i.} + \mu_{.j} + e_{ij}, \qquad (10.9)$$

where the added factor e_{ij} is the sampling error deviation.

In the research situation, the sample mean is used as the best point estimate of the particular population mean. Generally when a single value is used per cell, the sample mean is for a sample of size one. Table 10.5 presents this condition in the general case.

TABLE 10.5

SAMPLE DATA FOR TWO-VARIABLE ANALYSIS OF VARIANCE, $n = 1$

Category I

		1	2	3	4	...	m	$T_{i.}$	$\overline{X}_{i.}$
C	1	X_{11}	X_{12}	X_{13}	X_{14}	...	X_{1m}	$T_{1.}$	$\overline{X}_{1.}$
a	2	X_{21}	X_{22}	X_{23}	X_{24}	...	X_{2m}	$T_{2.}$	$\overline{X}_{2.}$
t	3	X_{31}	X_{32}	X_{33}	X_{34}	...	X_{3m}	$T_{3.}$	$\overline{X}_{3.}$
e	4	X_{41}	X_{42}	X_{43}	X_{44}	...	X_{4m}	$T_{4.}$	$\overline{X}_{4.}$
g	.	.	.	.	.	...	.	.	.
o	.	.	.	.	.	...	.	.	.
r	.	.	.	.	.	...	.	.	.
y	n	X_{n1}	X_{n2}	X_{n3}	X_{n4}	...	X_{nm}	$T_{n.}$	$\overline{X}_{n.}$
	$T_{.j}$	$T_{.1}$	$T_{.2}$	$T_{.3}$	$T_{.4}$	...	$T_{.m}$	$T_{..}$	$\overline{\overline{X}}_{..}$
II	$\overline{X}_{.j}$	$\overline{X}_{.1}$	$\overline{X}_{.2}$	$\overline{X}_{.3}$	$\overline{X}_{.4}$	...	$\overline{X}_{.m}$		

These data are analyzed in a manner similar to that used for the single classification. However, instead of analyzing the differences between means of one category we now analyze the differences between the means of two categories. The sum of the squared deviations may be partitioned as:

$$SSD_t = SSD_{C_I} + SSD_{C_{II}} + SSD_e$$

where

SSD_t = total sum of squared deviations,
SSD_{C_I} = sum of squared deviations due to Category I effect,
$SSD_{C_{II}}$ = sum of squared deviations due to Category II effect,
SSD_e = sum of squared deviations not accounted for (residual error),

or,

$$\sum_{j=1}^{m} \sum_{i=1}^{n_j} (X_{ij} - \bar{\bar{X}})^2$$
$$= \sum\sum[(\bar{X}_{i.} - \bar{\bar{X}}) + (\bar{X}_{.j} - \bar{\bar{X}}) + (X_{ij} - \bar{X}_{i.} - \bar{X}_{.j} + \bar{\bar{X}})]^2 \quad (10.10)$$

To arrive at computational forms for the portion shown in Equation (10.10), let us start again with a single value of X_{ij} such that:

$$(X_{ij} - \bar{\bar{X}}_{..}) = [(\bar{X}_{i.} - \bar{\bar{X}}_{..}) + (\bar{X}_{.j} - \bar{\bar{X}}_{..}) + (X_{ij} - \bar{X}_{i.} - \bar{X}_{.j} + \bar{\bar{X}}_{..})]$$

When both sides of this equation are squared, it becomes:

$$(X_{ij} - \bar{\bar{X}}_{..})^2 = [(\bar{X}_{i.} - \bar{\bar{X}}_{..}) + (\bar{X}_{.j} - \bar{\bar{X}}_{..}) + (X_{ij} - \bar{X}_{i.} - \bar{X}_{.j} + \bar{\bar{X}}_{..})]^2$$
$$= (\bar{X}_{i.} - \bar{\bar{X}}_{..})^2 + (\bar{X}_{.j} - \bar{\bar{X}}_{..})^2 + (X_{ij} - \bar{X}_{i.} - \bar{X}_{.j} + \bar{\bar{X}}_{..})^2$$
$$+ 2(\bar{X}_{i.} - \bar{\bar{X}}_{..})(\bar{X}_{.j} - \bar{\bar{X}}_{..})$$
$$+ 2(\bar{X}_{i.} - \bar{\bar{X}}_{..})(X_{ij} - \bar{X}_{i.} - \bar{X}_{.j} + \bar{\bar{X}}_{..})$$
$$+ 2(\bar{X}_{.j} - \bar{\bar{X}}_{..})(X_{ij} - \bar{X}_{i.} - \bar{X}_{.j} + \bar{\bar{X}}_{..})$$

Summing this expression for all n row values of X_{ij} in any jth column, and since ideally all $n_{.j}$ values for each column should be equal, or $n_{.1} = n_{.2} = \cdots = n_{.k} = n$, we have:

$$\sum_{i=1}^{n} (X_{ij} - \bar{\bar{X}}_{..})^2 = \sum_{i=1}^{n} (\bar{X}_{i.} - \bar{\bar{X}}_{..}) + n(\bar{X}_{.j} - \bar{\bar{X}}_{..})^2$$
$$+ \sum_{i=1}^{n} (X_{ij} - \bar{X}_{i.} - \bar{X}_{.j} + \bar{\bar{X}}_{..})^2$$
$$+ 2(\bar{X}_{.j} - \bar{\bar{X}}_{..}) \sum_{i=1}^{n} (\bar{X}_{i.} - \bar{\bar{X}}_{..})$$
$$+ 2 \sum_{i=1}^{n} (\bar{X}_{i.} - \bar{\bar{X}}_{..})(X_{ij} - \bar{X}_{i.} - \bar{X}_{.j} + \bar{\bar{X}}_{..})$$
$$+ 2(\bar{X}_{.j} - \bar{\bar{X}}_{..}) \sum_{i=1}^{n} (X_{ij} - \bar{X}_{i.} - \bar{X}_{.j} + \bar{\bar{X}}_{..})$$

In the fourth term the value of $\sum(\bar{X}_{i.} - \bar{\bar{X}}_{..})$ is found. It has been shown earlier that this sum is zero. As such, the fourth term of the expansion disappears. The next step would be to sum the remaining expressions over the m columns:

$$\sum_{j=1}^{m}\sum_{i=1}^{n}(X_{ij}-\bar{\bar{X}}_{..})^2 = m\sum_{i=1}^{n}(\bar{X}_{i.}-\bar{\bar{X}}_{..})^2 + n\sum_{j=1}^{m}(\bar{X}_{.j}-\bar{\bar{X}}_{..})^2$$

$$+\sum_{j=1}^{m}\sum_{i=1}^{n}(X_{ij}-\bar{X}_{i.}-\bar{X}_{.j}+\bar{\bar{X}}_{..})^2$$

$$+2\sum_{j=1}^{m}\sum_{i=1}^{n}(\bar{X}_{i.}-\bar{\bar{X}}_{..})(X_{ij}-\bar{X}_{i.}-\bar{X}_{.j}+\bar{\bar{X}}_{..})$$

$$+2\sum_{j=1}^{m}\sum_{i=1}^{n}(\bar{X}_{.j}-\bar{\bar{X}}_{..})(X_{ij}-\bar{X}_{i.}-\bar{X}_{.j}+\bar{\bar{X}}_{..})$$

Now

$$2\sum_{j=1}^{m}\sum_{i=1}^{n}(\bar{X}_{i.}-\bar{\bar{X}}_{..})(X_{ij}-\bar{X}_{i.}-\bar{X}_{.j}+\bar{\bar{X}}_{..})$$

$$= 2\sum_{j=1}^{m}\sum_{i=1}^{n}(\bar{X}_{i.}-\bar{\bar{X}}_{..})[(X_{ij}-\bar{X}_{i.})+(\bar{X}_{.j}-\bar{\bar{X}}_{..})]$$

$$= 2\sum\sum(\bar{X}_{i.}-\bar{\bar{X}}_{..})(X_{ij}-\bar{X}_{i.})$$
$$-2\sum\sum(\bar{X}_{i.}-\bar{\bar{X}}_{..})(\bar{X}_{.j}-\bar{\bar{X}}_{..})$$

Each portion of this equation is equal to zero and, as such, this portion disappears. The same may be shown for

$$2\sum\sum(\bar{X}_{.j}-\bar{\bar{X}}_{..})(X_{ij}-\bar{X}_{i.}-\bar{X}_{.j}+\bar{\bar{X}}_{..})$$

leaving as the final expression:

$$\sum_{j=1}^{m}\sum_{i=1}^{n}(X_{ij}-\bar{\bar{X}}_{..})^2 = m\sum_{i=1}^{n}(\bar{X}_{i.}-\bar{\bar{X}}_{..})^2 + n\sum_{j=1}^{m}(\bar{X}_{.j}-\bar{\bar{X}}_{..})^2$$

$$+\sum_{j=1}^{m}\sum_{i=1}^{n}(X_{ij}-\bar{X}_{i.}-\bar{X}_{.j}+\bar{\bar{X}}_{..})^2 \quad (10.11)$$

Now, let

$$T_{i.} = \sum_{j=1}^{m}X_{ij} \text{ for } i=1,2,\ldots,n \qquad T_{.j} = \sum_{i=1}^{n}X_{ij} \text{ for } j=1,2,\ldots,m$$

$$T_{..} = \sum_{j=1}^{m}\sum_{i=1}^{n}X_{ij} = \sum_{j=1}^{m}T_{.j} = \sum_{i=1}^{n}T_{i.} \text{ for } i=1,2,\ldots,n \text{ and } j=1,2,\ldots,m$$

$$N = \sum_{j=1}^{m}n_{.j} = \sum_{i=1}^{n}m_{i.} = mn \text{ where } m_{1.} = m_{2.} = \cdots = m \text{ and}$$
$$n_{.1} = n_{.2} = \cdots = n$$

$$\bar{\bar{X}}_{..} = T_{..}/N \qquad \bar{X}_{i.} = T_{i.}/m \qquad \bar{X}_{.j} = T_{.j}/n$$

To get computational form for the *between columns* (Category I) variance estimator, the second portion of Equation (10.11) becomes:

$$n \sum_{j=1}^{m} (\overline{X}_{.j} - \overline{X}_{..})^2$$

$$= \Sigma n(\overline{X}_{.j}^2 - 2\overline{\overline{X}}_{..}\overline{X}_{.j} + \overline{\overline{X}}_{..}^2) = \Sigma(n\overline{X}_{.j}^2 - 2n\overline{\overline{X}}_{..}\overline{X}_{.j} + n\overline{\overline{X}}_{..}^2)$$

$$= \Sigma n\overline{X}_{.j}^2 - 2\overline{\overline{X}}_{..}\Sigma n\overline{X}_{.j} + mn\overline{\overline{X}}_{..}^2$$

$$= \Sigma n(T_{.j}/n)(T_{.j}/n) - 2(T_{..}/N)\Sigma n(T_{.j}/n) + N(T_{..}/N)(T_{..}/N)$$

$$= \Sigma(T_{.j}^2/n) - 2(T_{..}/N)(\Sigma T_{.j}) + (T_{..}^2/N)$$

$$= \Sigma(T_{.j}^2/n) - (T_{..}^2/N)$$

When this portion is divided by the $(m - 1)$ degrees of freedom we have:

$$s_{C_I}^2 = \frac{\Sigma(T_{.j}^2/n) - (T_{..}^2/N)}{m - 1} \tag{10.12}$$

The variance estimator or mean square value for the *between rows* (Category II) may be formed in the same manner using the appropriate substitutions yielding:

$$s_{C_{II}}^2 = \frac{\Sigma(T_{i.}^2/m) - (T_{..}^2/N)}{n - 1} \tag{10.13}$$

Since
$$SSD_T = SSD_{C_I} + SSD_{C_{II}} + SSD_e$$
$$SSD_e = SSD_T - SSD_{C_I} - SSD_{C_{II}}$$

Using $SSD_T = \sum_{j=1}^{m}\sum_{i=1}^{n}(X_{ij} - \overline{X}_{..})^2 = \Sigma\Sigma X_{ij}^2 - (T_{..}^2/N)$ and the numerator values of Equations (10.12) and (10.13) for SSD_{C_I} and $SSD_{C_{II}}$, respectively,

$$SSD_e = [\Sigma\Sigma X_{ij}^2 - (T_{..}^2/N)] - [\Sigma(T_{.j}^2/n) - (T_{..}^2/N)]$$
$$- [\Sigma(T_{i.}^2/m) - (T_{..}^2/N)]$$

$$= \Sigma\Sigma X_{ij}^2 - \Sigma(T_{.j}^2/n) - \Sigma(T_{i.}/m)$$
$$- (T_{..}^2/N) + (T_{..}^2/N) + (T_{..}^2/N)$$

$$= \Sigma\Sigma X_{ij}^2 - \Sigma(T_{.j}^2/n) - \Sigma(T_{i.}/m) + (T_{..}^2/N)$$

Dividing this numerator value by the degrees of freedom $[(m - 1)(n - 1)]$, we have the *residual* or *within sample* mean square or variance estimator value:

$$s_e^2 = \frac{\Sigma\Sigma X_{ij}^2 - \Sigma(T_{.j}^2/n) - \Sigma(T_{i.}^2/m) + (T_{..}^2/N)}{(m - 1)(n - 1)} \tag{10.14}$$

Table 10.6 presents that table format used in the computational process involved in the testing of the associated hypotheses. The last column

(F ratios) now has two entries, (1) between the first main effect (C_I) and the residual error, and (2) between the remaining main effect (C_II) and the residual error.

TABLE 10.6

COMPUTATION TABLE FOR
TWO-WAY CLASSIFICATION ANALYSIS OF VARIANCE (10.15)

Source of Variability	Sum of Squared Deviations (SSD)	Degrees of Freedom (d.f.)	Mean Square (MS)	F
Between Cat. I (columns)	$\sum(T_{.j}^2/n) - (T_{..}^2/N)$	$m-1$	$s_{C\mathrm{I}}^2$	$s_{C\mathrm{I}}^2/s_e^2$
Between Cat. II (rows)	$\sum(T_{i.}^2/m) - (T_{..}^2/N)$	$n-1$	$s_{C\mathrm{II}}^2$	$s_{C\mathrm{II}}^2/s_e^2$
Residual Error	$\sum\sum X_{ij}^2 - \sum(T_{.j}^2/n)$ $- \sum(T_{i.}^2/m) + (T_{..}^2/N)$	$(m-1)(n-1)$	s_e^2	
Total	$\sum\sum X_{ij}^2 - \dfrac{T_{..}^2}{N}$	$N-1$		

As an illustration let us consider the following hypothetical case. The researcher desires to see if there is a significant variation in verbal ability which may be attributed to the differences in total years of course-work in English and Social Studies. The data in Table 10.7a represent the averages for the various double categories.

TABLE 10.7a

SCORES ON A VERBAL ABILITY INSTRUMENT
FOR
VARYING LEVELS OF PREPARATION IN ENGLISH AND SOCIAL STUDIES

			Number of Courses in English				
			1	2	3	4	$T_{i.}$
Courses in Social Studies		1	67	71	69	74	281
		2	61	69	62	71	263
		3	73	76	74	68	291
		4	66	72	61	64	263
$T_{.j}$			267	288	266	277	$T_{..} = 1098$

For ease of computation the data may be coded. The data coded by subtracting 69 for all values are given in Table 10.7b.

TABLE 10.7b

DATA FROM TABLE 10.7a CODED BY SUBTRACTING 69 FROM ALL X's

	1	2	3	4	$T_{i.}$
1	−2(4)	2(4)	0(0)	5(25)	5(33)
2	−8(64)	0(0)	−7(49)	2(4)	−13(117)
3	4(16)	7(49)	5(25)	−1(1)	15(91)
4	−3(9)	3(9)	−8(64)	−5(25)	−13(107)
$T_{.j}$	−9(93)	12(62)	−10(138)	1(55)	−6(348)

The squares are presented in parentheses with the row, column, and total sums of squares. To follow the format of Table 10.6, it is necessary to complete the following computations:

$$\sum(T_{.j}^2/n_j) = \frac{-9^2}{4} + \frac{12^2}{4} + \frac{-10^2}{4} + \frac{1^2}{4} = 81.50$$

$$\sum(T_{i.}^2/n_i) = \frac{5^2}{4} + \frac{-13^2}{4} + \frac{15^2}{4} + \frac{-13^2}{4} = 147.00$$

$$T_{..}^2/N = \frac{-6^2}{16} = 2.25$$

The actual testing of the hypotheses would be as follows:

1. $H_o: \mu_1 = \mu_2 = \mu_3 = \mu_4$ (column effect)
   $\mu_1 = \mu_2 = \mu_3 = \mu_4$ (row effect)
2. $\alpha = 0.05$
3. Reject H_o if $F > F_{0.05(3,9)} = 3.86$.
4.

S of V	SSD	d.f.	MS	F
Bet. cols	81.50 − 2.25 = 79.25	3	26.42	26.42/13.53 = 1.95
Bet. rows	147.00 − 2.25 = 144.75	3	48.25	48.25/13.53 = 3.57
Residual	348 − 81.50 − 147.00 + 2.25 = 121.75	9	13.53	
Total	348 − 2.25 = 345.75	15		

5. Accept both hypotheses.

10.3 Two-Way Classification with Replication. Section 10.2 was devoted to a discussion of the method used to analyze separately and yet simultaneously the significance of the two classifying agents. The single observation case does not permit examination of the possible varying effects of combinations of the two major variables. This is termed the test for *significance of interaction*.

To obtain a variance estimator for this factor, several observations (*replications*) must be made for each of the cells as is shown in the expansion of the data of Table 10.7a to include four readings (*replicates*) per cell. These data are presented in original form in Table 10.8 with their coded values in parentheses.

TABLE 10.8

DATA FROM TABLE 10.7a EXPANDED TO SHOW FOUR REPLICATES

Category II

		1	2	3	4
		65(— 4)	66(—3)	66(—3)	78(9)
	1	68(— 1)	77(8)	69(0)	69(0)
		69(0)	69(0)	72(3)	75(6)
C		66(— 3)	72(3)	69(0)	74(5)
a					
t		57(—12)	67(—2)	58(—11)	76(7)
e	2	58(—11)	69(0)	59(—10)	69(0)
g		65(— 4)	74(5)	65(— 4)	73(4)
o		64(— 5)	66(—3)	66(— 3)	66(—3)
r					
y		75(6)	78(9)	72(3)	66(—3)
	3	67(—2)	83(14)	73(4)	69(0)
I		69(0)	71(2)	68(—1)	72(3)
		81(12)	72(3)	83(14)	65(—4)
		63(—6)	70(1)	55(—14)	61(—8)
	4	62(—7)	78(9)	63(— 6)	68(—1)
		60(0)	68(—1)	57(—12)	63(—6)
		70(1)	62(—7)	69(0)	64(—5)

The pattern previously presented of subdividing the total variability is complicated by the variance of the samples within each of the cells of the table. As an example, the values 65, 68, 69, and 66 represent a random sample of four items from the population possessing the characteristic (1) of Category I and characteristic (1) of Category II. These four values represent a population exhibiting the *interacting* effects of both Category I and Category II. With this factor in mind, the variance due to this *interaction* effect must also be tested for significance.

Each term of X_{ijk} in Table 10.8 has three factors:

$i =$ the specific Category I factor (row number),
$j =$ the specific Category II factor (column number),
$k =$ the specific member of the sample for the interacting i and j factors.

As an example, $X_{111} = 65$. The subscript notation on X indicates that this particular value is the first member of the sample ($k = 1$) from the population which has the combined attributes of the first population of the Category I universe ($i = 1$) and the first population of the Category II universe ($j = 1$). The value then is read as "$X_{(\text{one, one, one})}$ equals 65."

The total sum of squared deviations (SSD_T) is now composed of four parts: (1) the sum of squared deviations due to Category I ($SSD_{C_{\text{I}}}$), (2) the sum of the squared deviations due to Category II ($SSD_{C_{\text{II}}}$), (3) the sum of squared deviations due to the interaction of Categories I and II (SSD_{I}), and (4) the *within groups* sum of squared deviations due to sampling error (SSD_e). This may be expressed as

$$SSD_T = SSD_{C_{\mathrm{I}}} + SSD_{C_{\mathrm{II}}} + SSD_{\mathrm{I}} + SSD_e$$

or

$$\sum_{k=1}^{r}\sum_{j=1}^{m}\sum_{i=1}^{n}(X_{ijk} - \overline{X}_{...})^2 = \sum_{k=1}^{r}\sum_{j=1}^{m}\sum_{i=1}^{n}[(\overline{X}_{i..} - \overline{X}_{...}) + (\overline{X}_{.j.} - \overline{X}_{...})$$
$$+ (X_{ijk} - \overline{X}_{ij.}) + (\overline{X}_{ij.} - \overline{X}_{i..} - \overline{X}_{.j.} + \overline{X}_{...})]^2$$

For any single value of X_{ijk} the expression would be:

$$\begin{aligned}
(X_{ijk} - \overline{X}_{...})^2 &= [(\overline{X}_{i..} - \overline{X}_{...}) + (\overline{X}_{.j.} - \overline{X}_{...}) + (X_{ijk} - \overline{X}_{ij.}) \\
&\quad + (\overline{X}_{ij.} - \overline{X}_{i..} - \overline{X}_{.j.} + \overline{X}_{...})]^2 \\
&= (\overline{X}_{i..} - \overline{X}_{...})^2 + (\overline{X}_{.j.} - \overline{X}_{...})^2 + (X_{ijk} - \overline{X}_{ij.})^2 \\
&\quad + (\overline{X}_{ij.} - \overline{X}_{i..} - \overline{X}_{.j.} + \overline{X}_{...})^2 \\
&\quad + 2(\overline{X}_{i..} - \overline{X}_{...})(\overline{X}_{.j.} - \overline{X}_{...}) \\
&\quad + 2(\overline{X}_{i..} - \overline{X}_{...})(X_{ijk} - \overline{X}_{ij.}) \\
&\quad + 2(\overline{X}_{i..} - \overline{X}_{...})(\overline{X}_{ij.} - \overline{X}_{i..} - \overline{X}_{.j.} + \overline{X}_{...}) \\
&\quad + 2(\overline{X}_{.j.} - \overline{X}_{...})(X_{ijk} - \overline{X}_{ij.}) \\
&\quad + 2(\overline{X}_{.j.} - \overline{X}_{...})(\overline{X}_{ij.} - \overline{X}_{i..} - \overline{X}_{.j.} + \overline{X}_{...}) \\
&\quad + 2(X_{ijk} - \overline{X}_{...})(\overline{X}_{ij.} - \overline{X}_{i..} - \overline{X}_{.j.} + \overline{X}_{...})
\end{aligned}$$

When this expansion is summed over the replicate values in any cell and where all cells have equal replications, we have:

$$\begin{aligned}
\sum_{k=1}^{r}(X_{ijk} - \overline{X}_{...})^2 =\ & r(\overline{X}_{i..} - \overline{X}_{...})^2 + r(\overline{X}_{.j.} - \overline{X}_{...})^2 \\
& + \sum_{k=1}^{r}(X_{ijk} - \overline{X}_{ij.})^2 \\
& + r(\overline{X}_{ij.} - \overline{X}_{i..} - \overline{X}_{.j.} + \overline{X}_{...})^2 \\
& + 2r(\overline{X}_{i..} - \overline{X}_{...})(\overline{X}_{.j.} - \overline{X}_{...}) \\
& + 2(\overline{X}_{i..} - \overline{X}_{...})\sum_{k=1}^{r}(X_{ijk} - \overline{X}_{ij.}) \\
& + 2r(\overline{X}_{i..} - \overline{X}_{...})(\overline{X}_{ij.} - \overline{X}_{i..} - \overline{X}_{.j.} + \overline{X}_{...}) \\
& + 2(\overline{X}_{.j.} - \overline{X}_{...})\sum_{k=1}^{r}(X_{ijk} - \overline{X}_{ij.}) \\
& + 2r(\overline{X}_{.j.} - \overline{X}_{...})(\overline{X}_{ij.} - \overline{X}_{i..} - \overline{X}_{.j.} + \overline{X}_{...}) \\
& + 2(\overline{X}_{ij.} - \overline{X}_{i..} - \overline{X}_{.j.} + \overline{X}_{...})\sum_{k=1}^{r}(X_{ijk} - \overline{X}_{ij.})
\end{aligned}$$

In the 6th, 8th, and 10th terms, the value $\sum_{k=1}^{r} (X_{ijk} - \overline{X}_{ij.})$ is found. Since the sum of deviations of sample values from the mean of the sample is zero, these three terms disappear. When the remaining terms are summed in any row over the m values, the resultant is:

$$\sum_{k=1}^{r} \sum_{j=1}^{m} (X_{ijk} - \overline{X}_{...})^2$$
$$= mr(\overline{\overline{X}}_{i..} - \overline{X}_{...})^2 + r \sum_{j=1}^{m} (\overline{\overline{X}}_{.j.} - \overline{X}_{...})^2$$
$$+ \sum_{k=1}^{r} \sum_{j=1}^{m} (X_{ijk} - \overline{X}_{ij.})^2$$
$$+ r \sum_{j=1}^{m} (\overline{X}_{ij.} - \overline{X}_{i..} - \overline{\overline{X}}_{.j.} + \overline{X}_{...})^2$$
$$+ 2(\overline{\overline{X}}_{i..} - \overline{X}_{...}) \sum_{j=1}^{m} (\overline{\overline{X}}_{.j.} - \overline{X}_{...})$$
$$+ 2r(\overline{\overline{X}}_{i..} - \overline{X}_{...}) \sum_{j=1}^{m} (\overline{X}_{ij.} - \overline{X}_{i..} - \overline{\overline{X}}_{.j.} + \overline{X}_{...})$$
$$+ 2r \sum_{j=1}^{m} [(\overline{\overline{X}}_{.j.} - \overline{X}_{...})(\overline{X}_{ij.} - \overline{X}_{i..} - \overline{\overline{X}}_{.j.} + \overline{X}_{...})]$$

In the 5th term of this last summation, another sum of deviations is found and is again equal to zero. As such, this whole term disappears. In the 7th term it may be shown that:

$$2r \sum_{j=1}^{m} [(\overline{\overline{X}}_{.j.} - \overline{X}_{...})(\overline{X}_{ij.} - \overline{X}_{i..} - \overline{\overline{X}}_{.j.} - \overline{X}_{...})]$$
$$= 2r \sum_{j=1}^{m} [(\overline{\overline{X}}_{.j.} - \overline{X}_{...})(\overline{X}_{ij.} - \overline{\overline{X}}_{.j.})$$
$$- (\overline{\overline{X}}_{.j.} - \overline{X}_{...})(\overline{\overline{X}}_{i..} - \overline{X}_{...})]$$
$$= 2r \sum_{j=1}^{m} [(\overline{\overline{X}}_{.j.} - \overline{X}_{...})(\overline{X}_{ij.} - \overline{\overline{X}}_{.j.})]$$
$$- 2r \sum_{j=1}^{m} [(\overline{\overline{X}}_{.j.} - \overline{X}_{...})(\overline{\overline{X}}_{i..} - \overline{X}_{...})]$$

Both portions of this resulting subdivision are equal to zero due to the sum of deviations factor. As such, the total quantity disappears. After summing the remaining factors over the n rows for any column, we have the following equation.

$$\sum_{k=1}^{r} \sum_{j=1}^{m} \sum_{i=1}^{n} (X_{ijk} - \overline{X}_{...})^2$$

$$= mr \sum_{i=1}^{n} (\overline{\overline{X}}_{i..} - \overline{X}_{...})^2 + nr \sum_{j=1}^{m} (\overline{\overline{X}}_{.j.} - \overline{X}_{...})^2$$

$$+ \sum_{k=1}^{r} \sum_{j=1}^{m} \sum_{i=1}^{n} (X_{ijk} - \overline{X}_{ij.})^2$$

$$+ r \sum_{j=1}^{m} \sum_{i=1}^{n} (X_{ij.} - \overline{\overline{X}}_{i..} - \overline{\overline{X}}_{.j.} + \overline{X}_{...})^2$$

$$+ 2r \sum_{j=1}^{m} \sum_{i=1}^{n} [(\overline{\overline{X}}_{i..} - \overline{X}_{...})(\overline{X}_{ij.} - \overline{\overline{X}}_{i..} - \overline{\overline{X}}_{.j.} + \overline{X}_{...})]$$

Using the same procedure, the last term disappears leaving the final portion of the total sum of squared deviations, or:

$$\sum_{k=1}^{r} \sum_{j=1}^{m} \sum_{i=1}^{n} (X_{ijk} - \overline{X}_{...})^2 = mr \sum_{i=1}^{n} (\overline{\overline{X}}_{i..} - \overline{X}_{...})^2 + nr \sum_{j=1}^{m} (\overline{\overline{X}}_{.j.} - \overline{X}_{...})^2$$

$$+ \sum_{k=1}^{r} \sum_{j=1}^{m} \sum_{i=1}^{n} (X_{ijk} - \overline{X}_{ij.})^2$$

$$+ r \sum_{j=1}^{m} \sum_{i=1}^{n} (\overline{X}_{ij.} - \overline{\overline{X}}_{i..} - \overline{\overline{X}}_{.j.} + \overline{X}_{...})^2$$

where

$$SSD_T = \sum_{k=1}^{r} \sum_{j=1}^{m} \sum_{i=1}^{n} (X_{ijk} - \overline{X}_{...})^2$$

$$SSD_{C_{\mathrm{I}}} = mr \sum_{i=1}^{n} (\overline{\overline{X}}_{i..} - \overline{X}_{...})^2$$

$$SSD_{C_{\mathrm{II}}} = nr \sum_{j=1}^{m} (\overline{\overline{X}}_{.j.} - \overline{X}_{...})^2$$

$$SSD_{\mathrm{I}} = r \sum_{j=1}^{m} \sum_{i=1}^{n} (\overline{X}_{ij.} - \overline{\overline{X}}_{i..} - \overline{\overline{X}}_{.j.} + \overline{X}_{...})^2$$

$$SSD_e = \sum_{k=1}^{r} \sum_{j=1}^{m} \sum_{i=1}^{n} (X_{ijk} - \overline{X}_{ij.})^2$$

By using the following substitutions, each of the computational formulas given in Table 10.9 may be determined. When each of these sums of squared deviations is divided by its particular degrees of freedom as indicated in the same table, the variance estimator or mean squared value is obtained.

Let

$$T_{...} = \sum\sum\sum X_{ijk} \qquad \bar{X}_{...} = T_{...}/N$$

$$T_{i..} = \overset{r}{\sum}\overset{m}{\sum} X_{ijk} \qquad \bar{X}_{i..} = T_{i..}/mr$$

$$T_{.j.} = \overset{r}{\sum}\overset{n}{\sum} X_{ijk} \qquad \bar{X}_{.j.} = T_{.j.}/nr$$

$$T_{..k} = \overset{r}{\sum} X_{ijk} \qquad \bar{X}_{ij.} = T_{..k}/r$$

$$N = rmn$$

TABLE 10.9

COMPUTATION TABLE FOR TWO-WAY CLASSIFICATION ANALYSIS OF VARIANCE WITH REPLICATIONS

Source of Variability	Sum of Squared Deviations	Degrees of Freedom	Mean Square	F Ratios
Bet. cols. (m)	$\sum(T_{.j.}^2/nr) - (T_{...}^2/N)$	$(m-1)$	s_m^2	s_m^2/s_e^2
Bet. rows (n)	$\sum(T_{i..}^2/mr) - (T_{...}^2/N)$	$(n-1)$	s_n^2	s_n^2/s_e^2
Interaction $(m \times n)$	$\sum\sum(T_{ij.}^2/r) - \sum(T_{.j.}^2/nr)$ $- \sum(T_{i..}^2/mr) + (T_{...}^2/N)$	$(m-1)$ $\times (n-1)$	$s_{(m \times n)}^2$	$s_{(m \times n)}^2/s_e^2$
Residual Error	$\sum\sum\sum X_{ijk}^2 - \sum\sum(T_{ij.}^2/r)$	$mn(r-1)$	s_e^2	
Total	$\sum\sum\sum X_{ijk}^2 - (T_{...}^2/N)$	$mnr-1$		

To facilitate the computational process, a table showing $T_{ij.}$ as well as $T_{i..}$, $T_{.j.}$, and $T_{...}$ is appropriate. Table 10.10 presents the coded data from Table 10.8 with these additional features which will be used in the example on page 163. The following computations are also necessary for solving the problem.

$$\sum\sum\sum X_{ijk}^2 = 2382$$

$$\sum(T_{i..}^2/nr) = 10{,}548/16 = 659.25$$

$$T_{...}^2/N = 1156/64 = 18.0625$$

$$\sum\sum(T_{ij.}^2/r) = 5428/4 = 1357$$

$$\sum(T_{.j.}^2/nr) = 4356/16 = 272.25$$

$$SSD_m = 272.25 - 18.0625 = 254.1875$$

$$SSD_{mn} = 1357 - 659.25 - 272.25 + 18.0625$$
$$= 443.5625$$

$$SSD_n = 659.25 - 18.0625 = 641.1875$$

$$SSD_e = 2382 - 1357 = 1025$$

$$SSD_t = 2382 - 18.0625 = 2363.9375$$

TABLE 10.10

CODED REPLICATED DATA FOR TWO-WAY CLASSIFICATION ANALYSIS OF VARIANCE FROM TABLE 10.8

	1	2	3	4	$T_{i..}$
1	−4	−3	−3	9	
	−1	8	0	0	
	0	0	3	6	
	−3	3	0	5	
$T_{ij.}$	−8	8	0	20	20
2	−12	−2	−11	7	
	−11	0	−10	0	
	−4	5	−4	4	
	−5	−3	−3	−3	
$T_{ij.}$	−32	0	−28	8	−52
3	6	9	3	−3	
	−2	14	4	0	
	0	2	−1	3	
	12	3	14	−4	
$T_{ij.}$	16	28	20	−4	60
4	−6	1	−14	−8	
	−7	9	−6	−1	
	0	−1	−12	−6	
	1	−7	0	−5	
$T_{ij.}$	−12	2	−32	−20	−62
$T_{.j.}$	−36	38	−40	4	$T_{...} = -34$

A. Hypotheses: The test hypotheses for this problem are:
   1. No statistically significant difference exists between the levels of the main effects (column and row).
   2. There is no statistically significant interaction between levels of the two main effects.

B. $\alpha = 0.05$.

Source of Variability	SSD	d.f.	MS	F	Critical F
Bet. cols.	254.1875	3	$254.1875/3 = 84.73$	3.97	2.8064
Bet. rows	641.1875	3	$641.1875/3 = 213.73$	10.01	2.8064
Interaction	443.5625	9	$443.5625/9 = 49.28$	2.14	2.0904
Error	1025.00	48	$1025/48 = 21.35$		
Total	2363.938	63			

C. Since all the sample F ratios were significant at the 0.05 level, both of the test hypotheses were rejected.

When the analysis of variance test has been completed, a significant F ratio indicates that, somewhere within the combined set of samples, one or more values of μ_i, μ_j, and/or μ_{ij} are apparently different from the common μ. To establish relationships between the various μ's, it is necessary to run t tests between pairs.

10.4 *Three-Way Classification.* Quite often the data involved are the results of the actions of three factors and their associated interactions, such as the effect of sex, grade level, and different classes on the achievement within a certain subject. Thus the separate scores obtained by testing are expressions of:

$$X_{ijkl} = \mu_{....} + \mu_{i...} + \mu_{.j..} + \mu_{..k.} + \mu_{ij} + \mu_{i.k.} + \mu_{.jk.} + \mu_{ijk.} + e_{ijkl}$$

where i represents factor (1), sex; j represents factor (2), grade level; k represents factor (3), different classes; and l represents the individual sample replicate. As illustrated earlier in this chapter, the deviation of the separate replicate X_{ijkl} from the common mean estimator $\overline{\overline{X}}_{....}$ may be divided into a series and the separate estimators may be determined.

This three factor situation is diagrammatically presented in Tables 10.11 and 10.12.

TABLE 10.11

DIAGRAMMATIC REPRESENTATION OF THREE-WAY CLASSIFICATION DATA

Boys									Girls								
Grade A			Grade B			Grade C			Grade A			Grade B			Grade C		
Class I	Class II	Class III	Class I	Class II	Class III	Class I	Class II	Class III	Class I	Class II	Class III	Class I	Class II	Class III	Class I	Class II	Class III
X_{1111}	X_{1121}	X_{1131}	X_{1211}	X_{1221}	X_{1231}	X_{1311}	X_{1321}	X_{1331}	X_{2111}	X_{2121}	X_{2131}	X_{2211}	X_{2221}	X_{2231}	X_{2311}	X_{2321}	X_{2331}
X_{1112}	X_{1122}	X_{1132}	X_{1212}	X_{1222}	X_{1232}	X_{1312}	X_{1322}	X_{1332}	X_{2112}	X_{2122}	X_{2132}	X_{2212}	X_{2222}	X_{2232}	X_{2312}	X_{2322}	X_{2332}
X_{1113}	X_{1123}	X_{1133}	X_{1213}	X_{1223}	X_{1233}	X_{1313}	X_{1323}	X_{1333}	X_{2113}	X_{2123}	X_{2133}	X_{2213}	X_{2223}	X_{2233}	X_{2313}	X_{2323}	X_{2333}
...	...	...	...	...	...	...	...	...	...	...	...	...	...	...	...	...	...
X_{111n}	X_{112n}	X_{113n}	X_{121n}	X_{122n}	X_{123n}	X_{131n}	X_{132n}	X_{133n}	X_{211n}	X_{212n}	X_{213n}	X_{221n}	X_{222n}	X_{223n}	X_{231n}	X_{232n}	X_{233n}
$T_{111.}$	$T_{112.}$	$T_{113.}$	$T_{121.}$	$T_{122.}$	$T_{123.}$	$T_{131.}$	$T_{132.}$	$T_{133.}$	$T_{211.}$	$T_{212.}$	$T_{213.}$	$T_{221.}$	$T_{222.}$	$T_{223.}$	$T_{231.}$	$T_{232.}$	$T_{233.}$
$T_{11..}$			$T_{12..}$			$T_{13..}$			$T_{21..}$			$T_{22..}$			$T_{23..}$		
$T_{1...}$									$T_{2...}$								

These data may now be analyzed for:

(1) Between Sex Differences

(2) Between Grade Level Differences

(3) Between Class Differences

(4) Sex × Grade Interaction

(5) Sex × Class Interaction

(6) Grade × Class Interaction

(7) Sex × Grade × Class Interaction

The analysis of variance computational table is shown in Table 10.12.

TABLE 10.12

COMPUTATIONAL TABLE FOR THREE-WAY CLASSIFICATION ANALYSIS OF VARIANCE, WITH REPLICATIONS

Source of Variability	SSD	d.f.
Between Sexes (S)	$SSD_S = \sum (T_{i\ldots}^2/n_{i\ldots}) - (T_{\ldots}^2/N)$	$s-1$
Between Grades (G)	$SSD_G = \sum (T_{\cdot j\cdot\cdot}^2/n_{\cdot j\cdot\cdot}) - (T_{\ldots}^2/N)$	$g-1$
Between Classes (C)	$SSD_C = \sum (T_{\cdot\cdot k\cdot}^2/n_{\cdot\cdot k\cdot}) - (T_{\ldots}^2/N)$	$c-1$
Interactions:		
Sex × Grade (S × G)	$SSD_{SG} = \sum\sum (T_{ij\cdot\cdot}^2/n_{ij\cdot\cdot}) - \sum (T_{i\ldots}^2/n_{i\ldots}) \\ - \sum (T_{\cdot j\cdot\cdot}^2/n_{\cdot j\cdot\cdot}) + (T_{\ldots}^2/N)$	$(s-1)(g-1)$
Sex × Class (S × C)	$SSD_{SC} = \sum\sum (T_{i\cdot k\cdot}^2/n_{i\cdot k\cdot}) - \sum (T_{i\ldots}^2/n_{i\ldots}) \\ - \sum (T_{\cdot\cdot k\cdot}^2/n_{\cdot\cdot k\cdot}) + (T_{\ldots}^2/N)$	$(s-1)(c-1)$
Grade × Class (G × C)	$SSD_{GC} = \sum\sum (T_{\cdot jk\cdot}^2/n_{\cdot jk\cdot}) - \sum (T_{\cdot j\cdot\cdot}^2/n_{\cdot j\cdot\cdot}) \\ - \sum (T_{\cdot\cdot k\cdot}^2/n_{\cdot\cdot k\cdot}) + (T_{\ldots}^2/N)$	$(g-1)(c-1)$
Sex × Grade × Class (S × G × C)	$SSD_{SGC} = \sum\sum\sum (T_{ijk\cdot}^2/n_{ijk\cdot}) - \sum\sum (T_{ij\cdot\cdot}^2/n_{ij\cdot\cdot}) \\ - \sum\sum (T_{i\cdot k\cdot}^2/n_{i\cdot k\cdot}) - \sum\sum (T_{\cdot jk\cdot}^2/n_{\cdot jk\cdot}) \\ + \sum (T_{i\ldots}^2/n_{i\ldots}) + \sum (T_{\cdot j\cdot\cdot}^2/n_{\cdot j\cdot\cdot}) \\ + \sum (T_{\cdot\cdot k\cdot}^2/n_{\cdot\cdot k\cdot}) - (T_{\ldots}^2/N)$	$(s-1)(g-1)(c-1)$
Within Groups	$SSD_w = \sum\sum\sum\sum X_{ijkl}^2 - \sum\sum\sum (T_{ijk\cdot}^2/n_{ijk\cdot})$	$N-sgc$
Total	$SSD_T = \sum\sum\sum\sum X_{ijkl}^2 - (T_{\ldots}^2/N)$	$N-1$

As an illustration, consider the case where three different classes in three different grade levels have been presented with the same tasks. The researcher is interested in knowing whether or not any differences in degree of accomplishment may be attributed to the sex factor, grade level factor, separate class factor, or the interactions between any two or more of these factors as expressed by achievement. The data are shown in Table 10.13 and the variables are identified as:

$$C_1 = \text{Class 1} \qquad G_1 = \text{Grade Level 1} \qquad S_1 = \text{Boys}$$
$$C_2 = \text{Class 2} \qquad G_2 = \text{Grade Level 2} \qquad S_2 = \text{Girls}$$
$$C_3 = \text{Class 3} \qquad G_3 = \text{Grade Level 3}$$

The analysis is aided by making separate tables for $S \times G$, $S \times C$ and $G \times C$.

	S_1	S_2	$T_{.j..}$		S_1	S_2	$T_{..k.}$		G_1	G_2	G_3	$T_{..k.}$
G_1	2309	2254	4563	C_1	2296	2279	4575	C_1	1526	1522	1527	4575
G_2	2280	2269	4549	C_2	2297	2213	4510	C_2	1490	1507	1513	4510
G_3	2302	2253	4555	C_3	2298	2284	4582	C_3	1547	1520	1515	4582
$T_{i...}$	6891	6776	13667	$T_{i...}$	6891	6776	13667	$T_{..j.}$	4563	4549	4555	13667

$$\sum\sum\sum\sum X^2_{ijkl} = 43^2 + 72^2 + \cdots + 80^2 + 71^2 = 929463$$

$$T^2_{....}/N = (13667^2/216) = 864754.12$$

$$\sum(T^2_{i...}/n_{i...}) = [(6891^2/108) + (6776^2/108)] = 864815.34$$

$$\sum(T^2_{.j..}/n_{.j..}) = (4563^2 + 4549^2 + 4555^2)/72 = 864755.49$$

$$\sum(T^2_{..k.}/n_{..k.}) = (4575^2 + 4510^2 + 4582^2)/72 = 864797.90$$

$$\sum\sum(T^2_{ij..}/n_{ij..}) = (2309^2 + 2280^2 + \cdots + 2269^2 + 2253^2)/36 = 864832.53$$

$$\sum\sum(T^2_{i.k.}/n_{i.k.}) = (2296^2 + 2297^2 + \cdots + 2213^2 + 2284^2)/36 = 864903.42$$

$$\sum\sum(T^2_{.jk.}/n_{.jk.}) = (1526^2 + 1490^2 + \cdots + 1513^2 + 1515^2)/24 = 864835.04$$

$$\sum\sum\sum(T^2_{ijk.}/n_{ijk.})$$
$$= (766^2 + 759^2 + 784^2 + \cdots + 737^2 + 762^2)/12 = 864,984.25$$

TABLE 10.13

HYPOTHETICAL DATA FOR THREE-WAY ANALYSIS OF VARIANCE

Student	S_1									S_2								
	G_1			G_2			G_3			G_1			G_2			G_3		
	C_1	C_2	C_3	C_1	C_2	C_3	C_1	C_2	C_3	C_1	C_2	C_3	C_1	C_2	C_3	C_1	C_2	C_3
1	43	41	45	43	60	54	57	48	55	54	56	59	57	58	59	58	64	70
2	72	61	65	61	68	63	70	60	65	69	72	75	83	74	77	74	75	75
3	64	73	69	77	80	55	75	80	33	67	43	53	56	63	68	53	52	64
4	47	61	68	63	44	57	38	64	69	48	35	58	57	57	56	54	54	53
5	53	52	49	48	45	45	45	45	45	44	44	42	42	41	41	41	41	40
6	37	35	31	31	25	58	57	56	54	52	51	49	48	46	44	44	43	41
7	40	40	39	37	37	37	38	35	34	33	32	31	31	31	30	30	30	29
8	83	78	86	80	83	70	75	67	81	86	73	69	74	82	77	72	73	85
9	86	77	78	70	74	72	75	85	76	71	83	75	77	80	81	88	84	84
10	79	79	82	82	78	78	77	77	77	77	76	76	75	75	72	72	72	70
11	78	81	91	86	91	85	81	85	87	90	84	94	82	69	76	85	84	80
12	84	81	81	79	77	87	85	74	77	69	82	82	83	69	78	83	65	71
	766	759	784	757	762	761	773	776	753	760	731	763	765	745	759	754	737	762

The hypotheses which have been previously given are tested in the following format.

Source of Variability	SSD	d.f.	MS	F
Between S	61.22	1	61.22	$325.65/61.22 = 5.32$
Between G	1.37	2	0.685	$325.65/0.685 = 475.40 +++$
Between C	43.78	2	21.89	$325.65/21.89 = 14.88$
Interactions				
$S \times G$	15.82	2	7.91	$325.65/7.91 = 41.17 +$
$S \times C$	44.30	2	22.15	$325.65/22.15 = 14.70$
$G \times C$	35.77	4	8.94	$325.65/8.94 = 36.43 +++$
$S \times G \times C$	27.87	4	6.97	$325.65/6.97 = 46.72 ++++$
Within Groups	64478.75	198	325.65	

$+ =$ Significance at the 0.05 level,

$+++ =$ Significance at the 0.005 level,

$++++ =$ Significance at the 0.001 level.

The analysis of the data indicates that achievement is apparently affected by the primary factor of grade placement and all of the interactions (combinations) of the primary factors with the exception of the *Sex* × *Class* combination.

PROBLEMS

1. Sixty persons were randomly divided into six groups of 10 each. Treatments A, B, C, D, E, and F were randomly assigned. At the end of the treatment period, testing yielded the following results. Is there a difference in the mean results? If significance exists, test for differences within the table.

A	B	C	D	E	F
89	88	98	90	70	77
70	80	92	82	74	73
78	90	71	63	76	64
56	87	85	95	79	86
55	88	88	68	95	79
71	91	79	84	49	45
57	85	61	91	79	45
80	71	65	75	96	72
81	58	45	70	55	68
71	66	85	42	88	76

2. A group of psychologists were studying the reaction effects of three drugs on three types of nervous disorders. Eighteen subjects for each disorder were divided into groups of 6 and randomly assigned to drugs. Following are their reaction times to the experimental task (in seconds).

Disorder Form		Drug		
		A	B	C
	I	19	14	27
		39	36	17
		13	16	15
		27	14	19
		24	41	46
		35	17	12
	II	11	19	13
		28	16	29
		18	12	45
		19	39	45
		16	15	43
		39	30	46
	III	14	42	18
		10	12	38
		21	41	39
		12	43	32
		36	45	19
		47	18	23

What conclusions can you draw from the data?

3. If the data in each cell of Problem 2 were averaged and the analysis of variance technique applied, what difference in conclusions would result?

4. Show the tests for assumptions necessary to validate the conclusions for Problems 1–3.

5. It was desired to analyze the achievement of students taught by: (1) programmed text, (2) mass instruction (using one lecturer and several assistants), and (3) small classes. It was desired to know if the initial ability of the student contributed significantly to the end results, if reading comprehension contributed significantly, and if there was a sex difference. Three different groups of students were used in the study, each group

representing the various ability levels, each group containing the various reading comprehension levels. The final results are presented below. Test the implied hypotheses.

Girls

A_1			A_2			A_3		
R_1	R_2	R_3	R_1	R_2	R_3	R_1	R_2	R_3
166	91	156	58	130	183	112	120	124
88	95	108	157	66	109	140	80	131
149	107	112	126	79	88	106	205	129
129	130	125	120	115	116	127	133	132
121	122	120	124	124	119	134	123	122
123	135	130	115	128	116	124	134	116
125	125	127	136	139	95	116	118	128
148	99	122	96	130	95	118	126	99
129	96	123	121	137	111	126	188	143
143	134	128	137	146	155	143	132	153

Boys

A_1			A_2			A_3		
R_1	R_2	R_3	R_1	R_2	R_3	R_1	R_2	R_3
63	109	127	162	140	158	150	53	104
114	108	192	113	118	114	169	96	131
172	88	120	138	137	127	132	113	124
136	123	110	111	121	124	125	118	123
124	126	124	125	118	124	112	120	116
133	97	113	136	131	110	122	98	120
121	112	99	123	130	123	123	123	113
118	114	118	115	122	118	115	122	118
154	125	109	111	138	128	167	120	99
133	125	110	122	124	128	131	133	100

REFERENCES

Dixon, Wilfrid J., and Massey, Frank J., Jr. *Introduction to Statistical Analysis.* Second Edition. New York: McGraw-Hill Book Company, Inc., 1959. Chapter 10.

DuBois, Philip H. *An Introduction to Psychological Statistics.* New York: Harper and Row, Publishers, 1965. Chapter 14.

Ferguson, George A. *Statistical Analysis in Psychology and Education*. New York: McGraw-Hill Book Company, Inc., 1966. Chapter 18.

Freund, John C., and Williams, Frank J. *Elementary Business Statistics: The Modern Approach*. Englewood Cliffs, N. J.: Prentice-Hall, Inc., 1964. Chapter 12.

Guenther, William C. *Concepts of Statistical Inference*. New York: McGraw-Hill Book Company, Inc., 1965. Chapter 7.

McNemar, Quinn. *Psychological Statistics*. Third Edition. New York: John Wiley and Sons, Inc., 1962. Chapter 15.

Winer, B. J. *Statistical Principles in Experimental Design*. New York: McGraw-Hill Book Company, Inc., 1962. Chapter 3.

Yamane, Taro. *Statistics, An Introductory Analysis*. New York: Harper and Row, Publishers, 1964. Chapter 21.

11

LINEAR REGRESSION

11.1 *Regression*. In certain situations it may be useful to obtain an *estimate* or *prediction* of the most likely measurement in one variable when derived from a known measurement in another variable. For example, from these derived or predicted values an investigator may make statements concerning the expected performance of a secondary school student upon entering college; or statements may be made relative to expected performance in mathematics courses by those students whose scores on a mathematics aptitude test are known.

Sir Francis Galton used the term *"regression"* in reporting on the relationship between height of offspring and height of parent. In studying the inheritance of this particular characteristic Galton found that children of tall parents tend to be shorter than their parents, while children of short parents tend to be taller than their parents. Thus the tendency for the heights of offspring to "regress" toward the general mean for the species has been termed the *law of filial regression,* and this regression tendency is characteristic of any two variables possessing imperfect linear relationship.

11.2 *The Regression of Y on X*. This concept of predicting one variable from another may be developed by studying the data in Table 11.1. In this table data are presented representing 10 sets of paired measurements made on height and weight.

These data are plotted in Figure 11.1, a *scatter diagram* of the 10 pairs of measurements. The shape of the scatter diagram yields some information concerning the relationship between the height in inches, the *independent* variable, and the weight in pounds, the *dependent*, or *criterion* variable. Note that the independent variable is plotted along the horizontal axis.

TABLE 11.1

HEIGHTS AND WEIGHTS OF 10 COLLEGE FRESHMEN

	Height X	Weight Y	X^2	Y^2	XY
1	64	150	4096	22500	9600
2	68	150	4624	22500	10200
3	69	160	4761	25600	11040
4	70	160	4900	25600	11200
5	70	180	4900	32400	12600
6	71	170	5041	28900	12070
7	72	170	5184	28900	12240
8	72	180	5184	32400	12960
9	73	170	5329	28900	12410
10	74	190	5476	36100	14060
Total	703	1680	49495	283800	118380

$$\overline{X} = 70.3 \quad \overline{Y} = 168$$

If this relationship were exact, plotted points representing the 10 pairs of measurements would lie on the line. However, the relationships between variables are rarely exact and more often the points do not lie upon any line. Rather, a *line of best fit*, which may contain no point representing any pair of observations, may be found.

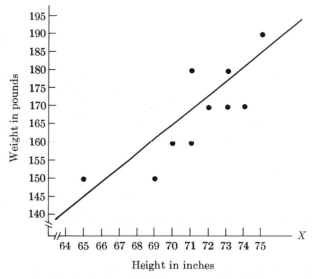

Figure 11.1 *Scatter diagram of 10 pairs of measurements shown in Table 11.1.*

If the rate of change for Y values is constant per unit change in X, the line of best fit is a straight line. This relationship is shown by the expression:

$$Y = a + bX$$

where

$Y =$ dependent or predicted value for a given value of X
$X =$ independent variable
$a =$ point of intersection of the straight line with the Y axis
$b =$ slope, or the rate of change of Y per unit change in X.

In working with related variables it should be remembered that there is a population of Y's for each of the X values. From rather casual observation this fact becomes apparent when we recall that not all individuals of a given height have the same weight. However, as height increases there is a tendency for the weight of the individual to increase. Each of the populations of weights Y for a given height X is normally distributed with a mean weight for the given height. This mean is represented as $\mu_{y.x}$ (read as mu sub y dot x, where x is the specific value). Each of these populations also has a measure of dispersion, $\sigma_{y.x}$ (read as sigma sub y dot x).

11.2.1 *The Regression Equation.* Utilizing the equation for a straight line, the expression for the linear regression equation is:

$$\mu_{y.x} = A_{y.x} + B_{y.x}X \qquad (11.1)$$

This is the equation for the straight line passing through $\mu_{y.x}$ for all values of X.

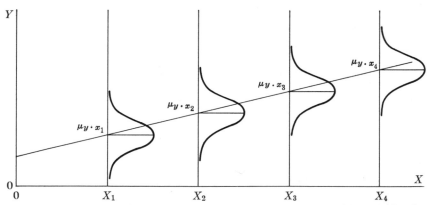

Figure 11.2 *The theoretical presentation of the regression equation,*
$$\mu_{y.x} = A_{y.x} + B_{y.x}X.$$

Only in rare instances will the population mean value of Y be available for all the involved values of X; therefore, it is necessary to make use of an expression involving statistics rather than parameters.

This expression is:

$$Y_c = a_{y.x} + b_{y.x}X \tag{11.2}$$

where

$$Y_c \quad \text{estimates } \mu_{y.x}$$

$$a_{y.x} \text{ estimates } A_{y.x}$$

and

$$b_{y.x} \text{ estimates } B_{y.x}$$

When Y is the independent variable and X is the dependent variable the expression becomes:

$$X_c = a_{x.y} + b_{x.y}Y \tag{11.3}$$

The primary point in question is the method for the computation of the sample statistics.

11.2.2 *The Concept of Least Squares.* By referring to Figure 11.3, we see that the sampled dependent values do not fall on the regression line, owing to the effects of sampling error.

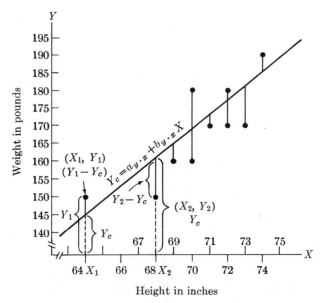

Figure 11.3 *Scatter diagram of 10 pairs of measurements shown in Table 11.1 with deviations of observations from the line.*

The sum of the squares of deviations from *the line of best fit* should be as small as possible. It may be written as $(Y - Y_c)^2$ to represent the squared deviations of the observed Y_c from the estimated values of Y. Thus the line represented by $Y_c = a_{y.x} + b_{y.x}X$ will meet the requirement for these minimum values. Any other line drawn through these points will result in a larger sum of squared deviations.   If

$$(Y_1 - Y_c)^2 + (Y_2 - Y_c)^2 + (Y_3 - Y_c)^2 + \cdots + (Y_{10} - Y_c)^2 = \text{a minimum}$$

then, extended to a sample of size n:

$$\Sigma(Y - Y_c)^2 = \text{a minimum}$$

so that substituting $(a + bX)$ for Y_c, and summing,

$$f = \Sigma(Y - a - bX)^2 = \text{a minimum}$$

By taking the derivative of the function with respect to a and b, and setting the derivative equal to zero:

$$\frac{\partial f}{\partial a} = 2\Sigma(Y - a - bX)(-1) = 0$$

$$\frac{\partial f}{\partial b} = 2\Sigma(Y - a - bX)(-X) = 0$$

$$-2\Sigma Y + 2na + 2b\Sigma X = 0$$

or

$$\Sigma Y = na + b\Sigma X \tag{11.4}$$

and

$$-2\Sigma XY + 2a\Sigma X + 2b\Sigma X^2 = 0$$

or

$$\Sigma XY = a\Sigma X + b\Sigma X^2 \tag{11.5}$$

The values for a and b may be determined directly by solving first for $a_{y.x}$:

$$\Sigma Y = na + b\Sigma X$$

$$na = \Sigma Y - b\Sigma X$$

$$a_{y.x} = \frac{\Sigma Y - b\Sigma X}{n} \tag{11.6}$$

then substituting and solving for $b_{y.x}$:

$$\Sigma XY = a\Sigma X + b\Sigma X^2$$

$$\Sigma XY = \left(\frac{\Sigma Y - b\Sigma X}{n}\right)\Sigma X + b\Sigma X^2$$

$$n\Sigma XY = (\Sigma X)(\Sigma Y) - b(\Sigma X)^2 + bn\Sigma X^2$$

$$n\Sigma XY - (\Sigma X)(\Sigma Y) = b[n\Sigma X^2 - (\Sigma X)^2]$$

$$b_{y.x} = \frac{n\Sigma XY - (\Sigma X)(\Sigma Y)}{n\Sigma X^2 - (\Sigma X)^2} \tag{11.7}$$

For the solution by simultaneous equations, using the data in Table 11.1

$$\Sigma Y = na_{y.x} + b_{y.x}\Sigma X$$
$$\Sigma XY = a_{y.x}\Sigma X + b_{y.x}\Sigma X^2$$
$$1680 = 10a + 703b$$
$$118380 = 703a + 49495b$$
$$1181040 = 7030a + 494209b$$
$$1183800 = 7030a + 494950b$$
$$-2760 = -741b$$
$$b = 3.72$$

Substituting the computed value of $b = 3.72$ into Equation (11.4)

$$1680 = 10a + 703(3.72)$$
$$1680 = 10a + 2615.16$$
$$a = -93.52$$

The regression equation for the data shown in Table 11.1 is

$$Y_c = -93.52 + 3.72X$$

The values of a and b indicate that the regression line cuts the Y axis at -93.52 and that the average value of Y increases 3.72 units for each unit increase in X.

The values for a and b may be determined by using Equations (11.6) and (11.7).

$$b = \frac{(10)(118380) - (703)(1680)}{(10)(49495) - (703)(703)} = \frac{2760}{741} = 3.72$$

$$a = \frac{1680 - (3.72)(703)}{10} = \frac{-935.16}{10} = -93.52$$

The values for a and b may also be obtained by using determinants:

$$a = \frac{\begin{vmatrix} 1680 & 703 \\ 118380 & 49495 \end{vmatrix}}{\begin{vmatrix} 10 & 703 \\ 703 & 49495 \end{vmatrix}}, \quad a = \frac{(1680 \times 49495) - (118380 \times 703)}{(10 \times 49495) - (703 \times 703)} = -93.84$$

$$b = \frac{\begin{vmatrix} 10 & 1680 \\ 703 & 118380 \end{vmatrix}}{\begin{vmatrix} 10 & 703 \\ 703 & 49495 \end{vmatrix}}, \quad b = \frac{(10 \times 118380) - (703 \times 1680)}{(10 \times 49495) \times (703 \times 703)} = 3.72$$

We may then substitute in the regression equation $Y_c = -93.52 + 3.72X$ to predict the weight of a person whose height is 68.5 inches:

$$Y_c = -93.52 + (3.72)(68.5) = 161.3 \text{ lbs.}$$

11.3 *The Regression of X on Y.* In deriving the equation showing the regression of Y on X we have minimized the sum of squares of the distances from the plotted points for $X_1Y_1, X_2Y_2, \ldots, X_{10}Y_{10}$ to the line when taken parallel to the Y-axis. If we wish to predict weight from a known measurement of the height of an individual, the regression line of X on Y is used, where $X_c = a_{x.y} + b_{x.y}Y$, and

$$\sum X = na + b\sum Y \tag{11.8}$$

$$\sum XY = a\sum Y + b\sum Y^2 \tag{11.9}$$

The regression line thus obtained will minimize the sum of the squares of the distances from the plotted points, X_1Y_1, etc., to the line when taken parallel to the X-axis. From this line a prediction of X may be made, with $b_{x.y}$ showing the slope of the regression line, and $a_{x.y}$ indicating the point where the line cuts the X-axis. Then, for the data shown in Table 11.1:

$$\sum X = na + b\sum Y \qquad\qquad \sum XY = a\sum Y + b\sum Y^2$$

$$703 = 10a + 1680b \qquad\qquad 118380 = 1680a + 283800b$$

$$(168)703 = (168)10a + (168)1680b \qquad 703 = 10a + 1680b$$

$$118380 = 1680a + 283800b \qquad\qquad 703 = 10a + 287.28$$

$$-266 = -1560b \qquad\qquad 10a = 415.72$$

$$b_{x.y} = 0.171 \qquad\qquad a_{x.y} = 41.6$$

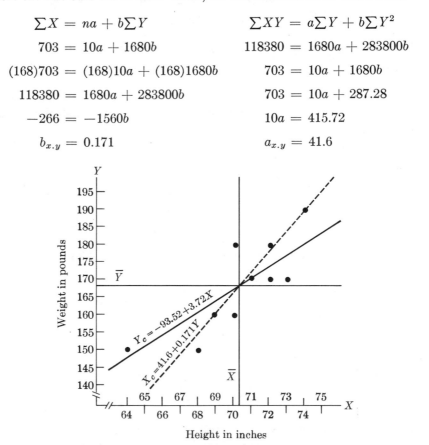

Figure 11.4   *Two regression lines for the data shown in Table 11.1.*

The equation for the regression line of X on Y is:

$$X_c = 41.6 + 0.171Y$$

We may then substitute in this regression equation to predict the height of a person whose weight is 150 pounds:

$$X_c = 41.6 + 0.171 \times 150$$
$$= 67.25 \text{ inches}$$

11.4 *The Sum of Products and Covariance.* In Section 11.2.2, the two normal equations were obtained:

$$\Sigma Y = na + b\Sigma X \qquad (11.4)$$
$$\Sigma XY = a\Sigma X + b\Sigma X^2 \qquad (11.5)$$

Dividing Equation (11.4) by n and solving for a,

$$a = \bar{Y} - b\bar{X} \qquad (11.10)$$

substituting $\bar{Y} - b\bar{X}$ for a in (11.5), and solving for b (see Equation (11.7)):

$$b = \frac{\Sigma XY - \dfrac{\Sigma X \Sigma Y}{n}}{\Sigma X^2 - \dfrac{(\Sigma X)^2}{n}} \qquad (11.11)$$

It may be remembered that the sum of the products of the deviations of X and Y (written as x and y) from their respective means is:

$$\Sigma xy = \Sigma(X - \bar{X})(Y - \bar{Y})$$
$$= \Sigma XY - \frac{(\Sigma X)(\Sigma Y)}{n}$$

and that

$$\Sigma x^2 = \Sigma X^2 - \frac{(\Sigma X)^2}{n}$$

so that Equation (11.11) may be written as:

$$b = \frac{\Sigma xy}{\Sigma x^2} \qquad (11.12)$$

where $x = (X - \bar{X})$, and $y = (Y - \bar{Y})$.

By dividing the numerator and denominator of Equation (11.12) by $(n-1)$, we see that two variance estimators are formed. The resulting numerator value, $\Sigma xy/(n-1)$, is the sample *covariance*, s_{xy}^2, of X and Y. The obtained denominator value should be recognized as the sample variance of the X values, s_x^2. Or:

$$b_{y.x} = \frac{\dfrac{\Sigma xy}{(n-1)}}{\dfrac{\Sigma x^2}{(n-1)}}$$

$$= \frac{s_{xy}^2}{s_x^2} \tag{11.13}$$

From the previous discussion in this section, the covariance may be recognized as a mean-product deviation involved in any case of the joint-variation of two or more variables.

11.5 *The Standard Error of Estimate.* In Section 11.2.2 we obtained *the line of best fit* by determining the values of a and b so that:

$$\Sigma(Y - Y_c)^2 = \text{a minimum}$$

Substituting $(a + bX)$ for Y_c, and summing:

$$\Sigma(Y - Y_c)^2 = \Sigma[Y - (a + bX)]^2$$

The residual sum of squares, or error of prediction, represents a measure of the variation of Y values about the regression line.

Since $Y_c = a + bX$, we may substitute from (11.10), thus obtaining:

$$Y_c = \bar{Y} - b\bar{X} + bX$$

$$= \bar{Y} + b(X - \bar{X})$$

$$= \bar{Y} + bx$$

$$Y_c - \bar{Y} = \bar{Y} + bx - \bar{Y}$$

$$y_c = bx \tag{11.14}$$

where
$$y_c = \text{predicted value of } Y \text{ in deviation units}$$
$$x = \text{deviation of } X \text{ from mean of } X \text{ distribution}$$
$$b = \text{regression coefficient.}$$

Then

$$(y - y_c) = (y - bx)$$

Squaring each side of this equation and summing over the n values,

$$\Sigma(y - y_c)^2 = \Sigma y^2 - 2b\Sigma xy + b^2\Sigma x^2$$

Substituting $b = \dfrac{\Sigma yx}{\Sigma x^2}$,

$$\Sigma(y - y_c)^2 = \Sigma y^2 - 2\frac{\Sigma xy}{\Sigma x^2} \cdot \Sigma xy + \frac{(\Sigma xy)^2}{(\Sigma x^2)^2} \cdot \Sigma x^2$$

$$\Sigma(y - y_c)^2 = \Sigma y^2 - \frac{(\Sigma xy)^2}{\Sigma x^2} \tag{11.15}$$

The difference between the actual deviation, $y = Y - \bar{Y}$, and the predicted deviation, $y_c = Y_c - \bar{Y}$, is the prediction error.

The residual variance may be obtained by dividing the residual sum of squares by $(n - 2)$:

$$\frac{\Sigma(y - y_c)^2}{n - 2} = s_{y.x}^2$$

Extracting the square root, we have the *standard error of estimate:*

$$s_{y.x} = \sqrt{\frac{\Sigma(y - y_c)^2}{n - 2}} \tag{11.16}$$

$$= \sqrt{\left[\frac{n - 1}{n - 2}\right][s_y^2 - b_{y.x}^2 s_x^2]} \tag{11.17}$$

11.6 *The Regression Concept.* From the standard error of estimate we are able to determine how successfully the regression equation is able to predict Y scores when X scores are known. Since $\sigma_{y.x}$ is the standard deviation of the differences between observed values of Y and values obtained from the regression equation, the standard error is then a measure of the scatter of the observed Y scores about the regression line. In Table 11.2, we have 50 pairs of scores. These pairs of scores were obtained by administering tests of aptitude and achievement after one semester of instruction in unified mathematics.

TABLE 11.2

TABLE 11.2

SCORES OF 50 STUDENTS ON MATHEMATICS APTITUDE TEST (X) AND MATHEMATICS ACHIEVEMENT TEST (Y)

Student	X	X^2	Y	Y^2	XY
1	37	1369	34	1156	1258
2	27	729	16	256	432
3	32	1024	33	1089	1056
4	13	169	7	49	91
5	24	576	13	169	312
6	29	841	36	1296	1044
7	30	900	31	961	930
8	25	625	10	100	250
9	20	400	22	484	440
10	15	225	8	64	120
11	16	256	20	400	320
12	27	729	25	625	675
13	33	1089	25	625	825
14	32	1024	27	729	864
15	36	1296	36	1296	1296
16	23	529	39	1521	897
17	10	100	5	25	50
18	11	121	16	256	176
19	21	441	18	324	378
20	24	576	28	784	672
21	25	625	21	441	525
22	18	324	12	144	216
23	23	529	9	81	207
24	21	441	23	529	483
25	22	484	30	900	660
26	20	400	23	529	460
27	24	576	23	529	552
28	24	576	23	529	552
29	19	361	13	169	247
30	34	1156	48	2304	1632
31	23	529	9	81	207
32	22	484	22	484	484
33	24	576	6	36	144
34	26	676	30	900	780
35	24	576	5	25	120

TABLE 11.2 (*continued*)

Student	X	X²	Y	Y²	XY
36	25	625	18	324	450
37	32	1024	26	676	832
38	25	625	27	729	675
39	18	324	9	81	162
40	24	576	18	324	432
41	12	144	14	196	168
42	20	400	18	324	360
43	16	256	15	225	240
44	23	529	22	484	506
45	35	1225	18	324	630
46	30	900	29	841	870
47	15	225	6	36	90
48	28	784	23	529	644
49	16	256	21	441	336
50	24	576	37	1369	888

$$\sum X = 1177 \quad \sum X^2 = 29{,}801 \quad \sum Y = 1047 \quad \sum Y^2 = 26{,}793 \quad \sum XY = 26{,}638$$

$$\overline{X} = 23.54 \qquad\qquad \overline{Y} = 20.94$$

$$s_x^2 = 42.74 \qquad\qquad s_y^2 = 99.36$$

To obtain the values of a and b in the general expression $Y_c = a + bX$:

$$b_{y.x} = \frac{n\sum XY - \sum X \sum Y}{n\sum X^2 - (\sum X)^2}$$

$$a_{y.x} = \frac{\sum Y - b\sum X}{n}$$

Substituting:

$$b_{y.x} = \frac{(50)(26{,}638) - (1177)(1047)}{(50)(29{,}801) - (1177)(1177)} = 0.9509$$

$$a_{y.x} = \frac{1047 - (0.9509)(1177)}{50} = -1.44$$

$$Y_c = -1.44 + 0.9509X$$

When the mean of X is substituted in the regression equation, the predicted value of Y will equal the mean of Y, which implies that the regression line passes through the point $\overline{X}, \overline{Y}$.

$$Y_c = -1.44 + (0.9509)(23.54) = 20.94 = \overline{Y}$$

The regression equation, $Y = -1.44 + 0.9509X$, is used in plotting the line shown in Figure 11.5. By choosing two values of X, one at the upper end of the scattergram and the other at the lower end of the diagram, we may establish the regression line as follows:

Let $X_1 = 35$, $X_2 = 14$; then

$$(1)\ \ Y_c = -1.44 + (0.9509)(35) = 31.84$$

$$(2)\ \ Y_c = -1.44 + (0.9509)(14) = 11.87$$

From Equation (11.17), we may obtain a measure of the error of our predictions:

$$s_{y.x} = \sqrt{\frac{(n-1)}{(n-2)}\,[s_y^2 - b_{y.x}^2 s_x^2]}$$

Substituting and solving for $s_{y.x}$:

$$s_{y.x} = \sqrt{\tfrac{49}{48}[99.36 - (0.9509)^2(42.74)]}$$

$$= 7.9 \text{ (standard error of estimate)}$$

Achievement Y / X Aptitude	5–7	8–10	11–13	14–16	17–19	20–22	23–25	26–28	29–31	32–34	35–37	38–40	41–43	44–46	47–49
36–37										/	/				
34–35				/					●(35, 31.84)					/	
32–33						/	//		/						
30–31								//							
28–29						/			/						
26–27			/			/		/							
24–25	//	/	/		//	/	//	//	/						
22–23		1t				1 X, Y	/		/						
20–21					1/	//									
18–19			/	//											
16–17				/		N									
14–15	/	/		(14, 11.87)											
12–13	/			/											
10–11	/			/											

Figure 11.5 *Scattergram of the fifty pairs of scores shown in Table 11.2, with regression of Y on X.*

11.7 Tests for Basic Assumptions. Regression analysis involves certain basic assumptions about the data. Included in these assumptions are: (1) normality of distributions, (2) randomness of sampling, and (3) homoscedasticity of the variances. In addition, the assumptions of linearity of data and dependency of the X and Y variables must be satisfied.

11.7.1 Test for Linearity of Data. The concept of linear regression assumes that *the line of best fit* is a straight line. Thus before computing the coefficients of the regression equation, it is necessary to determine the validity of this assumption for the data involved.

Earlier the concept of linear regression was presented graphically in Figure 11.2. From the regression equation, it may be seen that the factor $b_{y.x}$ contributes to the difference in the values of $\mu_{y.x}$. In the linear relationship, the value of $b_{y.x}$ is constant at all points on the line. This indicates a constant rate of change of the dependent variable Y per unit change in the independent variable X. As such, all values of $\mu_{y.x}$ would be equal if the value of $b_{y.x}$ was made to be zero. In essence, the removal of the regression effect $(b_{y.x})$, and the subsequent use of the single classification analysis of variance technique is utilized to test the data linear-relationship hypothesis.

In Chapter 10, the concept of the single classification analysis of variance was discussed. It was predicated upon the division of the total sum of squared deviations into two component parts: (1) the sum of squared deviations with each sample about the sample mean and (2) the sum of squared deviations of the sample means about the overall or grand mean:

$$\Sigma(X_{ij} - \bar{\bar{X}})^2 = \Sigma(X_{ij} - \bar{X}_j)^2 + \Sigma(\bar{X}_j - \bar{\bar{X}})^2$$

Using this same principle without modification would lead one to think that (in the case of regression) the variability of the Y values would be divided in a similar fashion:

$$\Sigma\Sigma(Y_{ij} - \bar{\bar{Y}})^2 = \Sigma(Y_{ij} - \bar{Y}_{ij})^2 + \Sigma(\bar{Y}_{ij} - \bar{\bar{Y}})^2$$

This does not suffice since the variability due to regression is not considered in this expression. Rather,

$$(Y_{ij} - \bar{\bar{Y}}) = (Y_{ij} - \bar{Y}_{ij}) + (\bar{Y}_{ij} - \bar{\bar{Y}})$$

the deviation must be broken into three portions:

$$(Y_{ij} - \bar{\bar{Y}}) = (Y_{ij} - \bar{Y}_{ij}) + (\bar{Y}_{ij} - Y_{ci}) + (Y_{ci} - \bar{\bar{Y}})$$

When these deviations are squared and summed over all the sample values $(i = 1, 2, \ldots, n_j)$ and all samples $(j = 1, 2, \ldots, k)$, the resulting partitioning is:

$$\Sigma\Sigma(Y_{ij} - \bar{\bar{Y}})^2 = \Sigma\Sigma(Y_{ij} - \bar{Y}_{i\cdot})^2 + \Sigma n_j(\bar{Y}_{ij} - Y_{ci})^2 + \Sigma n_j(Y_{ci} - \bar{\bar{Y}})^2$$

where

$\Sigma\Sigma(Y_{ij} - \bar{\bar{Y}})^2 = $ total sum of squared deviations,

$\Sigma\Sigma(Y_{ij} - \bar{Y}_{ij})^2 = $ sum of squared deviations *within* the samples,

$\Sigma n_j(\bar{Y}_{ij} - Y_{ci})^2 = $ sum of squared deviations of sample means *about* the *regression* line,

$\Sigma n_j(Y_{ci} - \bar{\bar{Y}})^2 = $ sum of squared deviations *between* the predicted Y_c values for each given X and the grand mean.

The degrees of freedom associated with this expression are:

$$(\Sigma n_j - 1) = (\Sigma n_j - k) + (k - 2) + (1)$$

To remove the necessity for the computation of all Y_{ci} values,

$$\Sigma n_j(Y_{ci} - \bar{\bar{Y}})^2 = b_{y\cdot x}^2 \Sigma n_j(X_{ij} - \bar{X})^2 \qquad (11.18)$$

Computationally the resulting analysis of variance form would be:

Source of Variability (S of V)	Sum of Squared Deviations (SSD)	Degrees of Freedom (d.f.)	Mean Square (MS)	F
Between	$b_{y\cdot x}^2\left[\Sigma\Sigma X_{i\cdot j}^2 - \dfrac{T_{x\cdot\cdot}^2}{N}\right] = SSD_B$	1	$SSD_B/1 = s_B^2$	
About Regression	Difference $SSD_A = SSD_T - SSD_B$	$k - 2$	$SSD_A/(k - 2) = s_A^2$	s_A^2/s_i^2
Within	$\Sigma\Sigma Y_{ij}^2 - \Sigma\dfrac{T_{y\cdot j}^2}{n_j} = SSD_W$	$\Sigma n_j - k$	$SSD_W/(\Sigma n_j - k) = s_W^2$	
Total	$\Sigma\Sigma Y_{ij}^2 - \dfrac{T_{Y\cdot\cdot}^2}{n} = SSD_T$	$\Sigma n_j - 1$		

As an example, the data given in Table 11.1 will be tested for linearity. Before pursuing the test the data must be rearranged as shown in the table on the next page.

	X_1	Y	X_2	Y	X_3	Y	X_4	Y	X_5	Y	X_6	Y	X_7	Y	X_8	Y
	64	150	68	150	69	160	70	160	71	170	72	170	73	170	74	190
							70	180			72	180				
$\sum X_{.j}$	64		68		69		140		71		144		73		74	
$\sum Y_{.j}$		150		150		160		340		170		350		170		190
$\sum X_{.j}^2$	4096		4624		4761		9800		5041		10368		5329		5476	
$\sum\sum XY$	9600		10200		11040		23800		12070		25200		12410		14060	
$\sum Y_{.j}^2$	22500		22500		25600		58000		28900		61300		28900		36100	

$$\sum\sum X_{ij} = 703$$

$$\sum\sum Y_{ij} = 1680$$

$$\sum\sum X_{ij}^2 = 49495$$

$$\sum\sum Y_{ij}^2 = 283800$$

$$\sum\sum X_{ij}Y_{ij} = 118380$$

$$b_{y.x} = 3.72$$

1. H_o: The regression line is linear.
2. $\alpha = 0.05$
3. Reject H_o if $F > F_{0.95(2,6)} = 5.14$.

4.

S of V	SSD	d.f.	MS	F
Between	1025.425	1		
About Reg.	534.574	6	89.096	
Within	250.00	2	125.00	$\dfrac{125.000}{89.096} = 1.403$
Total	1560.00	9		

5. Accept H_o.

The analysis for this example does not have a significant F ratio, and on this basis the hypothesis of linearity of the implied regression equation is accepted.

11.7.2 *Test for Independence of Variables.* The hypothesis to be tested is that the value of the variable Y is independent of the variable X; or that the value of Y will be the same for all values of X. To test this hypothesis is to test whether or not $B_{y.x} = 0$ by using the sample statistic $b_{y.x}$. This statistic is normally distributed with:

$$\sigma_f^2 = \sigma_{y.x}^2 / n\sigma_x^2 \tag{11.19}$$

Replacing these parameter values with estimators and using Equation (11.17), the expression becomes:

$$s_b^2 = s_{y.x}^2 / (n-1)s_x^2 = \frac{\dfrac{(n-1)}{(n-2)} [s_y^2 - b_{y.x}^2 s_x^2]}{(n-1)s_x^2} \tag{11.20}$$

The distribution of the $b_{y.x}$ values is a t distribution with d.f. $= n - 2$ and:

$$t = \frac{b_{y.x} - B_{y.x}}{s_b} \tag{11.21}$$

Again using the data in Table 11.1, the hypothesis of $B = 0$, or independence of the X and Y variables, will be presented as an example.

1. $H_o : B_{y.x} = 0$
2. $\alpha = 0.05$, test (c)

3. Reject H_o if $t < t_{0.025,8} = -2.306$ or if $t > t_{0.975,8} = 2.306$.

4. $t = \dfrac{3.72 - 0}{\sqrt{\dfrac{\left[\dfrac{(9)}{(8)}\right][173.33 - (3.72)^2(8.23)]}{(9)(8.23)}}}$

$= \dfrac{3.72}{\sqrt{\dfrac{59.443301}{65.84}}}$

$= \dfrac{3.72}{0.95} = 3.92$

5. Reject H_o and conclude that Y is dependent upon X.

11.8 Tests of Hypotheses and Confidence Interval Estimates. It may be seen that the occasion may arise where it will be necessary to test hypotheses about the parametric values of the regression equation.

11.8.1 Discussion of $A_{y.x}$. The statistic $a_{y.x}$, which is the point where the regression line intercepts the Y-axis, has a t distribution with $(n-2)$ degrees of freedom. The test statistic is:

$$t = \frac{a_{y.x} - A_{y.x}}{s_{a_{y.x}}} \tag{11.22}$$

where

$$s_{a_{y.x}}^2 = \frac{s_{y.x}^2}{n} \tag{11.23}$$

and the associated confidence interval estimate is:

$$P\left[a_{y.x} + t_{\frac{\alpha}{2},(n-2)} \frac{s_{y.x}}{\sqrt{n}} < A_{y.x} < a_{y.x} + t_{1-\frac{\alpha}{2},(n-2)} \frac{s_{y.x}}{\sqrt{n}}\right] = 1 - \alpha \tag{11.24}$$

11.8.2 Discussion of $B_{y.x}$. The test statistic for this variable has been presented in Section 11.7.2. The confidence interval estimate is:

$$P\left[b_{y.x} + t_{\frac{\alpha}{2},(n-2)} \frac{s_{y.x}}{s_x\sqrt{n-1}} < B_{y.x} < b_{y.x} + t_{1-\frac{\alpha}{2},(n-2)} \frac{s_{y.x}}{s_x\sqrt{n-1}}\right] = 1 - \alpha \tag{11.25}$$

11.8.3 *Discussion of* $\mu_{y.x}$. The sample statistic for this distribution is Y_c as computed for a specific value of X. This is a t distribution with $(n-2)$ degrees of freedom where:

$$t = \frac{Y_c - \mu_{y.x}}{s_{Y_c}} \tag{11.26}$$

and

$$s_{Y_c}^2 = s_{y.x}^2 \left[\frac{1}{n} + \frac{(X - \overline{X})^2}{(n-1)s_x^2} \right] \tag{11.27}$$

It should be noted that this is for $\mu_{y.x}$ and *not* for an individual value of Y, even though a specific value of X is called for. It is possible to obtain k regression lines as determined by the k possible samples of n pairs of values drawn from the populations of X's and Y's. Following the idea presented earlier in preceding chapters, a confidence interval estimate of $\mu_{y.x}$ is appropriate. This is:

$$P\left[Y_c + t_{\frac{\alpha}{2},(n-2)} \sqrt{s_{y.x}^2 \left[\frac{1}{n} + \frac{(X - \overline{X})^2}{(n-1)s_x^2} \right]} < \mu_{y.x} \right.$$

$$\left. < Y_c + t_{1-\frac{\alpha}{2},(n-2)} \sqrt{s_{y.x}^2 \left[\frac{1}{n} + \frac{(X - \overline{X})^2}{(n-1)s_x^2} \right]} \right] = 1 - \alpha \tag{11.28}$$

11.8.4 *Discussion of Individual Values of* Y. Where Section 11.8.3 is concerned with the estimation of $\mu_{y.x}$, a means for computing a confidence interval estimate of a single predicted value of Y for a given value of X is necessary. These values of Y follow a t distribution with $(n-2)$ degrees of freedom. The $(1-\alpha)$ confidence interval estimate is:

$$P\left\{ Y_c + t_{\frac{\alpha}{2},(n-2)} \sqrt{s_{y.x}^2 \left[1 + \frac{1}{n} + \frac{(X - \overline{X})^2}{(n-1)s_x^2} \right]} < Y \right.$$

$$\left. < Y_c + t_{1-\frac{\alpha}{2},(n-2)} \sqrt{s_{y.x}^2 \left[1 + \frac{1}{n} + \frac{(X - \overline{X})^2}{(n-1)s_x^2} \right]} \right\} = 1 - \alpha \tag{11.29}$$

11.8.5 *Discussion of* $\sigma_{y.x}^2$. As with other values of σ^2, the sampling distribution of $\sigma_{y.x}^2$ is a $\chi^2/\text{d.f.}$ distribution of the ratios of $s_{y.x}^2/\sigma_{y.x}^2$ with $(n-2)$ degrees of freedom. The $(1-\alpha)$ confidence interval estimate is:

$$P\left[\frac{\dfrac{s_{y.x}^2}{\chi_{1-\frac{\alpha}{2},\text{d.f.}}^2}}{\text{d.f.}} < \sigma_{y.x}^2 < \frac{\dfrac{s_{y.x}^2}{\chi_{\frac{\alpha}{2},\text{d.f.}}^2}}{\text{d.f.}} \right] = 1 - \alpha$$

PROBLEMS

1. The data shown in the table below are measurements of the performance of 30 students on an algebra test and on a test of achievement in general science.

X (Algebra)	Y (General Science)	X (Algebra)	Y (General Science)
100	75	110	86
108	75	104	75
110	77	84	68
99	75	80	65
93	74	94	68
117	84	96	65
98	70	80	51
62	60	78	63
85	67	69	54
98	74	72	57
96	78	72	52
61	46	63	51
96	66	75	57
101	72	84	64
94	67	75	66

(a) Make a scattergram for the data.

(b) Find $\overline{X}$, $\overline{Y}$, s_x, s_y, and $s_{y.x}$.
   Construct the two regression lines on the scattergram.

(c) Test the basic assumptions, and compute confidence interval estimates of the parameters.

(d) Write out the regression equations in score form.

2. What statements can be made concerning a point on one of the regression lines plotted in Exercise 1?

3. Using the method of least squares, find the value of a and b for $Y_c = a + bX$ for the data shown in tabular form. Plot each pair of values on coordinate paper and draw the regression line of Y on X.

X	Y
50	36
50	43
70	58
68	47
63	52
77	61
54	45
60	43
63	46
58	40

4. For the data shown in Tables 1, 2, 3, and 4:
   (a) Make a scatter diagram of these points and draw a *"line of best fit"* by estimate.
   (b) Compute the regression line by the procedure shown in Section 11.2.2.
   (c) Estimate from your regression line the expected score on Y for $X = 3.5$ in each case.

Table (1)		Table (2)		Table (3)		Table (4)	
X	Y	X	Y	X	Y	X	Y
1	50	1	250	1	91	1	1400
2	61	2	400	2	85	2	1250
3	68	3	500	3	80	3	1100
4	65	4	800	4	78	4	1050
5	70	5	1050	5	77	5	900
6	71			6	78	6	600
7	80			7	92	7	300
				8	70	8	250
				9	69		
				10	71		

REFERENCES

Ferguson, George A. *Statistical Analysis in Psychology and Education.* New York: McGraw-Hill Book Company, Inc., 1966. Chapter 8.

Freeman, Linton C. *Elementary Applied Statistics.* New York: John Wiley and Sons, Inc., 1965. Chapter 9.

Freund, John C., and Williams, Frank J. *Elementary Business Statistics: The Modern Approach.* Englewood Cliffs, New Jersey: Prentice-Hall, Inc., 1964. Chapter 10.

Guenther, William C. *Concepts of Statistical Inference.* New York: McGraw-Hill Book Company, Inc., 1965. Chapter 8.

Kurtz, Thomas E. *Basic Statistics.* Englewood Cliffs, New Jersey: Prentice-Hall, Inc., 1963. Chapter 9.

McNemar, Quinn. *Psychological Statistics.* Third Edition. New York: John Wiley and Sons, Inc., 1962. Chapter 9.

Peatman, John. *Introduction to Applied Statistics.* New York: Harper and Row, Publishers, 1963. Chapter 5.

Tate, Merle W. *Statistics in Education and Psychology: A First Course.* New York: The Macmillan Company, 1965. Chapter 7.

Yamane, Taro. *Statistics, An Introductory Analysis.* New York: Harper and Row, Publishers, 1964. Chapters 10 and 14.

12

LINEAR CORRELATION

In addition to computing statistical measures that provide information about the performance of an individual or a group, it may become necessary to find a means for comparing sets of data and to determine, if possible, the relationship between two or more variables. It may be observed that tall men tend to weigh more than short men; that there is a relationship between the amount of rainfall and the number of bushels of corn produced in a midwestern state over a given period of years; and that sales of fuel in winter months are related to the severity of temperatures. In many instances the relationship does not necessarily imply that changes in one set of conditions cause changes in the other. Both sets of conditions may show a relationship because they are related to a third set. The relationship may be due to chance; the two variables may be interacting; or one variable may actually be the cause of changes in the other.

12.1 *The Meaning of Correlation.* Let us assume that 10 students, designated A through J, took two tests, with the results indicated in Table 12.1. The result of the two tests indicates that there is perfect position relationship between the two sets; that is, each student obtained the same rank on both tests. Moreover, there is a positive relationship between the two variables, as shown in the scattergram of Figure 12.1.

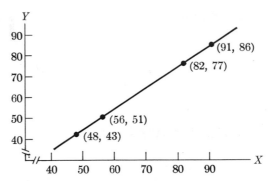

Figure 12.1 *Positive relationship, r = 1.00.*

TABLE 12.1

POSITIVE CORRELATION

Student	Test 1(X)	Rank	Test 2(Y)	Rank
A	94	1	89	1
B	91	2	86	2
C	85	3	80	3
D	82	4	77	4
E	74	5	69	5
F	65	6	60	6
G	62	7	57	7
H	56	8	51	8
I	50	9	45	9
J	48	10	43	10

For convenience, we label the first variable (Test 1) as X, and the second variable (Test 2) as Y, plotting the X values on the abscissa and the Y values on the ordinate, with each point on the graph representing a student's score for both X and Y. At this point it should be emphasized that a *scattergram* should be made for each set of paired values used in computing an index of relationship, the (correlation coefficient) r. It may be observed from the graph that

$$\frac{\Delta Y \text{ (Change in } Y)}{\Delta X \text{ (Change in } X)} = \text{a constant.}$$

When these pairs of values are plotted they fall on a straight line. This straight line runs from the lower left of the scattergram to the upper right, with a *coefficient of correlation*, r, equal to +1.00.

In another case we find the opposite of a positive correlation, that is, a negative relationship occurs if the individual with the highest score on the X variable obtains the lowest score on the Y variable. The second high on the X variable is next to the lowest on Y, and so on, as shown in Figure 12.2 where the coefficient of correlation, r, is equal to −1.00.

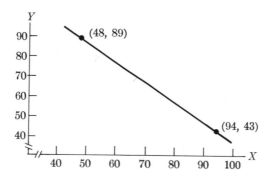

Figure 12.2   *Negative relationship, r = −1.00.*

While these two extremes represent the maximum and minimum values of the coefficient of correlation, measurements made in actual cases usually yield data in which the relationship is somewhere between these two values. In Figure 12.3 we have a case of positive correlation that is less than 1.00, with the 10 pairs of scores diverging from a straight line, but showing definite relationship.

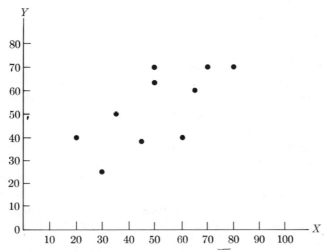

Figure 12.3   *Positive correlation less than 1.00, r = 0.71.*

In another case the trend of the points is along a diagonal from upper left to lower right, as shown in Figure 12.4. From this diagram we may observe that students obtaining high scores on the X variable are likely to obtain low scores on the Y variable, and those obtaining low scores on the X variable tend to obtain high scores on the Y variable. This *inverse* relationship has a coefficient of correlation with a negative sign, thus indicating the direction of the relationship between the two variables, X and Y.

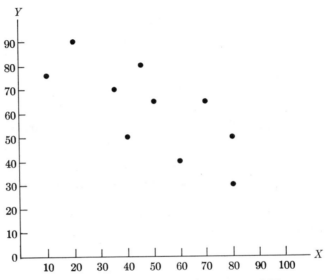

Figure 12.4   *Negative relationship, $r = -0.70$.*

12.2 *Underlying Assumptions.* Before computing the coefficient of correlation a scattergram should be made to obtain an indication of the sign of the relationship as well as its magnitude. While this operation may serve as a rough check on computational work, it also helps to determine if one of the two basic assumptions is satisfied. The first assumption is that the data under examination have a *linear relationship*, that is, the points plotted in the scattergram tend to fall along a straight line, as shown in Figures 12.3 and 12.4. From Figure 12.5 it may be observed that an increase in the X variable is accompanied by an increase in the Y variable until a maximum is reached; then as X increases, Y continues to decrease. When the data are nonlinear the size of the computed r tends to underestimate the amount of relationship. A second assumption on which correlation theory is based is that the variance of the columns and rows is homogeneous, thus meeting the criterion of *homoscedasticity*, with the array dispersions nearly equal. Most of the uses to which an r is put presuppose that each variable is normally distributed.

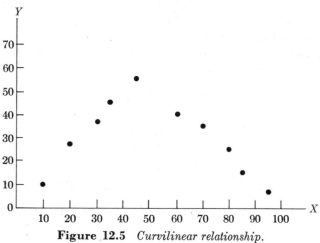

Figure 12.5 *Curvilinear relationship.*

Each pair of coordinates is generated by three factors: (1) the variance due to distribution of X values, (2) the variance due to distribution of all Y values, and (3) the variance due to Y values associated with each distinct X value (known as the covariance of X and Y). The coefficient of correlation is an expression of the amount of variance which may be attributed to standard deviations of the X values and Y values, or the *population coefficient*,

$$\rho = \frac{\sigma_{xy}^2}{\sigma_x \sigma_y}$$

$$= \frac{\sum (X - \mu_x)(Y - \mu_y)/N}{\sigma_x \sigma_y} \tag{12.1}$$

$$= \frac{1}{N} \frac{\sum (X - \mu_x)(Y - \mu_y)}{\sigma_x \sigma_y}$$

$$= \frac{1}{N} \sum \frac{(X - \mu_x)}{\sigma_x} \frac{(Y - \mu_y)}{\sigma_y}$$

$$\rho = \frac{1}{N} \sum z_x z_y \tag{12.2}$$

Thus the index of relationship between two variables, X and Y (the coefficient of correlation), is the mean of the cross products of the standardized deviate values for the pairs of coordinate values.

The expression for ρ, denoting population coefficient of correlation, may also be given in deviation units (where $x = X - \mu_x$, and $y = Y - \mu_y$)

$$\rho = \frac{\sum xy/N}{\sigma_x \sigma_y} = \frac{\sum xy}{N \sigma_x \sigma_y} \qquad (12.3)$$

Since the investigator rarely deals with the population, sample statistics, $\bar{X}$, $\bar{Y}$, s_x, s_y, and n, may be substituted in (12.3), with the symbol r denoting the *sample coefficient of correlation*, or:

$$r = \frac{s_{xy}^2}{s_x s_y} \qquad (12.4)$$

$$r = \frac{\sum z_x z_y}{n} \qquad (12.5)$$

$$r = \frac{[\sum (X - \bar{X})(Y - \bar{Y})]/n}{\sqrt{\{[\sum (X - \bar{X})^2]/n\}\{[\sum (Y - \bar{Y})^2]/n\}}} \qquad (12.6)$$

The formula for machine calculation of ungrouped data may be obtained by setting:

$$r^2 = \frac{\{\sum [(X - \bar{X})(Y - \bar{Y})]/n\}^2}{\{[\sum (X - \bar{X})^2]/n\}\{[\sum (Y - \bar{Y})^2]/n\}}$$

$$= \frac{[\sum (XY - Y\bar{X} - X\bar{Y} + \bar{X}\bar{Y})]^2/n^2}{\{[\sum (X^2 - 2\bar{X}X + \bar{X}^2)]/n\}\{[\sum (Y^2 - 2\bar{Y}Y + \bar{Y}^2)]/n\}}$$

$$= \frac{[\sum XY - \bar{X}\sum Y - \bar{Y}\sum X + n\bar{X}\bar{Y}]^2/n^2}{[\sum X^2 - 2\bar{X}\sum X + n\bar{X}^2][\sum Y^2 - 2\bar{Y}\sum Y + n\bar{Y}^2]/n^2}$$

$$= \frac{\left[\sum XY - \frac{(\sum X)(\sum Y)}{n}\right]^2}{\left[\sum X^2 - \frac{(\sum X)^2}{n}\right]\left[\sum Y^2 - \frac{(\sum Y)^2}{n}\right]}$$

$$= \frac{[n\sum XY - (\sum X)(\sum Y)]^2/n^2}{\{[n\sum X^2 - (\sum X)^2]/n\}\{[n\sum Y^2 - (\sum Y)^2]/n\}}$$

$$= \frac{[n\sum XY - (\sum X)(\sum Y)]^2}{[n\sum X^2 - (\sum X)^2][n\sum Y^2 - (\sum Y)^2]}$$

The positive square root of r:

$$r_{xy} = \frac{n\sum XY - (\sum X)(\sum Y)}{\sqrt{[n\sum X^2 - (\sum X)^2][n\sum Y^2 - (\sum Y)^2]}} \qquad (12.7)$$

12.3 *Methods of Calculation of r*. In illustrating the calculation of r, both hand and calculating machine methods will be presented. Although the hand calculation procedure shown first may appear laborious, it has the advantage of making clear the general nature and direction of relationship between the two variables, while at the same time supplying the scattergram that should always precede computation of the coefficient of correlation. In preparing for computation from a correlation table it is necessary to use a sheet of coordinate paper, or paper ruled off in squares, which permits the tallying of frequencies where both variables are entered simultaneously.

12.3.1 *The Correlation Table from Grouped Data*. In Table 12.2 the scores of 50 students completing the tests in mathematics aptitude and mathematics achievement, shown earlier in Table 11.2, are again entered in

TABLE 12.2

SCORES OF 50 STUDENTS ON A TEST OF MATHEMATICS APTITUDE (X) AND ON A TEST OF MATHEMATICS ACHIEVEMENT (Y)

Student	Aptitude X	Achievement Y	Student	Aptitude X	Achievement Y
1	37	34	26	20	23
2	27	16	27	24	23
3	32	33	28	24	23
4	13	7	29	19	13
5	24	13	30	34	48
6	29	36	31	23	9
7	30	31	32	22	22
8	25	10	33	24	6
9	20	22	34	26	30
10	15	8	35	24	5
11	16	20	36	25	18
12	27	25	37	32	26
13	33	25	38	25	27
14	32	27	39	18	9
15	36	36	40	24	18
16	23	39	41	12	14
17	10	5	42	20	18
18	11	16	43	16	15
19	21	18	44	23	22
20	24	28	45	35	18
21	25	21	46	30	29
22	18	12	47	15	6
23	23	9	48	28	23
24	21	23	49	16	21
25	22	30	50	24	37

the scattergram. To obtain the *Pearson product moment coefficient of correlation* for the two sets of measurements, the following steps are indicated:

1. Two grouped frequency distribution tables, shown in Table 12.3, are set up in the manner presented in Chapter 11, entering the scores on mathematics aptitude on the X-axis, and the scores on mathematics achievement on the Y-axis. It should be noted that the number of units in the class interval for the data on the X-axis is two, and the number on the Y-axis is three.

2. In the first row beneath the scattergram we sum the frequencies, obtaining a total sum equal to $N(50)$, the number of pairs of scores shown in Table 12.2. The entries in the row of fX_s are obtained by multiplying the frequency of the cell by the value of the substitute scale shown in the upper right of the cells of the topmost row. The values entered in the row fX_sX_s are obtained in the usual manner, multiplying the values of fX_s by the X_s of the substitute scale. Both rows are then summed.

3. To obtain the entries for the row headed by $\sum fY'_s$, we use the first column, headed by 5–7, as an example. In this column we find five tallies, one each in the Y-axis intervals 10–11, 12–13, and 14–15 and two in the Y-axis interval 24–25. By multiplying the number of entries in the cell by the value of the substitute scale shown at the upper left of each cell in the first column and summing, $(1 \times 0) + (1 \times 1) + (1 \times 2) + (2 \times 7)$, we obtain 17, the first entry in the row. In a similar manner we enter the column headed by 8–10 and sum the products $(1 \times 2) + (1 \times 4) + (2 \times 6) + (1 \times 7)$, obtaining 25, the second entry in the row. The sum of the entries in this row is obtained by summing the separate values thus obtained and entered in the cells.

4. The entries in the row headed by $X_s(\sum fY'_s)$ are obtained by multiplying the value of the substitute scale for the X-axis by the entries in each cell of the row immediately above. For example, the first entry in the row is obtained by multiplying $(\sum fY'_s)$, (17), by the value of the substitute scale on the X-axis, (0).

5. On the right-hand side of the scattergram we compute entries for the columns headed by f, fY_s, and fY_sY_s, proceeding in the usual manner.

6. Although the column headed by fX'_s is not used in the formula for computing r from the correlation table, the sum of this column serves as a computational check. This sum is the same as the value obtained by summing the row headed by fX_s and equals 248. It may be further observed that the sum of the column headed by fY_s equals the value obtained by summing the row headed by fY'_s, and is equal to 328, as shown in Table 12.3 on pages 202–203.

7. The value of r is obtained by substituting and solving:

$$r = \frac{\sum[X_s(\sum fY_s')] - \dfrac{\sum fX_s \cdot \sum fY_s}{n}}{\sqrt{\sum fX_sX_s - \dfrac{(\sum fX_s)(\sum fX_s)}{n}}\sqrt{\sum fY_sY_s - \dfrac{(\sum fY_s)(\sum fY_s)}{n}}} \qquad (12.8)$$

$$= \frac{1961 - \dfrac{248 \times 328}{50}}{\sqrt{1766 - \dfrac{248 \times 248}{50}}\sqrt{2678 - \dfrac{328 \times 328}{50}}}$$

$$= 0.62$$

The means and standard deviations for each of the distributions may be obtained from the scattergram:

$$\overline{X} = X_o + i\left(\frac{\sum fX}{n}\right) = 6.5 + 3\left(\frac{248}{50}\right)$$

$$= 21.38$$

$$s_x = \sqrt{\frac{\sum fX_sX_s - \dfrac{\sum fX_s \cdot \sum fX_s}{n}}{n}} \qquad (12.9)$$

$$= \sqrt{\frac{1766 - \dfrac{248 \times 248}{50}}{50}}$$

$$= 9.86$$

$$\overline{Y} = Y_o + i\left(\frac{\sum fY}{n}\right) = 11 + 2\left(\frac{328}{50}\right)$$

$$= 24.12$$

$$s_y = \sqrt{\frac{\sum fY_sY_s - \dfrac{\sum fY_s \cdot \sum fY_s}{n}}{n}} \qquad (12.10)$$

$$= \sqrt{\frac{2678 - \dfrac{328 \times 328}{50}}{50}}$$

$$= 6.48$$

TABLE 12.3

COMPUTING r FROM A CORRELATION TABLE 12.2

Aptitude		Achievement 5–7	8–10	11–13	14–16	17–19	20–22	23–25	26–28
36–37	13	0	1	2	3	4	5	6	7
34–35	12					1			
32–33	11							1	2
30–31	10								
28–29	9							1	
26–27	8				1			1	
24–25	7	2	1	1		2	1	2	2
22–23	6		2				2		
20–21	5					2	1	2	
18–19	4		1	2					
16–17	3				1		2		
14–15	2	1	1						
12–13	1	1			1				
10–11	0	1			1				
f		5	5	3	4	5	6	7	4
fX_s		0	5	6	12	20	30	42	28
fX_sX_s		0	5	12	36	80	150	252	196
$\sum fY'_s$		17	25	15	12	36	30	52	36
$X_s(\sum fY'_s)$		0	25	30	36	144	150	312	252

TABLE 12.3 (*Continued*)

29–31	32–34	35–37	38–40	41–43	44–46	47–49	f	fY_s	fY_sY_s	$\sum fX'_s$
[8] 1	[9] 1	[10]	[11]	[12]	[13]	[14]	2	26	338	19
						1	2	24	288	18
	1						4	44	484	29
2							2	20	200	16
		1					2	18	162	16
1							3	24	192	17
		1					12	84	588	52
1			1				6	36	216	31
							5	25	125	25
							3	12	48	5
							3	9	27	13
							2	4	8	1
							2	2	2	3
							2	–	–	3
4	2	3	1	0	0	1	50	328	2678	248
32	18	30	11	0	0	14	248			
256	162	300	121	0	0	196	1766			
34	24	29	6	0	0	12	328			
272	216	290	66	0	0	168	1961			

12.3.2 *Calculation of r from the deviations from the means.* When deviations are taken from the means of the two distributions the basic formula for the coefficient of correlation as shown in Formula (12.3) is:

$$\rho = \frac{\sum xy}{N\sigma_x\sigma_y}, \quad \text{and} \quad r = \frac{\sum xy}{ns_x s_y} \tag{12.11}$$

where

x is the deviation of any X score from the mean of the X distribution,
y is the deviation of any Y score from the mean of the Y distribution,
$\sum xy$ is the sum of the products of deviations,
s_x is the standard deviation of the X distribution,
s_y is the standard deviation of the Y distribution.

In Figure 12.4 ten pairs of measurements were plotted and the general indication is that of a negative correlation. These values are shown in Table 12.4, along with computations for entries in the basic formula for r above.

TABLE 12.4

THE PEARSON PRODUCT MOMENT r COMPUTED FROM DEVIATION SCORES FOR DATA SHOWN IN FIGURE 12.4

X	Y	x	y	x^2	y^2	xy
10	75	−40	15	1600	225	−600
20	90	−30	30	900	900	−900
35	70	−15	10	225	100	−1500
45	50	−5	−10	25	100	50
45	80	−5	20	25	400	−100
55	60	5	0	25	0	0
60	40	10	−20	100	400	−200
70	60	20	0	400	0	0
80	25	30	−35	900	1225	−1050
80	50	30	−10	900	100	−300
$\sum = 500$	600	0	0	5100	3450	−3250

$\overline{X} = 50 \quad \overline{Y} = 60$

$$s_x = \sqrt{\frac{5100}{9}} = 23.8$$

$$s_y = \sqrt{\frac{3450}{9}} = 19.6$$

$$r_{xy} = \frac{\sum xy}{ns_x s_y}$$

$$= \frac{-3250}{(10)(23.8)(19.6)} = -0.70$$

12.3.3 *Machine Calculation of r from Raw Scores.* In Figure 12.3 ten pairs of measurements were plotted and the general indication is that of a positive correlation less than 1.00. These values are shown in Table 12.5, along with computations for entries in the computing formula for r:

$$r = \frac{\sum XY - \frac{\sum X \sum Y}{n}}{\sqrt{\sum X^2 - \frac{\sum X \sum X}{n}} \sqrt{\sum Y^2 - \frac{\sum Y \sum Y}{n}}}$$

$$= \frac{28400 - \frac{505 \times 525}{10}}{\sqrt{28675 - \frac{505 \times 505}{10}} \sqrt{29825 - \frac{525 \times 525}{10}}}$$

$$= 0.71$$

TABLE 12.5

THE PEARSON PRODUCT MOMENT r COMPUTED FROM RAW SCORES SHOWN IN FIGURE 12.3

X	Y	X^2	Y^2	XY
20	40	400	1600	800
30	25	900	625	750
35	50	1225	2500	1750
45	40	2025	1600	1800
50	60	2500	3600	3000
50	70	2500	4900	3500
60	40	3600	1600	2400
65	60	4225	3600	3900
70	70	4900	4900	4900
80	70	6400	4900	5600
$\sum 505$	525	28,675	29,825	28,400

12.3.4 *Regression and the Coefficient of Correlation.* From Section 11.4 of Chapter 11:

$$b_{y.x} = \frac{\sum XY - \frac{(\sum X)(\sum Y)}{n}}{\sum X^2 - \frac{(\sum X)^2}{n}} = \frac{\sum xy}{\sum x^2}$$

$$b_{x.y} = \frac{\sum XY - \frac{(\sum X)(\sum Y)}{n}}{\sum Y^2 - \frac{(\sum Y)^2}{n}} = \frac{\sum xy}{\sum y^2}$$

Let us use a common computing formula for $r_{xy} = \sum xy / \sqrt{\sum x^2 \sum y^2}$ and multiply both numerator and denominator of $b_{y.x} = \sum xy / \sum x^2$ by $\sqrt{\sum x^2 \sum y^2} / \sqrt{\sum x^2 \sum y^2}$. Substituting:

$$b_{y.x} = \left(\frac{\sum xy}{\sum x^2}\right) \left(\frac{\sqrt{\sum x^2 \sum y^2}}{\sqrt{\sum x^2 \sum y^2}}\right)$$

$$b_{y.x} = r_{xy} \frac{\sqrt{\sum x^2 \sum y^2}}{\sum x^2} = \frac{r s_x s_y}{s_x^2}$$

$$b_{y.x} = r_{xy} \frac{s_y}{s_x} \qquad (12.12)$$

For the regression coefficient of X on Y:

$$b_{x.y} = r_{xy} \frac{s_x}{s_y} \qquad (12.13)$$

Multiplying the regression coefficient of Formulas (12.12) and (12.13), we obtain:

$$(r_{xy}) \left(\frac{s_y}{s_x}\right) (r_{xy}) \left(\frac{s_x}{s_y}\right) = (b_{y.x})(b_{x.y}), \quad \text{or} \quad r_{xy}^2 = (b_{y.x})(b_{x.y})$$

In Section 11.6, Chapter 11, we found the value of $b_{y.x} = 0.9509$. Using the data from Table 11.2, $b_{x.y}$ may be computed and found to be 0.4091. In Section 12.3.1, the value of r_{xy} for these same data was found to be 0.62. Then:

$$r_{xy}^2 = (0.62)^2 = 0.3844$$

and

$$(b_{x.y})(b_{y.x}) = (0.4091)(0.9509) = 0.3890$$

An alternate formula for the standard error of estimate may be written:

$$s_{y.x} = s_y \sqrt{1 - r_{xy}^2} \qquad (12.14)$$

For the data shown in Section 12.3.1:

$$s_{y.x} = 6.48\sqrt{1 - (0.62)^2}$$

$$s_{y.x} = (6.48)(0.7846) = 5.08$$

$$s_{x.y} = (9.86)(0.7846) = 7.69$$

If we substitute $(Y - \bar{Y})$ for y, and $(X - \bar{X})$ for x in the equation, then:

$$y = bx$$

$$Y - \bar{Y} = b_{y.x}(X - \bar{X}) \qquad (12.15)$$

$$b_{y.x} = r_{xy} \frac{s_y}{s_x}$$

$$Y - \bar{Y} = r_{xy} \frac{s_y}{s_x} (X - \bar{X}) \qquad (12.16)$$

For the data shown in Table 12.2, we have:

$$Y - 24.12 = 0.62 \left(\frac{6.48}{9.86}\right)(X - 21.38)$$

$$Y = 0.401X + 15.56$$

12.4 The Transformation of r into Fisher's ζ. A useful technique developed by R. A. Fisher is the logarithmic transformation of r which is referred to as the ζ statistic, with a sampling distribution that is normal for all values. Since the sampling distribution of r is non-uniform in shape and r lies between the limits of 1.00 and -1.00, as the population correlation, ρ, approaches these limits, the sampling distribution departs radically from a symmetrical curve. It may be observed that while the distribution is always symmetrical for $\rho = 0$, there is no case in which the distribution of r is normal. For large samples the distributions approach normality; however, it is inadvisable to assume normality of distribution of r.

Through the use of Fisher's ζ, we may change the correlation coefficients, r's, to ζ's, and test the difference between the two ζ's for significance. The transformation formula is:

$$\zeta = \tfrac{1}{2} \log_e \frac{1 + r}{1 - r}$$

$$\zeta = 1.1513 \log_{10} \frac{1 + r}{1 - r} \tag{12.17}$$

A table giving ζ values for different values of r may be found in Appendix A, Table VI. Accepted practice indicates that the researcher will convert from the ζ value to the appropriate r in preparing the research report. The standard deviation of ζ is:

$$\sigma_{\zeta_r} = \frac{1}{\sqrt{n - 3}} \tag{12.18}$$

For example, in transforming r to ζ, if we have a correlation coefficient equal to 0.50, and $n = 52$: from Table VI, $\zeta = 0.549$ and, using the ζ transformation:

$$\zeta = \tfrac{1}{2} \log_e \left(\frac{1 + r}{1 - r}\right) = \tfrac{1}{2} \log_e \left(\frac{1.5}{0.5}\right) = 0.5493$$

with a standard deviation of ζ equal to:

$$\sigma_\zeta = \frac{1}{\sqrt{n - 3}} = \frac{1}{\sqrt{49}} = \frac{1}{7} = 0.143$$

12.5 Tests of Hypotheses about the Correlation Coefficient. If we assume normality for the parent populations of both variables under study, Fisher's "t" ratio for testing the significance of a coefficient of correlation may be used.

12.5.1 Test of the Hypothesis $\rho = 0$. Test of the hypothesis H_o when $\rho = 0$, we have:

$$t = \frac{r\sqrt{n-2}}{\sqrt{1-r^2}} \; ; \text{d.f.} = n - 2 \qquad (12.19)$$

where r is the obtained correlation coefficient and n is the number of paired observations. In the following example, where $r = 0.50$, and $n = 10$,

$$t = \frac{0.50\sqrt{8}}{\sqrt{0.75}} = \frac{1.414}{0.866} = 1.633; \text{d.f.} = n - 2 = 10 - 2 = 8$$

A table giving significant values of r for H_o: $\rho = 0$ and different levels of α is found in Table V, Appendix A.

The hypothesis that the population correlation is zero can be accepted at the 0.05 level. From Table II, Appendix A, with eight degrees of freedom, the "t" required for significance at 0.05 is 2.31. In using the ς transformation:

$$\varsigma = \tfrac{1}{2} \log_e \left(\frac{1.5}{5}\right) = 0.5493, \text{ and } \frac{1}{\sqrt{n-3}} = \frac{1}{\sqrt{7}} = 0.378$$

$$z = \frac{\varsigma}{\sigma_\varsigma} = \frac{0.5493}{0.378} = 1.45, \text{ where } z = \frac{\varsigma_r - \varsigma_\rho}{\sigma_{\varsigma_r}} \qquad (12.20)$$

Hence, we may again accept the hypothesis that the population correlation is zero.

12.5.2 Establishing Confidence Interval for ρ. In a sample of 40 students selected at random from an entering class of 1,125 college freshmen, a correlation of 0.61 was found between scores on mathematics aptitude and high school grade point average. The ς corresponding to the observed r is 0.709, and computing the standard deviation of ς for a sample of size 40, we obtain:

$$\sigma_\varsigma = \frac{1}{\sqrt{40-3}} = 0.164$$

For the 95 per cent confidence limits, multiplying 0.164×1.96 yields 0.321. In ς units, the limits are 0.709 ± 0.321, which are 1.03 and 0.388 respectively. From Table VI we convert these limits of ς to r values, 0.78

and 0.31, the interval which includes all values of ρ falling within the 95 per cent confidence limits. Unlike previous illustrations of confidence intervals, the limits for the interval shown are at different distances from r, which results from the skewness of the sampling distribution of r.

12.5.3 *Test of the Hypothesis H_o: $\rho \neq 0$.* If we wish to test the hypothesis $\rho = 0.70$ for a reported correlation between reading speed and reading comprehension, the researcher may select from this population a random sample of 50 cases, obtaining X and Y scores for each. The correlation, r, for this sample is found to be 0.76.

1. H_o: $\rho = 0.70$; H_a: $\rho \neq 0.70$

2. $\alpha = 0.05$, test (c)

3. Reject H_o if $z < z_{0.025} = -1.96$ of if $z > z_{0.975} = 1.96$.

4. $z = \dfrac{\zeta_r - \zeta_\rho}{\sigma_{\zeta_r}} = \dfrac{0.996 - 0.867}{\dfrac{1}{\sqrt{50-3}}} = \dfrac{0.129}{\dfrac{1}{6.86}} = 0.88$

5. Accept H_o.

12.5.4 *Differences Between Two Correlation Coefficients, a Test of the Hypothesis $\rho_1 = \rho_2 = \rho$.* From the significance of difference test between two correlation coefficients obtained from independent groups, we may apply the principle developed in connection with the variance of differences of the paired measures. If two variables are independent and normally distributed, their differences are normally distributed with variance equal to the sum of the variances of the measures.

In transforming the two correlation coefficients we find the variance of the differences equals the sum of the variances:

$$\sigma^2_{\zeta_1 - \zeta_2} = \left(\frac{1}{n_1 - 3}\right) + \left(\frac{1}{n_2 - 3}\right) \tag{12.21}$$

$$z = \frac{\zeta_1 - \zeta_2}{\sqrt{\dfrac{1}{n_1 - 3} + \dfrac{1}{n_2 - 3}}} \tag{12.22}$$

where

$$\zeta_1 = \tfrac{1}{2}\log_e\left(\frac{1 + r_1}{1 - r_1}\right)$$

$$\zeta_2 = \tfrac{1}{2}\log_e\left(\frac{1 + r_2}{1 - r_2}\right)$$

For example, in a study of the relationship between manual dexterity and skill in laboratory performance, tests were administered to two groups of students. One group consisted of 16 students whose grade point average exceeded 3.0, and the second group consisted of 10 students whose grade point average was less than 2.0. The correlations were 0.61 and 0.54 respectively:

$$n_1 = 16 \qquad n_2 = 10$$
$$r_1 = 0.61 \qquad r_2 = 0.54$$

Using the transformation for r_1, $\zeta_1 = 0.709$, and for r_2, $\zeta_2 = 0.604$:

1. $H_o: \rho_1 = \rho_2$; $H_a: \rho_1 \neq \rho_2$

2. $\alpha = 0.05$, test (c)

3. Reject H_o if $z < z_{0.025} = -1.96$ or if $z > z_{0.975} = 1.96$.

4. $z = \dfrac{0.709 - 0.604}{\sqrt{\dfrac{1}{16 - 3} + \dfrac{1}{10 - 3}}} = \dfrac{0.105}{\sqrt{0.077 + 0.1429}} = 0.22$

5. Accept H_o.

By referring to the table of the normal probability values (Table I, Appendix A), we find that the probability of obtaining a value of $z \geq 0.99$ is approximately 0.82. The hypothesis as such is not rejected. We may conclude that the two values of ζ and the associated values of r_{xy} apparently do not differ significantly.

QUESTIONS

1. What are some examples in which the regression of a given factor in a population is not a straight line?
2. Mark each of the following as to your estimate of:
   Positive correlated   P
   Negatively correlated N
   Uncorrelated   U
   a. Grade point average in secondary school and grade point average in college.
   b. Horsepower of engine and fuel consumption in gallons/hour.
   c. Student's age and his I.Q.
   d. Age of individual and his number of permanent teeth.
   e. Age of an automobile and its trade-in value.
   f. Height and age of a stand of hardwood trees.

g. Density of a material and its mass.

h. Size of game fish and availability of food in a lake.

i. Time spent in processing a manufactured product and quality of product.

3. Why does the value of the Pearson product moment r tend to underestimate the amount of relationship between two variables when the assumption of linearity is not met?

4. Outline a sampling experiment that illustrates linear correlation.

5. What are some variables related to each of the following: (a) intelligence, (b) socio-economic status, (c) college grade point average?

6. If a research worker wished to determine the relationship between the age of an individual and his tendency toward rigidity in response to political issues, how should he proceed?

PROBLEMS

1. In the selection of 30 sophomore boys for participation in a special program in chemistry and physics each student was administered a standardized achievement test in science and in second year algebra with the following results.

Student	Science	Algebra	Student	Science	Algebra
1	47	63	16	48	43
2	51	54	17	52	43
3	48	53	18	51	42
4	46	52	19	46	42
5	52	51	20	50	41
6	59	51	21	47	41
7	55	50	22	50	41
8	49	50	23	48	40
9	47	48	24	54	39
10	49	46	25	47	39
11	46	45	26	52	39
12	55	45	27	48	39
13	54	44	28	48	38
14	46	44	29	48	38
15	49	43	30	54	37

(a) Find the coefficient of correlation. (Answer 0.015.)

(b) Test the hypothesis that $\rho = 0$.

(c) Compute the 95% confidence interval estimate of ρ.

2. The following scores were established on two successive tests taken by eight students:

Student	Test 1	Test 2
1	78	89
2	75	86
3	70	80
4	61	72
5	60	71
6	57	67
7	50	61
8	48	59

(a) Rewrite these entries so that the data show perfect rank correlation.
(b) Can these data be ordered to yield a correlation coefficient equal to 1.00 without also having perfect rank correlation?

3. Draw two samples of ten numbers each having two digits by using the table of random numbers in the appendix. Compute the coefficient of correlation after first guessing the value of r.

4. Use the data shown in the table below to find answers to parts (a) through (e):

X	4	5	6	7	8	10
Y	0	3	5	6	7	15

(a) Show the X set and Y set as x and y values.
(b) Find the value of xy.
(c) Give the value of Σx^2 and Σy^2.
(d) Find the value of the coefficient of correlation.
(e) Give the standard deviation of both the X set and the Y set.

5. Test the hypothesis that $\rho = 0.00$ if a sample of size 25 gives $r = 0.36$.

6. Test the hypothesis that $\rho = 0.60$ when a sample of size 25 gives $r = 0.50$ and find a 95% confidence interval for ρ.

7. For the problems shown below:
   (a) Prepare a graph for the data.
   (b) Calculate the regression equation and draw the line.
   (c) Calculate r.
   (d) Test the hypothesis that ρ is equal to zero.

8.1	X	3	4	5	8	11	12
	Y	1	1	3	3	4	6

8.2	X	1	3	5	7	9	11
	Y	7	12	14	19	22	30

8. The following data were obtained from the administration of a test in algebra and English:

Algebra X	English Y
$\overline{X} = 60$	$\overline{Y} = 70$
$s_x = 6$	$s_y = 7$
	$r = 0.70$

(a) Give the regression equation in score form.

(b) Predict the grade in English for a student who scores 58 in algebra and give the standard error of estimate of this prediction.

REFERENCES

DuBois, Philip H. *An Introduction to Psychological Statistics.* New York: Harper and Row, Publishers, 1965. Chapter 6.

Freeman, Linton C. *Elementary Applied Statistics.* New York: John Wiley and Sons, Inc., 1965. Chapter 9.

Ferguson, George A. *Statistical Analysis in Psychology and Education.* New York: McGraw-Hill Book Company, Inc., 1966. Chapter 7.

Freund, John C., and Williams, Frank J. *Elementary Business Statistics: The Modern Approach.* Englewood Cliffs, New Jersey: Prentice-Hall, Inc., 1964. Chapter 10.

Guenther, William C. *Concepts of Statistical Inference.* New York: McGraw-Hill Book Company, Inc., 1965. Chapter 8.

Kurtz, Thomas E. *Basic Statistics.* Englewood Cliffs, New Jersey: Prentice-Hall Inc., 1963. Chapter 9.

McNemar, Quinn. *Psychological Statistics.* Third Edition. New York: John Wiley and Sons, Inc., 1962. Chapters 8 and 9.

Peatman, John. *Introduction to Applied Statistics.* New York: Harper and Row, Publishers, 1963. Chapter 5.

Tate, Merle W. *Statistics in Education and Psychology: A First Course.* New York: The Macmillan Company, 1965. Chapter 7.

Yamane, Taro. *Statistics, An Introductory Analysis.* New York: Harper and Row, Publishers, 1964. Chapter 15.

SPECIAL TOPICS

13

FURTHER CONSIDERATION OF THE ANALYSIS OF VARIANCE

The previous discussions of the analysis of variance technique were concerned with the determination of significance of experimental factors, affecting multiple ($n > 2$) populations. These discussions were centered around the condition referred to as a fixed model or *fixed factor model*. This means that the factor levels considered were the only ones of interest. However, in many instances there are multiple treatments (factor levels) available and only a few are selected at random. Here a *random factor model* is used. In other cases "fixed factors" and "random factors" are combined for study to form a *mixed factor model*.

13.1 *Estimate of Variance.* The formation of the F ratios to test the associated hypotheses is dependent upon which of the three models is being utilized. The fixed factor model was used in the analysis. In Section 10.3 the separate "mean squares" computed are, in essence, the estimates of the "true" mean square. As such, another column might be added to Table 10.9 and entitled "Expected Mean Square." The entries in this column would be the components of the variance being estimated. For example, opposite s_m^2 would be $(\sigma_e^2 + \sigma_m^2)$ where σ_e^2 is the random error not accounted for by m and n, and σ_m^2 is the bias due exclusively to the effect of the m factor. The resulting configuration is given in Table 13.1.

TABLE 13.1

EXPECTED MEAN SQUARE VALUES FOR A TWO-WAY CLASSIFICATION FIXED FACTOR MODEL ANALYSIS OF VARIANCE

Source of Variability	MS	Expected Mean Square (EMS)
Bet. Cols. (m)	s_m^2	$\sigma_e^2 + nr[m/(m-1)]\sigma_m^2$
Bet. Rows (n)	s_n^2	$\sigma_e^2 + mr[n/(n-1)]\sigma_n^2$
Interaction ($m \times n$)	$s_{m\times n}^2$	$\sigma_e^2 + r[m/(m-1)][n/(n-1)]\sigma_{m\times n}^2$
Within Groups (e)	s_e^2	σ_e^2

For the data in Table 10.10, the expected mean square values would be:

$$\text{Bet. Cols. } (m): \sigma_e^2 + (4)(4)(4/3)\sigma_m^2$$
$$\text{Bet. Rows } (n): \sigma_e^2 + (4)(4)(4/3)\sigma_n^2$$
$$\text{Interaction } (m \times n): \sigma_e^2 + (4)(4/3)(4/3)\sigma_{m\times n}^2$$

The addition of this column to the computational table is of great significance. The entries give an indication of the "proper" F ratios to be made in testing the hypothesis. This will be explored later when the "components of variance" forms (random and mixed factor models) are discussed. This added column will also permit an estimation of the portion of the total variance attributable to each significant term in the analysis.

For the "fixed factor model," all of the effects are tested against the error term. This is quite clear when the "estimated mean square" column is checked. It may be seen that the value of σ_e^2 is included in each term and that a single variance estimator is also included. If the formed F ratio is non-significant, it would indicate that the specific σ^2 is zero. Conversely, if the F ratio is significantly different from one, the specific factor is not zero.

If all the "proper or correct" F ratios have been computed and the significant ones determined, the percentage of the total variability contributed by each of the significant factors may be determined. In the problem worked in Section 10.3, both main factors (rows and columns) as well as the interaction factor were significant. The following equations may be set up:

$$(1) \quad \sigma_e^2 + (64/3)\sigma_m^2 = 105.67$$

$$(2) \quad \sigma_e^2 + (64/3)\sigma_n^2 = 193.00$$

$$(3) \quad \sigma_e^2 + (64/9)\sigma_{m\times n}^2 = 54.11$$

$$(4) \quad \sigma_e^2 = 19.79$$

Equation (4) may then be substituted in turn in (1), (2), and (3) and the values of σ_m^2, σ_n^2, and $\sigma_{m\times n}^2$ determined.

$$(5) \quad 19.79 + (64/3)\sigma_m^2 = 105.67$$
$$(64/3)\sigma_m^2 = 85.88$$
$$\sigma_m^2 = 4.03$$

$$(6) \quad 19.79 + (64/3)\sigma_n^2 = 193.00$$
$$(64/3)\sigma_n^2 = 173.21$$
$$\sigma_n^2 = 8.12$$

$$(7) \quad 19.79 + (64/9)\sigma_{m\times n}^2 = 54.11$$
$$(64/9)\sigma_{m\times n}^2 = 34.32$$
$$\sigma_{m\times n}^2 = 4.83$$

The estimate of the total variance due to these three specific factors is

$$4.03 + 8.12 + 4.83 = 16.98$$

The m factor contributes

$$[(4.03/16.98)100] \quad \text{or} \quad 23.74\%$$

of the total variability; the n factor contributes

$$[(8.12/16.98)100] \quad \text{or} \quad 47.82\%$$

while the interaction $(m \times n)$ factor contributes

$$[(4.83/16.98)100] \quad \text{or} \quad 28.44\%$$

This indicates that even though all were significant, the n factor contributes almost one-half of the total variability.

The computation of the F ratios and also the variance estimates are different for the "random" and "mixed" models. If it could be assumed that the "grade" factor and the "class" factor in the data presented in Table 10.13 were randomly chosen from many different grade levels and many different classes, the estimated mean square column would indicate different F ratios from those indicated by a fixed factor — linear hypothesis analysis of variance form. These differences are indicated in Table 13.2.

From these estimated mean squares shown in Table 13.2, the F ratios would be formed differently. The specific form would be totally dependent upon the type of data being analyzed, and the specific factor (A, B, C, AB, AC, BC, ABC) being tested. This also points out that it is appropriate to combine the nonsignificant higher order interaction SSD with the "within groups" SSD thus increasing the value of σ_e^2 and reducing the number of F ratios.

TABLE 13.2

COMPONENTS OF VARIANCE
THREE FACTOR CLASSIFICATION WITH r REPLICATIONS

Source of Variability	*d.f.*	*Expected Mean Square*
	Case I	
	A, B, C — Fixed Factors	
Bet. A	$(a-1)$	$\sigma_e^2 + bcr[a/(a-1)]\sigma_A^2$
Bet. B	$(b-1)$	$\sigma_e^2 + acr[b/(b-1)]\sigma_B^2$
Bet. C	$(c-1)$	$\sigma_e^2 + abr[c/(c-1)]\sigma_C^2$
Interactions		
$A \times B$	$(a-1)(b-1)$	$\sigma_e^2 + cr[a/(a-1)][b/(b-1)]\sigma_{AB}^2$
$A \times C$	$(a-1)(c-1)$	$\sigma_e^2 + br[a/(a-1)][c/(c-1)]\sigma_{AC}^2$
$B \times C$	$(b-1)(c-1)$	$\sigma_e^2 + ar[b/(b-1)][c/(c-1)]\sigma_{BC}^2$
$A \times B \times C$	$(a-1)(b-1)(c-1)$	$\sigma_e^2 + r[a/(a-1)][b/(b-1)][c/(c-1)]\sigma_{ABC}^2$
Within Groups	$abc(r-1)$	σ_e^2
	Case II	
	A, B, C — Random Factors	
Bet. A	$(a-1)$	$\sigma_e^2 + r\sigma_{ABC}^2 + rc\sigma_{AB}^2 + rb\sigma_{AC}^2 + bcr\sigma_A^2$
Bet. B	$(b-1)$	$\sigma_e^2 + r\sigma_{ABC}^2 + rc\sigma_{AB}^2 + ra\sigma_{BC}^2 + acr\sigma_B^2$
Bet. C	$(c-1)$	$\sigma_e^2 + r\sigma_{ABC}^2 + rb\sigma_{AC}^2 + ra\sigma_{BC}^2 + acr\sigma_C^2$
Interactions		
$A \times B$	$(a-1)(b-1)$	$\sigma_e^2 + r\sigma_{ABC}^2 + rc\sigma_{AB}^2$
$A \times C$	$(a-1)(c-1)$	$\sigma_e^2 + r\sigma_{ABC}^2 + rb\sigma_{AC}^2$
$B \times C$	$(b-1)(c-1)$	$\sigma_e^2 + r\sigma_{ABC}^2 + ra\sigma_{BC}^2$
$A \times B \times C$	$(a-1)(b-1)(c-1)$	$\sigma_e^2 + r\sigma_{ABC}^2$
Within Groups	$abc(r-1)$	σ_e^2
	Case III (a)	
	A — Fixed	
	B, C — Random	
Bet. A	$(a-1)$	$\sigma_e^2 + r[a/(a-1)]\sigma_{ABC}^2 + rb[a/(a-1)]\sigma_{AC}^2$ $\quad + rc[a/(a-1)]\sigma_{AB}^2 + rbc[a/(a-1)]\sigma_A^2$
Bet. B	$(b-1)$	$\sigma_e^2 + ra\sigma_{BC}^2 + rac\sigma_B^2$
Bet. C	$(c-1)$	$\sigma_e^2 + ra\sigma_{BC}^2 + rab\sigma_C^2$

nteractions

$A \times C$	$(a-1)(c-1)$	$\sigma_e^2 + r[a/(a-1)]\sigma_{ABC}^2 + rb[a/(a-1)]\sigma_{AC}^2$
$A \times B$	$(a-1)(b-1)$	$\sigma_e^2 + r[a/(a-1)]\sigma_{ABC}^2 + rc[a/(a-1)]\sigma_{AB}^2$
$B \times C$	$(b-1)(c-1)$	$\sigma_e^2 + ra\sigma_{BC}^2$
$A \times B \times C$	$(a-1)(b-1)(c-1)$	$\sigma_e^2 + r[a/(a-1)]\sigma_{ABC}^2$
Within Groups	$abc(r-1)$	σ_e^2

Case III (b)

A, B — Fixed

C — Random

Bet. A	$(a-1)$	$\sigma_e^2 + rb[a/(a-1)]\sigma_{AC}^2 + bcr[a/(a-1)\sigma_A^2$
Bet. B	$(b-1)$	$\sigma_e^2 + ra[b/(b-1)]\sigma_{BC}^2 + rac[b/(b-1)]\sigma_B^2$
Bet. C	$(c-1)$	$\sigma_e^2 + rab\sigma_C^2$

nteractions

$A \times B$	$(a-1)(b-1)$	$\sigma_e^2 + r[a/(a-1)][b/(b-1)]\sigma_{ABC}^2$ $+ rc[a/(a-1)][b/(b-1)]\sigma_{AB}^2$
$A \times C$	$(a-1)(c-1)$	$\sigma_e^2 + rb[a/(a-1)]\sigma_{AC}^2$
$B \times C$	$(b-1)(c-1)$	$\sigma_e^2 + ra[b/(b-1)]\sigma_{BC}^2$
$A \times B \times C$	$(a-1)(b-1)(c-1)$	$\sigma_e^2 + r[a/(a-1)][b/(b-1)]\sigma_{ABC}^2$
Within Groups	$abc(r-1)$	σ_e^2

13.2 *Completely Randomized Block Design*. Many times the researcher is faced with the situation which does not permit the consideration of single factors. An example might be the study of different methods of instruction and their effects on achievement. It may be recognized readily that if more than one teacher is used, the factor of teacher differences enters into the situation. If the study is carried out in more than one school, school differences appear. The *completely randomized block design* is one which permits the researcher to continue his study and at the same time control these extraneous yet very important factors.

To set up the analysis and follow the idea of "block" design, several factors must be considered.

(1) The experimental treatment units within the groups must be fairly homogeneous in nature;

(2) The treatments are assigned *at random* to the various experimental treatment units within each group.

Suppose it was desired to know if the type of answer sheet had any effect on the individuals' scores obtained on a test. One company produces answer sheets which are:

(1) Marked by punching out the proper response with a pin.
(2) Marked in a box by use of an electrographic pencil.
(3) Marked in various positions on a punchable card using a card punch machine.

Mental maturity is a factor which may influence the results. To offset this, the researcher randomly divides the respective classrooms in each grade level into three groups, rather than having one class use Form A, one class use Form B, and one class use Form C. The grouping may then be shown diagrammatically as:

	Group 1	Group 2	Group 3
Class 1	Form A	Form C	Form B
Class 2	Form B	Form A	Form C
Class 3	Form C	Form B	Form A

The mean scores of the students on the tests are shown in Table 13.3.

TABLE 13.3

MEAN TEST SCORES OF STUDENTS USING THREE ANSWER SHEET FORMS

Classes	Answer Sheet Forms			
	A	B	C	$T_{i.}$
1	75	83	82	240
2	79	81	86	246
3	78	78	85	241
$T_{.j}$	232	242	253	$727 = T_{..}$

In this design the total variability may be subdivided into three portions rather than the two considered in Chapter 10. The computational table is shown in Table 13.4, where

$$SSD_B = (\sum T_{i.}^2/f) - (T_{..}^2/bf) \tag{13.1}$$

$$SSD_F = (\sum T_{.j}^2/b) - (T_{..}^2/bf) \tag{13.2}$$

$$SSD_e = \sum\sum X_{ij}^2 - (\sum T_{i.}^2/f) - (\sum T_{.j}^2/b) + (T_{..}^2/bf) \tag{13.3}$$

$$SSD_T = \sum\sum X_{ij}^2 - (T_{..}^2/bf) \tag{13.4}$$

TABLE 13.4

COMPUTATIONAL TABLE
FOR
COMPLETELY RANDOMIZED BLOCK DESIGN ANALYSIS OF VARIANCE

(a) General Form

Source of Variability	SSD	d.f.	MS
Blocks (B)	SSD_B	$(b-1)$	$SSD_B/(b-1)$
Answer Forms (F)	SSD_F	$(f-1)$	$SSD_F/(f-1)$
Within Groups	SSD_e	$(b-1)(f-1)$	$SSD_e/[(b-1)(f-1)]$
Total	SSD_T	$(bf-1)$	

(b) Problem

Source of Variability	SSD	d.f.	MS	F
Blocks	6.89	2	3.44	
Answer Forms	73.56	2	36.78	$36.78/5.78 = 6.36$
Within Groups	23.11	4	5.78	
Total	103.56	8		

F ratio non-significant

$$\sum T_{i.}^2/f) = (240^2 + 246^2 + 241^2)/3 = 58732.33$$

$$\sum (T_{.j}^2/b) = (232^2 + 242^2 + 253^2)/3 = 58799.00$$

$$\sum\sum X_{ij}^2 = 75^2 + 79^2 + \cdots + 86^2 + 85^2 = 58829.00$$

$$T_{..}^2/bf = 727^2/9 = 58725.44$$

To fully understand and utilize the results of our computation, we must keep in mind the assumptions basic to this design:

1. All variables are randomly drawn from normal distributions with mean μ_j.

2. All normal populations involved have homoscedastic variances.

3. The parameters for each block *and* each treatment are additive, or

$$\mu_{ij} = \mu_{..} + \mu_{i.} + \mu_{.j}$$

where $\mu_{i.}$ is the block factor and $\mu_{.j}$ is the treatment factor.

4. Each individual observation may be represented by the expression

$$X_{ij} = \mu_{..} + \mu_{i.} + \mu_{.j} + e_{ij} \tag{13.5}$$

The example used to illustrate this design is of the Case I type. It is possible (and quite probable) that Cases II and III may be involved. In that case it will be necessary to form the expected mean square column in order that the proper F ratios may be formed.

In essence, this particular design allows the conventional analysis of variance null hypothesis to be tested while the factors of within group variation due to unmeasured factors are somewhat controlled. More complete discussion of this design may be found in the references listed at the end of this chapter.

13.3 *Latin Square Design*.   The block design allowed us to control *one* factor or place *one restriction* upon the data. The *Latin square design* permits us to place *two restrictions* upon the data (or control two outside factors). A major restriction in the usefulness of this design is the lack of a significance test of the interactions of main effect factors. Furthermore, it is apparent from the name that if k treatments are to be studied, k^2 experimental cells must be available.

As such, each of the individual observations included may be represented by the expression:

$$X_{ij(k)} = \mu_{...} + \mu_{i..} + \mu_{.j.} + \mu_{..(k)} + e_{ij(k)} \tag{13.6}$$

where i is the row effect, j is the column effect, and k is the treatment effect. There is a further stipulation that each member of the k treatments *must* appear once and only once in each row and each column. These treatments are assigned randomly to each of the blocks or cells.

To further illustrate this design, consider the case where a particular subject is to be taught by television, teaching machine, program text, and conventional lecture ($k = 1, 2, 3, 4$). These methods will be tried out in a large school using the four sections ($i = 1, 2, 3, 4$) of each of four teachers ($j = 1, 2, 3, 4$). In this situation it would be desirable to control the teacher difference factor and the differences between classes factor.

To set up this design would require the random assignment of the method to the various classes under the different teachers. This is illustrated by the letters in parentheses in Table 13.5.

TABLE 13.5

**ACHIEVEMENT SCORES OF STUDENTS TAUGHT BY
FOUR DIFFERENT METHODS AS SHOWN IN A
LATIN SQUARE DESIGN**

Classes	Teachers				$T_{i..}$
	1	2	3	4	
1	93 (C)	80 (B)	80 (A)	73 (D)	326
2	87 (B)	74 (C)	86 (D)	84 (A)	331
3	86 (D)	87 (A)	77 (C)	84 (B)	334
4	72 (A)	88 (D)	77 (B)	79 (C)	316
$T_{.j.}$	338	329	320	320	$1307 = T_{...}$

Achievement score data will be used to test the single hypothesis of equality of means for the different methods of instruction. The analysis of variance computational form for the Latin square design is shown in Table 13.6 and computed for the sample data in Table 13.7.

TABLE 13.6

**COMPUTATIONAL TABLE FOR THE
LATIN SQUARE ANALYSIS OF VARIANCE DESIGN**

Source of Variability	SSD	d.f.	MS
Row Effect	SSD_i	$(m-1)$	$SSD_i/(m-1)$
Column Effect	SSD_j	$(m-1)$	$SSD_j/(m-1)$
Treatment	$SSD_{(k)}$	$(m-1)$	$SSD_{(k)}/(m-1)$
Within Group	SSD_e	$(m-1)(m-2)$	$SSD_e/[(m-1)(m-2)]$
Total	SSD_T	(m^2-1)	

In Table 13.6:

$$SSD_i = (\sum T_{i..}^2/m) - (T_{...}^2/m^2) \tag{13.7}$$

$$SSD_j = (\sum T_{.j.}^2/m) - (T_{...}^2/m^2) \tag{13.8}$$

$$SSD_{(k)} = (\sum T_{..(k)}^2/m) - (T_{...}^2/m^2) \tag{13.9}$$

$$SSD_e = \sum\sum X_{ij(k)}^2 - [(\sum T_{i..}^2 + \sum T_{.j.}^2 + \sum T_{..(k)}^2)/m] + 2(T_{...}^2/m^2) \tag{13.10}$$

$$SSD_T = \sum\sum X_{ij(k)}^2 - (T_{...}^2/m^2) \tag{13.11}$$

TABLE 13.7

ANALYSIS OF VARIANCE, LATIN SQUARE DESIGN
OF
MEAN ACHIEVEMENT SCORES IN TABLE 13.6

Source of Variability	SSD	d.f.	MS	F
Rows	46.69	3	15.56	
Columns	55.69	3	18.56	
Methods	17.19	3	5.73	72.98/5.73 = 12.74
Within	437.87	6	72.98	
Total	557.44	15		

$$\sum T_{i..}^2/m = (326^2 + \cdots + 316^2)/4 = 106812.25$$
$$\sum T_{.j.}^2/m = (338^2 + \cdots + 320^2)/4 = 106821.25$$
$$\sum T_{..(k)}^2/m = (323^2 + \cdots + 333^2)/4 = 106782.75$$
$$\sum\sum X_{ij(k)}^2 = 93^2 + 87^2 + \cdots + 84^2 + 79^2 = 107323.00$$
$$T_{...}^2/m^2 = 1307^2/4^2 = 106765.56$$

The resulting F ratio value of 12.74 is significant at the 0.05 level thus indicating a difference in achievement by method.

If there are multiple values obtained for each of the cells in the original design, it will be necessary to add into the computational table a sampling error as another source of variation. The sum of squared deviations for this new factor would be:

$$SSD_s = \sum\sum\sum X_{ij(k)l}^2 - (\sum\sum T_{ij..}^2/r) \tag{13.12}$$

with $m^2(r - 1)$ degrees of freedom. The original "Within Groups" term now becomes

$$SSD_e = (\sum\sum T_{ij..}^2/r) - [(\sum T_{i...}^2 + \sum T_{.j..}^2 + \sum T_{..(k).}^2)/m] + 2(T_{....}^2/m^2r) \tag{13.13}$$

retaining the same number of degrees of freedom.

13.4 *Factorial Design.* Many times the behavioral science researcher is faced with data classified beyond the conventional row, column, block, or replicate designation. The experimental subjects may be classified as to age, sex, education, experience, race, etc. The researcher then becomes interested in the results as these various factors vary in degree and at the same time interact in varying combinations. This design then uses the format of the randomized complete block and tests the effect of various factors and is called the *factorial analysis in a randomized complete block design*. The factorial analysis concept "can" be imposed upon the completely randomized design or the Latin square design as well.

For purposes of illustration, a two-factor problem will be considered with factor A at three levels and factor B at four levels. The hypothetical data is presented in Table 13.8.

TABLE 13.8

HYPOTHETICAL DATA FOR A TWO-FACTOR FACTORIAL RANDOMIZED COMPLETE BLOCK DESIGN

	A_1				A_2				A_3				
	B_1	B_2	B_3	B_4	B_1	B_2	B_3	B_4	B_1	B_2	B_3	B_4	$T_{i..}$
	39	33	53	49	26	30	35	52	50	34	56	47	504
	57	47	56	43	51	34	36	47	34	30	48	40	523
	36	34	54	48	50	38	36	33	38	50	46	31	494
	54	35	39	41	36	31	41	30	27	52	27	55	468
	38	53	48	36	35	29	51	36	37	52	36	35	486
	29	48	29	41	50	46	39	45	58	47	47	52	531
	53	35	52	41	52	42	32	47	41	43	54	44	536
	55	36	36	40	30	48	36	29	46	54	52	37	499
	42	43	53	34	49	31	37	36	38	49	45	33	490
	39	30	53	30	33	35	46	28	38	37	45	39	453
$T_{.jk}$	442	394	473	403	412	364	389	383	407	448	456	413	
$T_{.j.}$	1712				1548				1724				4984

Each member of this table may be represented by the following expression:

$$X_{ijk} = \mu_{...} + \mu_{i..} + \mu_{.j.} + \mu_{..k} + \mu_{.jk} + e_{ijk} \qquad (13.14)$$

where

$\mu_{...}$ = grand mean

$\mu_{i..}$ = effect of mean of replicate

$\mu_{.j.}$ = effect of mean of j factor (A)

$\mu_{..k}$ = effect of mean of k factor (B)

$\mu_{.jk}$ = effect of interaction of (AB)

e_{ijk} = sampling effect.

The computational table utilized in the two-factor analysis is given in Table 13.9 and actually computed for the problem data in 13.10.

TABLE 13.9

COMPUTATIONAL TABLE FOR TWO-FACTOR FACTORIAL RANDOMIZED COMPLETE BLOCK DESIGN

Source of Variability	SSD	d.f.
Replicates	SSD_R	$(r-1)$
Factors		
A	SSD_A	$(a-1)$
B	SSD_B	$(b-1)$
Interaction		
AB	SSD_{AB}	$(a-1)(b-1)$
Within	SSD_e	$(r-1)(ab-1)$
Total	SSD_T	$(rab-1)$

In Table 13.9:

$$SSD_R = (\textstyle\sum T_{i..}^2/ab) - (T_{...}^2/rab) \tag{13.15}$$

$$SSD_A = (\textstyle\sum T_{.j.}^2/rb) - (T_{...}^2/rab) \tag{13.16}$$

$$SSD_B = (\textstyle\sum T_{..k}^2/ra) - (T_{...}^2/rab) \tag{13.17}$$

$$SSD_{AB} = (\textstyle\sum\sum T_{.jk}^2/r) - (\textstyle\sum T_{.j.}^2/rb) - (\textstyle\sum T_{..k}^2/ra) + (T_{...}^2/rab) \tag{13.18}$$

$$SSD_e = \textstyle\sum\sum\sum X_{ijk}^2 - (\textstyle\sum T_{i..}^2/ab) - (\textstyle\sum\sum T_{.jk}^2/r) + (T_{...}^2/rab) \tag{13.19}$$

$$SSD_T = \textstyle\sum\sum\sum X_{ijk}^2 - (T_{...}^2/rab) \tag{13.20}$$

TABLE 13.10

ANALYSIS OF TWO-FACTOR DATA PRESENTED IN TABLE 13.8

Source of Variability	SSD	d.f.	MS	F
Replicates	528.54	9	58.73	
Factors				
A	483.47	2	241.74	$241.74/68.94 = 3.51^*$
B	307.27	3	102.42	$102.42/68.94 = 1.49$
Interaction				
AB	391.73	6	65.29	$68.94/65.29 = 1.06$
Within Groups	6824.86	99	68.94	
Total	8535.87	119		

*Significant at the 0.05 level

$$(\textstyle\sum T_{i..}^2/ab) = (504^2 + \cdots + 453^2)/12 = 207530.67$$
$$(\textstyle\sum T_{.j.}^2/rb) = (1712^2 + \cdots + 1724^2)/40 = 207485.60$$
$$(\textstyle\sum T_{..k}^2/ra) = (1261^2 + \cdots + 1199^2)/40 = 207309.40$$
$$(\textstyle\sum\sum T_{.jk}^2/r) = (442^2 + \cdots + 413^2)/10 = 208184.60$$

$$\Sigma\Sigma\Sigma X_{ijk}^2 = 39^2 + 57^2 + \cdots + 33^2 + 39^2 = 215538.00$$
$$(T_{...}^2/rab) = 4984^2/120 = 207002.13$$

The concept of "interaction" is presented clearly in the factorial analysis. In the problem presented as an example, there were three levels of Factor A (A_1, A_2, A_3) and four levels of factor B (B_1, B_2, B_3, B_4). As such there are many ways (to be exact there are twelve) in which one of the A levels may interact with one of the B levels:

	B_1	B_2	B_3	B_4
A_1	A_1B_1	A_1B_2	A_1B_3	A_1B_4
A_2	A_2B_1	A_2B_2	A_2B_3	A_2B_4
A_3	A_3B_1	A_3B_2	A_3B_3	A_3B_4

The interaction term of the analysis considers *all* of these level-to-level interactions simultaneously for significance. Thus the hypothesis of no significant differences between levels of each of the main effects as well as the hypothesis of no significant change between different level-to-level combinations may be tested.

By extending the concepts presented earlier in this chapter, the factorial design may be extended to n factors at m levels as well as the use of completely random and mixed models.

This has been a very superficial glance at *some* of the available designs. If the reader is interested in further study, he may refer to the references at the end of this chapter.

REFERENCES

Ferguson, George A. *Statistical Analysis in Psychology and Education.* New York: McGraw-Hill Book Company, Inc., 1966. Chapters 18 and 19.

Freund, John C., and Williams, Frank J. *Elementary Business Statistics: The Modern Approach.* Englewood Cliffs, New Jersey: Prentice-Hall, Inc., 1964. Chapter 12.

Guenther, William C. *Concepts of Statistical Inference.* New York: McGraw-Hill Book Company, Inc,. 1965. Chapter 7.

Lindquist, E. F. *Design and Analysis of Experiments in Psychology and Education.* Boston: Houghton Mifflin Company, 1953. Chapter 4.

McNemar, Quinn. *Psychological Statistics.* Third Edition. New York: John Wiley and Sons, Inc., 1962. Chapter 16.

Ostle, Bernard. *Statistics in Research.* Ames, Iowa: The Iowa State University Press, 1954. Chapter 10.

Winer, B. J. *Statistical Principles in Experimental Design.* New York: McGraw-Hill Book Company, Inc., 1962. Chapters 5 and 6.

Yamane, Taro. *Statistics, An Introductory Analysis.* New York: Harper and Row, Publishers, 1964. Chapter 21.

14

ANALYSIS OF COVARIANCE

After studying the chapters on linear regression and analysis of variance, the reader may appreciate the value of these two techniques. When combined, the basic concepts of these two different techniques are of great value to the behavioral scientists. Many studies have had the purpose of testing hypotheses about the effects of treatments upon achievement. Many of these researches overlooked such factors as intelligence, prior knowledge, aptitude, etc., as they affected achievement scores. As the intelligence level rises, it is reasonable to assume that achievement should rise also. The real test of effectiveness of the various involved treatments would come when the achievement scores have been "adjusted" to remove the effects of these linear regression factors. If the regression effect for all values of the independent variable X (i.e., intelligence) is reduced to zero, the condition of no significant effect would result in all $\mu_{y.x}$ values lying on the horizontal regression equation of $Y_c = a_{y.x}$. The technique which in essence "removes" the linear regression effect and then tests the hypotheses of no significant differences among the adjusted means is called the *analysis of covariance*.

14.1 *Basic Assumptions.* In addition to the assumptions basic to the analysis of variance technique, we have the added assumptions of:

(1) All variables of Y are to be independent and normally distributed (or nearly so);
(2) Where possible, all variances should be homoscedastic;
(3) Fixed values of the independent variable should be used;
(4) The regression equation between the independent values of X and values of $\mu_{y.x}$ must be linear.

The variables for the four basic designs considered in Chapters 10 and 13 are:

(1) For completely randomized design (one-way classification)
$$Y_{ij} = \mu_{..} + \mu_{i.} + B_{y.x}X_{ij} + e_{ij} \tag{14.1}$$

(2) For randomized complete block design

$$Y_{ij} = \mu_{..} + \mu_{i.} + \mu_{.j} + B_{y.x}X_{ij} + e_{ij} \qquad (14.2)$$

(3) For Latin square design

$$Y_{ijk} = \mu_{...} + \mu_{i..} + \mu_{.j.} + \mu_{..(k)} + B_{y.x}X_{ij(k)} + e_{ij(k)} \qquad (14.3)$$

(4) For randomized complete block two-factor factorial design

$$Y_{ijk} = \mu_{...} + \mu_{i...} + \mu_{.j.} + \mu_{..k} + \mu_{.jk} + B_{y.x}X_{ijk} + e_{ijk} \qquad (14.4)$$

14.2 Completely Randomized Design. To illustrate each of the co-variance designs the same basic problem will be used but with variations. Suppose that a researcher desires to test the effectiveness of five different motivational devices as demonstrated by test scores. A point of interest to the investigator is the amount of initial knowledge possessed by the student. At the beginning of the experiment, a test is given to determine the basic knowledge of the students involved. These values are identified as the X values in Table 14.1. After the completion of the experiment, an equivalent form of this test is given and these scores are indicated in Table 14.1 as the Y values.

TABLE 14.1

CODED PRE-TEST (X) SCORES AND POST-TEST (Y) SCORES OF 50 STUDENTS UNDER FIVE DIFFERENT MOTIVATIONAL STIMULI

| Student Number | Stimulus Type | | | | | | | | | |
| | I | | II | | III | | IV | | V | |
	X	Y	X	Y	X	Y	X	Y	X	Y
1	27	25	26	42	27	43	28	51	19	24
2	33	40	22	47	39	52	12	24	43	47
3	26	40	37	34	43	45	33	47	21	30
4	40	50	33	51	36	42	33	24	40	46
5	39	50	17	30	27	50	29	45	45	41
6	29	42	29	50	43	38	34	45	34	40
7	16	40	27	30	24	33	15	18	40	40
8	30	44	41	41	37	43	22	52	19	30
9	29	45	34	47	39	37	41	46	27	42
10	36	39	36	28	28	30	32	44	35	36
Σ	305	415	302	400	334	413	279	396	323	376
$\Sigma X_{ij}Y_{ij}$	12872		12124		13944		11602		12686	

$$\Sigma\Sigma X_{ij} = T_{X..} = 1543 \qquad \Sigma\Sigma X_{ij}^2 = 50653$$
$$\Sigma\Sigma Y_{ij} = T_{Y..} = 2000 \qquad \Sigma\Sigma Y_{ij}^2 = 83602$$
$$\Sigma\Sigma X_{ij}Y_{ij} = T_{(XY)..} = 63259$$

These test scores for testing the hypothesis of no significant difference between motivational stimuli are shown in Table 14.1. Table 14.2 presents the computational table for the covariance analysis for a completely randomized design. The problem is analyzed and presented in Table 14.3.

In Table 14.2:

$$SSD_X = (\sum T_{X_{ij}}^2/n_{.j}) - (T_{X..}^2/N) \tag{14.5}$$

$$SSD_{WX} = \sum\sum X_{ij}^2 - (\sum T_{X_{ij}}^2/n_{.j}) \tag{14.6}$$

$$SSD_{TX} = \sum\sum X_{ij}^2 - (T_{X..}^2/N) \tag{14.7}$$

$$SSP_{XY} = \{\sum[(T_{X_{ij}})(T_{Y_{ij}})]/n_{.j}\} - [(T_{X..})(T_{Y..})/N] \tag{14.8}$$

$$SSP_{WXY} = T_{(XY)..} - \{\sum[(T_{X..})(T_{Y..})]/n_{.j}\} \tag{14.9}$$

$$SSP_{TXY} = T_{(XY)..} - [(T_{X..})(T_{Y..})/N] \tag{14.10}$$

$$SSD_Y = (\sum T_{Y_{ij}}^2/n_{.j}) - (T_{Y..}^2/N) \tag{14.11}$$

$$SSD_{WY} = \sum\sum Y_{ij}^2 - (\sum T_{Y_{ij}}^2/n_{.j}) \tag{14.12}$$

$$SSD_{TY} = \sum\sum Y_{ij}^2 - (T_{Y..}^2/N) \tag{14.13}$$

$$SSD_{AW} = SSD_{WY} - (SSD_{WXY}^2/SSD_{WX}) \tag{14.14}$$

$$SSD_{AT} = SSD_{TY} - (SSD_{TXY}^2/SSD_{TX}) \tag{14.15}$$

$$SSD_{AAT} = SSD_{AT} - SSD_{AW} \tag{14.16}$$

$$F = MS_W/MS_{AAT} \tag{14.17}$$

$$MS_W = SSD_{AW}/(N - k - 1) \tag{14.18}$$

$$MS_{AAT} = SSD_{AAT}/(k - 1) \tag{14.19}$$

Using the data and computations of Table 14.1, we find that:

$$(\sum T_{X_{ij}}^2/n_{.j}) = (305^2 + \cdots + 323^2)/10 = 47795.50$$

$$(\sum T_{Y_{ij}}^2/n_{.j}) = (415^2 + \cdots + 376^2)/10 = 80098.60$$

$$\sum[(T_{X_{ij}})(T_{Y_{ij}})]/n_{.j} = [(305)(415) + \cdots + (323)(376)]/10 = 61724.90$$

$$T_{X..}^2/N = 1543^2/50 = 47616.98$$

$$T_{Y..}^2/N = 80000.00$$

$$[(T_{X..})(T_{Y..})]/N = [(1543)(2000)]/50 = 61720.00$$

The F ratio is not significant, at the 0.05 level; therefore no difference may be attributed in the post-test scores to the different motivational stimuli.

To utilize the covariance analysis technique properly, we need to have some evidence that a regression factor is entering into the test results. The

TABLE 14.2

COMPUTATIONAL TABLE FOR ANALYSIS OF COVARIANCE OF COMPLETELY RANDOMIZED DESIGN

Source of Variability	Sum of Squared Deviations (SSD) and Sum of Deviation Cross Products (SSP)			About Regression Deviation		
	$\sum x^2$	$\sum xy$	$\sum y^2$	$\sum y^2 - (\sum xy)^2/\sum x^2$	d.f.	MS
Between Treatments	SSD_X	SSP_{XY}	SSD_Y	– – – –	– – –	– –
Within Treatments	SSD_{WX}	SSP_{WXY}	SSD_{WY}	SSD_{AW}	$N-k-1$	MS_W
Total	SSD_{TX}	SSP_{TXY}	SSD_{TY}	SSD_{AT}	$N-2$	– – –
Among Adjusted Treatments				SSD_{AAT}	$k-1$	MS_{AAT}

TABLE 14.3

ANALYSIS OF COVARIANCE FOR COMPLETELY RANDOMIZED DESIGN EXAMPLE PROBLEM

Source of Variability	SSD and SSP			About Regression Deviation			
	$\sum x^2$	$\sum xy$	$\sum y^2$	$\sum y^2 - [(\sum xy)^2/\sum x^2]$	d.f.	MS	F
Between Tmts.	178.52	4.90	98.60	– – – –	– –	– – –	– – – – –
Within Tmts.	2957.50	1534.10	3503.40	2707.64	44	61.54	61.54/34.78 = 1.77
Total	3136.02	1539.00	3602.00	2846.74	48	– –	– – – – –
Among Adjusted Tmt. Means				139.10	4	34.78	

TABLE 14.4

COMPUTATIONAL FORMAT FOR COVARIANCE ANALYSIS
OF
RANDOMIZED COMPLETE BLOCK DESIGN

Source of Variability	SSD and SSP		
	$\sum x^2$	$\sum xy$	$\sum y^2$
Between Blocks	SSD_{BX}	SSP_{BXY}	SSD_{BY}
Between Treatments	SSD_{TX}	SSP_{TXY}	SSD_{TY}
Within Groups	SSD_{WX}	SSP_{WXY}	SSD_{WY}
Total	SSD_{TTX}	SSP_{TTXY}	SSD_{TTY}
Among Adjusted Treatments			

reader may remember from the discussion on regression that it is possible to test the hypothesis of $H_o : B_{y.x} = 0$, or of no regression effect. This hypothesis should be tested prior to the covariance analysis. This may be done by use of the following F ratio:

$$F = (SSD_{WXY}/SSD_{WX})/MS_W, \quad \text{d.f.} = 1, (N - k - 1) \quad (14.20)$$

For our problem, this would be

$$F = [(1534.10)^2/2957.50]/61.54 = 12.93$$

When this F ratio is checked for significance, it is found to exceed the value of $F_{0.01(1,44)} = 7.27$ thus rejecting the null hypothesis of no regression effect ($B_{y.x} = 0$) and thereby justifying the use of the covariance technique.

14.3 Randomized Complete Block Design. When the appropriate basic design is that of the randomized complete block and the null hypothesis of no regression effect ($B_{y.x} = 0$) is rejected, the covariance analysis form for the randomized complete block is appropriate. The computational format is given in Table 14.4, where:

$$SSD_{BX} = \left(\sum_{i=1}^{b} T_{X_{ij}}^2/k \right) - (T_{X..}^2/bk) \qquad (14.21)$$

$$SSD_{TX} = \left(\sum_{j=1}^{k} T_{X_{ij}}^2/b \right) - (T_{X..}^2/bk) \qquad (14.22)$$

About Regression Deviation			
$\sum y^2 - (\sum xy)^2/\sum x^2$	d.f.	MS	F
- - - - - - - - - - -	- - - - - - - - - - - -	- - - -	- - - - - - - -
- - - - - - - - - - -	- - - - - - - - - - - -	- - - -	- - - - - - - -
SSD_{AW}	$[(b-1)(k-1)] - 1$	MS_W	MS_{AAT}/MS_{AW}
SSD_{ATT}	$[b(k-1)] - 1$	- - - -	- - - - - - - -
SSD_{AAT}	$k - 1$	MS_{AAT}	

$$SSD_{WX} = \sum\sum X_{ij}^2 - \left(\sum_{i=1}^{b} T_{X_{ij}}^2/k\right) - \left(\sum_{j=1}^{k} T_{X_{ij}}^2/b\right) + (T_{X..}^2/bk) \tag{14.23}$$

$$SSD_{TTX} = \sum\sum X_{ij}^2 - \left(\sum_{i=1}^{b} T_{X_{ij}}^2/k\right) \tag{14.24}$$

$$SSP_{BXY} = \left\{\sum_{i=1}^{b} [(T_{X_{ij}})(T_{Y_{ij}})]/k\right\} - [(T_{X..})(T_{Y..})/bk] \tag{14.25}$$

$$SSP_{TXY} = \sum_{j=1}^{k} [(T_{X_{ij}})(T_{Y_{ij}})]/b - [(T_{X..})(T_{Y..})/bk] \tag{14.26}$$

$$SSP_{WXY} = \sum\sum [X_{ij}Y_{ij}] - \left\{\sum_{i=1}^{b} [(T_{X_{ij}})(T_{Y_{ij}})]/k\right\}$$
$$- \left\{\sum_{j=1}^{k} [(T_{X_{ij}})(T_{Y_{ij}})]/b\right\}$$
$$+ [(T_{X..})(T_{Y..})/bk] \tag{14.27}$$

$$SSP_{TTXY} = \sum\sum [X_{ij}Y_{ij}] - \left\{\sum_{i=1}^{b} [(T_{X_{ij}})(T_{Y_{ij}})]/k\right\} \tag{14.28}$$

$$SSD_{BY} = \left(\sum_{i=1}^{b} T_{Y_{ij}}^2/k\right) - (T_{Y..}^2/bk) \tag{14.29}$$

$$SSD_{TY} = \left(\sum_{j=1}^{k} T^2_{Y_{ij}}/b \right) - (T^2_{Y..}/bk) \tag{14.30}$$

$$SSD_{WY} = \sum\sum Y^2_{ij} - \left(\sum_{i=1}^{b} T^2_{Y_{ij}}/k \right) - \left(\sum_{j=1}^{k} T^2_{Y_{ij}}/b \right) + (T^2_{Y..}/bk) \tag{14.31}$$

$$SSD_{TTY} = \sum\sum Y^2_{ij} - \left(\sum_{i=1}^{b} T^2_{Y_{ij}}/k \right) \tag{14.32}$$

$$SSD_{AW} = SSD_{WY} - [(SSP^2_{WXY})/SSD_{WX}] \tag{14.33}$$

$$SSD_{ATT} = SSD_{TTY} - [(SSP^2_{TTXY})/SSD_{TTX}] \tag{14.34}$$

$$SSD_{AAT} = SSD_{ATT} - SSD_{AW} \tag{14.35}$$

$$MS_W = SSD_{AW}/\{[(b-1)(k-1)]-1\} \tag{14.36}$$

$$MS_{AAT} = SSD_{AAT}/(k-1) \tag{14.36a}$$

For purposes of an example, let us expand the data in Table 13.3 to include a regression factor X. These data are shown in Table 14.5.

TABLE 14.5

MEAN TEST SCORES (Y) OF STUDENTS AND INTELLIGENCE SCORES (X) USING THREE DIFFERENT ANSWER FORMS

Classes	Answer Sheet Forms								
	A		B		C				
	X	Y	X	Y	X	Y	$\sum X$	$\sum Y$	$\sum XY$
1	106	75	119	83	115	82	340	240	27257
2	118	79	111	81	101	86	330	246	26999
3	102	78	102	78	119	85	323	241	26027
Σ	326	232	332	242	335	253	993	727	
$\sum XY$	25228		26824		28231				80283

$$\sum\sum X_{ij}^2 = 110037$$

$$\sum\sum Y_{ij}^2 = 58829$$

$$\sum_{i=1}^{b} T_{X_{ij}}^2/k = (340^2 + \cdots + 323^2)/3 = 109609.67$$

$$\sum_{j=1}^{k} T_{X_{ij}}^2/b = (326^2 + \cdots + 335^2)/3 = 109575.00$$

$$\sum_{i=1}^{b} T_{Y_{ij}}^2/k = (240^2 + \cdots + 241^2)/3 = 58732.33$$

$$\sum_{j=1}^{k} T_{Y_{ij}}^2/b = (232^2 + \cdots + 253^2)/3 = 58799.00$$

$$\sum_{i=1}^{b} [(T_{X_{ij}})(T_{Y_{ij}})]/k = [(340)(240) + \cdots + (323)(241)]/3 = 80207.67$$

$$\sum_{j=1}^{k} [(T_{X_{ij}})(T_{Y_{ij}})]/b = [(326)(232) + \cdots + (335)(253)]/3 = 80243.67$$

$$T_{X..}^2/bk = 993^2/9 = 109561$$

$$T_{Y..}^2/bk = 727^2/9 = 58725.44$$

$$[(T_{X..})(T_{Y..})]/bk = [(993)(727)]/9 = 80212.33$$

To test the hypothesis that $B_{y.x} = 0$, the F ratio of

$$F = 43.99^2/[(413.33)(3)] = 1.56$$

which actually is not significant, thus indicating that the covariance analysis was not really needed.

14.4 *Latin Square Design.* Without further illustration, the computational format for the covariance analysis of the Latin square design is presented in Table 14.7. This variation of the Latin square design presented in Chapter 13 permits the analysis of data when a regression factor is present.

TABLE 14.6

COVARIANCE ANALYSIS OF THE RANDOMIZED COMPLETE BLOCK DESIGN EXAMPLE PROBLEM

Source of Variability	SSD and SSP			About Regression Deviation			
	$\sum x^2$	$\sum xy$	$\sum y^2$	dev.	d.f.	MS	F
Between Blocks	48.67	−4.66	6.89	− − −	− −	− − −	− − −
Between Treatments	14.00	31.34	73.56	− − −	− −	− − −	− − −
Within Groups	413.33	43.99	23.11	18.43	3	6.14	32.48/6.14 = 5.29
Total	427.33	75.33	96.67	83.39	5	− − −	− − −
Among Adjusted Treatments				64.96	2	32.48	

TABLE 14.7

COMPUTATIONAL FORMAT FOR THE COVARIANCE ANALYSIS OF THE LATIN SQUARE DESIGN OF SIZE $(m \times m)$

Source of Variability	SSD and SSP			About Regression Deviation			
	$\sum x^2$	$\sum xy$	$\sum y^2$	dev.	d.f.	MS	F
Row Effect	SSD_{XR}	SSP_{XYR}	SSD_{YR}	− − −	− − −	− − −	− − −
Column Effect	SSD_{XC}	SSP_{XYC}	SSD_{YC}	− − −	− − −	− − −	− − −
Between Treatments (m)	SSD_{XT}	SSP_{XYT}	SSD_{YT}	− − −	− − −	− − −	− − −
Within Groups	SSD_{XW}	SSP_{XYW}	SSD_{YW}	SSD_{AW}	$[(m-1)(m-2)-1]$	MS_W	MS_{AAT}/MS_{AW}
Total	SSD_{XTT}	SSP_{XYTT}	SSD_{YTT}	SSD_{ATT}	$[(m-1)^2-1]$	− − −	− − −
Among Adjusted Treatments				SSD_{AAT}	$(m-1)$	MS_{AAT}	

The entries in Table 14.7 are computed as follows:

$$SSD_{XR} = \left(\sum_{i=1}^{m} T^2_{X_{i..}}/m \right) - (T^2_{X...}/m^2) \tag{14.37}$$

$$SSD_{XC} = \left(\sum_{j=1}^{m} T^2_{X_{.j.}}/m \right) - (T^2_{X...}/m^2) \tag{14.38}$$

$$SSD_{XT} = \left(\sum_{k=1}^{m} T^2_{X_{..k}}/m \right) - (T^2_{X...}/m^2) \tag{14.39}$$

$$SSD_{XW} = \sum\sum X^2_{ijk} - \left(\sum_{i=1}^{m} T^2_{X_{i..}}/m \right) - \left(\sum_{j=1}^{m} T^2_{X_{.j.}}/m \right) + (T^2_{X...}/m^2) \tag{14.40}$$

$$SSD_{XTT} = \sum\sum X^2_{ijk} - (\sum T^2_{X_{i..}}/m) - (\sum T^2_{X_{.j.}}/m) + (\sum T^2_{X_{..k}}/m) \tag{14.41}$$

$$SSP_{XYR} = \sum[(T_{X_{i..}})(T_{Y_{i..}})]/m - (T_X...)(T_Y...)/m^2 \tag{14.42}$$

$$SSP_{XYC} = \sum[(T_{X_{.j.}})(T_{Y_{.j.}})]/m - (T_X...)(T_Y...)/m^2 \tag{14.43}$$

$$SSP_{XYT} = \sum[(T_{X_{..k}})(T_{Y_{..k}})]/m - (T_X...)(T_Y...)/m^2 \tag{14.44}$$

$$SSP_{XYW} = \sum\sum[(X_{ijk})(Y_{ijk})] - \sum[(T_{X_{i..}})(T_{Y_{i..}})]/m \\ - \sum[(T_{X_{.j.}})(T_{Y_{.j.}})]/m + (T_X...)(T_Y...)/m^2 \tag{14.45}$$

$$SSP_{XYTT} = \sum\sum[(X_{ijk})(Y_{ijk})] - \sum[(T_{X_{i..}})(T_{Y_{i..}})]/m \\ - \sum[(T_{X_{.j.}})(T_{Y_{.j.}})]/m + \sum[(T_{X_{..k}})(T_{Y_{..k}})]/m \tag{14.46}$$

$$SSD_{YR} = \sum T^2_{Y_{i..}}/m - T^2_Y.../m^2 \tag{14.47}$$

$$SSD_{YC} = \sum T^2_{Y_{.j.}}/m - T^2_Y.../m^2 \tag{14.48}$$

$$SSD_{YT} = \sum T^2_{Y_{..k}}/m - T^2_Y.../m^2 \tag{14.49}$$

$$SSD_{YW} = \sum\sum Y^2_{ijk} - \sum T^2_{Y_{i..}}/m - \sum T^2_{Y_{.j.}}/m + T^2_Y.../m^2 \tag{14.50}$$

$$SSD_{YTT} = \sum\sum Y^2_{ijk} - \sum T^2_{Y_{i..}}/m - \sum T^2_{Y_{.j.}}/m + \sum T^2_{Y_{..k}}/m \tag{14.51}$$

The test of significance is the F ratio between the adjusted mean squares of the "within group" factor and the "adjusted treatment means" factor.

TABLE 14.8

COMPUTATIONAL FORMAT FOR COVARIANCE ANALYSIS OF TWO-FACTOR FACTORIAL RANDOMIZED COMPLETE BLOCK DESIGN

Source of Variability	SSD_X	SSP_{XY}	SSD_Y
Replicates (i)	SSD_{FRX}	SSP_{FRXY}	SSD_{FRY}
Factor			
A	SSD_{FAX}	SSP_{FAXY}	SSD_{FAY}
B	SSD_{FBX}	SSP_{FBXY}	SSD_{FBY}
Interaction			
AB	$SSD_{F(AB)X}$	$SSP_{F(AB)XY}$	$SSD_{F(AB)Y}$
Within Groups (W)	SSD_{FWX}	SSP_{FWXY}	SSD_{FWY}
Total $(A+W)$	$SSD_{F(A+W)X}$	$SSP_{F(A+W)XY}$	$SSD_{F(A+W)Y}$
Total $(B+W)$	$SSD_{F(B+W)X}$	$SSP_{F(B+W)XY}$	$SSD_{F(B+W)Y}$
Total $(AB+W)$	$SSD_{F(AB+W)X}$	$SSP_{F(AB+W)XY}$	$SSD_{F(AB+W)Y}$

Adjusted A Factor
Adjusted B Factor
Adjusted AB Interaction

14.5 *Two-Factor Factorial Randomized Complete Block.* As previously discussed, this particular design allows for the testing of significance for *all* main effects, and interactions. The reader should remember that the factorial concept may be applied to *all* three models or types as well as to *all* of the basic designs presented in Chapter 13. The necessary computations for testing the implied hypotheses are indicated in Table 14.8, where:

$$SSD_{FRX} = (\sum T^2_{X_{i..}}/ab) - (T^2_X.../rab) \tag{14.52}$$

$$SSD_{FAX} = (\sum T^2_{X_{.j.}}/rb) - (T^2_X.../rab) \tag{14.53}$$

$$SSD_{FBX} = (\sum T^2_{X_{..k}}/ra) - (T^2_X.../rab) \tag{14.54}$$

$$SSD_{F(AB)X} = (\sum\sum T^2_{X_{.jk}}/r) - (\sum T^2_{X_{.j.}}/rb) \\ - (\sum T^2_{X_{..k}}/ra) + (T^2_X.../rab) \tag{14.55}$$

$$SSD_{FWX} = \sum\sum\sum X^2_{ijk} - (\sum T^2_{X_{i..}}/ab) \\ - (\sum\sum T^2_{X_{.jk}}/r) + (T^2_X.../rab) \tag{14.56}$$

	About Regression		
ASSD	d.f.	AMS	F
- - - - - - -	- -	- - - - -	- - - - - - - - -
- - - - - - -	- -	- - - - -	- - - - - - - - -
- - - - - - -	- -	- - - - -	- - - - - - - - -
- - - - - - -	- -	- - - - -	- - - - - - - - -
SSD_{FW}	$[(r-1)(ab-1)]-1$	AMS_{FW}	- - - - - - - - -
$SSD_{F(A+W)}$	$\{(a-1)+[(r-1)(ab-1)]-1\}$	- - - - -	- - - - - - - - -
$SSD_{F(B+W)}$	$\{(b-1)+[(r-1)(ab-1)]-1\}$	- - - - -	- - - - - - - - -
$SSD_{F(AB+W)}$	$\{[(a-1)(b-1)]+[(r-1)(ab-1)]-1\}$	- - - - -	- - - - - - - - -
FD_{FA}	$(a-1)$	AMS_{FA}	AMS_{FA}/AMS_{FW}
FD_{FB}	$(b-1)$	AMS_{FB}	AMS_{FB}/AMS_{FW}
FD_{FAB}	$(a-1)(b-1)$	AMS_{FAB}	AMS_{FAB}/AMS_{FW}

$$SSD_{F(A+W)X} = \sum\sum\sum X_{ijk}^2 - (\sum T_{X_{i..}}^2/ab)$$
$$- (\sum\sum T_{X_{.jk}}^2/r) + (\sum T_{X_{.j.}}^2/rb) \quad (14.57)$$

$$SSD_{F(B+W)X} = \sum\sum\sum X_{ijk}^2 - (\sum T_{X_{i..}}^2/ab)$$
$$- (\sum\sum T_{X_{.jk}}^2/r) + (\sum T_{X_{..k}}^2/ra) \quad (14.58)$$

$$SSD_{F(AB+W)X} = \sum\sum\sum X_{ijk}^2 - (\sum T_{X_{i..}}^2/ab) - (\sum T_{X_{.j.}}^2/rb)$$
$$- (\sum T_{X_{..k}}^2/ra) + 2(T_{X_{...}}^2/rab) \quad (14.59)$$

$$SSP_{FRXY} = \{\sum[(T_{X_{i..}})(T_{Y_{i..}})]/ab\} - [(T_{X_{...}})(T_{Y_{...}})/rab] \quad (14.60)$$

$$SSP_{FAXY} = \{\sum[(T_{X_{.j.}})(T_{Y_{.j.}})]/rb\} - [(T_{X_{...}})(T_{Y_{...}})/rab] \quad (14.61)$$

$$SSP_{FBXY} = \{\sum[(T_{X_{..k}})(T_{Y_{..k}})]/ra\} - [(T_{X_{...}})(T_{Y_{...}})/rab] \quad (14.62)$$

$$SSP_{F(AB)XY} = \{\sum\sum[(T_{X_{.jk}})(T_{Y_{.jk}})]/r\} - \{\sum[(T_{X_{.j.}})(T_{Y_{.j.}})]/rb\}$$
$$- \{\sum[(T_{X_{..k}})(T_{Y_{..k}})]/ra\}$$
$$+ [(T_{X_{...}})(T_{Y_{...}})/rab] \quad (14.63)$$

$$SSP_{FWXY} = \sum\sum\sum[(X_{ijk})(Y_{ijk})] - \{\sum[(T_{X_{i..}})(T_{Y_{i..}})]/ab\}$$
$$- \{\sum\sum[(T_{X_{.jk}})(T_{Y_{.jk}})]/r\}$$
$$+ [(T_{X...})(T_{Y...})/rab] \qquad (14.64)$$

$$SSP_{F(A+W)XY} = \sum\sum\sum[(X_{ijk})(Y_{ijk})] - \sum[(T_{X_{i..}})(T_{Y_{i..}})]/ab$$
$$- \sum\sum[(T_{X_{.jk}})(T_{Y_{.jk}})]/r$$
$$+ \sum[(T_{X_{.j.}})(T_{Y_{.j.}})]/rb \qquad (14.65)$$

$$SSP_{F(B+W)XY} = \sum\sum\sum[(X_{ijk})(Y_{ijk})] - \sum[(T_{X_{i..}})(T_{Y_{i..}})]/ab$$
$$- \sum\sum[(T_{X_{.jk}})(T_{Y_{.jk}})]/r$$
$$+ \sum[(T_{X_{..k}})(T_{Y_{..k}})]/ra \qquad (14.66)$$

$$SSP_{F(AB+W)XY} = \sum\sum\sum[(X_{ijk})(Y_{ijk})] - \sum[(T_{X_{i..}})(T_{Y_{i..}})]/ab$$
$$- \sum[(T_{X_{.j.}})(T_{Y_{.j.}})]/rb$$
$$- \sum[(T_{X_{..k}})(T_{Y_{..k}})]/ra$$
$$+ 2[(T_{X...})(T_{Y...})]/rab \qquad (14.67)$$

$$SSD_{FRY} = (\sum T^2_{Y_{i..}}/ab) - (T^2_{Y...}/rab) \qquad (14.68)$$

$$SSD_{FAY} = (\sum T^2_{Y_{.j.}}/rb) - (T^2_{Y...}/rab) \qquad (14.69)$$

$$SSD_{FBY} = (\sum T^2_{Y_{..k}}/ra) - (T^2_{Y...}/rab) \qquad (14.70)$$

$$SSD_{FABY} = (\sum\sum T^2_{Y_{.jk}}/r) - (\sum T^2_{Y_{.j.}}/rb)$$
$$- (\sum T^2_{Y_{..k}}/ra) + (T^2_{Y...}/rab) \qquad (14.71)$$

$$SSD_{FWY} = \sum\sum\sum Y^2_{ijk} - (\sum T^2_{Y_{i..}}/ab)$$
$$- (\sum\sum T^2_{Y_{.jk}}/r) + (T^2_{Y...}/rab) \qquad (14.72)$$

$$SSD_{F(A+W)Y} = \sum\sum\sum Y^2_{ijk} - (\sum T^2_{Y_{i..}}/ab)$$
$$- (\sum\sum T^2_{Y_{.jk}}/r) + (\sum T^2_{Y_{.j.}}/rb) \qquad (14.73)$$

$$SSD_{F(B+W)Y} = \sum\sum\sum Y^2_{ijk} - (\sum T^2_{Y_{i..}}/ab)$$
$$- (\sum\sum T^2_{Y_{.jk}}/r) + (\sum T^2_{Y_{..k}}/ra) \qquad (14.74)$$

$$SSD_{F(AB+W)Y} = \sum\sum\sum Y^2_{ijk} - (\sum T^2_{Y_{i..}}/ab)$$
$$- (\sum T^2_{Y_{.j.}}/rb) - (\sum T^2_{Y_{..k}}/ra)$$
$$+ 2[(T^2_{Y...}/rab)] \qquad (14.75)$$

$$ASSD_{FW} = SSD_{FWY} - [(SSP_{FWXY})^2/SSD_{FWX}] \tag{14.76}$$

$$ASSD_{F(A+W)} = SSD_{F(A+W)Y} - [(SSP_{F(A+W)XY})^2/SSD_{F(A+W)X}] \tag{14.77}$$

$$ASSD_{F(B+W)} = SSD_{F(B+W)Y} - [(SSP_{F(B+W)XY})^2/SSD_{F(B+W)X}] \tag{14.78}$$

$$ASSD_{F(AB+W)} = SSD_{F(AB+W)Y} - [(SSP_{F(AB+W)XY})^2/SSD_{F(AB+W)X}] \tag{14.79}$$

$$AFD_{FA} = ASSD_{F(A+W)} - ASSD_{FW} \tag{14.80}$$

$$AFD_{FB} = ASSD_{F(B+W)} - ASSD_{FW} \tag{14.81}$$

$$AFD_{FAB} = ASSD_{F(AB+W)} - ASSD_{FW} \tag{14.82}$$

$$AMS_{FW} = ASSD_{FW}/[(r-1)(ab-1)-1] \tag{14.83}$$

$$AMS_{FA} = AFD_{FA}/(a-1) \tag{14.84}$$

$$AMS_{FB} = AFD_{FB}/(b-1) \tag{14.85}$$

$$AMS_{FAB} = AFD_{FAB}/[(a-1)(b-1)] \tag{14.86}$$

REFERENCES

Federer, Walter T. *Experimental Design: Theory and Application.* New York: The Macmillan Company, Inc., 1955. Chapter XVI.

Ferguson, George A. *Statistical Analysis in Psychology and Education.* New York: McGraw-Hill Book Company, Inc., 1966. Chapter 20.

Lindquist, E. F. *Design and Analysis of Experiments in Psychology and Education.* Boston: Houghton Mifflin Company, 1953. Chapter 14.

McNemar, Quinn. *Psychological Statistics.* Third Edition. New York: John Wiley and Sons, Inc., 1962. Chapter 18.

Ostle, Bernard. *Statistics in Research.* Ames, Iowa: The Iowa State University Press, 1954. Chapter 13.

Scheffé, Henry. *The Analysis of Variance.* New York: John Wiley and Sons, Inc., 1959. Chapter 6.

Winer, B. J. *Statistical Principles in Experimental Design.* New York: McGraw-Hill Book Company, Inc., 1962. Chapter 11.

15

OTHER STATISTICAL PROCEDURES

In many instances the researcher is unable to meet all the necessary underlying assumptions for the utilization of the conventional parametric statistical techniques.   In cases where data are in a rating form, or are non-normal, or qualitative in nature, the investigator must resort to certain techniques referred to as non-parametric techniques.   For the reader who desires further discussion of these techniques, a presentation of non-parametric techniques is made in texts by Fraser, Siegel, and Tate.

15.1 *Single Sample Techniques.* There are several techniques available which are appropriate for use with single samples.   The use of the *binomial probability distribution* to determine the likelihood of the occurrence of a sequence of dichotomous events is one procedure which may be used. Another is that of the *Chi-square test for goodness of fit* which was discussed at some length in Chapter 9.   Another test used quite frequently involves the testing for the *randomness* of a given sample.   The technique used for this is the *runs test* for single samples.   In essence, the test evaluates the occurrence of events in a sample as they fall around some median value.   The procedure for this technique will be demonstrated through the use of two problems — one where the sample has $n > 20$ and the other where the sample size is $n < 20$.

A physics teacher used an assessment of laboratory technique as part of his final evaluation.   Since all of the students could not be observed and rated on the same day, it was of interest to know whether or not evaluation on different days would have a demonstrable effect on the scores.   The teacher had a class of 26 students and each day rated as many as three students.

The median for the distribution of scores shown in Table 15.1 was determined and the position of the student's score relative to this median score

TABLE 15.1

**SCORES GIVEN ON AN EVALUATION
OF LABORATORY TECHNIQUE**

Student Number	Rating Score	Position of Score Around Median
1	83	+
2	59	−
3	67	−
4	79	+
5	76	−
6	70	−
7	62	−
8	84	+
9	71	−
10	88	+
11	95	+
12	79	+
13	90	+
14	90	+
15	68	−
16	47	−
17	95	+
18	72	−
19	83	+
20	92	+
21	78	−
22	79	+
23	78	−
24	58	+
25	68	−
26	82	+

was noted. A plus (+) sign denotes an above median value, and a minus (−) sign denotes a below median value. Placing these scores on a horizontal, the runs may be seen more clearly:

$$\underset{(1)}{+} \quad \underset{(2)}{--} \quad \underset{(3)}{+} \quad \underset{(4)}{---} \quad \underset{(5)}{+} \quad \underset{(6)}{-} \quad \underset{(7)}{+++++} \quad \underset{(8)}{--} \quad \underset{(9)}{+} \quad \underset{(10)}{-} \quad \underset{(11)}{++}$$

$$\underset{(12)}{-} \quad \underset{(13)}{+} \quad \underset{(14)}{-} \quad \underset{(15)}{+} \quad \underset{(16)}{-} \quad \underset{(17)}{+}$$

In this problem, the number of runs is $r = 17$. The question to be answered is:

1. Is it reasonable to suppose that the pluses and minuses do not occur in a random manner thus implying the presence of an influencing factor?
2. H_o: The pluses and minuses do occur in a random manner.

3. $\alpha = 0.05$, $n = 26$, $n_1 = 13$ (number of scores above the median, or pluses), $n_2 = 13$ (number of scores below the median, or minuses), test (c)

4. Reject H_o if $r < r_{0.025} = 8$ (Critical values from Table VII) or if $r > r_{0.975} = 20$.

5. $r = 17$

6. Accept H_o. This would be interpreted as indicating that the rating on different days apparently does not bias the results.

For large samples, where it is possible for either n_1 or n_2 to be greater than 20, the normal approximation is more appropriate. In this instance:

$$\mu_r = \frac{2n_1 n_2}{n_1 + n_2} + 1 \tag{15.1}$$

and

$$\sigma_r^2 = \frac{2n_1 n_2 (2n_1 n_2 - n_1 - n_2)}{(n_1 + n_2)^2 (n_1 + n_2 - 1)} \tag{15.2}$$

To test the null hypothesis, the test statistic is:

$$z = \frac{r - \mu_r}{\sigma_r} \tag{15.3}$$

An example using this variation could be illustrated by the following problem. An English teacher assigned term papers to all students in her senior class. Of necessity, several evenings were spent grading the papers (grades were given in letter fashion: A+, A, A−, B+, B, B−, C+, C, C−, D+, D, D−, F). Table 15.2 gives the grades marked by the teacher and indicates the position of each of these grades relative to the median grade of C+.

1. Is it reasonable to suppose that since the number of papers to be marked is high, the grades shall rise and thus the number of papers having grades higher than C+ will result in a non-random fashion?

2. H_o: The grades shall be random in nature, that is, obvious runs may not be attributed to a conscious effort to compensate for the fatigue factor.

3. $\alpha = 0.05$, test (a)

4. Reject H_o if $z < z_{0.05} = -1.645$.

5. $z = \dfrac{32 - \dfrac{(2)(38)(37)}{38 + 37} + 1}{\sqrt{\dfrac{(2)(38)(37)\{[(2)(38)(37)] - 38 - 37\}}{(38 + 37)^2(38 + 37 - 1)}}} = -1.608$

6. Accept H_o.

TABLE 15.2

GRADES OF 80 SENIOR ENGLISH STUDENTS ON A TERM PAPER

Student Number	Grade	Position Relative to Median Grade (C+)	Student Number	Grade	Position Relative to Median Grade (C+)
1	C	—	41	C	—
2	B+	+	42	B+	+
3	B+	+	43	C	—
4	C—	—	44	D—	—
5	C	—	45	B+	+
6	D—	—	46	C	—
7	D	—	47	C+	0
8	B—	+	48	C	—
9	C	—	49	D	—
10	C	—	50	B	+
11	C+	0	51	D	—
12	C	—	52	A	+
13	C	—	53	C	—
14	D	—	54	C	—
15	B+	+	55	A	+
16	C+	0	56	F	—
17	D	—	57	B+	+
18	C	—	58	B	+
19	F	—	59	B—	+
20	D+	—	60	A+	+
21	C—	—	61	B—	+
22	C	—	62	B	+
23	B+	+	63	A—	+
24	C	—	64	C	—
25	C	—	65	C—	—
26	C—	—	66	B+	+
27	B+	+	67	B—	+
28	C+	0	68	A	+
29	D—	—	69	B	+
30	B+	+	70	B	+
31	B	+	71	B—	+
32	B	+	72	A	+
33	D	—	73	B	+
34	C—	—	74	A	+
35	C—	—	75	B—	+
36	B+	+	76	B	+
37	C+	0	77	A	+
38	B+	+	78	C	—
39	D+	—	79	B	+
40	B	+	80	B	+

15.2 *Techniques for Two Samples.* In the presentation of the discussion of the parametric statistics it was observed that tests involving two samples and two populations are more frequently used than single sample cases. In this discussion two types of tests were presented — one for correlated data, one for uncorrelated data. Similarly there are several nonparametric forms or techniques for each of these two variations.

15.2.1 *Uncorrelated Data.* Material used in these tests (like their parametric counterparts) involve independent samples. There are several techniques used when working with data of this type which cannot meet all of the assumptions required for parametric analysis. The one which shall be presented in this discussion is the *Mann-Whitney U test*. This test is, for all practical purposes, an equivalent of the *t* test and is one of the most powerful techniques available. Essentially this technique analyzes the samples to determine whether or not they come from populations having the same distribution, thus in essence testing for equality of the two parent populations.

Basically the method involved in this test will be presented with the technique used to analyze the data in Table 7.1.

1. Assign the values of n_1 and n_2. The larger sample is denoted by n_2 and the smaller by n_1. If the samples are of equal size as in the problem to be analyzed, n_1 and n_2 are randomly assigned. (Since both of the samples in the problem are of size 20, random assignment is the only way it could be fairly accomplished. We will assign the teaching machine group (TM) to be n_1 and the conventional group (C) to be n_2.)
2. Rank both samples in a single array assigning the rank of 1 to the lowest algebraic value and then proceeding to the rank of $N = n_1 + n_2$. In the case of ties, assign the mean of the tied ranks.
3. Determine the value of the U statistic; if n_1 and n_2 are both less than 8, a procedure involving counting is given by Seigel (see references). A commonly used practice where $9 \leq n_2 \leq 20$ to determine U is:

$$U = n_1 n_2 + \frac{n_1(n_1 + 1)}{2} - R_1 \qquad (15.4)$$

$$U = n_1 n_2 + \frac{n_2(n_2 + 1)}{2} - R_2 \qquad (15.5)$$

where $R_1 =$ sum of n_1 ranks, and $R_2 =$ sum of n_2 ranks.

In the problem under analysis:

$$U = (20)(20) + \frac{(20)(21)}{2} - 328.5 \text{ (using } R_1)$$

$$U = 400 + 210 - 328.5 = 281.5$$

or
$$U = (20)(20) + \frac{(20)(21)}{2} - 491.5 \text{ (using } R_2)$$

$$= 400 + 210 - 491.5 = 118.5$$

4. Determine the significance of the obtained value of U.

   a. If $n_2 \leq 8$, the exact probability of obtaining a value as small as the observed value of U may be found in Table IX. If test (c) is appropriate, double the significant value of p. If the obtained U is not found in Table IX, it is U' and should be converted to U by:

   $$U = n_1 n_2 - U' \tag{15.6}$$

   b. If $9 \leq n_2 \leq 20$, the significance of U may be found in Table IX. If the obtained value of $U > n_1 n_2/2$, it is U' and must be converted to U. (In the problem this value would be $(20)(20)/2 = 200$.) Where $n_1 = n_2$ the smaller obtained value of U may be used. (As such, the value of $U = 118.5$ should be used.)

5. If the probability of the obtained value of $U \leq \alpha$, reject H_o.

Example

1. Is it reasonable to suppose that the students taught by the teaching machines (TM) and those taught by the conventional (C) method are not from the same population in terms of their achievement? (Data given in Table 15.3.)

TABLE 15.3

RANK COMPARISON OF TABLE 7.1

TM	Rank	C	Rank
1	8.5	15	40.0
3	15.0	2	12.0
7	27.0	6	22.5
2	12.0	1	8.5
−3	5.0	14	38.5
3	15.0	8	30.5
14	38.5	7	27.0
3	15.0	10	34.5
1	8.5	11	37.0
6	22.5	8	30.5
10	34.5	7	27.0
6	22.5	−6	1.5
−6	1.5	4	17.0
5	19.0	6	22.5
0	6.0	10	34.5
−4	4.0	−5	3.0
1	8.5	9	32.0
2	12.0	5	19.0
10	34.5	7	27.0
5	19.0	7	27.0
R_1 = 328.5		R_2 = 491.5	

2. H_o: TM = C

3. $\alpha = 0.05$, test (c)

4. Reject H_o if $U \leq U_{0.025} = 127$.

5. $U = 118.5$

6. Reject H_o.

If $n_2 > 20$ the normal approximation may be used where

$$\mu_U = \frac{n_1 n_2}{2} \qquad (15.7)$$

and

$$\sigma_U^2 = \frac{(n_1 n_2)(n_1 + n_2 + 1)}{12} \qquad (15.8)$$

such that

$$z = \frac{U - \mu_U}{\sigma U} \qquad (15.9)$$

In this case U or U' may be used, the only effect being in terms of the sign of the value of z computed.

In using the normal approximation, a correction for tied ranks should be used where

$$T = \frac{t^3 - t}{12} \qquad (15.10)$$

such that t is the number of observations tied for the same rank.

Solely for the purpose of illustration the data just analyzed will be used.

$$\mu_U = \frac{(20)(20)}{2} = 200$$

and using the correction for tied ranks

$$\sigma_U^2 = \left[\frac{n_1 n_2}{N(N-1)} \right]\left[\frac{N^3 - N}{12} - \Sigma T \right] \qquad (15.11)$$

where $N = n_1 + n_2$.

To find ΣT it is necessary to determine the number of scores involving tied ranks. Observation of the data used in the problem indicates that there were:

$$\begin{array}{rl}
2 & \text{scores of } -6 \\
4 & \text{scores of } 1 \\
3 & \text{scores of } 2 \\
3 & \text{scores of } 3 \\
3 & \text{scores of } 5 \\
4 & \text{scores of } 6 \\
5 & \text{scores of } 7 \\
2 & \text{scores of } 8 \\
4 & \text{scores of } 10 \\
2 & \text{scores of } 14
\end{array}$$

If

$$T = \frac{t^3 - t}{12} \text{ such that } T_1 = \frac{2^3 - 2}{12} \text{ and } T_2 = \frac{4^3 - 4}{12}$$

then

$$\Sigma T = \frac{(2^3 - 2)}{12} + \frac{(4^3 - 4)}{12} + \frac{(3^3 - 3)}{12} + \frac{(3^3 - 3)}{12}$$

$$+ \frac{(3^3 - 3)}{12} + \frac{(4^3 - 4)}{12} + \frac{(5^3 - 5)}{12} + \frac{(2^3 - 2)}{12}$$

$$+ \frac{(4^3 - 4)}{12} + \frac{(2^3 - 2)}{12}$$

$$\Sigma T = \frac{3(2^3 - 2)}{12} + \frac{3(3^3 - 3)}{12} + \frac{3(4^3 - 4)}{12} + \frac{(5^3 - 5)}{12}$$

$$= \frac{[(3)(6)] + [(3)(24)] + [(3)(60)] + 120}{12} = 32.5$$

Using Equation (15.11), we find that:

$$\sigma_U^2 = \left[\frac{(20)(20)}{(40)(39)}\right]\left[\frac{(40^3 - 40)}{12} - 32.5\right]$$

$$= \left[\frac{400}{1560}\right]\left[\frac{63570}{12}\right]$$

$$= 1358.33$$

$$\sigma_U = 36.86$$

$$z = \frac{281.5 - 200}{36.86} = 2.21106 \text{ (which is significant at the 0.025 level)}.$$

15.2.2 *Correlated Data.* There are several non-parametric techniques available to the researcher when the design necessitates the use of correlated data. The selection of the technique is controlled by the type of information obtained. When the measurements can be obtained only in a *nominal* sense, the *McNemar test* is used. When the measurement is continuous but crude in nature, the *sign test* may be effectively used.

15.2.2.1 *Wilcoxon Signed Rank Test.* One of the more favored techniques used is the *Wilcoxon signed rank test*. This technique is designed to take into account the direction of change occurring after treatment as well as the size of the change. This technique would be appropriate when working with "matched pairs" of students where one is used as a control and the other is used as the experimental subject. This procedure likewise is applicable in the field of experimental psychology when discussing effects of treatments on litter mates of animals.

Suppose a group of students were matched as to prior achievement level, age, weight, sex, height, and socio-economic background such that 20 pairs of students were finally included in a study of the effect of lack of carbohydrate in the daily diet on achievement in a physical proficiency examination. Table 15.4 presents the scores obtained by 20 pairs of students.

TABLE 15.4

SCORES ON A PHYSICAL PROFICIENCY EXAMINATION OF 20 PAIRS OF STUDENTS ON DIFFERENT CARBOHYDRATE CONTENT DIETS

Student Pair Number	With Carbohydrate	Without Carbohydrate	d	Rank of d	Rank with less frequent sign
1	48	48	0		
2	56	48	8	6.5	
3	88	72	16	12	
4	88	56	32	16.5	
5	88	56	32	16.5	
6	64	56	8	6.5	
7	80	48	32	16.5	
8	80	88	−8	−6.5	6.5
9	72	80	−8	−6.5	6.5
10	72	80	−8	−6.5	6.5
11	80	64	16	12	
12	56	80	−24	−14	14
13	72	40	32	16.5	
14	56	56	0		
15	64	72	−8	−6.5	6.5
16	48	64	−16	−12	12
17	56	54	2	1	
18	56	50	6	2	
19	72	64	8	6.5	
20	88	80	8	6.5	
					$T = 52$

To test the effect of diet on physical proficiency, the following process would be followed (using the Wilcoxon technique). The amount of carbohydrate intake for the experimental group would be controlled.

1. H_o: The physical proficiency is not affected by the lack of carbohydrate in the diet.
2. $\alpha = 0.05$, $N = 20 - 2 = 18$ (N is the total number of pairs minus the number of pairs having a d value of 0.)
3. Reject H_o if $T \leq T_{0.025, 18} = 40$.
4. $T = 52$
5. Accept H_o.

The procedure in an outline form for the determination of T is:

1. Determine the value of d representing the difference between the two scores for each pair.
2. Rank the values of d_i without respect to sign and omit all values of $d_i = 0$.
3. Assign the sign of each d_i to its respective rank.
4. Sum the values of the ranks of like sign. Select the smallest sum of ranks and this value is T.
5. Select the appropriate significant value of T for the selected α and N from Table X, Appendix A.

Where $N > 25$ the normal approximation may be used. In this case the distribution of the sum of ranks (T) rapidly approaches normality as N increases beyond 25 and as such has the parameters of:

$$\mu_T = \frac{N(N+1)}{4} \tag{15.12}$$

$$\sigma_T^2 = \frac{N(N+1)(2N+1)}{24} \tag{15.13}$$

Thus
$$z = \frac{T - \dfrac{N(N+1)}{4}}{\sqrt{\dfrac{N(N+1)(2N+1)}{24}}} \tag{15.14}$$

Using the data in Table 15.4:

$$z = \frac{52 - \dfrac{18(18+1)}{4}}{\sqrt{\dfrac{(18)(18+1)([2][18]+1)}{24}}} = -\frac{33.5}{22.96}$$

$$= -1.459 \text{ (which is not significant at the 0.025 level)}.$$

15.2.2.2 *Walsh Test*. The Walsh test may be applied if the distributions sampled are continuous, symmetrical, $N \leq 15$, and the data are in at least interval scale. This means that the mean and median will be synonymous, permitting the testing of the $H_o:\mu < 0; \mu > 0; \mu \neq 0$.

The procedure is as follows:

1. Obtain the difference values (d_i) of each pair of scores.
2. Rank the d_i values from *low to high*, letting $i = 1, 2, \ldots, N$. The sign of the difference is considered in the ranking.
3. Consult Table VIII, Appendix A, using the appropriate row as determined by the sample size, to determine the probability of occurrence.

Table 15.5 contains data on 10 students giving the number of errors made on a manual dexterity test before and after exercise. The lowest value of $d_i = -1$, therefore $d_1 = -1$, and $d_2 = 0$, $d_3 = 1$. There are four values of $d_i = 2$, therefore, $d_4 = 2$, $d_5 = 2$, $d_6 = 2$, $d_7 = 2$. Proceeding in like fashion $d_8 = 4$, $d_9 = 4$, and $d_{10} = 5$.

Table VIII, Appendix A, shows that for a sample of $N = 10$, the hypothesis for a test (b) situation is rejected at the $\alpha = 0.056$ level of significance if

$$\text{Max} \left[d_6, \tfrac{1}{2}(d_4 + d_{10}) \right] < 0$$

The hypothesis for a test (a) situation is rejected at the same level of significance if

$$\text{Min} \left[d_5, \tfrac{1}{2}(d_1 + d_7) \right] > 0$$

The hypothesis under a test (c) situation is rejected at the $\alpha = 0.111$ level of significance if either of these conditions is found to exist.

TABLE 15.5

**ERRORS MADE ON A MANUAL DEXTERITY TEST
BEFORE AND AFTER EXERCISE**

Student Number	Before Exercise	After Exercise	d_i
1	6	10	4
2	3	8	5
3	5	7	2
4	9	13	4
5	12	13	1
6	2	4	2
7	8	7	−1
8	4	6	2
9	3	5	2
10	5	5	0

The "maximum" term in the statistic means that the larger of the two alternate values, d_6 or $\tfrac{1}{2}(d_4 + d_{10})$, will be used to determine significance in the left tail, and the "minimum" (or smaller value of the two alternatives, d_5 or $\tfrac{1}{2}(d_1 + d_7)$) will be used to reject the hypothesis in the right tail.

1. $H_o: \mu_o = 0$, $H: \mu \neq 0$.
2. $\alpha = 0.111$.
3. Reject H_o if d_7 or $\tfrac{1}{2}(d_4 + d_{10}) < 0$ (whichever is larger)
   or if d_5 or $\tfrac{1}{2}(d_1 + d_7) > 0$ (whichever is smaller).
4. a. $d_7 = 2$, $\tfrac{1}{2}(d_4 + d_{10}) = \tfrac{1}{2}(2 + 5) = 3.5$,
   b. $d_5 = 2$, $\tfrac{1}{2}(d_1 + d_7) = \tfrac{1}{2}(-1 + 2) = 0.5$.

5. Reject H_o since $\frac{1}{2}(d_1 + d_7) = 0.5 > 0$ and conclude that the exercise apparently decreases manual dexterity.

15.3 *The Median Test*. If normality of the sampled population cannot be assumed, a non-parametric equivalent may be used to test the hypothesis concerning the differences between two groups. One technique employed is the *Median test*, which is the non-parametric equivalent of the t test for differences between two population means. This procedure uses the χ^2 statistic as given in Equation (15.15) below and is included in this chapter for that reason.

The test is centered around the randomness of the samples. If the samples are random and are from similar populations, it is equally likely that they will occur on both sides of the common median value. The data are listed and designated as being values above the common median $(+)$ or values below the common median $(-)$. Afterward the number of pluses and minuses for the two populations are presented in a 2×2 contingency table. The modification for computing χ^2 in this special case is then used. If a significant χ^2 value is obtained, this is indicative of a difference in the central tendency values (median) for the two populations. Thus, it is correct to assume this is the evidence of dissimilarity of the two parent populations.

Table 15.6 presents two samples $(n_1 = n_2 = 82)$ having a common median value of 50. Associated with each value is a $(+)$ if the value is above the median and $(-)$ if below. In the case of those values which are the same as the median value, the sign $(+)$ or $(-)$ is assigned at random.

TABLE 15.6

COMPARISON OF TWO SAMPLES $(n_1 = n_2 = 82)$ AS TO MEDIAN VALUES

Sample I						Sample II					
49−	51−	59+	42−	54+	68+	68+	52+	38−	59+	62+	46−
56+	35−	62+	54+	42−	51−	48−	38−	63+	46−	66+	63+
59+	55+	54+	55+	55+	65+	44−	66+	42−	63+	59+	52+
60+	45−	48−	51+	55+	59+	48−	41−	49−	45−	63+	59+
60+	62+	44−	51−	78+	44−	63+	41−	42−	48−	56+	46−
51+	45−	39−	62+	49−	38−	45−	49−	59+	45−	55+	34−
52+	65+	56+	52+	54+	52+	45−	58+	42−	42−	54+	65+
42−	48−	66+	45−	46−		51+	58+	62+	51−	68+	
59+	48−	49−	56+	46−		48−	46−	63+	51+	42−	
60+	46−	49−	55+	51+		42−	45−	46−	63+	66+	
45−	65+	45−	39−	45−		42−	48−	55+	54+	54+	
45−	54+	71+	52+	45−		55+	55+	68+	58+	55+	
49−	55+	39−	44−	54+		55+	49−	49−	49−	51−	
42−	54+	49−	59+	59+		66+	42−	49−	49−	68+	
54+	42−	60+	45−	44−		42−	63+	49−	42−	45−	

1. H_o: There is no difference in the median scores of the populations represented by the two samples in the test used. H_1: The second is greater than the first.

2. $\alpha = 0.05$.

3. Reject H_o if $\chi^2 < \chi^2_{0.025,1} = 0.0982$ or if $\chi^2 > \chi^2_{0.975,1} = 5.02$.

4.

	Position with respect to median		
	above $(+)$	below $(-)$	total
Sample I	44	38	82
Sample II	40	42	82
Total	84	80	164

$$\chi^2 = \frac{164[|(44)(40) - (38)(42)| - \frac{164}{2}]^2}{(82)(82)(84)(80)}$$

$$= \frac{164[|1760 - 1596| - 82]^2}{45185280} = 0.244$$

5. Accept the H_o.

In the case where $n_1 + n_2 = N > 40$ or if $20 \leq N \leq 40$ and all cell expected values are greater than 5, use

$$\chi^2 = \frac{N\left[|ac - bd| - \dfrac{N}{2}\right]^2}{(a+b)(c+d)(a+c)(b+d)} \qquad (15.15)$$

If $N < 20$, use Fisher's exact probability formula

$$p = \frac{(a+b)!(c+d)!(a+c)!(b+d)!}{N!a!b!c!d!} \qquad (15.16)$$

15.4 Correlated Data for $(k > 2)$ Samples. This section will be concerned with the cases where the data are representative of data obtained as multiple observations on the same subject. Sometimes the responses are dichotomous or *nominal* in nature. In other cases the observational values are *ordinal*.

15.4.1 Cochran Q Test. This test is used to determine whether or not more than two samples differ significantly among themselves. For purposes of illustration consider the responses to six items in a test using a sample of 41 students. The responses are recorded as (1) when the person correctly answered the item and (0) when the item was missed. The data are presented in Table 15.7.

TABLE 15.7

RESPONSES TO 6 ITEMS IN A TEST INVOLVING 41 STUDENTS

Student	Item 1	Item 2	Item 3	Item 4	Item 5	Item 6	L_i	L_i^2
1	0	0	0	0	0	0	0	0
2	0	0	1	0	0	0	1	1
3	0	1	0	0	0	0	1	1
4	0	1	0	0	0	0	1	1
5	1	1	1	0	0	1	4	16
6	1	1	0	0	0	1	3	9
7	1	1	1	0	0	0	3	9
8	1	1	1	1	0	0	4	16
9	0	0	1	0	0	0	1	1
10	0	1	0	0	0	0	1	1
11	1	1	1	0	0	1	4	16
12	1	0	0	0	0	0	1	1
13	0	0	0	0	0	0	0	0
14	1	0	1	0	0	0	2	4
15	0	0	0	0	0	0	0	0
16	0	1	1	0	0	0	2	4
17	1	1	1	0	0	1	4	16
18	0	0	0	0	0	0	0	0
19	0	1	1	0	0	0	2	4
20	1	0	1	1	0	0	3	9
21	1	1	1	0	1	0	4	16
22	0	0	1	0	0	0	1	1
23	1	1	0	0	0	1	3	9
24	1	0	0	0	0	0	1	1
25	0	0	1	0	0	0	1	1
26	1	0	1	1	0	0	3	9
27	1	1	1	0	0	0	3	9
28	1	1	1	0	0	0	3	9
29	1	1	1	0	0	0	3	9
30	1	1	0	0	1	0	3	9
31	0	0	0	0	0	0	0	0
32	0	1	1	0	0	0	2	4
33	1	1	1	0	0	1	4	16
34	0	1	1	0	0	0	2	4
35	0	0	0	0	0	0	0	0
36	0	0	1	0	0	0	1	1
37	0	0	1	0	0	0	1	1
38	1	1	1	0	0	1	4	16
39	1	1	1	0	0	0	3	9
40	1	1	0	0	0	0	2	4
41	0	0	0	0	0	1	1	1
G_j	21	23	25	3	2	8	$\sum L_i = 82$	$\sum L_i^2 = 238$

The statistic used is:

$$Q = \frac{(k-1)[k\sum G_j^2 - (\sum G_j)^2]}{k\sum L_i - \sum L_i^2} \tag{15.17}$$

where G_j is the total right responses for any one of the items for all 41 students. In the cases of the sample data, $G_1 = 21$, meaning that 21 of the total of 41 students answered the item correctly. L_i represents the total right responses for each student. An example would be: according to the data of Table 15.7 student number 5 answered four of the six items correctly and as such has a L_4 value of 4.

For the problem under consideration

$$Q = \frac{(6-1)[(6)(21^2 + 23^2 + 25^2 + 3^2 + 2^2 + 8^2) - (82)^2]}{(6)(82) - 238}$$
$$= 65.11$$

The significance of Q is assessed by using the table of the χ^2 distribution (see Table III) for d.f. $= k - 1$. The obtained value of Q for the problem has a $p < 0.0005$ for chance occurrence. The result may be interpreted to say that the probability of getting items 1–6 right is different for each item.

15.5 Independent Data for ($k > 2$) Samples.   In the case of uncorrelated data, several techniques are possible. One of these is the conventional χ^2 test for independency of data. Other commonly used techniques are the extension of the median test, and the Kruskal-Wallis test.

Of the last two tests mentioned, the Kruskal-Wallis test is of greater value. Where the median test requires dichotomization of the data into above and below the median categories, the Kruskal-Wallis technique converts all of the variable values into ranks thus utilizing more information.

The major limitation of this technique is the restriction of a one-way classification. It does not permit extension to 2^n factorial analysis and interaction evaluation.

The technique tests the hypothesis of no difference between averages of several groups of ordinal evaluations, the concept being that the sums of rank values assigned will not be so different as to imply that different populations were sampled. In any case the obtained statistic, H, is distributed as the x^2 distribution with d.f. $= k - 1$. Where three populations are sampled and $n < 5$ in any sample, Table XI may be used.

Essentially the technique involves the following steps:

1. Rank all observations for all samples in *one* continuous series, assigning the rank of 1 to the lowest score and N to the highest score.
2. Sum the ranks (R_j) for the n_j values of *each* of the k samples.
3. After steps 1 and 2 have been completed, you are now ready to use the formula for the determination of the H statistic which is:

$$H = \left[\frac{12}{N(N+1)}\right]\left[\Sigma\left(\frac{\Sigma R_j^2}{n_j}\right)\right] - 3(N+1) \qquad (15.18)$$

In many instances there are multiple values of the same score, thus introducing the factor of tied rank values. As such, a correction factor is introduced, the reciprocal value of

$$1 - \left[\frac{\Sigma T}{N^3 - N}\right]$$

which is multiplied by the uncorrected value of H obtained by use of formula (15.18). The formula for the statistic H using the correction notation would then be:

$$H = \frac{\left[\frac{12}{N(N+1)}\right]\left[\Sigma\left(\frac{\Sigma R_j^2}{n_j}\right)\right] - 3(N+1)}{1 - \left[\frac{\Sigma T}{N^3 - N}\right]} \qquad (15.19)$$

where $\Sigma T = t^3 - t$ (using t as the number of times a given score is in the tied condition).

4. After the value of H has been computed, it should be compared with the x^2 table (Table III) to determine significance. Where all n_j's < 5 for a three sample case, Table XI, Appendix A, may be used.
5. Act upon the test hypothesis.

For illustrative purposes, a problem is presented in Table 15.8 where four samples of $n_1 = n_2 = n_3 = n_4 = 41$ test scores are considered to determine if there is evidence of a difference between the groups being sampled. Inspection of the table reveals the fact that there are several tied scores; thus Equation (15.19) will be used.

TABLE 15.8

EXAMINATION SCORES OF 4 SAMPLES OF
$n_1 = n_2 = n_3 = n_4 = 41$ SUBJECTS

Student	Sample and Rank							
	1	R	2	R	3	R	4	R
1	49	69	49	69	60	134	55	108.5
2	49	69	45	38	68	160	68	160
3	56	116.5	71	163	48	57.5	49	69
4	59	126.5	39	7	44	28	49	69
5	60	134	42	18	48	57.5	49	69
6	60	134	54	97	63	145.5	59	126.5
7	51	81.5	55	108.5	45	38	46	49.5
8	52	89	51	81.5	45	38	63	145.5
9	42	18	51	81.5	51	81.5	45	38
10	59	126.5	62	139	48	57.5	48	57.5
11	60	134	52	89	42	18	45	38
12	45	38	45	38	42	18	42	18
13	45	38	45	38	55	108.5	51	81.5
14	49	69	56	116.5	55	108.5	51	81.5
15	42	18	55	108.5	66	155	63	145.5
16	54	97	39	7	42	18	54	97
17	51	81.5	52	89	52	89	58	120
18	35	2	44	28	38	4	49	69
19	55	108.5	59	126.5	66	155	49	69
20	45	38	54	97	41	9.5	42	18
21	62	139	42	18	41	9.5	62	139
22	45	38	55	108.5	49	69	66	155
23	65	151	55	108.5	58	120	59	126.5
24	48	57.5	78	164	58	120	63	145.5
25	48	57.5	49	69	46	49.5	56	116.5
26	46	49.5	54	97	45	38	55	108.5
27	65	151	46	49.5	48	57.5	54	97
28	54	97	46	49.5	55	108.5	68	160
29	55	108.5	51	81.5	49	69	42	18
30	54	97	45	38	42	18	66	155
31	42	18	45	38	63	145.5	54	97
32	59	126.5	54	97	38	4	55	108.5
33	62	139	59	126.5	63	145.5	51	81.5
34	54	97	44	28	42	18	68	160
35	48	57.5	68	160	49	69	45	38
36	44	28	51	81.5	42	18	46	49.5
37	39	7	65	151	59	126.5	63	145.5
38	60	134	59	126.5	42	18	52	89
39	56	116.5	44	28	62	139	59	126.5
40	66	155	38	4	63	145.5	46	49.5
41	49	69	49	69	46	49.5	34	1
$\sum R_j$		3481.5		3233.0		3018.5		3797.0

To pursue the problem just posed, we make the following analysis.

1. H_o: The average score on the examination is the same for all populations sampled.

2. $\alpha = 0.05$

3. Reject the H_o if $H \leq \chi^2_{0.025,3} = 0.216$

      or if $H \geq \chi^2_{0.975,3} = 9.35$.

4.

$$H = \frac{\dfrac{12}{164(164+1)}\left[\dfrac{3481.5^2 + 3233.0^2 + 3018.5^2 + 3797.0^2}{41}\right] - 3(164+1)}{1 - \dfrac{17490}{164^3 - 164}}$$

$= 3.654$

5. Accept the H_o.

Computation of $\sum T$ for tied scores is:

X	t	$T = t^3 - t$	X	t	$T = t^3 - t$
38	3	24	54	11	1320
39	3	24	55	12	1716
41	2	6	56	4	60
42	15	3360	58	3	24
44	5	120	59	10	990
45	15	3360	60	5	120
46	8	504	62	5	120
48	8	504	63	8	504
49	15	3360	65	3	24
51	10	990	66	5	120
52	5	120	68	5	120
				$\sum T$	$= 17490$

15.6 *Spearman's Rank-Difference Correlation, R.* The rank-difference method of correlation may be applied when pairs of measures on individuals are not obtainable but the data are presented in rank order. This procedure is particularly useful when the samples are small, and while it was originally used as an estimate of the Pearson r, the Spearman R may also be used as a means for testing the independence of ranks.

For computation of the Spearman R it is necessary to assign rank orders for the available measures if the data are not already reported in rank orders.

In Table 15.9 we have the ratings of eight mathematics teachers on years of experience and effectiveness in the classroom.

TABLE 15.9

SPEARMAN RANK-DIFFERENCE CORRELATION BETWEEN YEARS OF EXPERIENCE AND PERFORMANCE AS A MATHEMATICS TEACHER

Teacher	Experience	Effectiveness	D	D^2
A	1	2	1	1
B	2	1	1	1
C	3	4	1	1
D	4	6	2	4
E	5	3	2	4
F	6	5	1	1
G	7	8	1	1
H	8	7	1	1
				$\sum D^2 = 14$

In assigning ranks to the eight mathematics teachers it is necessary to obtain the number of years of experience for each and to rank the person with the greatest number of years of experience as number one, next greatest as number two, and so on. The ratings on effectiveness in the classroom are those submitted by a supervisor and indicate a judgement as to the relative effectiveness of the eight as mathematics teachers. This procedure has the advantage that it is applicable to populations other than those which are normally distributed.

For every pair of ranks we determine the difference in ranks, without indicating the algebraic sign of this difference, since these values are squared and entered under the column headed D^2. The formula for the Spearman rank-difference correlation is:

$$R = 1 - \frac{6\sum D^2}{n(n^2 - 1)} \tag{15.20}$$

where

$\sum D^2$ = sum of the squared differences in ranks
n = number of paired ranks

Substituting the values obtained from Table 15.9:

$$R = 1 - \frac{6 \times 14}{8(64 - 1)} = 1 - 0.17 = 0.83$$

By referring to Table XII, Appendix A, we see that this value is significant at $\alpha = 0.05$.

It may prove useful to recall that the denominator of the computing formula for R can be factored to give three consecutive integers, $(n - 1)$, (n), and $(n + 1)$. Since the product of three consecutive integers is always divisible by 6, cancellation of factors in numerator and denominator may bring about some saving in computation.

$$R = 1 - \frac{6 \times 14}{7 \times 8 \times 9}$$

Since the Spearman R is usually restricted to small samples, the main use of this correlation coefficient is to test the hypothesis of zero correlation. If R is to be used as an estimate of the product-moment r, where ranks have been assigned to measurements on X and Y, the usual assumptions of linearity of regression and homoscedasticity should apply.

The significance of the obtained value of R for n may be determined by use of the t statistic with d.f. $= n - 2$.

$$t = R \sqrt{\frac{n - 2}{1 - R^2}} \tag{15.21}$$

Critical values for the Spearman Rank Coefficient, R, may also be found in Table XIIb, Appendix A.

PROBLEMS

1. Analyze the following data using the runs test for single samples. 50, 45, 57, 48, 57, 40, 56, 49, 55, 62, 55, 62, 38, 48, 48, 53, 36, 54, 55, 35, 44, 43, 45, 48, 44, 59, 59, 44, 57, 46, 53, 35, 44, 59, 51, 50.

2. Following are 36 pairs of scores. The first score (X) prediction was based upon a mathematical expression (equation) and the second score (Y) is the actual test score. Using the Wilcoxon technique, analyze the data and determine whether or not the predicted score overestimated or underestimated the student's actual score.

X	Y	X	Y	X	Y	X	Y	X	Y	X	Y
49	50	51	56	38	45	55	68	44	45	53	59
50	45	50	49	48	49	35	42	59	68	35	44
52	57	49	55	48	52	44	54	59	59	44	51
44	48	57	62	53	58	43	63	44	42	59	59
50	57	58	55	36	48	45	48	57	60	51	56
43	40	55	53	54	59	48	62	46	52	50	65

3. Following are the scores of two mathematics classes taught by two different methods. Using the Mann-Whitney technique, determine whether or not the data indicate superiority of technique in relation to student achievement. The first score of the pair is that belonging to a student taught by method A and the second score that of a student taught by method B.

A	B	A	B	A	B	A	B	A	B	A	B
60	42	59	72	96	54	24	42	78	36	90	60
90	48	108	60	42	48	72	66	60	66	90	42
60	72	30	42	72	60	66	48	49	49	42	90
30	54	54	66	30	72	42	66	72	60	24	60
30	54	42	78	54	60	66	66	78	54	54	24
42	42	60	96	102	66	56	55	84	78	79	77

4. An investigator was studying the effects of the lack of sleep on response to stimuli. A group of 14 students were given a series of stimuli and the number of errors recorded. These same students were then kept awake for 48 hours. After this period, they were again given the series of stimuli and the number of errors recorded. The findings were:

Student No.	Before	After
1	6	6
2	3	4
3	2	3
4	7	2
5	5	10
6	8	1
7	1	7
8	1	11
9	0	5
10	6	12
11	12	2
12	3	1
13	2	11
14	6	10

Analyze these data using the Walsh technique.

REFERENCES

DuBois, Philip H. *An Introduction to Psychological Statistics*. New York: Harper and Row, Publishers, 1965. Chapter 9.

Ferguson, George A. *Statistical Analysis in Psychology and Education*. New York: McGraw-Hill Book Company, Inc., 1966. Chapter 22.

Freund, John C., and Williams, Frank J. *Elementary Business Statistics: The Modern Approach*. Englewood Cliffs, New Jersey: Prentice-Hall, Inc., 1964. Chapter 11.

Kurtz, Thomas E. *Basic Statistics*. Englewood Cliffs, New Jersey: Prentice-Hall, Inc., 1963. Chapters 7 and 8.

McNemar, Quinn. *Psychological Statistics*. Third Edition. New York: John Wiley and Sons, Inc., 1962. Chapter 19.

Siegel, Sidney. *Nonparametric Statistics for the Behavioral Sciences*. New York: McGraw-Hill Book Company, Inc., 1956.

Walsh, John E. *Handbook of Nonparametric Statistics: Investigation of Randomness, Moments, Percentiles and Distributions*. Princeton, New Jersey: D. Van Nostrand Company, Inc., 1962.

APPENDIX

APPENDIX A

TABLES

TABLE I.   The Normal Probability Integral   270
TABLE II.   The t Distribution   271
TABLE III.   Percentile Values of the χ^2 Distribution   272
TABLE IVa. F Distribution: 50% Points   276
TABLE IVb. F Distribution: 25% Points   277
TABLE IVc. F Distribution: 10% Points   278
TABLE IVd. F Distribution: 5% Points   279
TABLE IVe. F Distribution: 1% Points   280
TABLE IVf. F Distribution: 0.5% Points   281
TABLE IVg. F Distribution: 0.1% Points   282
TABLE V.   Values of the Correlation Coefficient for Different Levels of
Significance   283
TABLE VI.   Fisher's Transformation of r to ζ 284
TABLE VIIa.   Probability for Total Number of Runs in Samples of
Size (N_1, N_2) 285
TABLE VIIb.   Significance Level of r 294
TABLE VIII.   Critical Values for the Walsh Test   300
TABLE IXa.   Probabilities Associated with Observed Small Values of U
in the Mann-Whitney Test   301
TABLE IXb.   Critical Values of U in the Mann-Whitney Test   303
TABLE X.   Critical Values of T in the Wilcoxon Test for Paired Data   306
TABLE XI.   Critical Values of H (for three samples) for the
Kruskal-Wallis Test   307
TABLE XIIa.   Values of $\sum d^2$ for Spearman Rank Correlation   308
TABLE XIIb.   Critical Values for the Spearman Rank Coefficient, R 310
TABLE XIII.   Squares, Square Roots, and Reciprocals   311
TABLE XIV.   Values of the Exponential e^{-x} 328
TABLE XV.   Common Logarithms of Numbers (Five Decimal Places)   331
TABLE XVI.   Natural Logarithms of Numbers (Five Decimal Places)   350
TABLE XVII.   Ten Thousand Randomly Assorted Digits   352
TABLE XVIII.   Factorials   356
TABLE XIX.   Logarithms of the Binomial Coefficients   357

TABLE 1. THE NORMAL PROBABILITY INTEGRAL

z		0	1	2	3	4	5	6	7	8	9
0.0	0.	50000	49601	49202	48803	48405	48006	47608	47210	46812	46414
.1		46017	45620	45224	44828	44433	44038	43644	43251	42858	42465
.2		42074	41683	41294	40905	40517	40129	39743	39358	38974	38591
.3		38209	37828	37448	37070	36693	36317	35942	35569	35197	34827
.4		34458	34090	33724	33360	32997	32636	32276	31918	31561	31207
0.5		30854	30503	30153	29806	29460	29116	28774	28434	28096	27760
.6		27425	27093	26763	26435	26109	25785	25463	25143	24825	24510
.7		24196	23885	23576	23270	22965	22663	22363	22065	21770	21476
.8		21186	20897	20611	20327	20045	19766	19489	19215	18943	18673
.9		18406	18141	17879	17619	17361	17106	16853	16602	16354	16109
1.0		15866	15625	15386	15151	14917	14686	14457	14231	14007	13786
1.1		13567	13350	13136	12924	12714	12507	12302	12100	11900	11702
1.2		11507	11314	11123	10935	10749	10565	10383	10204	10027/	98525
1.3	0.0	96800	95098	93418	91759	90123	88508	86915	85343	83793	82264
1.4		80757	79270	77804	76359	74934	73529	72145	70781	69437	68112
1.5		66807	65522	64255	63008	61780	60571	59380	58208	57053	55917
1.6		54799	53699	52616	51551	50503	49471	48457	47460	46479	45514
1.7		44565	43633	42716	41815	40930	40059	39204	38364	37538	36727
1.8		35930	35148	34380	33625	32884	32157	31443	30742	30054	29379
1.9		28717	28067	27429	26803	26190	25588	24998	24419	23852	23295
2.0		22750	22216	21692	21178	20675	20182	19699	19226	18763	18309
2.1		17864	17429	17003	16586	16177	15778	15386	15003	14629	14262
2.2		13903	13553	13209	12874	12545	12224	11911	11604	11304	11011
2.3		10724	10444	10170/	99031	96419	93867	91375	88940	86563	84242
2.4	0.0^{2}*	81975	79763	77603	75494	73436	71428	69469	67557	65691	63872
2.5		62097	60366	58677	57031	55426	53861	52336	50849	49400	47988
2.6		46612	45271	43965	42692	41453	40246	39070	37926	36811	35726
2.7		34670	33642	32641	31667	30720	29798	28901	28028	27179	26354
2.8		25551	24771	24012	23274	22557	21860	21182	20524	19884	19262
2.9		18658	18071	17502	16948	16411	15889	15382	14890	14412	13949
3.0		13499	13062	12639	12228	11829	11442	11067	10703	10350	10008
3.1	0.0^{3}	96760	93544	90426	87403	84474	81635	78885	76219	73638	71136
3.2		68714	66367	64095	61895	59765	57703	55706	53774	51904	50094
3.3		48342	46648	45009	43423	41889	40406	38971	37584	36243	34946
3.4		33693	32481	31311	30179	29086	28029	27009	26023	25071	24151
3.5		23263	22405	21577	20778	20006	19262	18543	17849	17180	16534
3.6		15911	15310	14730	14171	13632	13112	12611	12128	11662	11213
3.7		10780	10363/	99611	95740	92010	88417	84957	81624	78414	75324
3.8	0.0^{4}	72348	69483	66726	64072	61517	59059	56694	54418	52228	50122
3.9		48096	46148	44274	42473	40741	39076	37475	35936	34458	33037
4.0		31671	30359	29099	27888	26726	25609	24536	23507	22518	21569
4.1		20658	19783	18944	18138	17365	16624	15912	15230	14575	13948
4.2		13346	12769	12215	11685	11176	10689	10221/	97736	93447	89337
4.3	0.0^{5}	85399	81627	78015	74555	71241	68069	65031	62123	59340	56675
4.4		54125	51685	49350	47117	44979	42935	40980	39110	37322	35612
4.5		33977	32414	30920	29492	28127	26823	25577	24386	23249	22162
4.6		21125	20133	19187	18283	17420	16597	15810	15060	14344	13660
4.7		13008	12386	11792	11226	10686	10171/	96796	92113	87648	83391
4.8	0.0^{6}	79333	75465	71779	68267	64920	61731	58693	55799	53043	50418
4.9		47918	45538	43272	41115	39061	37107	35247	33476	31792	30190

Table I is abridged from Table II$_I$ of R.A. Fisher and F. Yates, Statistical Tables for Biological, Agricultural and Medical Research, published by Oliver & Boyd Ltd., Edinburgh, and by permission of the authors and publishers.
*0.0^{2} is to be read 0.00; etc.

TABLE II. THE t DISTRIBUTION

d.f. \ α	0.50	0.40	0.30	0.20	0.10	0.05	0.01	0.001
1	1.0005	1.376	1.963	3.078	6.314	12.706	63.657	636.619
2	0.816	1.061	1.386	1.886	2.920	4.303	9.925	31.598
3	.765	0.978	1.250	1.638	2.353	3.182	5.841	12.941
4	.741	.941	1.190	1.533	2.132	2.776	4.604	8.610
5	.727	.920	1.156	1.476	2.015	2.571	4.032	6.859
6	0.718	0.906	1.134	1.440	1.943	2.447	3.707	5.959
7	.711	.896	1.119	1.415	1.895	2.365	3.499	5.405
8	.706	.889	1.108	1.397	1.860	2.306	3.355	5.041
9	.703	.883	1.100	1.383	1.833	2.262	3.250	4.781
10	.700	.879	1.093	1.372	1.812	2.228	3.169	4.587
11	0.697	0.876	1.088	1.363	1.796	2.201	3.106	4.437
12	.695	.873	1.083	1.356	1.782	2.179	3.055	4.318
13	.694	.870	1.079	1.350	1.771	2.160	3.012	4.221
14	.692	.868	1.076	1.345	1.761	2.145	2.977	4.140
15	.691	.866	1.074	1.341	1.753	2.131	2.947	4.073
16	0.690	0.866	1.071	1.337	1.746	2.120	2.921	4.015
17	.689	.863	1.069	1.333	1.740	2.110	2.898	3.965
18	.688	.862	1.067	1.330	1.734	2.101	2.878	3.922
19	.688	.861	1.066	1.328	1.729	2.093	2.861	3.883
20	.687	.860	1.064	1.325	1.725	2.086	2.845	3.850
21	0.686	0.859	1.063	1.323	1.721	2.080	2.831	3.819
22	.686	.858	1.061	1.321	1.717	2.074	2.819	3.792
23	.685	.858	1.060	1.319	1.714	2.069	2.807	3.767
24	.685	.857	1.059	1.318	1.711	2.064	2.797	3.745
25	.684	.856	1.058	1.316	1.708	2.060	2.787	3.725
26	0.684	0.856	1.058	1.315	1.706	2.056	2.779	3.707
27	.684	.855	1.057	1.314	1.703	2.052	2.771	3.690
28	.683	.855	1.056	1.313	1.701	2.048	2.763	3.674
29	.683	.854	1.055	1.311	1.699	2.045	2.756	3.659
30	.683	.854	1.055	1.310	1.697	2.042	2.750	3.646
35	0.682	0.852	1.052	1.306	1.690	2.030	2.724	3.591
40	.681	.851	1.050	1.303	1.684	2.021	2.704	3.551
45	.680	.850	1.048	1.301	1.680	2.014	2.690	3.520
50	.680	.849	1.047	1.299	1.676	2.008	2.678	3.496
55	.679	.849	1.047	1.297	1.673	2.004	2.669	3.476
60	0.679	0.848	1.046	1.296	1.671	2.000	2.660	3.460
70	.678	.847	1.045	1.294	1.667	1.994	2.648	3.435
80	.678	.847	1.044	1.293	1.665	1.990	2.638	3.416
90	.678	.846	1.043	1.291	1.662	1.987	2.632	3.402
100	.677	.846	1.042	1.290	1.661	1.984	2.626	3.390
200	0.676	0.844	1.039	1.286	1.653	1.972	2.601	3.340
300	.676	.843	1.038	1.285	1.650	1.968	2.592	3.323
400	.676	.843	1.038	1.284	1.649	1.966	2.588	3.315
500	.676	.843	1.037	1.284	1.648	1.965	2.586	3.310
1000	.675	.842	1.037	1.283	1.647	1.962	2.581	3.301
∞	0.67449	0.84162	1.03643	1.28155	1.64485	1.95996	2.57582	3.29053

Table II is abridged from:
(1) Table III of R.A. Fisher and F. Yates, Statistical Tables for Biological, Agricultural and Medical Research, published by Oliver & Boyd Ltd., Edinburgh, and by permission of the authors and publishers.
(2) Appendix 6 of B. Ostle, Statistics in Research, published by the Iowa State University Press, Ames, Iowa, by permission of the author and publisher.

TABLE III. PERCENTILE VALUES OF THE χ^2 DISTRIBUTION

CUMULATIVE PROBABILITY

f \ P	0.0005	0.001	0.005	0.01	0.025	0.05	0.10	0.20	0.30	0.40
1	0.0^6393	0.0^5157	0.0^4393	0.0^3157	0.0^3982	0.0^2393	0.0158	0.0642	0.148	0.275
2	0.0^2100	0.0^2200	0.0100	0.0201	0.0506	0.103	0.211	0.446	0.713	1.022
3	0.0153	0.0243	0.0717	0.115	0.216	0.352	0.584	1.005	1.424	1.869
4	0.0639	0.0908	0.207	0.297	0.484	0.711	1.064	1.649	2.195	2.753
5	0.158	0.210	0.412	0.554	0.831	1.145	1.610	2.343	3.000	3.655
6	0.299	0.381	0.676	0.872	1.237	1.635	2.204	3.070	3.828	4.570
7	0.485	0.598	0.989	1.239	1.690	2.167	2.833	3.822	4.671	5.493
8	0.710	0.857	1.344	1.646	2.180	2.733	3.490	4.594	5.527	6.423
9	0.972	1.153	1.735	2.088	2.700	3.325	4.168	5.380	6.393	7.357
10	1.265	1.479	2.156	2.558	3.247	3.940	4.865	6.179	7.267	8.295
11	1.587	1.834	2.603	3.053	3.816	4.575	5.578	6.989	8.148	9.237
12	1.934	2.214	3.074	3.571	4.404	5.226	6.304	7.807	9.034	10.182
13	2.305	2.617	3.565	4.107	5.009	5.892	7.042	8.634	9.926	11.129
14	2.697	3.041	4.075	4.660	5.629	6.571	7.790	9.467	10.821	12.079
15	3.108	3.483	4.601	5.229	6.262	7.261	8.547	10.307	11.721	13.030
16	3.536	3.942	5.142	5.812	6.908	7.962	9.312	11.152	12.624	13.983
17	3.980	4.416	5.697	6.408	7.564	8.672	10.085	12.002	13.531	14.937
18	4.439	4.905	6.265	7.015	8.231	9.390	10.865	12.857	14.440	15.893
19	4.912	5.407	6.844	7.633	8.907	10.117	11.651	13.716	15.352	16.850
20	5.398	5.921	7.434	8.260	9.591	10.851	12.443	14.578	16.266	17.809
21	5.896	6.447	8.034	8.897	10.283	11.591	13.240	15.445	17.182	18.768
22	6.405	6.983	8.643	9.542	10.982	12.338	14.041	16.314	18.101	19.729
23	6.924	7.529	9.260	10.196	11.688	13.091	14.848	17.187	19.021	20.690
24	7.453	8.085	9.886	10.856	12.401	13.848	15.659	18.062	19.943	21.652
25	7.991	8.649	10.520	11.524	13.120	14.611	16.473	18.940	20.867	22.616
26	8.538	9.222	11.160	12.198	13.844	15.379	17.292	19.820	21.792	23.579
27	9.093	9.803	11.808	12.879	14.573	16.151	18.114	20.703	22.719	24.544
28	9.656	10.391	12.461	13.565	15.308	16.928	18.939	21.588	23.647	25.509
29	10.227	10.986	13.121	14.256	16.047	17.708	19.768	22.475	24.577	26.475
30	10.804	11.588	13.787	14.953	16.791	18.493	20.599	23.364	25.508	27.442
31	11.389	12.196	14.458	15.655	17.539	19.281	21.434	24.255	26.440	28.409
32	11.979	12.811	15.134	16.362	18.291	20.072	22.271	25.148	27.373	29.376
33	12.576	13.431	15.815	17.073	19.047	20.867	23.110	26.042	28.307	30.344
34	13.179	14.057	16.501	17.789	19.806	21.664	23.952	26.938	29.242	31.313
35	13.788	14.688	17.192	18.509	20.569	22.465	24.797	27.836	30.178	32.282
36	14.401	15.324	17.887	19.233	21.336	23.269	25.643	28.735	31.115	33.252
37	15.020	15.965	18.586	19.960	22.106	24.075	26.492	29.635	32.053	34.222
38	15.644	16.611	19.289	20.691	22.878	24.884	27.343	30.537	32.992	35.192
39	16.273	17.261	19.996	21.426	23.654	25.695	28.196	31.441	33.932	36.163
40	16.906	17.916	20.707	22.164	24.433	26.509	29.051	32.345	34.872	37.134
41	17.544	18.575	21.421	22.906	25.215	27.326	29.907	33.251	35.813	38.105
42	18.186	19.238	22.138	23.650	25.999	28.144	30.765	34.157	36.755	39.077
43	18.832	19.905	22.859	24.398	26.785	28.965	31.625	35.065	37.698	40.050
44	19.482	20.576	23.584	25.148	27.575	29.787	32.487	35.974	38.641	41.022
45	20.136	21.251	24.311	25.901	28.366	30.612	33.350	36.884	39.585	41.995
46	20.794	21.929	25.041	26.657	29.160	31.439	34.215	37.795	40.529	42.968
47	21.456	22.610	25.774	27.416	29.956	32.268	35.081	38.708	41.474	43.942
48	22.121	23.295	26.511	28.177	30.755	33.098	35.949	39.621	42.420	44.915
49	22.789	23.983	27.249	28.941	31.555	33.930	36.818	40.534	43.366	45.889
50	23.461	24.674	27.991	29.707	32.357	34.764	37.689	41.449	44.313	46.864

Example: $P\left\{\chi^2 < 4.404\right\} = 2.5\%$ for $f = 12$.

Approximate formula: $\chi_P^2 \approx \frac{1}{2}\left(\sqrt{2f-1} + z_P\right)^2$ for $f > 30$.†

*Table III is from A. Hald and S.A. Sinkbaek, "A Table of Percentage Points of the χ^2 Distribution," Skandinavisk Aktuarietidskrift, 168-175 (1950), by permission of the author and publisher.

†Thompson, Catherine M., "Table of Percentage Points of the χ^2 Distribution," Biometrika, XXII: 187-191, 1941-42.

TABLE III. PERCENTILE VALUES OF THE χ^2 DISTRIBUTION
(Continued)

CUMULATIVE PROBABILITY												
.50	.60	.70	.80	.90	.95	.975	.99	.995	.999	.9995	P	f
.455	.708	1.074	1.642	2.706	3.841	5.024	6.635	7.879	10.828	12.116	1
1.386	1.833	2.408	3.219	4.605	5.991	7.378	9.210	10.597	13.816	15.202	2
2.366	2.946	3.665	4.642	6.251	7.815	9.348	11.345	12.838	16.266	17.730	3
3.357	4.045	4.878	5.989	7.779	9.488	11.143	13.277	14.860	18.467	19.998	4
4.351	5.132	6.064	7.289	9.236	11.070	12.832	15.086	16.750	20.515	22.105	5
5.348	6.211	7.231	8.558	10.645	12.592	14.449	16.812	18.548	22.458	24.103	6
6.346	7.283	8.383	9.803	12.017	14.067	16.013	18.475	20.278	24.322	26.018	7
7.344	8.351	9.524	11.030	13.362	15.507	17.535	20.090	21.955	26.125	27.868	8
8.343	9.414	10.656	12.242	14.684	16.919	19.023	21.666	23.589	27.877	29.666	9
9.342	10.473	11.781	13.442	15.987	18.307	20.483	23.209	25.188	29.588	31.419	10
10.341	11.530	12.899	14.631	17.275	19.675	21.920	24.725	26.757	31.264	33.136	11
11.340	12.584	14.011	15.812	18.549	21.026	23.336	26.217	28.300	32.909	34.821	12
12.340	13.636	15.119	16.985	19.812	22.362	24.736	27.688	29.819	34.528	36.478	13
13.339	14.685	16.222	18.151	21.064	23.685	26.119	29.141	31.319	36.123	38.109	14
14.339	15.733	17.322	19.311	22.307	24.996	27.488	30.578	32.801	37.697	39.719	15
15.338	16.780	18.418	20.465	23.542	26.296	28.845	32.000	34.267	39.252	41.308	16
16.338	17.824	19.511	21.615	24.769	27.587	30.191	33.409	35.718	40.790	42.879	17
17.338	18.868	20.601	22.760	25.989	28.869	31.526	34.805	37.156	42.312	44.434	18
18.338	19.910	21.689	23.900	27.204	30.144	32.852	36.191	38.582	43.820	45.973	19
19.337	20.951	22.775	25.038	28.412	31.410	34.170	37.566	39.997	45.315	47.498	20
20.337	21.991	23.858	26.171	29.615	32.671	35.479	38.932	41.401	46.797	49.010	21
21.337	23.031	24.939	27.301	30.813	33.924	36.781	40.289	42.796	48.268	50.511	22
22.337	24.069	26.018	28.429	32.007	35.172	38.076	41.638	44.181	49.728	52.000	23
23.337	25.106	27.096	29.553	33.196	36.415	39.364	42.980	45.558	51.179	53.479	24
24.337	26.143	28.172	30.675	34.382	37.652	40.646	44.314	46.928	52.620	54.947	25
25.336	27.179	29.246	31.795	35.563	38.885	41.923	45.642	48.290	54.052	56.407	26
26.336	28.214	30.319	32.912	36.741	40.113	43.194	46.963	49.645	55.476	57.858	27
27.336	29.249	31.391	34.027	37.916	41.337	44.461	48.278	50.993	56.892	59.300	28
28.336	30.283	32.461	35.139	39.087	42.557	45.722	49.588	52.336	58.302	60.734	29
29.336	31.316	33.530	36.250	40.256	43.773	46.979	50.892	53.672	59.703	62.161	30
30.336	32.349	34.598	37.359	41.422	44.985	48.232	52.191	55.003	61.098	63.582	31
31.336	33.381	35.665	38.466	42.585	46.194	49.480	53.486	56.328	62.487	64.995	32
32.336	34.413	36.731	39.572	43.745	47.400	50.725	54.776	57.648	63.870	66.402	33
33.336	35.444	37.795	40.676	44.903	48.602	51.966	56.061	58.964	65.247	67.803	34
34.336	36.475	38.859	41.778	46.059	49.802	53.203	57.342	60.275	66.619	69.198	35
35.336	37.505	39.922	42.879	47.212	50.998	54.437	58.619	61.581	67.985	70.588	36
36.336	38.535	40.984	43.978	48.363	52.192	55.668	59.892	62.883	69.346	71.972	37
37.335	39.564	42.045	45.076	49.513	53.384	56.895	61.162	64.181	70.703	73.351	38
38.335	40.593	43.105	46.173	50.660	54.572	58.120	62.428	65.476	72.055	74.725	39
39.335	41.622	44.165	47.269	51.805	55.758	59.342	63.691	66.766	73.402	76.095	40
40.335	42.651	45.224	48.363	52.949	56.942	60.561	64.950	68.053	74.745	77.459	41
41.335	43.679	46.282	49.456	54.090	58.124	61.777	66.206	69.336	76.084	78.820	42
42.335	44.706	47.339	50.548	55.230	59.304	62.990	67.459	70.616	77.418	80.176	43
43.335	45.734	48.396	51.639	56.369	60.481	64.201	68.709	71.893	78.749	81.528	44
44.335	46.761	49.452	52.729	57.505	61.656	65.410	69.957	73.166	80.077	82.876	45
45.335	47.787	50.507	53.818	58.641	62.830	66.617	71.201	74.437	81.400	84.220	46
46.335	48.814	51.562	54.906	59.774	64.001	67.821	72.443	75.704	82.720	85.560	47
47.335	49.840	52.616	55.993	60.907	65.171	69.023	73.683	76.969	84.037	86.897	48
48.335	50.866	53.670	57.079	62.038	66.339	70.222	74.919	78.231	85.350	88.231	49
49.335	51.892	54.723	58.164	63.167	67.505	71.420	76.154	79.490	86.661	89.561	50

Example: $P\{\chi^2 < 23.3\} = 97.5\%$ for $f = 12$.

Approximate formula: $\chi^2_P \approx \frac{1}{2}(\sqrt{2f-1} + z_P)^2$ for $f > 30$.

273

TABLE III. PERCENTILE VALUES OF THE χ^2 DISTRIBUTION
(Continued)

f \ P	0.0005	0.001	0.005	0.01	0.025	0.05	0.10	0.20	0.30	0.40
				CUMULATIVE PROBABILITY						
51	24.136	25.368	28.735	30.475	33.162	35.600	38.560	42.365	45.261	47.838
52	24.814	26.065	29.481	31.246	33.968	36.437	39.433	43.281	46.209	48.813
53	25.495	26.765	30.230	32.018	34.776	37.276	40.308	44.199	47.157	49.788
54	26.179	27.468	30.981	32.793	35.586	38.116	41.183	45.117	48.106	50.764
55	26.866	28.173	31.735	33.570	26.398	38.958	42.060	46.036	49.056	51.739
56	27.556	28.881	32.490	34.350	37.212	39.801	42.937	46.955	50.005	52.715
57	28.248	29.592	33.248	35.131	38.027	40.646	43.816	47.876	50.956	53.691
58	28.943	30.305	34.008	35.913	38.844	41.492	44.696	48.797	51.906	54.667
59	29.640	31.021	34.771	36.698	39.662	42.339	45.577	49.718	52.857	55.643
60	30.340	31.739	35.535	37.485	40.482	43.188	46.459	50.641	53.809	56.620
61	31.043	32.459	36.301	38.273	41.303	44.038	47.342	51.564	54.761	57.597
62	31.748	33.181	37.068	39.063	42.126	44.889	48.226	52.487	55.714	58.574
63	32.455	33.906	37.838	39.855	42.950	45.741	49.111	53.411	56.666	59.551
64	33.165	34.633	38.610	40.649	43.776	46.595	49.996	54.336	57.619	60.528
65	33.877	35.362	39.383	41.444	44.603	47.450	50.883	55.262	58.573	61.506
66	34.591	36.093	40.158	42.240	45.431	48.305	51.770	56.188	59.527	62.484
67	35.307	36.826	40.935	43.038	46.261	49.162	52.659	57.115	60.481	63.461
68	36.025	37.561	41.713	43.838	47.092	50.020	53.548	58.042	61.436	64.440
69	36.745	38.298	42.494	44.639	47.924	50.879	54.438	58.970	62.391	65.418
70	37.467	39.036	43.275	45.442	48.758	51.739	55.329	59.898	63.346	66.396
71	38.192	39.777	44.058	46.246	49.592	52.600	56.221	60.827	64.302	67.375
72	38.917	40.520	44.843	47.051	50.428	53.462	57.113	61.756	65.258	68.353
73	39.646	41.264	45.629	47.858	51.265	54.325	58.006	62.686	66.214	69.332
74	40.376	42.010	46.417	48.666	52.103	55.189	58.900	63.616	67.170	70.311
75	41.107	42.757	47.206	49.475	52.942	56.054	59.795	64.547	68.127	71.290
76	41.841	43.506	47.998	50.286	53.782	56.920	60.690	65.478	69.084	72.270
77	42.576	44.257	48.788	51.097	54.623	57.786	61.586	66.409	70.042	73.249
78	43.313	45.010	49.582	51.910	55.466	58.654	62.483	67.341	70.999	74.228
79	44.051	45.764	50.376	52.725	56.309	59.522	63.380	68.274	71.957	75.208
80	44.791	46.520	51.172	53.540	57.153	60.391	64.278	69.207	72.915	76.188
81	45.533	47.277	51.969	54.357	57.998	61.261	65.176	70.140	73.874	77.168
82	46.276	48.036	52.767	55.174	58.845	62.132	66.076	71.074	74.833	78.148
83	47.021	48.796	53.567	55.993	59.692	63.004	66.976	72.008	75.792	79.128
84	47.767	49.557	54.368	56.813	60.540	63.876	67.876	72.943	76.751	80.108
85	48.515	50.320	55.170	57.634	61.389	64.749	68.777	73.878	77.710	81.089
86	49.264	51.085	55.973	58.456	62.239	65.623	69.679	74.813	78.670	82.069
87	50.015	51.850	56.777	59.279	63.089	66.498	70.581	75.749	79.630	83.050
88	50.767	52.617	57.582	60.103	63.941	67.373	71.484	76.685	80.590	84.031
89	51.521	53.386	58.389	60.928	64.793	68.249	72.387	77.622	81.550	85.012
90	52.276	54.155	59.196	61.754	65.647	69.126	73.291	78.558	82.511	85.993
91	53.032	54.926	60.005	62.581	66.501	70.003	74.196	79.496	83.472	86.974
92	53.790	55.698	60.815	63.409	67.356	70.882	75.101	80.433	84.433	87.955
93	54.549	56.471	61.625	64.238	68.211	71.760	76.006	81.371	85.394	88.936
94	55.309	57.246	62.437	65.068	69.068	72.640	76.912	82.309	86.356	89.917
95	56.070	58.022	63.250	65.898	69.925	73.520	77.818	83.248	87.317	90.899
96	56.833	58.799	64.063	66.730	70.783	74.400	78.725	84.187	88.279	91.881
97	57.597	59.577	64.878	67.562	71.642	75.282	79.633	85.126	89.241	92.862
98	58.362	60.356	65.694	68.396	72.501	76.164	80.541	86.065	90.204	93.844
99	59.128	61.136	66.510	69.230	73.361	77.046	81.449	87.005	91.166	94.826
100	59.896	61.918	67.328	70.065	74.222	77.929	82.358	87.945	92.129	95.808

Example: $P\{\chi^2 < 43.8\} = 2.5\%$ for $f = 64$.

Approximate formula: $\chi_P^2 \approx \frac{1}{2}(\sqrt{2f-1} + z_P)^2$ for $f > 30$.

TABLE III. PERCENTILE VALUES OF THE χ^2 DISTRIBUTION
(Continued)

| CUMULATIVE PROBABILITY | | | | | | | | | | | P | |
.50	.60	.70	.80	.90	.95	.975	.99	.995	.999	.9995		f
50.335	52.917	55.775	59.248	64.295	68.669	72.616	77.386	80.747	87.968	90.887		51
51.335	53.942	56.827	60.332	65.422	69.832	73.810	78.616	82.001	89.272	92.211		52
52.335	54.967	57.879	61.414	66.548	70.993	75.002	79.843	83.253	90.573	93.532		53
53.335	55.992	58.930	62.496	67.673	72.153	76.192	81.069	84.502	91.872	94.849		54
54.335	57.016	59.980	63.577	68.796	73.311	77.380	82.292	85.749	93.167	96.163		55
55.335	58.040	61.031	64.658	69.918	74.468	78.567	83.513	86.994	94.460	97.475		56
56.335	59.064	62.080	65.737	71.040	75.624	79.752	84.733	88.236	95.751	98.784		57
57.335	60.088	63.129	66.816	72.160	76.778	80.936	85.950	89.477	97.039	100.090		58
58.335	61.111	64.178	67.894	73.279	77.931	82.117	87.166	90.715	98.324	101.394		59
59.335	62.135	65.226	68.972	74.397	79.082	83.298	88.379	91.952	99.607	102.695		60
60.335	63.158	66.274	70.049	75.514	80.232	84.476	89.591	93.186	100.888	103.993		61
61.335	64.181	67.322	71.125	76.630	81.381	85.654	90.802	94.419	102.166	105.289		62
62.335	65.204	68.369	72.201	77.745	82.529	86.830	92.010	95.649	103.442	106.583		63
63.335	66.226	69.416	73.276	78.860	83.675	88.004	93.217	96.878	104.716	107.874		64
64.335	67.249	70.462	74.351	79.973	84.821	89.177	94.422	98.105	105.988	109.164		65
65.335	68.271	71.508	75.425	81.086	85.965	90.349	95.626	99.330	107.258	110.451		66
66.335	69.293	72.554	76.498	82.197	87.108	91.519	96.828	100.554	108.525	111.735		67
67.334	70.315	73.600	77.571	83.308	88.250	92.688	98.028	101.776	109.791	113.018		68
68.334	71.337	74.645	78.643	84.418	89.391	93.856	99.227	102.996	111.055	114.299		69
69.334	72.358	75.689	79.715	85.527	90.531	95.023	100.425	104.215	112.317	115.577		70
70.334	73.380	76.734	80.786	86.635	91.670	96.189	101.621	105.432	113.577	116.854		71
71.334	74.401	77.778	81.857	87.743	92.808	97.353	102.816	106.648	114.835	118.129		72
72.334	75.422	78.822	82.927	88.850	93.945	98.516	104.010	107.862	116.091	119.402		73
73.334	76.443	79.865	83.997	89.956	95.081	99.678	105.202	109.074	117.346	120.673		74
74.334	77.464	80.908	85.066	91.061	96.217	100.839	106.393	110.286	118.599	121.942		75
75.334	78.485	81.951	86.135	92.166	97.351	101.999	107.583	111.495	119.851	123.209		76
76.334	79.505	82.994	87.203	93.270	98.484	103.158	108.771	112.704	121.100	124.475		77
77.334	80.526	84.036	88.271	94.374	99.617	104.316	109.958	113.911	122.348	125.739		78
78.334	81.546	85.078	89.338	95.476	100.749	105.473	111.144	115.117	123.594	127.001		79
79.334	82.566	86.120	90.405	96.578	101.879	106.629	112.329	116.321	124.839	128.261		80
80.334	83.586	87.161	91.472	97.680	103.009	107.783	113.512	117.524	126.083	129.520		81
81.334	84.606	88.202	92.538	98.780	104.139	108.937	114.695	118.726	127.324	130.777		82
82.334	85.626	89.243	93.604	99.880	105.267	110.090	115.876	119.927	128.565	132.033		83
83.334	86.646	90.284	94.669	100.980	106.395	111.242	117.057	121.126	129.804	133.287		84
84.334	87.665	91.325	95.734	102.079	107.522	112.393	118.236	122.325	131.041	134.540		85
85.334	88.685	92.365	96.799	103.177	108.648	113.544	119.414	123.522	132.277	135.792		86
86.334	89.704	93.405	97.863	104.275	109.773	114.693	120.591	124.718	133.512	137.042		87
87.334	90.723	94.445	98.927	105.372	110.898	115.841	121.767	125.912	134.745	138.290		88
88.334	91.742	95.484	99.991	106.469	112.022	116.989	122.942	127.106	135.977	139.537		89
89.334	92.761	96.524	101.054	107.565	113.145	118.136	124.116	128.299	137.208	140.783		90
90.334	93.780	97.563	102.116	108.661	114.268	119.282	125.289	129.491	138.438	142.027		91
91.334	94.799	98.602	103.179	109.756	115.390	120.427	126.462	130.681	139.666	143.270		92
92.334	95.818	99.641	104.242	110.850	116.511	121.571	127.633	131.871	140.893	144.511		93
93.334	96.836	100.679	105.303	111.944	117.632	122.715	128.803	133.059	142.119	145.751		94
94.334	97.855	101.717	106.364	113.038	118.752	123.858	129.973	134.247	143.343	146.990		95
95.334	98.873	102.755	107.425	114.131	119.871	125.000	131.141	135.433	144.567	148.228		96
96.334	99.892	103.793	108.486	115.223	120.990	126.141	132.309	136.619	145.789	149.464		97
97.334	100.910	104.831	109.547	116.315	122.106	127.282	133.476	137.803	147.010	150.699		98
98.334	101.928	105.868	110.607	117.406	123.225	128.422	134.642	138.987	148.230	151.934		99
99.334	102.946	106.906	111.667	118.498	124.342	129.561	135.807	140.169	149.449	153.167		100

Example: $P\{\chi^2 < 88.0\} = 97.5\%$ for $f = 64$.

Approximate formula: $\chi_P^2 \approx \frac{1}{2}\left(\sqrt{2f-1} + z_P\right)^2$ for $f > 30$.

TABLE IVa. F DISTRIBUTION: 50% POINTS (Values of F for which $I_F(f_1, f_2) = 0.50$; $F = s_1^2/s_2^2$.)

f_2 \ f_1	1	2	3	4	5	6	7	8	9	10	12	15	20	24	30	40	60	120	∞
1	1.0000	1.5000	1.7092	1.8227	1.8937	1.9422	1.9774	2.0041	2.0250	2.0419	2.0674	2.0931	2.1190	2.1321	2.1452	2.1584	2.1716	2.1848	2.1981
2	0.66667	1.0000	1.1349	1.2071	1.2519	1.2824	1.3045	1.3213	1.3344	1.3450	1.3610	1.3771	1.3933	1.4014	1.4096	1.4178	1.4261	1.4344	1.4427
3	.58506	.88110	1.0000	1.0632	1.1024	1.1289	1.1482	1.1627	1.1741	1.1833	1.1972	1.2111	1.2252	1.2322	1.2393	1.2464	1.2536	1.2608	1.2680
4	.54863	.82843	.94054	1.0000	1.0367	1.0617	1.0797	1.0933	1.1040	1.1126	1.1255	1.1386	1.1517	1.1583	1.1649	1.1716	1.1782	1.1849	1.1916
5	0.52807	0.79877	0.90715	0.96456	1.0000	1.0240	1.0414	1.0545	1.0648	1.0730	1.0855	1.0980	1.1106	1.1170	1.1234	1.1297	1.1361	1.1426	1.1490
6	.51489	.77976	.88578	.94191	.97654	1.0000	1.0169	1.0298	1.0398	1.0478	1.0600	1.0722	1.0845	1.0907	1.0969	1.1031	1.1093	1.1156	1.1219
7	.50572	.76655	.87095	.92619	.96026	.98334	1.0000	1.0126	1.0224	1.0304	1.0423	1.0543	1.0664	1.0724	1.0785	1.0846	1.0908	1.0969	1.1031
8	.49898	.75683	.86004	.91464	.94831	.97111	.98757	1.0000	1.0097	1.0175	1.0293	1.0412	1.0531	1.0591	1.0651	1.0711	1.0771	1.0832	1.0893
9	.49382	.74938	.85168	.90580	.93916	.96175	.97805	.99037	1.0000	1.0077	1.0194	1.0311	1.0429	1.0489	1.0548	1.0608	1.0667	1.0727	1.0788
10	0.48973	.74349	.84508	.89882	.93193	.95436	.97054	.98276	.99232	1.0000	1.0116	1.0232	1.0349	1.0408	1.0467	1.0526	1.0585	1.0645	1.0705
11	.48644	.73872	.83973	.89316	.92608	.94837	.96445	.97661	.98610	.99373	1.0052	1.0168	1.0284	1.0343	1.0401	1.0460	1.0519	1.0578	1.0637
12	.48369	.73477	.83530	.88848	.92124	.94342	.95943	.97152	.98097	.98856	1.0000	1.0115	1.0231	1.0289	1.0347	1.0405	1.0464	1.0523	1.0582
13	.48141	.73145	.83159	.88454	.91718	.93926	.95520	.96724	.97665	.98421	.99560	1.0071	1.0186	1.0243	1.0301	1.0360	1.0418	1.0476	1.0535
14	.47944	.72862	.82842	.88119	.91371	.93573	.95161	.96360	.97298	.98051	.99186	1.0033	1.0147	1.0205	1.0263	1.0321	1.0379	1.0437	1.0495
15	0.47775	.72619	.82569	.87830	.91073	.93267	.94850	.96046	.96981	.97732	.98863	1.0000	1.0114	1.0172	1.0229	1.0287	1.0345	1.0403	1.0461
16	.47628	.72406	.82330	.87578	.90812	.93001	.94580	.95773	.96705	.97454	.98582	.99716	1.0086	1.0143	1.0200	1.0258	1.0315	1.0373	1.0431
17	.47499	.72219	.82121	.87357	.90584	.92767	.94342	.95532	.96462	.97209	.98334	.99466	1.0060	1.0117	1.0174	1.0232	1.0289	1.0347	1.0405
18	.47385	.72053	.81936	.87161	.90381	.92560	.94132	.95319	.96247	.96993	.98116	.99245	1.0038	1.0095	1.0152	1.0209	1.0267	1.0324	1.0382
19	.47284	.71906	.81771	.86987	.90200	.92375	.93944	.95129	.96056	.96800	.97920	.99047	1.0018	1.0075	1.0132	1.0189	1.0246	1.0304	1.0361
20	0.47192	.71773	.81621	.86830	.90038	.92210	.93776	.94959	.95884	.96626	.97746	.98870	1.0000	1.0057	1.0114	1.0171	1.0228	1.0285	1.0343
21	.47108	.71653	.81487	.86688	.89891	.92060	.93624	.94805	.95728	.96470	.97587	.98710	.99838	1.0040	1.0097	1.0154	1.0211	1.0268	1.0326
22	.47033	.71545	.81365	.86559	.89759	.91924	.93486	.94665	.95588	.96328	.97444	.98565	.99692	1.0026	1.0082	1.0139	1.0196	1.0253	1.0311
23	.46965	.71446	.81255	.86442	.89638	.91800	.93360	.94538	.95459	.96199	.97313	.98433	.99558	1.0012	1.0069	1.0126	1.0183	1.0240	1.0297
24	.46902	.71356	.81153	.86335	.89527	.91687	.93245	.94422	.95342	.96081	.97194	.98312	.99436	1.0000	1.0057	1.0113	1.0170	1.0227	1.0284
25	0.46844	.71272	.81061	.86236	.89425	.91583	.93140	.94315	.95234	.95972	.97084	.98201	.99324	.99887	1.0045	1.0102	1.0159	1.0215	1.0273
26	.46793	.71195	.80975	.86145	.89331	.91487	.93042	.94217	.95135	.95872	.96983	.98099	.99220	.99783	1.0035	1.0091	1.0148	1.0205	1.0262
27	.46744	.71124	.80894	.86061	.89244	.91399	.92952	.94126	.95044	.95779	.96889	.98004	.99125	.99687	1.0025	1.0082	1.0138	1.0195	1.0252
28	.46697	.71059	.80820	.85983	.89164	.91317	.92869	.94041	.94958	.95694	.96802	.97917	.99036	.99598	1.0016	1.0073	1.0129	1.0186	1.0243
29	.46654	.70999	.80753	.85911	.89089	.91241	.92791	.93963	.94879	.95614	.96722	.97835	.98954	.99515	1.0008	1.0064	1.0121	1.0177	1.0234
30	0.46616	.70941	.80689	.85844	.89019	.91169	.92719	.93889	.94805	.95540	.96647	.97759	.98877	.99438	1.0000	1.0056	1.0113	1.0170	1.0226
40	.46330	.70531	.80228	.85357	.88516	.90654	.92197	.93361	.94272	.95003	.96104	.97211	.98323	.98880	.99440	1.0000	1.0056	1.0113	1.0169
60	.46053	.70122	.79770	.84873	.88017	.90144	.91679	.92838	.93743	.94471	.95566	.96667	.97773	.98328	.98884	.99441	1.0000	1.0056	1.0112
120	.45774	.69717	.79314	.84392	.87521	.89637	.91164	.92318	.93218	.93943	.95032	.96128	.97228	.97780	.98333	.98887	.99443	1.0000	1.0056
∞	.45494	.69315	.78866	.83918	.87029	.89135	.90654	.91802	.92698	.93418	.94503	.95593	.96687	.97236	.97787	.98339	.98891	.99445	1.0000

Tables iVa-IVg are abridged from:
(1) M. Merrington and C.M. Thompson, "Tables of Percentage Points of the Inverted Beta (F) Distribution," Biometrika, 33:73-88 (1943), by permission of E.S. Pearson and the Biometrika Trustees, London.
(2) S.K. Banerjee, "The One-Tenth Per Cent Level of the Ratio of Variances," Sankhya, 2:427-428 (1936), by permission of the Editor of Sankhya and the Statistical Publishing Society.

TABLE IVb. F DISTRIBUTION: 25% POINTS (Values of F for which $I_F(f_1, f_2) = 0.25$; $F = s_1^2/s_2^2$.)

f_2 \ f_1	1	2	3	4	5	6	7	8	9	10	12	15	20	24	30	40	60	120	∞
1	5.8285	7.5000	8.1999	8.5810	8.8198	8.9833	9.1021	9.1922	9.2631	9.3202	9.4064	9.4934	9.5813	9.6255	9.6698	9.7144	9.7591	9.8041	9.8492
2	2.5714	3.0000	3.1534	3.2320	3.2799	3.3121	3.3352	3.3526	3.3661	3.3770	3.3934	3.4098	3.4263	3.4345	3.4428	3.4511	3.4594	3.4677	3.4761
3	2.0239	2.2798	2.3555	2.3901	2.4095	2.4218	2.4302	2.4364	2.4410	2.4447	2.4500	2.4552	2.4602	2.4626	2.4650	2.4674	2.4697	2.4720	2.4742
4	1.8074	2.0000	2.0467	2.0642	2.0723	2.0766	2.0790	2.0805	2.0814	2.0820	2.0826	2.0829	2.0828	2.0827	2.0825	2.0821	2.0817	2.0812	2.0806
5	1.6925	1.8528	1.8843	1.8927	1.8947	1.8945	1.8935	1.8923	1.8911	1.8899	1.8877	1.8851	1.8820	1.8802	1.8784	1.8763	1.8742	1.8719	1.8694
6	1.6214	1.7622	1.7844	1.7872	1.7852	1.7821	1.7789	1.7760	1.7733	1.7708	1.7668	1.7621	1.7569	1.7540	1.7510	1.7477	1.7443	1.7407	1.7368
7	1.5732	1.7010	1.7169	1.7157	1.7111	1.7059	1.7011	1.6969	1.6931	1.6898	1.6843	1.6781	1.6712	1.6675	1.6635	1.6593	1.6548	1.6502	1.6452
8	1.5384	1.6569	1.6683	1.6642	1.6575	1.6508	1.6448	1.6396	1.6350	1.6310	1.6244	1.6170	1.6088	1.6043	1.5996	1.5945	1.5892	1.5836	1.5777
9	1.5121	1.6236	1.6315	1.6253	1.6170	1.6091	1.6022	1.5961	1.5909	1.5863	1.5788	1.5705	1.5611	1.5560	1.5506	1.5450	1.5389	1.5325	1.5257
10	1.4915	1.5975	1.6028	1.5949	1.5853	1.5765	1.5688	1.5621	1.5563	1.5513	1.5430	1.5338	1.5235	1.5179	1.5119	1.5056	1.4990	1.4919	1.4843
11	1.4749	1.5767	1.5798	1.5704	1.5598	1.5502	1.5418	1.5346	1.5284	1.5230	1.5140	1.5041	1.4930	1.4869	1.4805	1.4737	1.4664	1.4587	1.4504
12	1.4613	1.5595	1.5609	1.5503	1.5389	1.5286	1.5197	1.5120	1.5054	1.4996	1.4902	1.4796	1.4678	1.4613	1.4544	1.4471	1.4393	1.4310	1.4221
13	1.4500	1.5452	1.5451	1.5336	1.5214	1.5105	1.5011	1.4931	1.4861	1.4801	1.4701	1.4590	1.4465	1.4397	1.4324	1.4247	1.4164	1.4075	1.3980
14	1.4403	1.5331	1.5317	1.5194	1.5066	1.4952	1.4854	1.4770	1.4697	1.4634	1.4530	1.4414	1.4284	1.4212	1.4136	1.4055	1.3967	1.3874	1.3772
15	1.4321	1.5227	1.5202	1.5071	1.4938	1.4820	1.4718	1.4631	1.4556	1.4491	1.4383	1.4263	1.4127	1.4052	1.3973	1.3888	1.3796	1.3698	1.3591
16	1.4249	1.5137	1.5103	1.4955	1.4827	1.4705	1.4601	1.4511	1.4433	1.4366	1.4255	1.4130	1.3990	1.3913	1.3830	1.3742	1.3646	1.3543	1.3432
17	1.4186	1.5057	1.5015	1.4873	1.4730	1.4605	1.4497	1.4405	1.4325	1.4256	1.4142	1.4014	1.3869	1.3790	1.3704	1.3613	1.3514	1.3406	1.3290
18	1.4130	1.4988	1.4938	1.4790	1.4644	1.4516	1.4406	1.4312	1.4230	1.4159	1.4042	1.3911	1.3762	1.3680	1.3592	1.3497	1.3395	1.3284	1.3162
19	1.4081	1.4925	1.4870	1.4717	1.4568	1.4437	1.4325	1.4228	1.4145	1.4073	1.3953	1.3819	1.3666	1.3582	1.3492	1.3394	1.3289	1.3174	1.3048
20	1.4037	1.4870	1.4808	1.4652	1.4500	1.4366	1.4252	1.4153	1.4069	1.3995	1.3873	1.3736	1.3580	1.3494	1.3401	1.3301	1.3193	1.3074	1.2943
21	1.3997	1.4820	1.4753	1.4593	1.4438	1.4302	1.4186	1.4086	1.4000	1.3925	1.3801	1.3661	1.3502	1.3414	1.3319	1.3217	1.3105	1.2983	1.2848
22	1.3961	1.4774	1.4703	1.4540	1.4382	1.4244	1.4126	1.4025	1.3937	1.3861	1.3735	1.3593	1.3431	1.3341	1.3245	1.3140	1.3025	1.2900	1.2761
23	1.3928	1.4733	1.4657	1.4491	1.4331	1.4191	1.4072	1.3969	1.3880	1.3803	1.3675	1.3531	1.3366	1.3275	1.3176	1.3069	1.2952	1.2824	1.2681
24	1.3898	1.4695	1.4615	1.4447	1.4285	1.4143	1.4022	1.3918	1.3828	1.3750	1.3621	1.3474	1.3307	1.3214	1.3113	1.3004	1.2885	1.2754	1.2607
25	1.3870	1.4661	1.4577	1.4406	1.4242	1.4099	1.3976	1.3871	1.3780	1.3701	1.3570	1.3422	1.3252	1.3158	1.3056	1.2945	1.2823	1.2689	1.2538
26	1.3845	1.4629	1.4542	1.4368	1.4203	1.4058	1.3935	1.3828	1.3737	1.3656	1.3524	1.3374	1.3202	1.3106	1.3002	1.2889	1.2765	1.2628	1.2474
27	1.3822	1.4600	1.4510	1.4334	1.4166	1.4021	1.3896	1.3788	1.3696	1.3615	1.3481	1.3329	1.3155	1.3058	1.2953	1.2838	1.2712	1.2572	1.2414
28	1.3800	1.4572	1.4480	1.4302	1.4133	1.3986	1.3860	1.3752	1.3658	1.3576	1.3441	1.3288	1.3112	1.3013	1.2906	1.2790	1.2662	1.2519	1.2358
29	1.3780	1.4547	1.4452	1.4272	1.4102	1.3953	1.3826	1.3717	1.3623	1.3541	1.3404	1.3249	1.3071	1.2971	1.2863	1.2745	1.2615	1.2470	1.2306
30	1.3761	1.4524	1.4426	1.4244	1.4073	1.3923	1.3795	1.3685	1.3590	1.3507	1.3369	1.3213	1.3033	1.2933	1.2823	1.2703	1.2571	1.2424	1.2256
40	1.3626	1.4355	1.4239	1.4045	1.3863	1.3706	1.3571	1.3455	1.3354	1.3266	1.3119	1.2952	1.2758	1.2649	1.2529	1.2397	1.2249	1.2080	1.1883
60	1.3493	1.4188	1.4055	1.3848	1.3657	1.3491	1.3349	1.3226	1.3119	1.3026	1.2870	1.2691	1.2481	1.2361	1.2229	1.2081	1.1912	1.1715	1.1474
120	1.3362	1.4024	1.3873	1.3634	1.3453	1.3278	1.3128	1.2999	1.2886	1.2787	1.2621	1.2428	1.2200	1.2068	1.1921	1.1752	1.1555	1.1314	1.0987
∞	1.3233	1.3863	1.3694	1.3463	1.3251	1.3068	1.2910	1.2774	1.2654	1.2549	1.2371	1.2163	1.1914	1.1767	1.1600	1.1404	1.1164	1.0838	1.0000

TABLE IVc. F DISTRIBUTION: 10% POINTS (Values of F for which $I_F(f_1, f_2) = 0.10$; $F = s_1^2/s_2^2$.)

f_2 \ f_1	1	2	3	4	5	6	7	8	9	10	12	15	20	24	30	40	60	120	∞
1	39.864	49.500	53.593	55.833	57.241	58.204	58.906	59.439	59.858	60.195	60.705	61.220	61.740	62.002	62.265	62.529	62.794	63.061	63.328
2	8.5263	9.0000	9.1618	9.2434	9.2926	9.3255	9.3491	9.3668	9.3805	9.3916	9.4081	9.4247	9.4413	9.4496	9.4579	9.4663	9.4746	9.4829	9.4913
3	5.5383	5.4624	5.3908	5.3427	5.3092	5.2847	5.2662	5.2517	5.2400	5.2304	5.2156	5.2003	5.1845	5.1764	5.1681	5.1597	5.1512	5.1425	5.1337
4	4.5448	4.3246	4.1908	4.1073	4.0506	4.0098	3.9790	3.9549	3.9357	3.9199	3.8955	3.8689	3.8443	3.8310	3.8174	3.8036	3.7896	3.7753	3.7607
5	4.0604	3.7797	3.6195	3.5202	3.4530	3.4045	3.3679	3.3393	3.3163	3.2974	3.2682	3.2380	3.2067	3.1905	3.1741	3.1573	3.1402	3.1228	3.1050
6	3.7760	3.4633	3.2888	3.1808	3.1075	3.0546	3.0145	2.9830	2.9577	2.9369	2.9047	2.8712	2.8363	2.8183	2.8000	2.7812	2.7620	2.7423	2.7222
7	3.5894	3.2574	3.0741	2.9605	2.8833	2.8274	2.7849	2.7516	2.7247	2.7025	2.6681	2.6322	2.5947	2.5753	2.5555	2.5351	2.5142	2.4928	2.4708
8	3.4579	3.1131	2.9238	2.8064	2.7265	2.6683	2.6241	2.5893	2.5612	2.5380	2.5020	2.4642	2.4246	2.4041	2.3830	2.3614	2.3391	2.3162	2.2926
9	3.3603	3.0065	2.8129	2.6927	2.6106	2.5509	2.5053	2.4694	2.4403	2.4163	2.3789	2.3396	2.2983	2.2768	2.2547	2.2320	2.2085	2.1843	2.1592
10	3.2850	2.9245	2.7277	2.6053	2.5216	2.4606	2.4140	2.3772	2.3473	2.3226	2.2841	2.2435	2.2007	2.1784	2.1554	2.1317	2.1072	2.0818	2.0554
11	3.2252	2.8595	2.6602	2.5362	2.4512	2.3891	2.3416	2.3040	2.2735	2.2482	2.2087	2.1671	2.1230	2.1000	2.0762	2.0516	2.0261	1.9997	1.9721
12	3.1765	2.8068	2.6055	2.4801	2.3940	2.3310	2.2828	2.2446	2.2135	2.1878	2.1474	2.1049	2.0597	2.0360	2.0115	1.9861	1.9597	1.9323	1.9036
13	3.1362	2.7632	2.5603	2.4337	2.3467	2.2830	2.2341	2.1953	2.1638	2.1376	2.0966	2.0532	2.0070	1.9827	1.9576	1.9315	1.9043	1.8759	1.8462
14	3.1022	2.7265	2.5222	2.3947	2.3069	2.2426	2.1931	2.1539	2.1220	2.0954	2.0537	2.0095	1.9625	1.9377	1.9119	1.8852	1.8572	1.8280	1.7973
15	3.0732	2.6952	2.4898	2.3614	2.2730	2.2081	2.1582	2.1185	2.0862	2.0593	2.0171	1.9722	1.9243	1.8990	1.8728	1.8454	1.8168	1.7867	1.7551
16	3.0481	2.6682	2.4618	2.3327	2.2438	2.1783	2.1280	2.0880	2.0553	2.0281	1.9854	1.9399	1.8913	1.8656	1.8388	1.8108	1.7816	1.7507	1.7182
17	3.0262	2.6446	2.4374	2.3077	2.2183	2.1524	2.1017	2.0613	2.0284	2.0009	1.9577	1.9117	1.8624	1.8362	1.8090	1.7805	1.7506	1.7191	1.6856
18	3.0070	2.6239	2.4160	2.2858	2.1958	2.1296	2.0785	2.0379	2.0047	1.9770	1.9333	1.8868	1.8368	1.8103	1.7827	1.7537	1.7232	1.6910	1.6567
19	2.9899	2.6056	2.3970	2.2663	2.1760	2.1094	2.0580	2.0171	1.9836	1.9557	1.9117	1.8647	1.8142	1.7873	1.7592	1.7298	1.6988	1.6659	1.6308
20	2.9747	2.5893	2.3801	2.2489	2.1582	2.0913	2.0397	1.9985	1.9649	1.9367	1.8924	1.8449	1.7938	1.7667	1.7382	1.7083	1.6768	1.6433	1.6074
21	2.9609	2.5746	2.3649	2.2333	2.1423	2.0751	2.0232	1.9819	1.9480	1.9197	1.8750	1.8272	1.7756	1.7481	1.7193	1.6890	1.6569	1.6228	1.5862
22	2.9486	2.5613	2.3512	2.2193	2.1279	2.0605	2.0084	1.9668	1.9327	1.9043	1.8593	1.8111	1.7590	1.7312	1.7021	1.6714	1.6389	1.6042	1.5668
23	2.9374	2.5493	2.3387	2.2065	2.1149	2.0472	1.9949	1.9531	1.9189	1.8903	1.8450	1.7964	1.7439	1.7159	1.6864	1.6554	1.6224	1.5871	1.5490
24	2.9271	2.5383	2.3274	2.1949	2.1030	2.0351	1.9826	1.9407	1.9063	1.8775	1.8319	1.7831	1.7302	1.7019	1.6721	1.6407	1.6073	1.5715	1.5327
25	2.9177	2.5283	2.3170	2.1843	2.0922	2.0241	1.9714	1.9292	1.8947	1.8658	1.8200	1.7708	1.7175	1.6890	1.6589	1.6272	1.5934	1.5570	1.5176
26	2.9091	2.5191	2.3075	2.1745	2.0822	2.0139	1.9610	1.9188	1.8841	1.8550	1.8090	1.7596	1.7059	1.6771	1.6468	1.6147	1.5805	1.5437	1.5036
27	2.9012	2.5106	2.2987	2.1655	2.0730	2.0045	1.9515	1.9091	1.8743	1.8451	1.7989	1.7492	1.6951	1.6662	1.6356	1.6032	1.5686	1.5313	1.4906
28	2.8939	2.5028	2.2906	2.1571	2.0645	1.9959	1.9427	1.9001	1.8652	1.8359	1.7895	1.7395	1.6852	1.6560	1.6252	1.5925	1.5575	1.5198	1.4784
29	2.8871	2.4955	2.2831	2.1494	2.0566	1.9878	1.9345	1.8918	1.8568	1.8274	1.7808	1.7306	1.6759	1.6465	1.6155	1.5825	1.5472	1.5090	1.4670
30	2.8807	2.4887	2.2761	2.1422	2.0492	1.9803	1.9269	1.8841	1.8490	1.8195	1.7727	1.7223	1.6673	1.6377	1.6065	1.5732	1.5376	1.4989	1.4564
40	2.8354	2.4404	2.2261	2.0909	1.9968	1.9269	1.8725	1.8289	1.7929	1.7627	1.7146	1.6624	1.6052	1.5741	1.5411	1.5056	1.4672	1.4248	1.3769
60	2.7914	2.3932	2.1774	2.0410	1.9457	1.8747	1.8194	1.7748	1.7380	1.7070	1.6574	1.6034	1.5435	1.5107	1.4755	1.4373	1.3952	1.3476	1.2915
120	2.7478	2.3473	2.1300	1.9923	1.8959	1.8238	1.7675	1.7220	1.6843	1.6524	1.6012	1.5450	1.4821	1.4472	1.4094	1.3676	1.3203	1.2646	1.1926
∞	2.7055	2.3026	2.0838	1.9449	1.8473	1.7741	1.7167	1.6702	1.6315	1.5987	1.5458	1.4871	1.4206	1.3832	1.3419	1.2951	1.2400	1.1686	1.0000

TABLE IVd. F DISTRIBUTION: 5% POINTS (Values of F for which $I_F(f_1, f_2) = 0.05$; $F = s_1^2 / s_2^2$.)

f_2 \ f_1	1	2	3	4	5	6	7	8	9	10	12	15	20	24	30	40	60	120	∞
1	161.45	199.50	215.71	224.58	230.16	233.99	236.77	238.88	240.54	241.88	243.91	245.95	248.01	249.05	250.09	251.14	252.20	253.25	254.32
2	18.513	19.000	19.164	19.247	19.296	19.330	19.353	19.371	19.385	19.396	19.413	19.429	19.446	19.454	19.462	19.471	19.479	19.487	19.496
3	10.128	9.5521	9.2766	9.1172	9.0135	8.9406	8.8868	8.8452	8.8123	8.7855	8.7446	8.7029	8.6602	8.6385	8.6166	8.5944	8.5720	8.5494	8.5265
4	7.7086	6.9443	6.5914	6.3883	6.2560	6.1631	6.0942	6.0410	5.9988	5.9644	5.9117	5.8578	5.8025	5.7744	5.7459	5.7170	5.6878	5.6581	5.6281
5	6.6079	5.7861	5.4095	5.1922	5.0503	4.9503	4.8759	4.8183	4.7725	4.7351	4.6777	4.6188	4.5581	4.5272	4.4957	4.4638	4.4314	4.3984	4.3650
6	5.9874	5.1433	4.7571	4.5337	4.3874	4.2839	4.2066	4.1468	4.0990	4.0600	3.9999	3.9381	3.8742	3.8415	3.8082	3.7743	3.7398	3.7047	3.6688
7	5.5914	4.7374	4.3468	4.1203	3.9715	3.8660	3.7870	3.7257	3.6767	3.6365	3.5747	3.5108	3.4445	3.4105	3.3758	3.3404	3.3043	3.2674	3.2298
8	5.3177	4.4590	4.0662	3.8378	3.6875	3.5806	3.5005	3.4381	3.3881	3.3472	3.2840	3.2184	3.1503	3.1152	3.0794	3.0428	3.0053	2.9669	2.9276
9	5.1174	4.2565	3.8626	3.6331	3.4817	3.3738	3.2927	3.2296	3.1789	3.1373	3.0729	3.0061	2.9365	2.9005	2.8637	2.8259	2.7872	2.7475	2.7067
10	4.9646	4.1028	3.7083	3.4780	3.3258	3.2172	3.1355	3.0717	3.0204	2.9782	2.9130	2.8450	2.7740	2.7372	2.6996	2.6609	2.6211	2.5801	2.5379
11	4.8443	3.9823	3.5874	3.3567	3.2039	3.0946	3.0123	2.9480	2.8962	2.8536	2.7876	2.7186	2.6464	2.6090	2.5705	2.5309	2.4901	2.4480	2.4045
12	4.7472	3.8853	3.4903	3.2592	3.1059	2.9961	2.9134	2.8486	2.7964	2.7534	2.6866	2.6169	2.5436	2.5055	2.4663	2.4259	2.3842	2.3410	2.2962
13	4.6672	3.8056	3.4105	3.1791	3.0254	2.9153	2.8321	2.7669	2.7144	2.6710	2.6037	2.5331	2.4589	2.4202	2.3803	2.3392	2.2966	2.2524	2.2064
14	4.6001	3.7389	3.3439	3.1122	2.9582	2.8477	2.7642	2.6987	2.6458	2.6021	2.5342	2.4630	2.3879	2.3487	2.3082	2.2664	2.2230	2.1778	2.1307
15	4.5431	3.6823	3.2874	3.0556	2.9013	2.7905	2.7066	2.6408	2.5876	2.5437	2.4753	2.4035	2.3275	2.2878	2.2468	2.2043	2.1601	2.1141	2.0658
16	4.4940	3.6337	3.2389	3.0069	2.8524	2.7413	2.6572	2.5911	2.5377	2.4935	2.4247	2.3522	2.2756	2.2354	2.1938	2.1507	2.1058	2.0589	2.0096
17	4.4513	3.5915	3.1968	2.9647	2.8100	2.6987	2.6143	2.5480	2.4943	2.4499	2.3807	2.3077	2.2304	2.1898	2.1477	2.1040	2.0584	2.0107	1.9604
18	4.4139	3.5546	3.1599	2.9277	2.7729	2.6613	2.5767	2.5102	2.4563	2.4117	2.3421	2.2686	2.1906	2.1497	2.1071	2.0629	2.0166	1.9681	1.9168
19	4.3808	3.5219	3.1274	2.8951	2.7401	2.6283	2.5435	2.4768	2.4227	2.3779	2.3080	2.2341	2.1555	2.1141	2.0712	2.0264	1.9796	1.9302	1.8780
20	4.3513	3.4928	3.0984	2.8661	2.7109	2.5990	2.5140	2.4471	2.3928	2.3479	2.2776	2.2033	2.1242	2.0825	2.0391	1.9938	1.9464	1.8963	1.8432
21	4.3248	3.4668	3.0725	2.8401	2.6848	2.5727	2.4876	2.4205	2.3661	2.3210	2.2504	2.1757	2.0960	2.0540	2.0102	1.9645	1.9165	1.8657	1.8117
22	4.3009	3.4434	3.0491	2.8167	2.6613	2.5491	2.4638	2.3965	2.3419	2.2967	2.2258	2.1508	2.0707	2.0283	1.9842	1.9380	1.8895	1.8380	1.7831
23	4.2793	3.4221	3.0280	2.7955	2.6400	2.5277	2.4422	2.3748	2.3201	2.2747	2.2036	2.1282	2.0476	2.0050	1.9605	1.9139	1.8649	1.8128	1.7570
24	4.2597	3.4028	3.0088	2.7763	2.6207	2.5082	2.4226	2.3551	2.3002	2.2547	2.1834	2.1077	2.0267	1.9838	1.9390	1.8920	1.8424	1.7897	1.7331
25	4.2417	3.3852	2.9912	2.7587	2.6030	2.4904	2.4047	2.3371	2.2821	2.2365	2.1649	2.0889	2.0075	1.9643	1.9192	1.8718	1.8217	1.7684	1.7110
26	4.2252	3.3690	2.9751	2.7426	2.5868	2.4741	2.3883	2.3205	2.2655	2.2197	2.1479	2.0716	1.9898	1.9464	1.9010	1.8533	1.8027	1.7488	1.6906
27	4.2100	3.3541	2.9604	2.7278	2.5719	2.4591	2.3732	2.3053	2.2501	2.2043	2.1323	2.0558	1.9736	1.9299	1.8842	1.8361	1.7851	1.7307	1.6717
28	4.1960	3.3404	2.9467	2.7141	2.5581	2.4453	2.3593	2.2913	2.2360	2.1900	2.1179	2.0411	1.9586	1.9147	1.8687	1.8203	1.7689	1.7138	1.6541
29	4.1830	3.3277	2.9340	2.7014	2.5454	2.4324	2.3463	2.2782	2.2229	2.1768	2.1045	2.0275	1.9446	1.9005	1.8543	1.8055	1.7537	1.6981	1.6377
30	4.1709	3.3158	2.9223	2.6896	2.5336	2.4205	2.3343	2.2662	2.2107	2.1646	2.0921	2.0148	1.9317	1.8874	1.8409	1.7918	1.7396	1.6835	1.6223
40	4.0848	3.2317	2.8387	2.6060	2.4495	2.3359	2.2490	2.1802	2.1240	2.0772	2.0035	1.9245	1.8389	1.7929	1.7444	1.6928	1.6373	1.5766	1.5089
60	4.0012	3.1504	2.7581	2.5252	2.3683	2.2540	2.1665	2.0970	2.0401	1.9926	1.9174	1.8364	1.7480	1.7001	1.6491	1.5943	1.5343	1.4673	1.3893
120	3.9201	3.0718	2.6802	2.4472	2.2900	2.1750	2.0867	2.0164	1.9588	1.9105	1.8337	1.7505	1.6587	1.6084	1.5543	1.4952	1.4290	1.3519	1.2539
∞	3.8415	2.9957	2.6049	2.3719	2.2141	2.0986	2.0096	1.9384	1.8799	1.8307	1.7522	1.6664	1.5705	1.5173	1.4591	1.3940	1.3180	1.2214	1.0000

TABLE IVe. F DISTRIBUTION: 1% POINTS (Values of F for which $I_F(f_1, f_2) = 0.01$; $F = s_1^2/s_2^2$)

f_2 \\ f_1	1	2	3	4	5	6	7	8	9	10	12	15	20	24	30	40	60	120	∞
1	4052.2	4999.5	5403.3	5624.6	5763.7	5859.0	5928.3	5981.6	6022.5	6055.8	6106.3	6157.3	6208.7	6234.6	6260.7	6286.8	6313.0	6339.4	6366.0
2	98.503	99.000	99.166	99.249	99.299	99.332	99.356	99.374	99.388	99.399	99.416	99.432	99.458	99.449	99.466	99.474	99.483	99.491	99.501
3	34.116	30.817	29.457	28.710	28.237	27.911	27.672	27.489	27.345	27.229	27.052	26.872	26.690	26.598	26.505	26.411	26.316	26.221	26.125
4	21.198	18.000	16.694	15.977	15.522	15.207	14.976	14.799	14.659	14.546	14.374	14.198	14.020	13.929	13.838	13.745	13.652	13.558	13.463
5	16.258	13.274	12.060	11.392	10.967	10.672	10.456	10.289	10.158	10.051	9.8883	9.7222	9.5527	9.4665	9.3793	9.2912	9.2020	9.1118	9.0204
6	13.745	10.925	9.7795	9.1483	8.7459	8.4661	8.2600	8.1016	7.9761	7.8741	7.7183	7.5590	7.3958	7.3127	7.2285	7.1432	7.0568	6.9690	6.8801
7	12.246	9.5466	8.4513	7.8467	7.4604	7.1914	6.9928	6.8401	6.7188	6.6201	6.4691	6.3143	6.1554	6.0743	5.9921	5.9084	5.8236	5.7372	5.6495
8	11.259	8.6491	7.5910	7.0060	6.6318	6.3707	6.1776	6.0289	5.9106	5.8143	5.6668	5.5151	5.3591	5.2793	5.1981	5.1156	5.0316	4.9460	4.8588
9	10.561	8.0215	6.9919	6.4221	6.0569	5.8018	5.6129	5.4671	5.3511	5.2565	5.1114	4.9621	4.8080	4.7290	4.6486	4.5667	4.4831	4.3978	4.3105
10	10.044	7.5594	6.5523	5.9943	5.6363	5.3858	5.2001	5.0567	4.9424	4.8492	4.7059	4.5582	4.4054	4.3269	4.2469	4.1653	4.0819	3.9965	3.9090
11	9.6460	7.2057	6.2167	5.6683	5.3160	5.0692	4.8861	4.7445	4.6315	4.5393	4.3974	4.2509	4.0990	4.0209	3.9411	3.8596	3.7761	3.6904	3.6025
12	9.3302	6.9266	5.9526	5.4119	5.0643	4.8206	4.6395	4.4994	4.3875	4.2961	4.1553	4.0096	3.8584	3.7805	3.7008	3.6192	3.5355	3.4494	3.3608
13	9.0738	6.7010	5.7394	5.2053	4.8616	4.6204	4.4410	4.3021	4.1911	4.1003	3.9603	3.8154	3.6646	3.5868	3.5070	3.4253	3.3413	3.2548	3.1654
14	8.8616	6.5149	5.5639	5.0354	4.6950	4.4558	4.2779	4.1399	4.0297	3.9394	3.8001	3.6557	3.5052	3.4274	3.3476	3.2656	3.1813	3.0942	3.0040
15	8.6831	6.3589	5.4170	4.8932	4.5556	4.3183	4.1415	4.0045	3.8948	3.8049	3.6662	3.5222	3.3719	3.2940	3.2141	3.1319	3.0471	2.9595	2.8684
16	8.5310	6.2262	5.2922	4.7726	4.4374	4.2016	4.0259	3.8896	3.7804	3.6909	3.5527	3.4089	3.2588	3.1808	3.1007	3.0182	2.9330	2.8447	2.7528
17	8.3997	6.1121	5.1850	4.6690	4.3359	4.1015	3.9267	3.7910	3.6822	3.5931	3.4552	3.3117	3.1615	3.0835	3.0032	2.9205	2.8348	2.7459	2.6530
18	8.2854	6.0129	5.0919	4.5790	4.2479	4.0146	3.8406	3.7054	3.5971	3.5082	3.3706	3.2273	3.0771	2.9990	2.9185	2.8354	2.7493	2.6597	2.5660
19	8.1850	5.9259	5.0103	4.5003	4.1708	3.9386	3.7653	3.6305	3.5225	3.4338	3.2965	3.1533	3.0031	2.9249	2.8442	2.7608	2.6742	2.5839	2.4893
20	8.0960	5.8489	4.9382	4.4307	4.1027	3.8714	3.6987	3.5644	3.4567	3.3682	3.2311	3.0880	2.9377	2.8594	2.7785	2.6947	2.6077	2.5168	2.4212
21	8.0166	5.7804	4.8740	4.3688	4.0421	3.8117	3.6396	3.5056	3.3981	3.3098	3.1729	3.0299	2.8796	2.8011	2.7200	2.6359	2.5484	2.4568	2.3603
22	7.9454	5.7190	4.8166	4.3134	3.9880	3.7583	3.5867	3.4530	3.3458	3.2576	3.1209	2.9780	2.8274	2.7488	2.6675	2.5831	2.4951	2.4029	2.3055
23	7.8811	5.6637	4.7649	4.2635	3.9392	3.7102	3.5390	3.4057	3.2986	3.2106	3.0740	2.9311	2.7805	2.7017	2.6202	2.5355	2.4471	2.3542	2.2559
24	7.8229	5.6136	4.7181	4.2184	3.8951	3.6667	3.4959	3.3629	3.2560	3.1681	3.0316	2.8887	2.7380	2.6591	2.5773	2.4923	2.4035	2.3099	2.2107
25	7.7698	5.5680	4.6755	4.1774	3.8550	3.6272	3.4568	3.3239	3.2172	3.1294	2.9931	2.8502	2.6993	2.6203	2.5383	2.4530	2.3637	2.2695	2.1694
26	7.7213	5.5263	4.6366	4.1400	3.8183	3.5911	3.4210	3.2884	3.1818	3.0941	2.9579	2.8150	2.6640	2.5848	2.5026	2.4170	2.3273	2.2325	2.1315
27	7.6767	5.4881	4.6009	4.1056	3.7848	3.5580	3.3882	3.2558	3.1494	3.0618	2.9256	2.7827	2.6316	2.5522	2.4699	2.3840	2.2938	2.1984	2.0965
28	7.6356	5.4529	4.5681	4.0740	3.7539	3.5276	3.3581	3.2259	3.1195	3.0320	2.8959	2.7530	2.6017	2.5223	2.4397	2.3535	2.2629	2.1670	2.0642
29	7.5976	5.4205	4.5378	4.0449	3.7254	3.4995	3.3302	3.1982	3.0920	3.0045	2.8685	2.7256	2.5742	2.4946	2.4118	2.3253	2.2344	2.1378	2.0342
30	7.5625	5.3904	4.5097	4.0179	3.6990	3.4735	3.3045	3.1726	3.0665	2.9791	2.8431	2.7002	2.5487	2.4689	2.3860	2.2992	2.2079	2.1107	2.0062
40	7.3141	5.1785	4.3126	3.8283	3.5138	3.2910	3.1238	2.9930	2.8876	2.8005	2.6648	2.5216	2.3689	2.2880	2.2034	2.1142	2.0194	1.9172	1.8047
60	7.0771	4.9774	4.1259	3.6491	3.3389	3.1187	2.9530	2.8233	2.7185	2.6318	2.4961	2.3523	2.1978	2.1154	2.0285	1.9360	1.8363	1.7263	1.6006
120	6.8510	4.7865	3.9493	3.4796	3.1735	2.9559	2.7918	2.6629	2.5586	2.4721	2.3363	2.1915	2.0346	1.9500	1.8600	1.7628	1.6557	1.5330	1.3805
∞	6.6349	4.6052	3.7816	3.3192	3.0173	2.8020	2.6393	2.5113	2.4073	2.3209	2.1848	2.0385	1.8783	1.7908	1.6964	1.5923	1.4730	1.3246	1.0000

TABLE IVf. F DISTRIBUTION: 0.5% POINTS (Values of F for which $I_F(f_1, f_2) = 0.005$; $F = s_1^2/s_2^2$.)

f_2 \ f_1	1	2	3	4	5	6	7	8	9	10	12	15	20	24	30	40	60	120	∞
1	16211.	20000.	21615.	22500.	23056.	23437.	23715.	23925.	24091.	24224.	24426.	24630.	24836.	24940.	25044.	25148.	25253.	25359.	25465.
2	198.50	199.00	199.17	199.25	199.30	199.33	199.36	199.37	199.39	199.40	199.42	199.43	199.45	199.46	199.47	199.47	199.48	199.49	199.51
3	55.552	49.799	47.467	46.195	45.392	44.838	44.434	44.126	43.882	43.686	43.387	43.085	42.778	42.622	42.466	42.308	42.149	41.989	41.829
4	31.333	26.284	24.259	23.155	22.456	21.975	21.622	21.352	21.139	20.967	20.705	20.438	20.167	20.030	19.892	19.752	19.611	19.468	19.325
5	22.785	18.314	16.530	15.556	14.940	14.513	14.200	13.961	13.772	13.618	13.384	13.146	12.903	12.780	12.656	12.530	12.402	12.274	12.144
6	18.635	14.544	12.917	12.028	11.464	11.073	10.786	10.566	10.391	10.250	10.034	9.8140	9.5888	9.4741	9.3583	9.2408	9.1219	9.0015	8.8793
7	16.236	12.404	10.882	10.050	9.5221	9.1554	8.8854	8.6781	8.5138	8.3803	8.1764	7.9678	7.7540	7.6450	7.5345	7.4225	7.3088	7.1933	7.0760
8	14.688	11.042	9.5965	8.8051	8.3018	7.9520	7.6942	7.4960	7.3386	7.2107	7.0149	6.8143	6.6082	6.5029	6.3961	6.2875	6.1772	6.0649	5.9505
9	13.614	10.107	8.7171	7.9559	7.4711	7.1338	6.8849	6.6933	6.5411	6.4171	6.2274	6.0325	5.8318	5.7292	5.6248	5.5186	5.4104	5.3001	5.1875
10	12.826	9.4270	8.0807	7.3428	6.8723	6.5446	6.3025	6.1159	5.9676	5.8467	5.6613	5.4707	5.2740	5.1732	5.0705	4.9659	4.8592	4.7501	4.6385
11	12.226	8.9122	7.6004	6.8809	6.4217	6.1015	5.8648	5.6821	5.5368	5.4182	5.2363	5.0489	4.8552	4.7557	4.6543	4.5508	4.4450	4.3367	4.2256
12	11.754	8.5096	7.2258	6.5211	6.0711	5.7570	5.5245	5.3451	5.2021	5.0855	4.9063	4.7214	4.5299	4.4315	4.3309	4.2282	4.1229	4.0149	3.9039
13	11.374	8.1865	6.9257	6.2335	5.7910	5.4819	5.2529	5.0761	4.9351	4.8199	4.6429	4.4600	4.2703	4.1726	4.0727	3.9704	3.8704	3.7577	3.6465
14	11.060	7.9217	6.6803	5.9984	5.5623	5.2574	5.0313	4.8566	4.7173	4.6034	4.4281	4.2468	4.0585	3.9614	3.8619	3.7600	3.6553	3.5473	3.4359
15	10.798	7.7008	6.4760	5.8029	5.3721	5.0708	4.8473	4.6743	4.5364	4.4236	4.2498	4.0698	3.8826	3.7859	3.6867	3.5850	3.4803	3.3722	3.2602
16	10.575	7.5138	6.3034	5.6378	5.2117	4.9134	4.6920	4.5207	4.3838	4.2719	4.0994	3.9205	3.7342	3.6378	3.5388	3.4372	3.3324	3.2240	3.1115
17	10.384	7.3536	6.1556	5.4967	5.0746	4.7789	4.5594	4.3893	4.2535	4.1423	3.9709	3.7929	3.6073	3.5112	3.4124	3.3107	3.2058	3.0971	2.9839
18	10.218	7.2148	6.0277	5.3746	4.9560	4.6627	4.4448	4.2759	4.1410	4.0305	3.8599	3.6827	3.4977	3.4017	3.3030	3.2014	3.0962	2.9871	2.8732
19	10.073	7.0935	5.9161	5.2681	4.8526	4.5614	4.3448	4.1770	4.0428	3.9329	3.7631	3.5866	3.4020	3.3062	3.2075	3.1058	3.0004	2.8908	2.7762
20	9.9439	6.9865	5.8177	5.1743	4.7616	4.4721	4.2569	4.0900	3.9564	3.8470	3.6779	3.5020	3.3178	3.2220	3.1234	3.0215	2.9159	2.8058	2.6904
21	9.8295	6.8914	5.7304	5.0911	4.6808	4.3931	4.1789	4.0128	3.8799	3.7709	3.6024	3.4270	3.2431	3.1474	3.0488	2.9467	2.8408	2.7302	2.6140
22	9.7271	6.8064	5.6524	5.0168	4.6088	4.3225	4.1094	3.9440	3.8116	3.7030	3.5350	3.3600	3.1764	3.0807	2.9821	2.8799	2.7736	2.6625	2.5455
23	9.6348	6.7300	5.5823	4.9500	4.5441	4.2591	4.0469	3.8822	3.7502	3.6420	3.4745	3.2999	3.1165	3.0208	2.9221	2.8198	2.7132	2.6016	2.4837
24	9.5513	6.6610	5.5190	4.8898	4.4857	4.2019	3.9905	3.8264	3.6949	3.5870	3.4199	3.2456	3.0624	2.9667	2.8679	2.7654	2.6585	2.5463	2.4276
25	9.4753	6.5982	5.4615	4.8351	4.4327	4.1500	3.9394	3.7758	3.6447	3.5370	3.3704	3.1963	3.0133	2.9176	2.8187	2.7160	2.6088	2.4960	2.3765
26	9.4059	6.5409	5.4091	4.7852	4.3844	4.1027	3.8928	3.7297	3.5989	3.4916	3.3252	3.1515	2.9685	2.8728	2.7738	2.6709	2.5633	2.4501	2.3297
27	9.3423	6.4885	5.3611	4.7396	4.3402	4.0594	3.8501	3.6875	3.5571	3.4499	3.2839	3.1104	2.9275	2.8318	2.7327	2.6296	2.5217	2.4078	2.2867
28	9.2838	6.4403	5.3170	4.6977	4.2996	4.0197	3.8110	3.6487	3.5186	3.4117	3.2460	3.0727	2.8899	2.7941	2.6949	2.5916	2.4834	2.3689	2.2469
29	9.2297	6.3958	5.2764	4.6591	4.2622	3.9830	3.7749	3.6130	3.4832	3.3765	3.2111	3.0379	2.8551	2.7594	2.6601	2.5565	2.4479	2.3330	2.2102
30	9.1797	6.3547	5.2388	4.6233	4.2276	3.9492	3.7416	3.5801	3.4505	3.3440	3.1787	3.0057	2.8230	2.7272	2.6278	2.5241	2.4151	2.2997	2.1760
40	8.8278	6.0664	4.9759	4.3738	3.9860	3.7129	3.5088	3.3498	3.2220	3.1167	2.9531	2.7811	2.5984	2.5020	2.4015	2.2958	2.1838	2.0635	1.9318
60	8.4946	5.7950	4.7290	4.1399	3.7600	3.4918	3.2911	3.1344	3.0083	2.9042	2.7419	2.5705	2.3872	2.2898	2.1874	2.0789	1.9622	1.8341	1.6885
120	8.1790	5.5393	4.4973	3.9207	3.5482	3.2849	3.0874	2.9330	2.8083	2.7052	2.5439	2.3727	2.1881	2.0890	1.9839	1.8709	1.7469	1.6055	1.4311
∞	7.8794	5.2983	4.2794	3.7151	3.3499	3.0913	2.8968	2.7444	2.6210	2.5188	2.3583	2.1868	1.9998	1.8983	1.7891	1.6691	1.5325	1.3637	1.0000

TABLE IVg. F DISTRIBUTION: 0.1% POINTS (Values of F for which $I_F(f_1, f_2) = 0.001$; $F = s_1^2/s_2^2$.)

f_2 \ f_1	1	2	3	4	5	6	7	8	9	10	12	15	20	24	30	40	60	120	∞
1	406491.	499976.	536657.	562482.	576375.	585906.	592860.	598100.	602181.	605563.	610549.	615699.	620893.	623381.	626506.	628640.	631286.	633942.	636483.
2	998.4	990.0	999.2	999.2	999.2	999.2	999.2	999.2	999.4	999.4	999.6	999.4	999.4	999.4	999.4	999.4	999.4	999.4	999.4
3	167.46	148.5	141.11	137.08	134.58	132.84	131.57	130.6	129.87	129.23	128.30	127.35	126.41	125.94	125.43	124.96	124.46	124.01	123.49
4	74.126	61.238	56.181	53.430	51.706	50.520	49.658	48.998	48.471	48.047	47.407	46.758	46.098	45.768	45.430	45.086	44.745	44.388	44.052
5	47.039	36.612	33.201	31.087	29.748	28.835	28.168	27.638	27.237	26.918	26.416	25.909	25.396	25.143	24.883	24.605	24.332	24.061	23.783
6	35.509	26.998	23.702	21.902	20.809	20.029	19.464	19.029	18.686	18.412	17.989	17.559	17.119	16.891	16.663	16.444	16.216	15.987	15.746
7	29.218	21.688	18.772	17.188	16.206	15.521	15.020	14.634	14.325	14.083	13.708	13.324	12.933	12.733	12.531	12.322	12.119	11.912	11.695
8	25.416	18.493	15.828	14.388	13.485	12.858	12.404	12.044	11.768	11.540	11.194	10.842	10.483	10.302	10.113	9.922	9.728	9.535	9.335
9	22.855	16.385	13.901	12.561	11.714	11.127	10.697	10.369	10.106	9.893	9.570	9.239	8.898	8.723	8.547	8.369	8.189	8.004	7.813
10	21.039	14.906	12.553	11.282	10.481	9.924	9.518	9.204	8.955	8.753	8.445	8.129	7.802	7.637	7.469	7.298	7.123	6.943	6.762
11	19.687	13.813	11.560	10.346	9.577	9.047	8.655	8.354	8.116	7.922	7.625	7.321	7.008	6.847	6.684	6.518	6.348	6.174	5.998
12	18.641	12.972	10.805	9.633	8.892	8.378	8.001	7.711	7.480	7.292	7.005	6.709	6.404	6.248	6.090	5.927	5.763	5.593	5.419
13	17.814	12.312	10.208	9.072	8.354	7.855	7.489	7.206	6.982	6.799	6.519	6.231	5.934	5.782	5.626	5.467	5.305	5.138	4.967
14	17.143	11.780	9.730	8.623	7.922	7.435	7.078	6.802	6.582	6.404	6.130	5.848	5.557	5.408	5.254	5.099	4.939	4.775	4.604
15	16.586	11.338	9.335	8.253	7.567	7.092	6.741	6.470	6.256	6.081	5.812	5.536	5.248	5.101	4.950	4.795	4.638	4.475	4.307
16	16.119	10.970	9.005	7.948	7.272	6.804	6.460	6.195	5.983	5.811	5.548	5.274	4.992	4.846	4.697	4.545	4.388	4.228	4.059
17	15.721	10.659	8.727	7.683	7.022	6.563	6.223	5.962	5.753	5.584	5.324	5.054	4.777	4.631	4.484	4.332	4.177	4.017	3.850
18	15.379	10.389	8.487	7.459	6.807	6.355	6.021	5.763	5.558	5.390	5.132	4.867	4.590	4.448	4.301	4.155	3.996	3.837	3.671
19	15.080	10.157	8.280	7.264	6.609	6.176	5.845	5.590	5.387	5.222	4.967	4.704	4.427	4.286	4.143	3.994	3.840	3.681	3.515
20	14.820	9.952	8.098	7.102	6.461	6.018	5.692	5.440	5.239	5.075	4.823	4.562	4.290	4.150	4.005	3.856	3.703	3.546	3.378
21	14.588	9.773	7.937	6.946	6.318	5.880	5.557	5.308	5.109	4.946	4.697	4.437	4.167	4.026	3.884	3.736	3.584	3.425	3.257
22	14.379	9.612	7.796	6.814	6.192	5.758	5.438	5.190	4.993	4.832	4.583	4.326	4.058	3.918	3.774	3.629	3.475	3.312	3.151
23	14.194	9.469	7.669	6.695	6.079	5.648	5.330	5.086	4.889	4.729	4.482	4.227	3.961	3.822	3.679	3.534	3.380	3.223	3.054
24	14.027	9.339	7.555	6.589	5.976	5.550	5.235	4.991	4.797	4.638	4.393	4.139	3.873	3.735	3.594	3.447	3.294	3.137	2.968
25	13.875	9.222	7.450	6.493	5.885	5.462	5.148	4.907	4.713	4.555	4.311	4.058	3.794	3.657	3.516	3.368	3.216	3.057	2.890
26	13.738	9.116	7.356	6.406	5.802	5.382	5.069	4.829	4.638	4.480	4.238	3.986	3.722	3.586	3.444	3.299	3.147	2.990	2.820
27	13.612	9.020	7.272	6.326	5.726	5.308	4.999	4.759	4.568	4.411	4.170	3.920	3.658	3.521	3.379	3.235	3.082	2.925	2.754
28	13.498	8.930	7.194	6.253	5.656	5.240	4.932	4.694	4.505	4.349	4.109	3.860	3.598	3.462	3.319	3.176	3.023	2.861	2.695
29	13.391	8.852	7.121	6.187	5.592	5.179	4.876	4.645	4.447	4.291	4.053	3.804	3.543	3.407	3.268	3.122	2.971	2.812	2.640
30	13.292	8.774	7.054	6.124	5.533	5.122	4.817	4.581	4.393	4.238	4.000	3.753	3.492	3.358	3.217	3.072	2.919	2.758	2.589
40	12.614	8.251	6.600	5.698	5.128	4.731	4.436	4.207	4.024	3.874	3.642	3.400	3.145	3.012	2.872	2.727	2.574	2.408	2.233
60	11.972	7.765	6.172	5.307	4.757	4.373	4.088	3.865	3.688	3.542	3.315	3.079	2.828	2.694	2.555	2.408	2.252	2.085	1.896
120	11.262	7.312	5.793	4.947	4.415	4.041	3.765	3.546	3.373	3.229	3.016	2.767	2.522	2.396	2.261	2.112	1.952	1.782	1.561
∞	10.826	6.908	5.423	4.616	4.103	3.743	3.474	3.265	3.098	2.959	2.742	2.513	2.266	2.132	1.990	1.835	1.660	1.448	1.000

TABLE V. VALUES OF THE CORRELATION COEFFICIENT FOR DIFFERENT LEVELS OF SIGNIFICANCE

n	0.1	0.05	0.02	0.01	0.001
1	0.98769	0.99692	0.999507	0.999877	0.9999988
2	.90000	.95000	.98000	.990000	.99900
3	.8054	.8783	.93433	.95873	.99116
4	.7293	.8114	.8822	.91720	.97406
5	.6694	.7545	.8329	.8745	.95074
6	0.6215	0.7067	0.7887	0.8343	0.92493
7	.5822	.6664	.7498	.7977	.8982
8	.5494	.6319	.7155	.7646	.8721
9	.5214	.6021	.6851	.7348	.8471
10	.4973	.5760	.6581	.7079	.8233
11	0.4762	0.5529	0.6339	0.6835	0.8010
12	.4575	.5324	.6120	.6614	.7800
13	.4409	.5139	.5923	.6411	.7603
14	.4259	.4973	.5742	.6226	.7420
15	.4124	.4821	.5577	.6055	.7246
16	0.4000	0.4683	0.5425	0.5897	0.7084
17	.3887	.4555	.5285	.5751	.6932
18	.3783	.4438	.5155	.5614	.6787
19	.3687	.4329	.5034	.5487	.6652
20	.3598	.4227	.4921	.5368	.6524
25	0.3233	0.3809	0.4451	0.4869	0.5974
30	.2960	.3494	.4093	.4487	.5541
35	.2746	.3246	.3810	.4182	.5189
40	.2573	.3044	.3578	.3932	.4896
45	.2428	.2875	.3384	.3721	.4648
50	0.2306	0.2732	0.3218	0.3541	0.4433
60	.2108	.2500	.2948	.3248	.4078
70	.1954	.2319	.2737	.3017	.3799
80	.1829	.2172	.2565	.2830	.3568
90	.1726	.2050	.2422	.2673	.3375
100	.1638	.1946	.2301	.2540	.3211

Table V is abridged from Table VII of R.A. Fisher and F. Yates, Statistical Tables for Biological, Agricultural and Medical Research, published by Oliver & Boyd Ltd., Edinburgh, and by permission of the authors and publishers.

TABLE VI. FISHER'S TRANSFORMATION OF r TO ζ

ζ	0.00	0.01	0.02	0.03	0.04	0.05	0.06	0.07	0.08	0.09
0.0	0.0000	0.0100	0.0200	0.0300	0.0400	0.0500	0.0599	0.0699	0.0798	0.0898
.1	.0997	.1096	.1194	.1293	.1391	.1489	.1586	.1684	.1781	.1877
.2	.1974	.2070	.2165	.2260	.2355	.2449	.2543	.2636	.2729	.2821
.3	.2913	.3004	.3095	.3185	.3275	.3364	.3452	.3540	.3627	.3714
.4	.3800	.3885	.3969	.4053	.4136	.4219	.4301	.4382	.4462	.4542
0.5	0.4621	0.4699	0.4777	0.4854	0.4930	0.5005	0.5080	0.5154	0.5227	0.5299
.6	.5370	.5441	.5511	.5580	.5649	.5717	.5784	.5850	.5915	.5980
.7	.6044	.6107	.6169	.6231	.6291	.6351	.6411	.6469	.6527	.6584
.8	.6640	.6696	.6751	.6805	.6858	.6911	.6963	.7014	.7064	.7114
.9	.7163	.7211	.7259	.7306	.7352	.7398	.7443	.7487	.7531	.7574
1.0	0.7616	0.7658	0.7699	0.7739	0.7779	0.7818	0.7857	0.7895	0.7932	0.7969
1.1	.8005	.8041	.8076	.8110	.8144	.8178	.8210	.8243	.8275	.8306
1.2	.8337	.8367	.8397	.8426	.8455	.8483	.8511	.8538	.8565	.8591
1.3	.8617	.8643	.8668	.8692	.8717	.8741	.8764	.8787	.8810	.8832
1.4	.8854	.8875	.8896	.8917	.8937	.8957	.8977	.8996	.9015	.9033
1.5	0.9051	0.9069	0.9087	0.9104	0.9121	0.9138	0.9154	0.9170	0.9186	0.9201
1.6	.9217	.9232	.9246	.9261	.9275	.9289	.9302	.9316	.9329	.9341
1.7	.9354	.9366	.9379	.9391	.9402	.9414	.9425	.9436	.9447	.9458
1.8	.94681	.94783	.94884	.94983	.95080	.95175	.95268	.95359	.95449	.95537
1.9	.95624	.95709	.95792	.95873	.95953	.96032	.96109	.96185	.96259	.96331
2.0	0.96403	0.96473	0.96541	0.96609	0.96675	0.96739	0.96803	0.96865	0.96926	0.96986
2.1	.97045	.97103	.97159	.97215	.97269	.97323	.97375	.97426	.97477	.97526
2.2	.97574	.97622	.97668	.97714	.97759	.97803	.97846	.97888	.97929	.97970
2.3	.98010	.98049	.98087	.98124	.98161	.98197	.98233	.98267	.98301	.98335
2.4	.98367	.98399	.98431	.98462	.98492	.98522	.98551	.98579	.98607	.98635
2.5	0.98661	0.98688	0.98714	0.98739	0.98764	0.98788	0.98812	0.98835	0.98858	0.98881
2.6	.98903	.98924	.98945	.98966	.98987	.99007	.99026	.99045	.99064	.99083
2.7	.99101	.99118	.99136	.99153	.99170	.99186	.99202	.99218	.99233	.99248
2.8	.99263	.99278	.99292	.99306	.99320	.99333	.99346	.99359	.99372	.99384
2.9	.99396	.99408	.99420	.99431	.99443	.99454	.99464	.99475	.99485	.99495

	0.0	0.1	0.2	0.3	0.4	0.5	0.6	0.7	0.8	0.9
3	0.99505	0.99595	0.99668	0.99728	0.99777	0.99818	0.99851	0.99878	0.99900	0.99918
4	.99933	.99945	.99955	.99963	.99970	.99975	.99980	.99983	.99986	.99989

Table VI is abridged from Table VIII₁ of R.A. Fisher and F. Yates, Statistical Tables for Biological, Agricultural and Medical Research, published by Oliver & Boyd Ltd., Edinburgh, and by permission of the authors and publishers.

TABLE VIIa. PROBABILITY FOR TOTAL NUMBER OF RUNS IN SAMPLES OF SIZE (N_1, N_2)

N_1 N_2	2	3	4	5	6	7	8	9	10
2,2	0.3333	0.6667	1.0000						
2,3	.2000	.5000	0.9000	1.0000					
2,4	.1333	.4000	.8000	1.0000					
2,5	.0952	.3333	.7143	1.0000					
2,6	.0714	.2857	.6429	1.0000					
2,7	.0556	.2500	.5833	1.0000					
2,8	.0444	.2222	.5333	1.0000					
2,9	.0364	.2000	.4909	1.0000					
2,10	.0303	.1818	.4545	1.0000					
2,11	.0256	.1667	.4231	1.0000					
2,12	.0220	.1538	.3956	1.0000					
2,13	.0190	.1429	.3714	1.0000					
2,14	.0167	.1333	.3500	1.0000					
2,15	.0147	.1250	.3309	1.0000					
2,16	.0131	.1176	.3137	1.0000					
2,17	.0117	.1111	.2982	1.0000					
2,18	.0105	.1053	.2842	1.0000					
2,19	.0095	.1000	.2714	1.0000					
2,20	.0087	.0952	.2597	1.0000					
3,3	0.1000	0.3000	0.7000	0.9000	1.0000				
3,4	.0571	.2000	.5429	.8000	0.9714	1.0000			
3,5	.0357	.1429	.4286	.7143	.9286	1.0000			
3,6	.0238	.1071	.3452	.6429	.8810	1.0000			
3,7	.0167	.0833	.2833	.5833	.8333	1.0000			
3,8	.0121	.0667	.2364	.5333	.7879	1.0000			
3,9	.0091	.0545	.2000	.4909	.7454	1.0000			
3,10	.0070	.0454	.1713	.4545	.7063	1.0000			
3,11	.0055	.0385	.1484	.4231	.6703	1.0000			
3,12	.0044	.0330	.1297	.3956	.6374	1.0000			
3,13	.0036	.0286	.1143	.3714	.6071	1.0000			
3,14	.0029	.0250	.1015	.3500	.5794	1.0000			
3,15	.0024	.0221	.0907	.3309	.5539	1.0000			
3,16	.0021	.0196	.0815	.3137	.5304	1.0000			
3,17	.0018	.0175	.0737	.2982	.5088	1.0000			
3,18	.0015	.0158	.0669	.2842	.4887	1.0000			
3,19	.0013	.0143	.0610	.2714	.4701	1.0000			
3,20	.0011	.0130	.0559	.2597	.4528	1.0000			

Table VIIa is abridged from F.S. Swed and C. Eisenhart, "Tables for Testing Randomness of Grouping in a Sequence of Alternatives," Annals of Mathematical Statistics,
14:66-87 (1943), by permission of the authors and publisher.

$N_1\ N_2$	2	3	4	5	6	7	8	9	10
4,4	0.0286	0.1143	0.3714	0.6286	0.8857	0.9714	1.0000		
4,5	.0159	.0714	.2619	.5000	.7857	.9286	0.9921	1.0000	
4,6	.0095	.0476	.1905	.4048	.6905	.8810	.9762	1.0000	
4,7	.0061	.0333	.1424	.3333	.6061	.8333	.9545	1.0000	
4,8	.0040	.0242	.1091	.2788	.5333	.7879	.9293	1.0000	
4,9	.0028	.0182	.0853	.2364	.4713	.7454	.9021	1.0000	
4,10	.0020	.0140	.0679	.2028	.4186	.7063	.8741	1.0000	
4,11	.0015	.0110	.0549	.1758	.3736	.6703	.8462	1.0000	
4,12	.0011	.0088	.0451	.1538	.3352	.6374	.8187	1.0000	
4,13	$.0^3840$	.0071	.0374	.1357	.3021	.6071	.7920	1.0000	
4,14	$.0^3654$	.0059	.0314	.1206	.2735	.5794	.7663	1.0000	
4,15	$.0^3516$	.0049	.0266	.1078	.2487	.5539	.7417	1.0000	
4,16	$.0^3413$	.0041	.0227	.0970	.2270	.5304	.7183	1.0000	
4,17	$.0^3334$	.0035	.0195	.0877	.2080	.5088	.6959	1.0000	
4,18	$.0^3273$	.0030	.0170	.0797	.1912	.4887	.6746	1.0000	
4,19	$.0^3226$	.0026	.0148	.0727	.1764	.4701	.6544	1.0000	
4,20	$.0^3188$	.0023	.0130	.0666	.1632	.4528	.6352	1.0000	
5,5	0.0^2794	0.0397	0.1667	0.3571	0.6429	0.8333	0.9603	0.9921	1.0000
5,6	$.0^2433$	.0238	.1104	.2619	.5216	.7381	.9112	.9762	0.9978
5,7	$.0^2252$	.0152	.0758	.1970	.4242	.6515	.8535	.9545	.9924
5,8	$.0^2155$	.0101	.0536	.1515	.3473	.5758	.7933	.9293	.9837
5,9	$.0^3999$	$.0^2699$	.0390	.1189	.2867	.5105	.7343	.9021	.9720
5,10	$.0^3666$	$.0^2500$	.0290	.0949	.2388	.4545	.6783	.8741	.9580
5,11	$.0^3458$	$.0^2366$	.0220	.0769	.2005	.4066	.6264	.8462	.9423
5,12	$.0^3323$	$.0^2275$	.0170	.0632	.1698	.3654	.5787	.8187	.9253
5,13	$.0^3233$	$.0^2210$	.0133	.0525	.1450	.3298	.5352	.7920	.9076
5,14	$.0^3172$	$.0^2163$	.0106	.0441	.1246	.2990	.4958	.7663	.8893
5,15	$.0^3129$	$.0^2129$	$.0^2851$	.0374	.1078	.2722	.4600	.7417	.8709
5,16	$.0^4983$	$.0^2103$	$.0^2693$	.0320	.0939	.2487	.4276	.7183	.8524
5,17	$.0^4759$	$.0^3835$	$.0^2570$	.0276	.0822	.2281	.3982	.6959	.8341
5,18	$.0^4594$	$.0^3684$	$.0^2472$	.0239	.0724	.2098	.3715	.6746	.8161
5,19	$.0^4471$	$.0^3565$	$.0^2395$	.0209	.0641	.1937	.3473	.6544	.7984
5,20	$.0^4376$	$.0^3470$	$.0^2333$	.0184	.0570	.1793	.3252	.6352	.7811
6,6	0.0^2216	0.0130	0.0671	0.1753	0.3918	0.6082	0.8247	0.9329	0.9870
6,7	$.0^2117$	$.0^2758$	.0425	.1212	.2960	.5000	.7331	.8788	.9662
6,8	$.0^3666$	$.0^2466$	.0280	.0862	.2261	.4126	.6457	.8205	.9371
6,9	$.0^3400$	$.0^2300$	.0190	.0629	.1748	.3427	.5664	.7622	.9021
6,10	$.0^3250$	$.0^2200$	.0132	.0470	.1369	.2867	.4965	.7063	.8636
6,11	$.0^3162$	$.0^2137$	$.0^2945$	.0357	.1084	.2418	.4357	.6538	.8235
6,12	$.0^3108$	$.0^3970$	$.0^2690$	.0276	.0869	.2054	.3832	.6054	.7831
6,13	$.0^4737$	$.0^3700$	$.0^2512$	.0217	.0704	.1758	.3379	.5609	.7434
6,14	$.0^4516$	$.0^3516$	$.0^2387$	.0173	.0575	.1514	.2990	.5204	.7048
6,15	$.0^4369$	$.0^3387$	$.0^2297$	.0139	.0475	.1313	.2655	.4835	.6680
6,16	$.0^4268$	$.0^3295$	$.0^2230$	.0114	.0395	.1146	.2365	.4500	.6329
6,17	$.0^4198$	$.0^3228$	$.0^2181$	$.0^2934$	.0331	.1005	.2114	.4195	.5998
6,18	$.0^4149$	$.0^3178$	$.0^2144$	$.0^2776$	.0280	.0886	.1896	.3917	.5685
6,19	$.0^4113$	$.0^3141$	$.0^2116$	$.0^2649$	.0238	.0785	.1706	.3665	.5392
6,20	$.0^5087$	$.0^3113$	$.0^3938$	$.0^2548$	.0203	.0698	.1540	.3434	.5118

11	12	13	14	15	16	17	18	19	20	21
1.0000										
1.0000										
1.0000										
1.0000										
1.0000										
1.0000										
1.0000										
1.0000										
1.0000										
1.0000										
1.0000										
1.0000										
1.0000										
1.0000										
1.0000										
0.9978	1.0000									
.9924	0.9994	1.0000								
.9837	.9977	1.0000								
.9720	.9944	1.0000								
.9580	.9895	1.0000								
.9423	.9830	1.0000								
.9253	.9751	1.0000								
.9076	.9659	1.0000								
.8893	.9557	1.0000								
.8709	.9447	1.0000								
.8524	.9329	1.0000								
.8341	.9207	1.0000								
.8161	.9080	1.0000								
.7984	.8952	1.0000								
.7811	.8822	1.0000								

$N_1\ N_2$	2	3	4	5	6	7	8	9	10
7,7	0.0^3583	0.0^2408	0.0251	0.0775	0.2086	0.3834	0.6166	0.7914	0.9225
7,8	$.0^3311$	$.0^2233$	$.0154$	$.0513$	$.1492$	$.2960$	$.5136$	$.7040$	$.8671$
7,9	$.0^3175$	$.0^2140$	$.0^2979$	$.0350$	$.1084$	$.2308$	$.4266$	$.6224$	$.8059$
7,10	$.0^3103$	$.0^3874$	$.0^2643$	$.0245$	$.0800$	$.1818$	$.3546$	$.5490$	$.7433$
7,11	$.0^4628$	$.0^3566$	$.0^2434$	$.0175$	$.0600$	$.1448$	$.2956$	$.4842$	$.6821$
7,12	$.0^4397$	$.0^3377$	$.0^2300$	$.0128$	$.0456$	$.1165$	$.2475$	$.4276$	$.6241$
7,13	$.0^4258$	$.0^3258$	$.0^2212$	$.0^2955$	$.0351$	$.0947$	$.2082$	$.3785$	$.5700$
7,14	$.0^4172$	$.0^3181$	$.0^2152$	$.0^2722$	$.0273$	$.0777$	$.1760$	$.3359$	$.5204$
7,15	$.0^4117$	$.0^3129$	$.0^2111$	$.0^2555$	$.0216$	$.0642$	$.1496$	$.2990$	$.4751$
7,16	$.0^4082$	$.0^4938$	$.0^3828$	$.0^2432$	$.0172$	$.0536$	$.1278$	$.2670$	$.4340$
7,17	$.0^4058$	$.0^4693$	$.0^3624$	$.0^2340$	$.0138$	$.0450$	$.1097$	$.2392$	$.3969$
7,18	$.0^4042$	$.0^4520$	$.0^3476$	$.0^2270$	$.0112$	$.0381$	$.0946$	$.2149$	$.3634$
7,19	$.0^4030$	$.0^4395$	$.0^3368$	$.0^2217$	$.0^2915$	$.0324$	$.0820$	$.1937$	$.3332$
7,20	$.0^4023$	$.0^4304$	$.0^3287$	$.0^2176$	$.0^2754$	$.0278$	$.0714$	$.1751$	$.3060$
8,8	0.0^3155	0.0^2124	0.0^2886	0.03170	0.1002	0.2144	0.4048	0.5952	0.7855
8,9	$.0^4823$	$.0^36993$	$.0^25306$	$.02028$	$.06865$	$.1573$	$.3186$	$.5000$	$.7016$
8,10	$.0^4457$	$.0^34114$	$.0^23291$	$.01337$	$.04792$	$.1170$	$.2514$	$.4194$	$.6209$
8,11	$.0^4265$	$.0^32514$	$.0^22104$	$.0^29050$	$.03406$	$.08824$	$.1994$	$.3522$	$.5467$
8,12	$.0^4159$	$.0^31588$	$.0^21381$	$.0^26271$	$.02461$	$.06740$	$.1591$	$.2966$	$.4800$
8,13	$.0^4098$	$.0^31032$	$.0^39288$	$.0^24438$	$.01806$	$.05212$	$.1278$	$.2508$	$.4210$
8,14	$.0^4063$	$.0^4688$	$.0^36380$	$.0^23199$	$.01344$	$.04076$	$.1034$	$.2129$	$.3694$
8,15	$.0^4041$	$.0^4469$	$.0^34467$	$.0^22345$	$.01014$	$.03223$	$.08419$	$.1816$	$.3245$
8,16	$.0^4027$	$.0^4326$	$.0^33182$	$.0^21746$	$.0^27742$	$.02573$	$.06904$	$.1556$	$.2856$
8,17	$.0^4018$	$.0^4231$	$.0^32302$	$.0^21318$	$.0^25977$	$.02073$	$.05698$	$.1340$	$.2518$
8,18	$.0^4013$	$.0^4166$	$.0^31690$	$.0^21007$	$.0^24663$	$.01685$	$.04732$	$.1159$	$.2225$
8,19	$.0^4009$	$.0^4122$	$.0^31257$	$.0^37784$	$.0^23673$	$.01380$	$.03953$	$.1006$	$.1971$
8,20	$.0^4006$	$.0^4090$	$.0^4946$	$.0^36081$	$.0^22919$	$.01139$	$.03322$	$.08777$	$.1751$
9,9	0.0^4411	0.0^33702	0.0^23003	0.01222	0.04447	0.1090	0.2380	0.3992	0.6008
9,10	$.0^4217$	$.0^32057$	$.0^21764$	$.0^27610$	$.02943$	$.07672$	$.1786$	$.3186$	$.5095$
9,11	$.0^4119$	$.0^31191$	$.0^21072$	$.0^24882$	$.01989$	$.05489$	$.1349$	$.2549$	$.4300$
9,12	$.0^4068$	$.0^4714$	$.0^36702$	$.0^23215$	$.01369$	$.03989$	$.1028$	$.2049$	$.3621$
9,13	$.0^4040$	$.0^4442$	$.0^34302$	$.0^22167$	$.0^29598$	$.02941$	$.07895$	$.1656$	$.3050$
9,14	$.0^4024$	$.0^4281$	$.0^32827$	$.0^21492$	$.0^26837$	$.02198$	$.06118$	$.1347$	$.2572$
9,15	$.0^4015$	$.0^4184$	$.0^31897$	$.0^21046$	$.0^24944$	$.01664$	$.04782$	$.1102$	$.2174$
9,16	$.0^4010$	$.0^4122$	$.0^31297$	$.0^37465$	$.0^23625$	$.01274$	$.03768$	$.09069$	$.1842$
9,17	$.0^4006$	$.0^4083$	$.0^4903$	$.0^35409$	$.0^22692$	$.0^29861$	$.02993$	$.07510$	$.1566$
9,18	$.0^4004$	$.0^4058$	$.0^4638$	$.0^33975$	$.0^22022$	$.0^27710$	$.02396$	$.06255$	$.1336$
9,19	$.0^4003$	$.0^4041$	$.0^4458$	$.0^32959$	$.0^21536$	$.0^26085$	$.01932$	$.05240$	$.1144$
9,20	$.0^4002$	$.0^4029$	$.0^4333$	$.0^32230$	$.0^21179$	$.0^24844$	$.01568$	$.04413$	$.09831$
10,10	0.0^4108	0.0^31083	0.0^39851	0.0^24492	0.01852	0.05126	0.1276	0.2422	0.4141
10,11	$.0^4057$	$.0^4595$	$.0^35699$	$.0^22739$	$.01192$	$.03489$	$.09205$	$.1849$	$.3350$
10,12	$.0^4031$	$.0^4340$	$.0^33402$	$.0^21718$	$.0^27842$	$.02417$	$.06704$	$.1421$	$.2707$
10,13	$.0^4017$	$.0^4201$	$.0^32089$	$.0^21106$	$.0^25259$	$.01703$	$.04933$	$.1099$	$.2189$
10,14	$.0^4010$	$.0^4122$	$.0^31315$	$.0^37281$	$.0^23592$	$.01218$	$.03668$	$.08568$	$.1775$
10,15	$.0^4006$	$.0^4076$	$.0^4847$	$.0^34895$	$.0^22494$	$.0^28841$	$.02755$	$.06731$	$.1445$
10,16	$.0^4004$	$.0^4049$	$.0^4557$	$.0^33353$	$.0^21759$	$.0^26503$	$.02089$	$.05327$	$.1180$
10,17	$.0^4002$	$.0^4032$	$.0^4373$	$.0^32336$	$.0^21258$	$.0^24842$	$.01599$	$.04248$	$.09684$
10,18	$.0^4002$	$.0^4021$	$.0^4255$	$.0^31654$	$.0^39115$	$.0^23648$	$.01235$	$.03412$	$.07982$
10,19	$.0^4001$	$.0^4014$	$.0^4176$	$.0^31187$	$.0^36687$	$.0^22777$	$.0^29621$	$.02759$	$.06608$
10,20	$.0^5001$	$.0^4010$	$.0^4124$	$.0^4864$	$.0^34962$	$.0^32135$	$.0^27554$	$.02245$	$.05496$

0

11	12	13	14	15	16	17	18	19	20	21
0.9749	0.9959	0.9994	1.0000							
.9487	.9879	.9977	0.9998	1.0000						
.9161	.9748	.9944	.9993	1.0000						
.8794	.9571	.9895	.9981	1.0000						
.8405	.9355	.9830	.9962	1.0000						
.8009	.9109	.9751	.9934	1.0000						
.7616	.8842	.9659	.9898	1.0000						
.7233	.8561	.9557	.9852	1.0000						
.6864	.8273	.9447	.9799	1.0000						
.6512	.7982	.9329	.9738	1.0000						
.6178	.7692	.9207	.9669	1.0000						
.5862	.7407	.9081	.9595	1.0000						
.5565	.7128	.8952	.9516	1.0000						
.5286	.6857	.8822	.9433	1.0000						
0.8998	0.9683	0.9911	0.9988	0.9998	1.0000					
.8427	.9394	.9797	.9958	.9993	0.99996	1.0000				
.7822	.9031	.9636	.9905	.9981	.99979	1.0000				
.7217	.8618	.9434	.9823	.9962	.99940	1.0000				
.6634	.8174	.9201	.9714	.9934	.99869	1.0000				
.6084	.7718	.8944	.9580	.9898	.99757	1.0000				
.5573	.7263	.8672	.9423	.9852	.99598	1.0000				
.5103	.6818	.8390	.9248	.9799	.99388	1.0000				
.4674	.6389	.8104	.9057	.9738	.99125	1.0000				
.4285	.5981	.7818	.8855	.9670	.9881	1.0000				
.3931	.5595	.7536	.8645	.9595	.9844	1.0000				
.3611	.5232	.7258	.8429	.9516	.9803	1.0000				
.3322	.4893	.6988	.8210	.9433	.9757	1.0000				
0.7620	0.8910	0.9555	0.9878	0.9970	0.9997	0.99996	1.0000			
.6814	.8342	.9233	.9742	.9924	.9986	.9998	0.99999	1.0000		
.6050	.7731	.8851	.9551	.9851	.9966	.9994	.99994	1.0000		
.5350	.7110	.8431	.9311	.9751	.9931	.9987	.99981	1.0000		
.4721	.6505	.7991	.9031	.9625	.9880	.9976	.99956	1.0000		
.4164	.5928	.7545	.8721	.9477	.9813	.9960	.99912	1.0000		
.3674	.5389	.7104	.8390	.9309	.9729	.9939	.99847	1.0000		
.3245	..4892	.6675	.8047	.9125	.9629	.9912	.99755	1.0000		
.2871	.4437	.6264	.7699	.8929	.9515	.9881	.99634	1.0000		
.2545	.4024	.5872	.7351	.8724	.9388	.9844	.99481	1.0000		
.2261	.3650	.5502	.7008	.8513	.9250	.9803	.99296	1.0000		
.2013	.3313	.5155	.6672	.8298	.9103	.9757	.99078	1.0000		
0.5859	0.7578	0.8724	0.9487	0.9815	0.9955	0.9990	0.9999	0.99999	1.0000	
.5000	.6800	.8151	.9151	.9651	.9896	.9973	.9996	.99994	0.999997	1.0000
.4250	.6050	.7551	.8751	.9437	.9804	.9942	.9988	.9998	.99998	1.0000
.3607	.5351	.6950	.8370	.9180	.9678	.9896	.9974	.9996	.99994	1.0000
.3062	.4715	.6369	.7839	.8889	.9519	.9834	.9952	.9991	.99985	1.0000
.2602	.4146	.5818	.7361	.8574	.9330	.9755	.9920	.9985	.99969	1.0000
.2216	.3641	.5303	.6886	.8243	.9115	.9660	.9879	.9976	.99943	1.0000
.1893	.3197	.4828	.6423	.7904	.8880	.9552	.9826	.9963	.99905	1.0000
.1621	.2809	.4393	.5978	.7562	.8629	.9429	.9763	.9948	.99852	1.0000
.1392	.2470	.3997	.5554	.7223	.8367	.9296	.9689	.9930	.99782	1.0000
.1200	.2175	.3638	.5155	.6889	.8096	.9153	.9606	.9908	.99692	1.0000

N_1 N_2	2	3	4	5	6	7	8	9	10
11,11	0.0^4028	0.0^4312	0.0^33147	0.0^21590	0.0^27332	0.02264	0.06347	0.1349	0.2599
11,12	$.0^4015$	$.0^4170$	$.0^31797$	$.0^39526$	$.0^24614$	$.01499$	$.04427$	$.09919$	$.2017$
11,13	$.0^4008$	$.0^4096$	$.0^31058$	$.0^35865$	$.0^22966$	$.01010$	$.03126$	$.07356$	$.1568$
11,14	$.0^4004$	$.0^4056$	$.0^4639$	$.0^33702$	$.0^21945$	$.0^26932$	$.02233$	$.05505$	$.1224$
11,15	$.0^4003$	$.0^4034$	$.0^4346$	$.0^32389$	$.0^21299$	$.0^24832$	$.01614$	$.04158$	$.09600$
11,16	$.0^4002$	$.0^4021$	$.0^4251$	$.0^31574$	$.0^38822$	$.0^23419$	$.01180$	$.03169$	$.07566$
11,17	$.0^4001$	$.0^4013$	$.0^4162$	$.0^31056$	$.0^36085$	$.0^22453$	$.0^28711$	$.02436$	$.05995$
11,18	$.0^4001$	$.0^4008$	$.0^4107$	$.0^4721$	$.0^34259$	$.0^21782$	$.0^26499$	$.01888$	$.04777$
11,19		$.0^4005$	$.0^4071$	$.0^4500$	$.0^33020$	$.0^21310$	$.0^24895$	$.01475$	$.03828$
11,20		$.0^4004$	$.0^4049$	$.0^4351$	$.0^32169$	$.0^39742$	$.0^23721$	$.01162$	$.03084$
12,12	0.0^4007	0.0^4089	0.0^4984	0.0^35458	0.0^22783	0.0^29495	0.02963	0.06990	0.1504
12,13	$.0^4004$	$.0^4048$	$.0^4556$	$.0^33221$	$.0^21718$	$.0^26139$	$.02010$	$.04977$	$.1126$
12,14	$.0^4002$	$.0^4027$	$.0^4323$	$.0^31952$	$.0^21084$	$.0^24045$	$.01382$	$.03581$	$.08467$
12,15	$.0^4001$	$.0^4016$	$.0^4193$	$.0^31211$	$.0^36970$	$.0^22712$	$.0^29622$	$.02603$	$.06404$
12,16	$.0^4001$	$.0^4009$	$.0^4118$	$.0^4769$	$.0^34565$	$.0^21849$	$.0^26784$	$.01912$	$.04874$
12,17		$.0^4006$	$.0^4073$	$.0^4497$	$.0^33041$	$.0^21279$	$.0^24840$	$.01419$	$.03733$
12,18		$.0^4003$	$.0^4047$	$.0^4328$	$.0^32057$	$.0^38976$	$.0^23492$	$.01063$	$.02879$
12,19		$.0^4002$	$.0^4030$	$.0^4220$	$.0^31412$	$.0^36381$	$.0^22546$	$.0^28032$	$.02234$
12,20		$.0^4001$	$.0^4020$	$.0^4150$	$.0^4983$	$.0^34593$	$.0^21876$	$.0^26124$	$.01745$
13,13	0.0^4002	0.0^4025	0.0^4302	0.0^31825	0.0^21020	0.0^23812	0.01312	0.03406	0.08118
13,14	$.0^4001$	$.0^4013$	$.0^4169$	$.0^31063$	$.0^36196$	$.0^22416$	$.0^28690$	$.02359$	$.05888$
13,15	$.0^4001$	$.0^4007$	$.0^4097$	$.0^4636$	$.0^33844$	$.0^21561$	$.0^25838$	$.01653$	$.04300$
13,16		$.0^4004$	$.0^4057$	$.0^4389$	$.0^32431$	$.0^21026$	$.0^23976$	$.01172$	$.03168$
13,17		$.0^4003$	$.0^4035$	$.0^4243$	$.0^31566$	$.0^36856$	$.0^22743$	$.0^28401$	$.02345$
13,18		$.0^4002$	$.0^4021$	$.0^4155$	$.0^31025$	$.0^34652$	$.0^21916$	$.0^26086$	$.01751$
13,19		$.0^4001$	$.0^4013$	$.0^4100$	$.0^4682$	$.0^33201$	$.0^21354$	$.0^24454$	$.01318$
13,20		$.0^4001$	$.0^4009$	$.0^4066$	$.0^4460$	$.0^32232$	$.0^39671$	$.0^23292$	$.0^29986$
14,14		0.0^4007	0.0^4095	0.0^4597	0.0^33630	0.0^21475	0.0^25553	0.01575	0.04123
14,15		$.0^4004$	$.0^4051$	$.0^4344$	$.0^32174$	$.0^39191$	$.0^23604$	$.01065$	$.02911$
14,16		$.0^4002$	$.0^4029$	$.0^4203$	$.0^31330$	$.0^35835$	$.0^22373$	$.0^27295$	$.02072$
14,17		$.0^4001$	$.0^4017$	$.0^4123$	$.0^4829$	$.0^33770$	$.0^21585$	$.0^25058$	$.01487$
14,18		$.0^4001$	$.0^4010$	$.0^4076$	$.0^4526$	$.0^32476$	$.0^21073$	$.0^23548$	$.01077$
14,19			$.0^4006$	$.0^4048$	$.0^4339$	$.0^31651$	$.0^37351$	$.0^22516$	$.0^27861$
14,20			$.0^4004$	$.0^4030$	$.0^4222$	$.0^31116$	$.0^35098$	$.0^21804$	$.0^25786$
15,15		0.0^4002	0.0^4027	0.0^4191	0.0^31259	0.0^35530	0.0^22261	0.0^26959	0.01988
15,16		$.0^4001$	$.0^4015$	$.0^4109$	$.0^4745$	$.0^33395$	$.0^21442$	$.0^24610$	$.01370$
15,17		$.0^4001$	$.0^4008$	$.0^4064$	$.0^4450$	$.0^32123$	$.0^39329$	$.0^23095$	$.0^29536$
15,18			$.0^4005$	$.0^4038$	$.0^4277$	$.0^31351$	$.0^36124$	$.0^22104$	$.0^26698$
15,19			$.0^4003$	$.0^4023$	$.0^4173$	$.0^4873$	$.0^34074$	$.0^21448$	$.0^24748$
15,20			$.0^4002$	$.0^4014$	$.0^4110$	$.0^4573$	$.0^32745$	$.0^21008$	$.0^23397$
16,16		0.0^4001	0.0^4008	0.0^4060	0.0^4427	0.0^32017	0.0^38905	0.0^22957	0.0^29157
16,17			$.0^4004$	$.0^4034$	$.0^4250$	$.0^31222$	$.0^35590$	$.0^21924$	$.0^26182$
16,18			$.0^4002$	$.0^4020$	$.0^4149$	$.0^4754$	$.0^33562$	$.0^21269$	$.0^24217$
16,19			$.0^4001$	$.0^4012$	$.0^4091$	$.0^4473$	$.0^32302$	$.0^38475$	$.0^22905$
16,20			$.0^4001$	$.0^4007$	$.0^4056$	$.0^4302$	$.0^31509$	$.0^35732$	$.0^22021$
17,17			0.0^4002	0.0^4019	0.0^4142	0.0^4718	0.0^33406	0.0^21214	0.0^24053
17,18			$.0^4001$	$.0^4011$	$.0^4083$	$.0^4430$	$.0^32109$	$.0^37773$	$.0^22686$
17,19			$.0^4001$	$.0^4006$	$.0^4049$	$.0^4262$	$.0^31325$	$.0^35046$	$.0^21800$
17,20				$.0^4004$	$.0^4029$	$.0^4163$	$.0^4845$	$.0^33318$	$.0^21219$
18,18			0.0^4001	0.0^4006	0.0^4047	0.0^4250	0.0^31269	0.0^34836	0.0^21732
18,19				$.0^4003$	$.0^4027$	$.0^4148$	$.0^4776$	$.0^33053$	$.0^21130$
18,20				$.0^4002$	$.0^4016$	$.0^4090$	$.0^4482$	$.0^31954$	$.0^37448$
19,19				0.0^4002	0.0^4015	0.0^4086	0.0^4462	0.0^31875	0.0^37174
19,20				$.0^4001$	$.0^4009$	$.0^4050$	$.0^4280$	$.0^31169$	$.0^34611$
20,20				0.0^4001	0.0^4005	0.0^4029	0.0^4165	0.0^4710	0.0^32890

TABLE VIIa. PROBABILITY FOR TOTAL NUMBER OF RUNS IN SAMPLES OF SIZE (N_1, N_2) (Continued)

11	12	13	14	15	16	17	18	19	20	21
0.4100	0.5900	0.7401	0.8651	0.9365	0.9774	0.9927	0.9984	0.9997	0.99997	0.999997
.3350	.5072	.6650	.8086	.9008	.9594	.9850	.9960	.9990	.9999	.99998
.2735	.4335	.5933	.7488	.8598	.9360	.9740	.9919	.9978	.9996	.9999
.2235	.3690	.5266	.6883	.8154	.9078	.9598	.9857	.9958	.9990	.9998
.1831	.3137	.4660	.6293	.7692	.8758	.9424	.9774	.9930	.9981	.9997
.1504	.2665	.4116	.5728	.7225	.8410	.9224	.9669	.9891	.9967	.9994
.1240	.2265	.3632	.5199	.6765	.8043	.9002	.9542	.9841	.9948	.9990
.1027	.1928	.3205	.4708	.6317	.7666	.8763	.9395	.9781	.9922	.9985
.08533	.1644	.2830	.4257	.5888	.7286	.8510	.9230	.9711	.9890	.9978
.07122	.1404	.2500	.3846	.5480	.6908	.8247	.9051	.9631	.9849	.9969
0.2632	0.4211	0.5789	0.7368	0.8496	0.9301	0.9704	0.9905	0.9972	0.9994	0.9999
.2068	.3475	.5000	.6642	.7932	.8937	.9502	.9816	.9939	.9985	.9997
.1628	.2860	.4296	.5938	.7345	.8518	.9251	.9691	.9886	.9968	.9992
.1286	.2351	.3681	.5277	.6759	.8062	.8958	.9528	.9813	.9940	.9984
.1020	.1932	.3149	.4669	.6189	.7585	.8632	.9330	.9718	.9899	.9971
.08131	.1591	.2693	.4118	.5646	.7101	.8283	.9101	.9602	.9844	.9953
.06511	.1312	.2304	.3626	.5137	.6621	.7919	.8847	.9465	.9774	.9929
.05240	.1085	.1973	.3189	.4665	.6153	.7548	.8572	.9311	.9690	.9898
.04238	.08996	.1693	.2803	.4231	.5703	.7176	.8281	.9140	.9590	.9860
0.1566	0.2772	0.4179	0.5821	0.7228	0.8434	0.9188	0.9659	0.9869	0.9962	0.9990
.1189	.2205	.3475	.5056	.6524	.7880	.8811	.9446	.9764	.9921	.9976
.09064	.1753	.2883	.4365	.5847	.7299	.8388	.9182	.9623	.9858	.9952
.06947	.1396	.2389	.3751	.5212	.6714	.7934	.8873	.9446	.9771	.9917
.05354	.1113	.1980	.3215	.4628	.6141	.7465	.8529	.9238	.9658	.9868
.04150	.08902	.1643	.2752	.4098	.5592	.6992	.8159	.9001	.9520	.9805
.03236	.07143	.1366	.2353	.3623	.5074	.6525	.7772	.8742	.9358	.9728
.02538	.05752	.1138	.2012	.3200	.4592	.6072	.7377	.8465	.9174	.9635
0.08711	0.1697	0.2798	0.4266	0.5734	0.7202	0.8303	0.9129	0.9588	0.9842	0.9944
.06417	.1306	.2247	.3576	.5000	.6519	.7753	.8749	.9358	.9727	.9893
.04756	.1007	.1804	.2986	.4336	.5854	.7183	.8322	.9081	.9574	.9820
.03548	.07788	.1450	.2486	.3745	.5226	.6614	.7863	.8765	.9382	.9721
.02665	.06044	.1168	.2068	.3227	.4643	.6058	.7386	.8418	.9155	.9598
.02015	.04709	.09422	.1720	.2776	.4110	.5527	.6903	.8049	.8898	.9450
.01534	.03684	.07626	.1432	.2387	.3640	.5027	.6425	.7667	.8616	.9281
0.04572	0.09739	0.1749	0.2912	0.4241	0.5759	0.7088	0.8251	0.9026	0.9543	0.9801
.03280	.07281	.1362	.2362	.3576	.5046	.6424	.7710	.8638	.9305	.9672
.02370	.05462	.1062	.1912	.3005	.4393	.5781	.7147	.8210	.9020	.9505
.01726	.04115	.08296	.1546	.2519	.3806	.5174	.6581	.7754	.8693	.9303
.01267	.03115	.06504	.1251	.2109	.3286	.4610	.6026	.7285	.8334	.9068
$.0^2 9370$	.02370	.05118	.1014	.1766	.2831	.4095	.5493	.6813	.7952	.8806
0.02280	0.05280	0.1028	0.1862	0.2933	0.4311	0.5689	0.7067	0.8138	0.8972	0.9472
.01598	.03846	.07781	.1465	.2397	.3659	.5000	.6420	.7603	.8584	.9222
.01129	.02816	.05907	.1153	.1956	.3091	.4369	.5789	.7050	.8155	.8928
$.0^2 8049$	.02072	.04502	.09079	.1594	.2603	.3801	.5188	.6498	.7697	.8596
$.0^2 5786$	.01534	.03446	.07162	.1300	.2188	.3297	.4628	.5959	.7224	.8237
0.01087	0.02722	0.05720	0.1122	0.1907	0.3028	0.4290	0.5710	0.6972	0.8093	0.8878
$.0^2 7460$	.01937	.04221	.08589	.1514	.2495	.3659	.5038	.6341	.7566	.8486
$.0^2 5168$	.01388	.03129	.06587	.1202	.2049	.3108	.4418	.5728	.7022	.8057
$.0^2 3614$	.01000	.02331	.05063	.09551	.1680	.2631	.3854	.5146	.6474	.7604
$0.0^2 4978$	0.01342	0.03029	0.06405	0.1171	0.2004	0.3046	0.4349	0.5651	0.6954	0.7996
$.0^2 3355$	$.0^2 9355$	.02186	.04786	.09057	.1606	.2525	.3729	.5000	.6338	.7475
$.0^2 2283$	$.0^2 6569$	.01586	.03586	.07014	.1285	.2088	.3182	.4398	.5736	.6940
$0.0^2 2201$	$0.0^2 6355$	0.01536	0.03486	0.06828	0.1256	0.2044	0.3127	0.4331	0.5669	0.6873
$.0^2 1459$	$.0^2 4350$	.01086	.02547	.05157	.09810	.1650	.2610	.3729	.5033	.6271
$0.0^3 9429$	$0.0^2 2905$	$0.0^2 7482$	0.01816	0.03800	0.07484	0.1301	0.2130	0.3143	0.4381	0.5619

N_1 N_2	22	23	24	25	26	27	28	29
11,11	1.0000							
11,12	0.999999	1.0000						
11,13	.99999	1.0000						
11,14	.99998	1.0000						
11,15	.99995	1.0000						
11,16	.99989	1.0000						
11,17	.9998	1.0000						
11,18	.9996	1.0000						
11,19	.9994	1.0000						
11,20	.9991	1.0000						
12,12	0.99999	0.999999	1.0000					
12,13	.99996	.99999	0.999999	1.0000				
12,14	.99986	.99998	.999999	1.0000				
12,15	.99966	.99995	.999995	1.0000				
12,16	.99930	.9999	.999985	1.0000				
12,17	.99872	.9998	.99996	1.0000				
12,18	.9978	.9996	.99993	1.0000				
12,19	.9966	.9994	.99987	1.0000				
12,20	.9950	.9991	.99978	1.0000				
13,13	0.9998	0.99997	0.999998	0.9999998	1.0000			
13,14	.9995	.9999	.99999	.999999	0.9999999	1.0000		
13,15	.9988	.9997	.99996	.999995	.9999996	1.0000		
13,16	.9975	.9994	.99988	.99999	.999998	1.0000		
13,17	.9957	.9989	.99975	.99996	.999995	1.0000		
13,18	.9930	.9981	.99951	.99993	.99999	1.0000		
13,19	.9894	.9969	.99914	.99987	.99998	1.0000		
13,20	.9848	.9954	.9986	.99978	.99995	1.0000		
14,14	0.9985	0.9996	0.9999	0.99999	0.999999	0.9999999	1.0000	
14,15	.9967	.9991	.9998	.99997	.999996	.9999996	0.99999999	1.0000
14,16	.9938	.9981	.9995	.99990	.999986	.9999985	.9999999	1.0000
14,17	.9894	.9965	.9990	.99978	.999961	.9999953	.9999995	1.0000
14,18	.9834	.9941	.9982	.99957	.999910	.9999885	.9999986	1.0000
14,19	.9756	.9909	.9970	.99923	.999817	.9999753	.9999963	1.0000
14,20	.9660	.9867	.9952	.99872	.999663	.9999527	.9999916	1.0000
15,15	0.9930	0.9977	0.9994	0.9999	0.99998	0.999997	0.9999998	0.9999999
15,16	.9872	.9954	.9987	.9997	.99994	.999989	.9999988	.9999999
15,17	.9789	.9918	.9974	.9992	.99983	.999968	.9999956	.9999995
15,18	.9678	.9866	.9953	.9985	.99963	.999923	.9999871	.9999986
15,19	.9540	.9798	.9923	.9975	.99928	.999839	.9999686	.9999963
15,20	.9375	.9712	.9881	.9959	.99872	.999699	.9999332	.9999916
16,16	0.9772	0.9908	0.9970	0.9991	0.9998	0.99996	0.99999	0.999999
16,17	.9634	.9840	.9942	.9981	.9995	.99988	.99998	.999997
16,18	.9457	.9747	.9900	.9964	.9989	.99971	.99994	.999989
16,19	.9244	.9626	.9840	.9938	.9980	.99942	.99986	.999973
16,20	.8996	.9479	.9761	.9902	.9965	.99894	.99972	.999942
17,17	0.9428	0.9728	0.9891	0.9959	0.9988	0.9997	0.9999	0.99999
17,18	.9172	.9578	.9816	.9925	.9975	.9992	.9998	.99996
17,19	.8872	.9391	.9714	.9876	.9954	.9985	.9996	.99989
17,20	.8534	.9168	.9584	.9808	.9924	.9972	.9992	.99977
18,18	0.8829	0.9360	0.9697	0.9866	0.9950	0.9983	0.9995	0.9999
18,19	.8438	.9094	.9540	.9782	.9911	.9966	.9990	.9997
18,20	.8010	.8788	.9345	.9670	.9856	.9941	.9980	.9994
19,19	0.7956	0.8744	0.9317	0.9651	0.9846	0.9936	0.9978	0.9993
19,20	.7444	.8350	.9048	.9484	.9756	.9891	.9959	.9985
20,20	0.6857	0.7870	0.8699	0.9252	0.9620	0.9818	0.9925	0.9971

30	31	32	33	34	35	36	37
1.0000							
1.0000							
1.0000							
0.9999999	1.0000						
.9999996	1.0000						
.9999988	1.0000						
0.9999999	1.0000						
.9999997	1.0000						
.9999986	0.9999999	1.0000					
.9999958	.9999996	1.0000					
.9999893	.9999988	0.9999999	1.0000				
0.9999981	0.9999998	1.0000					
.9999929	.9999989	0.9999999	1.0000				
.9999795	.9999965	.9999996	1.0000				
.9999499	.9999909	.9999986	0.9999999	1.0000			
0.99998	0.999995	0.999999	0.9999999	1.0000			
.99993	.999985	.999998	.9999997	1.0000			
.99984	.999962	.999993	.9999989	0.9999999	0.99999999	1.0000	
0.9998	0.99995	0.99999	0.999999	.9999998	0.9999999	1.0000	
.9996	.99988	.99997	.999995	.9999993	.9999999	1.0000	
0.9990	0.9997	0.99993	0.99998	0.999997	0.9999995	0.9999999	1.0000

$N = 10$	$r_{.005}$	$r_{.01}$	$r_{.025}$	$r_{.05}$	$r_{.95}$	$r_{.975}$	$r_{.99}$	$r_{.995}$
2,2					4	4	4	4
2,3					5	5	5	5
2,4					5	5	5	5
2,5					5	5	5	5
2,6					5	5	5	5
2,7					5	5	5	5
2,8				2	5	5	5	5
2,9				2	5	5	5	5
2,10				2	5	5	5	5
2,11				2	5	5	5	5
2,12			2	2	5	5	5	5
2,13			2	2	5	5	5	5
2,14			2	2	5	5	5	5
2,15			2	2	5	5	5	5
2,16			2	2	5	5	5	5
2,17			2	2	5	5	5	5
2,18			2	2	5	5	5	5
2,19		2	2	2	5	5	5	5
2,20		2	2	2	5	5	5	5
3,3					6	6	6	6
3,4					6	7	7	7
3,5				2	7	7	7	7
3,6			2	2	7	7	7	7
3,7			2	2	7	7	7	7
3,8			2	2	7	7	7	7
3,9		2	2	2	7	7	7	7
3,10		2	2	3	7	7	7	7
3,11		2	2	3	7	7	7	7
3,12	2	2	2	3	7	7	7	7
3,13	2	2	2	3	7	7	7	7
3,14	2	2	2	3	7	7	7	7
3,15	2	2	3	3	7	7	7	7
3,16	2	2	3	3	7	7	7	7
3,17	2	2	3	3	7	7	7	7
3,18	2	2	3	3	7	7	7	7
3,19	2	2	3	3	7	7	7	7
3,20	2	2	3	3	7	7	7	7

Table VIIb is abridged from F.S. Swed and C. Eisenhart, "Tables for Testing Random-ness of Grouping in a Sequence of Alternatives," Annals of Mathematical Statistics, 14:66–87 (1943), by permission of the authors and publisher.

N = 10	$r_{.005}$	$r_{.01}$	$r_{.025}$	$r_{.05}$	$r_{.95}$	$r_{.975}$	$r_{.99}$	$r_{.995}$
4,4				2	7	8	8	8
4,5			2	2	8	8	8	9
4,6		2	2	3	8	8	9	9
4,7		2	2	3	8	9	9	9
4,8	2	2	3	3	9	9	9	9
4,9	2	2	3	3	9	9	9	9
4,10	2	2	3	3	9	9	9	9
4,11	2	2	3	3	9	9	9	9
4,12	2	3	3	4	9	9	9	9
4,13	2	3	3	4	9	9	9	9
4,14	2	3	3	4	9	9	9	9
4,15	3	3	3	4	9	9	9	9
4,16	3	3	4	4	9	9	9	9
4,17	3	3	4	4	9	9	9	9
4,18	3	3	4	4	9	9	9	9
4,19	3	3	4	4	9	9	9	9
4,20	3	3	4	4	9	9	9	9
5,5		2	2	3	8	9	9	10
5,6	2	2	3	3	9	9	10	10
5,7	2	2	3	3	9	10	10	11
5,8	2	2	3	3	10	10	11	11
5,9	2	3	3	4	10	11	11	11
5,10	3	3	3	4	10	11	11	11
5,11	3	3	4	4	11	11	11	11
5,12	3	3	4	4	11	11	11	11
5,13	3	3	4	4	11	11	11	11
5,14	3	3	4	5	11	11	11	11
5,15	3	4	4	5	11	11	11	11
5,16	3	4	4	5	11	11	11	11
5,17	3	4	4	5	11	11	11	11
5,18	4	4	5	5	11	11	11	11
5,19	4	4	5	5	11	11	11	11
5,20	4	4	5	5	11	11	11	11
6,6	2	2	3	3	10	10	11	11
6,7	2	3	3	4	10	11	11	12
6,8	3	3	3	4	11	11	12	12
6,9	3	3	4	4	11	12	12	13
6,10	3	3	4	5	11	12	13	13
6,11	3	4	4	5	12	12	13	13
6,12	3	4	4	5	12	12	13	13
6,13	3	4	5	5	12	13	13	13
6,14	4	4	5	5	12	13	13	13
6,15	4	4	5	6	13	13	13	13
6,16	4	4	5	6	13	13	13	13
6,17	4	5	5	6	13	13	13	13
6,18	4	5	5	6	13	13	13	13
6,19	4	5	6	6	13	13	13	13
6,20	4	5	6	6	13	13	13	13

$N = 10$	$r_{.005}$	$r_{.01}$	$r_{.025}$	$r_{.05}$	$r_{.95}$	$r_{.975}$	$r_{.99}$	$r_{.995}$
7,7	3	3	3	4	11	12	12	12
7,8	3	3	4	4	12	12	13	13
7,9	3	4	4	5	12	13	13	14
7,10	3	4	5	5	12	13	14	14
7,11	4	4	5	5	13	13	14	14
7,12	4	4	5	6	13	13	14	15
7,13	4	5	5	6	13	14	15	15
7,14	4	5	5	6	13	14	15	15
7,15	4	5	6	6	14	14	15	15
7,16	5	5	6	6	14	15	15	15
7,17	5	5	6	7	14	15	15	15
7,18	5	5	6	7	14	15	15	15
7,19	5	6	6	7	14	15	15	15
7,20	5	6	6	7	14	15	15	15
8,8	3	4	4	5	12	13	13	14
8,9	3	4	5	5	13	13	14	14
8,10	4	4	5	6	13	14	14	15
8,11	4	5	5	6	14	14	15	15
8,12	4	5	6	6	14	15	15	16
8,13	5	5	6	6	14	15	16	16
8,14	5	5	6	7	15	15	16	16
8,15	5	5	6	7	15	15	16	17
8,16	5	6	6	7	15	16	16	17
8,17	5	6	7	7	15	16	17	17
8,18	6	6	7	8	15	16	17	17
8,19	6	6	7	8	15	16	17	17
8,20	6	6	7	8	16	16	17	17
9,9	4	4	5	6	13	14	15	15
9,10	4	5	5	6	14	15	15	16
9,11	5	5	6	6	14	15	16	16
9,12	5	5	6	7	15	15	16	17
9,13	5	6	6	7	15	16	17	17
9,14	5	6	7	7	16	16	17	17
9,15	6	6	7	8	16	17	17	18
9,16	6	6	7	8	16	17	17	18
9,17	6	7	7	8	16	17	18	18
9,18	6	7	8	8	17	17	18	19
9,19	6	7	8	8	17	17	18	19
9,20	7	7	8	9	17	17	18	19
10,10	5	5	6	6	15	15	16	16
10,11	5	5	6	7	15	16	17	17
10,12	5	6	7	7	16	16	17	18
10,13	5	6	7	8	16	17	18	18
10,14	6	6	7	8	16	17	18	18
10,15	6	7	7	8	17	17	18	19
10,16	6	7	8	8	17	18	19	19
10,17	7	7	8	9	17	18	19	19
10,18	7	7	8	9	18	18	19	20
10,19	7	8	8	9	18	19	19	20
10,20	7	8	9	9	18	19	19	20

TABLE VIIb. SIGNIFICANCE LEVEL OF r
(Continued)

$N = 10$	$r_{.005}$	$r_{.01}$	$r_{.025}$	$r_{.05}$	$r_{.95}$	$r_{.975}$	$r_{.99}$	$r_{.995}$
11,11	5	6	7	7	16	16	17	18
11,12	6	6	7	8	16	17	18	18
11,13	6	6	7	8	17	18	18	19
11,14	6	7	8	8	17	18	19	19
11,15	7	7	8	9	18	18	19	20
11,16	7	7	8	9	18	19	20	20
11,17	7	8	9	9	18	19	20	21
11,18	7	8	9	10	19	19	20	21
11,19	8	8	9	10	19	20	21	21
11,20	8	8	9	10	19	20	21	21
12,12	6	7	7	8	17	18	18	19
12,13	6	7	8	9	17	18	19	20
12,14	7	7	8	9	18	19	20	20
12,15	7	8	8	9	18	19	20	21
12,16	7	8	9	10	19	20	21	21
12,17	8	8	9	10	19	20	21	21
12,18	8	8	9	10	20	20	21	22
12,19	8	9	10	10	20	21	22	22
12,20	8	9	10	11	20	21	22	22
13,13	7	7	8	9	18	19	20	20
13,14	7	8	9	9	19	19	20	21
13,15	7	8	9	10	19	20	21	21
13,16	8	8	9	10	20	20	21	22
13,17	8	9	10	10	20	21	22	22
13,18	8	9	10	11	20	21	22	23
13,19	9	9	10	11	21	22	23	23
13,20	9	10	10	11	21	22	23	23
14,14	7	8	9	10	19	20	21	22
14,15	8	8	9	10	20	21	22	22
14,16	8	9	10	11	20	21	22	23
14,17	8	9	10	11	21	22	23	23
14,18	9	9	10	11	21	22	23	24
14,19	9	10	11	12	22	22	23	24
14,20	9	10	11	12	22	23	24	24
15,15	8	9	10	11	20	21	22	23
15,16	9	9	10	11	21	22	23	23
15,17	9	10	11	11	21	22	23	24
15,18	9	10	11	12	22	23	24	24
15,19	10	10	11	12	22	23	24	25
15,20	10	11	12	12	23	24	25	25
16,16	9	10	11	11	22	22	23	24
16,17	9	10	11	12	22	23	24	25
16,18	10	10	11	12	23	24	25	25
16,19	10	11	12	13	23	24	25	26
16,20	10	11	12	13	24	24	25	26
17,17	10	10	11	12	23	24	25	25
17,18	10	11	12	13	23	24	25	26
17,19	10	11	12	13	24	25	26	26
17,20	11	11	13	13	24	25	26	27

N = 10	$r_{.005}$	$r_{.01}$	$r_{.025}$	$r_{.05}$	$r_{.95}$	$r_{.975}$	$r_{.99}$	$r_{.995}$
18,18	11	11	12	13	24	25	26	26
18,19	11	12	13	14	24	25	26	27
18,20	11	12	13	14	25	26	27	28
19,19	11	12	13	14	25	26	27	28
19,20	12	12	13	14	26	26	28	28
20,20	12	13	14	15	26	27	28	29
21,21	13	14	15	16	27	28	29	30
22,22	14	14	16	17	28	29	31	31
23,23	14	15	16	17	30	31	32	33
24,24	15	16	17	18	31	32	33	34
25,25	16	17	18	19	32	33	34	35
26,26	17	18	19	20	33	34	35	36
27,27	18	19	20	21	34	35	36	37
28,28	18	19	21	22	35	36	38	39
29,29	19	20	22	23	36	37	39	40
30,30	20	21	22	24	37	39	40	41
31,31	21	22	23	25	38	40	41	42
32,32	22	23	24	25	40	41	42	43
33,33	23	24	25	26	41	42	43	44
34,34	23	24	26	27	42	43	45	46
35,35	24	25	27	28	43	44	46	47
36,36	25	26	28	29	44	45	47	48
37,37	26	27	29	30	45	46	48	49
38,38	27	28	30	31	46	47	49	50
39,39	28	29	30	32	47	49	50	51
40,40	29	30	31	33	48	50	51	52
41,41	29	31	32	34	49	51	52	54
42,42	30	31	33	35	50	52	54	55
43,43	31	32	34	35	52	53	55	56
44,44	32	33	35	36	53	54	56	57
45,45	33	34	36	37	54	55	57	58
46,46	34	35	37	38	55	56	58	59
47,47	35	36	38	39	56	57	59	60
48,48	35	37	38	40	57	59	60	62
49,49	36	38	39	41	58	60	61	63
50,50	37	38	40	42	59	61	63	64
51,51	38	39	41	43	60	62	64	65
52,52	39	40	42	44	61	63	65	66
53,53	40	41	43	45	62	64	66	67
54,54	41	42	44	45	64	65	67	68
55,55	42	43	45	46	65	66	68	69
56,56	42	44	46	47	66	67	69	71
57,57	43	45	47	48	67	68	70	72
58,58	44	46	47	49	68	70	71	73
59,59	45	46	48	50	69	71	73	74

TABLE VIIb. SIGNIFICANCE LEVEL OF r
(Continued)

N = 10	$r_{.005}$	$r_{.01}$	$r_{.025}$	$r_{.05}$	$r_{.95}$	$r_{.975}$	$r_{.99}$	$r_{.995}$
60,60	46	47	49	51	70	72	74	75
61,61	47	48	50	52	71	73	75	76
62,62	48	49	51	53	72	74	76	77
63,63	49	50	52	54	73	75	77	78
64,64	49	51	53	55	74	76	78	80
65,65	50	52	54	56	75	77	79	81
66,66	51	53	55	57	76	78	80	82
67,67	52	54	56	58	77	79	81	83
68,68	53	54	57	58	79	80	83	84
69,69	54	55	58	59	80	81	84	85
70,70	55	56	58	60	81	83	85	86
71,71	56	57	59	61	82	84	86	87
72,72	57	58	60	62	83	85	87	88
73,73	57	59	61	63	84	86	88	90
74,74	58	60	62	64	85	87	89	91
75,75	59	61	63	65	86	88	90	92
76,76	60	62	64	66	87	89	91	93
77,77	61	63	65	67	88	90	92	94
78,78	62	64	66	68	89	91	93	95
79,79	63	64	67	69	90	92	95	96
80,80	64	65	68	70	91	93	96	97
81,81	65	66	69	71	92	94	97	98
82,82	66	67	69	71	94	96	98	99
83,83	66	68	70	72	95	97	99	101
84,84	67	69	71	73	96	98	100	102
85,85	68	70	72	74	97	99	101	103
86,86	69	71	73	75	98	100	102	104
87,87	70	72	74	76	99	101	103	105
88,88	71	73	75	77	100	102	104	106
89,89	72	74	76	78	101	103	105	107
90,90	73	74	77	79	102	104	107	108
91,91	74	75	78	80	103	105	108	109
92,92	75	76	79	81	104	106	109	110
93,93	75	77	80	82	105	107	110	112
94,94	76	78	81	83	106	108	111	113
95,95	77	79	82	84	107	109	112	114
96,96	78	80	82	85	108	111	113	115
97,97	79	81	83	86	109	112	114	116
98,98	80	82	84	87	110	113	115	117
99,99	81	83	85	87	112	114	116	118
100,100	82	84	86	88	113	115	117	119

TABLE VIII. CRITICAL VALUES FOR THE WALSH TEST

N	Level of Probability Tests a or b	Level of Probability Test c	STATISTICAL TEST Test c — Test b	STATISTICAL TEST Test c — Test a
4	0.062	0.125	$d_4 < 0$	$d_1 > 0$
5	0.062	0.125	$\frac{1}{2}(d_4 + d_5) < 0$	$\frac{1}{2}(d_1 + d_2) > 0$
	0.031	0.062	$d_5 < 0$	$d_1 > 0$
6	0.047	0.094	$\max[d_5, \frac{1}{2}(d_4 + d_6)] < 0$	$\min[d_2, \frac{1}{2}(d_1 + d_3)] > 0$
	0.031	0.062	$\frac{1}{2}(d_5 + d_6) < 0$	$\frac{1}{2}(d_1 + d_2) > 0$
	0.016	0.031	$d_6 < 0$	$d_1 > 0$
7	0.055	0.109	$\max[d_5, \frac{1}{2}(d_4 + d_7)] < 0$	$\min[d_3, \frac{1}{2}(d_1 + d_4)] > 0$
	0.023	0.047	$\max[d_6, \frac{1}{2}(d_5 + d_7)] < 0$	$\min[d_2, \frac{1}{2}(d_1 + d_3)] > 0$
	0.016	0.031	$\frac{1}{2}(d_6 + d_7) < 0$	$\frac{1}{2}(d_1 + d_2) > 0$
	0.008	0.016	$d_7 < 0$	$d_1 > 0$
8	0.043	0.086	$\max[d_6, \frac{1}{2}(d_4 + d_8)] < 0$	$\min[d_3, \frac{1}{2}(d_1 + d_5)] > 0$
	0.027	0.055	$\max[d_6, \frac{1}{2}(d_5 + d_8)] < 0$	$\min[d_3, \frac{1}{2}(d_1 + d_4)] > 0$
	0.012	0.023	$\max[d_7, \frac{1}{2}(d_6 + d_8)] < 0$	$\min[d_2, \frac{1}{2}(d_1 + d_3)] > 0$
	0.008	0.016	$\frac{1}{2}(d_7 + d_8) < 0$	$\frac{1}{2}(d_1 + d_2) > 0$
	0.004	0.008	$d_8 < 0$	$d_1 < 0$
9	0.051	0.102	$\max[d_6, \frac{1}{2}(d_4 + d_9)] < 0$	$\min[d_4, \frac{1}{2}(d_1 + d_6)] > 0$
	0.022	0.043	$\max[d_7, \frac{1}{2}(d_5 + d_9)] < 0$	$\min[d_3, \frac{1}{2}(d_1 + d_5)] > 0$
	0.010	0.020	$\max[d_8, \frac{1}{2}(d_5 + d_9)] < 0$	$\min[d_2, \frac{1}{2}(d_1 + d_5)] > 0$
	0.006	0.012	$\max[d_8, \frac{1}{2}(d_7 + d_9)] < 0$	$\min[d_2, \frac{1}{2}(d_1 + d_3)] > 0$
	0.004	0.008	$\frac{1}{2}(d_8 + d_9) < 0$	$\frac{1}{2}(d_1 + d_2) > 0$
10	0.056	0.111	$\max[d_6, \frac{1}{2}(d_4 + d_{10})] < 0$	$\min[d_5, \frac{1}{2}(d_1 + d_7)] > 0$
	0.025	0.051	$\max[d_7, \frac{1}{2}(d_5 + d_{10})] < 0$	$\min[d_4, \frac{1}{2}(d_1 + d_6)] > 0$
	0.011	0.021	$\max[d_8, \frac{1}{2}(d_6 + d_{10})] < 0$	$\min[d_3, \frac{1}{2}(d_1 + d_5)] > 0$
	0.005	0.010	$\max[d_9, \frac{1}{2}(d_6 + d_{10})] < 0$	$\min[d_2, \frac{1}{2}(d_1 + d_5)] > 0$
11	0.048	0.097	$\max[d_7, \frac{1}{2}(d_4 + d_{11})] < 0$	$\min[d_5, \frac{1}{2}(d_1 + d_8)] > 0$
	0.028	0.056	$\max[d_7, \frac{1}{2}(d_5 + d_{11})] < 0$	$\min[d_5, \frac{1}{2}(d_1 + d_7)] > 0$
	0.011	0.021	$\max[\frac{1}{2}(d_6 + d_{11}), \frac{1}{2}(d_8 + d_9)] < 0$	$\min[\frac{1}{2}(d_1 + d_6), \frac{1}{2}(d_3 + d_4)] > 0$
	0.005	0.011	$\max[d_9, \frac{1}{2}(d_7 + d_{11})] < 0$	$\min[d_3, \frac{1}{2}(d_1 + d_5)] > 0$
12	0.047	0.094	$\max[\frac{1}{2}(d_4 + d_{12}), \frac{1}{2}(d_5 + d_{11})] < 0$	$\min[\frac{1}{2}(d_1 + d_9), \frac{1}{2}(d_2 + d_8)] > 0$
	0.024	0.048	$\max[d_8, \frac{1}{2}(d_5 + d_{12})] < 0$	$\min[d_5, \frac{1}{2}(d_1 + d_8)] > 0$
	0.010	0.020	$\max[d_9, \frac{1}{2}(d_6 + d_{12})] < 0$	$\min[d_4, \frac{1}{2}(d_1 + d_7)] > 0$
	0.005	0.011	$\max[\frac{1}{2}(d_7 + d_{12}), \frac{1}{2}(d_9 + d_{10})] < 0$	$\min[\frac{1}{2}(d_1 + d_6), \frac{1}{2}(d_3 + d_4)] > 0$
13	0.047	0.094	$\max[\frac{1}{2}(d_4 + d_{13}), \frac{1}{2}(d_5 + d_{12})] < 0$	$\min[\frac{1}{2}(d_1 + d_{10}), \frac{1}{2}(d_2 + d_9)] > 0$
	0.023	0.047	$\max[\frac{1}{2}(d_5 + d_{13}), \frac{1}{2}(d_6 + d_{12})] < 0$	$\min[\frac{1}{2}(d_1 + d_9), \frac{1}{2}(d_2 + d_8)] > 0$
	0.010	0.020	$\max[\frac{1}{2}(d_6 + d_{13}), \frac{1}{2}(d_9 + d_{10})] < 0$	$\min[\frac{1}{2}(d_1 + d_8), \frac{1}{2}(d_4 + d_5)] > 0$
	0.005	0.010	$\max[d_{10}, \frac{1}{2}(d_7 + d_{13})] < 0$	$\min[d_4, \frac{1}{2}(d_1 + d_7)] > 0$
14	0.047	0.094	$\max[\frac{1}{2}(d_4 + d_{14}), \frac{1}{2}(d_5 + d_{13})] < 0$	$\min[\frac{1}{2}(d_1 + d_{11}), \frac{1}{2}(d_2 + d_{10})] > 0$
	0.023	0.047	$\max[\frac{1}{2}(d_5 + d_{14}), \frac{1}{2}(d_6 + d_{13})] < 0$	$\min[\frac{1}{2}(d_1 + d_{10}), \frac{1}{2}(d_2 + d_9)] > 0$
	0.010	0.020	$\max[d_{10}, \frac{1}{2}(d_6 + d_{14})] < 0$	$\min[d_5, \frac{1}{2}(d_1 + d_9)] > 0$
	0.005	0.010	$\max[\frac{1}{2}(d_7 + d_{14}), \frac{1}{2}(d_{10} + d_{11})] < 0$	$\min[\frac{1}{2}(d_1 + d_8), \frac{1}{2}(d_4 + d_5)] > 0$
15	0.047	0.094	$\max[\frac{1}{2}(d_4 + d_{15}), \frac{1}{2}(d_5 + d_{14})] < 0$	$\min[\frac{1}{2}(d_1 + d_{12}), \frac{1}{2}(d_2 + d_{11})] > 0$
	0.023	0.047	$\max[\frac{1}{2}(d_5 + d_{15}), \frac{1}{2}(d_6 + d_{14})] < 0$	$\min[\frac{1}{2}(d_1 + d_{11}), \frac{1}{2}(d_2 + d_{10})] > 0$
	0.010	0.020	$\max[\frac{1}{2}(d_6 + d_{15}), \frac{1}{2}(d_{10} + d_{11})] < 0$	$\min[\frac{1}{2}(d_1 + d_{10}), \frac{1}{2}(d_5 + d_6)] > 0$
	0.005	0.010	$\max[d_{11}, \frac{1}{2}(d_7 + d_{15})] < 0$	$\min[d_5, \frac{1}{2}(d_1 + d_9)] > 0$

Table VIII is modified from J. E. Walsh, "Applications of Some Significance Tests for the Median Which Are Valid under Very General Conditions," Journal of American Statistical Association, 44:343 (1949), with the permission of the author and publisher.

TABLE IXa. PROBABILITIES ASSOCIATED WITH OBSERVED SMALL VALUES OF U IN THE MANN-WHITNEY TEST

n = 3

U \ m	1	2	3
0	.250	.100	.050
1	.500	.200	.100
2	.750	.400	.200
3		.600	.350
4			.500
5			.650

n = 4

U \ m	1	2	3	4
0	.200	.067	.028	.014
1	.400	.133	.057	.029
2	.600	.267	.114	.057
3		.400	.200	.100
4		.600	.314	.171
5			.429	.243
6			.571	.343
7				.443
8				.557

n = 5

U \ m	1	2	3	4	5
0	.167	.047	.018	.008	.004
1	.333	.095	.036	.016	.008
2	.500	.190	.071	.032	.016
3	.667	.286	.125	.056	.028
4		.429	.196	.095	.048
5		.571	.286	.143	.075
6			.393	.206	.111
7			.500	.278	.155
8			.607	.365	.210
9				.452	.274
10				.548	.345
11					.421
12					.500
13					.579

n = 6

U \ m	1	2	3	4	5	6
0	.143	.036	.012	.005	.002	.001
1	.286	.071	.024	.010	.004	.002
2	.428	.143	.048	.019	.009	.004
3	.571	.214	.083	.033	.015	.008
4		.321	.131	.057	.026	.013
5		.429	.190	.086	.041	.021
6		.571	.274	.129	.063	.032
7			.357	.176	.089	.047
8			.452	.238	.123	.066
9			.548	.305	.165	.090
10				.381	.214	.120
11				.457	.268	.155
12				.545	.331	.197
13					.396	.242
14					.465	.294
15					.535	.350
16						.409
17						.469
18						.531

Table IXa is abridged from H. B. Mann and D. R. Whitney, "On a Test Whether One of Two Random Variables Is Stochastically Larger Than the Other," Annals of Mathematical Statistics, 18:50-60 (1947), by permission of the authors and publisher.

(3) U VALUES FOR THE .025 LEVEL OF SIGNIFICANCE

m \ n	1	2	3	4	5	6	7	8	9	10	11	12	13	14	15	16	17	18	19	20
1	--	--	--	--	--	--	--	--	--	--	--	--	--	--	--	--	--	--	--	--
2	--	--	--	--	--	--	--	0	0	0	0	1	1	1	1	1	2	2	2	2
3	--	--	--	--	0	1	1	2	2	3	3	4	4	5	5	6	6	7	7	8
4	--	--	--	0	1	2	3	4	4	5	6	7	8	9	10	11	11	12	13	13
5	--	--	0	1	2	3	5	6	7	8	9	11	12	13	14	15	17	18	19	20
6	--	--	1	2	3	5	6	8	10	11	13	14	16	17	19	21	22	24	25	27
7	--	--	1	3	5	6	8	10	12	14	16	18	20	22	24	26	28	30	32	34
8	--	0	2	4	6	8	10	13	15	17	19	22	24	26	29	31	34	36	38	41
9	--	0	2	4	7	10	12	15	17	20	23	26	28	31	34	37	39	42	45	48
10	--	0	3	5	8	11	14	17	20	23	26	29	33	36	39	42	45	48	52	55
11	--	0	3	6	9	13	16	19	23	26	30	33	37	40	44	47	51	55	58	62
12	--	1	4	7	11	14	18	22	26	29	33	37	41	45	49	53	57	61	65	69
13	--	1	4	8	12	16	20	24	28	33	37	41	45	50	54	59	63	67	72	76
14	--	1	5	9	13	17	22	26	31	36	40	45	50	55	59	64	67	74	78	83
15	--	1	5	10	14	19	24	29	34	39	44	49	54	59	64	70	75	80	85	90
16	--	1	6	11	15	21	26	31	37	42	47	53	59	64	70	75	81	86	92	98
17	--	2	6	11	17	22	28	34	39	45	51	57	63	67	75	81	87	93	99	105
18	--	2	7	12	18	24	30	36	42	48	55	61	67	74	80	86	93	99	106	112
19	--	2	7	13	19	25	32	38	45	52	58	65	72	78	85	92	99	106	113	119
20	--	2	8	13	20	27	34	41	48	55	62	69	76	83	90	98	105	112	119	127

(4) U VALUES FOR THE .01 LEVEL OF SIGNIFICANCE

m \ n	1	2	3	4	5	6	7	8	9	10	11	12	13	14	15	16	17	18	19	20
1	--	--	--	--	--	--	--	--	--	--	--	--	--	--	--	--	--	--	--	--
2	--	--	--	--	--	--	--	--	--	--	--	--	0	0	0	0	0	0	1	1
3	--	--	--	--	--	--	0	0	1	1	1	2	2	2	3	3	4	4	4	5
4	--	--	--	--	0	1	1	2	3	3	4	5	5	6	7	7	8	9	9	10
5	--	--	--	0	1	2	3	4	5	6	7	8	9	10	11	12	13	14	15	16
6	--	--	--	1	2	3	4	6	7	8	9	11	12	13	15	16	18	19	20	22
7	--	--	0	1	3	4	6	7	9	11	12	14	16	17	19	21	23	24	26	28
8	--	--	0	2	4	6	7	9	11	13	15	17	20	22	24	26	28	30	32	34
9	--	--	1	3	5	7	9	11	14	16	18	21	23	26	28	31	33	36	38	40
10	--	--	1	3	6	8	11	13	16	19	22	24	27	30	33	36	38	41	44	47
11	--	--	1	4	7	9	12	15	18	22	25	28	31	34	37	41	44	47	50	53
12	--	--	2	5	8	11	14	17	21	24	28	31	35	38	42	46	49	53	56	60
13	--	0	2	5	9	12	16	20	23	27	31	35	39	43	47	51	55	59	63	67
14	--	0	2	6	10	13	17	22	26	30	34	38	43	47	51	56	60	65	69	73
15	--	0	3	7	11	15	19	24	28	33	37	42	47	51	56	61	66	70	75	80
16	--	0	3	7	12	16	21	26	31	36	41	46	51	56	61	66	71	76	82	87
17	--	0	4	8	13	18	23	28	33	38	44	49	55	60	66	71	77	82	88	93
18	--	0	4	9	14	19	24	30	36	41	47	53	59	65	70	76	82	88	94	100
19	--	1	4	9	15	20	26	32	38	44	50	56	63	69	75	82	88	94	101	107
20	--	1	5	10	16	22	28	34	40	47	53	60	67	73	80	87	93	100	107	114

(5) U VALUES FOR THE .005 LEVEL OF CONFIDENCE

m \ n	1	2	3	4	5	6	7	8	9	10	11	12	13	14	15	16	17	18	19	20
1	--	--	--	--	--	--	--	--	--	--	--	--	--	--	--	--	--	--	--	--
2	--	--	--	--	--	--	--	--	--	--	--	--	--	--	--	--	--	--	0	0
3	--	--	--	--	--	--	--	--	0	0	0	1	1	1	2	2	2	2	3	3
4	--	--	--	--	--	0	0	1	1	2	2	3	3	4	5	5	6	6	7	8
5	--	--	--	--	0	1	1	2	3	4	5	6	7	7	8	9	10	11	12	13
6	--	--	--	0	1	2	3	4	5	6	7	9	10	11	12	13	15	16	17	18
7	--	--	--	0	1	3	4	6	7	9	10	12	13	15	16	18	19	21	22	24
8	--	--	--	1	2	4	6	7	9	11	13	15	17	18	20	22	24	26	28	30
9	--	--	0	1	3	5	7	9	11	13	16	18	20	22	24	27	29	31	33	36
10	--	--	0	2	4	6	9	11	13	16	18	21	24	26	29	31	34	37	39	42
11	--	--	0	2	5	7	10	13	16	18	21	24	27	30	33	36	39	42	45	48
12	--	--	1	3	6	9	12	15	18	21	24	27	31	34	37	41	44	47	51	54
13	--	--	1	3	7	10	13	17	20	24	27	31	34	38	42	45	49	53	56	60
14	--	--	1	4	7	11	15	18	22	26	30	34	38	42	46	50	54	58	63	67
15	--	--	2	5	8	12	16	20	24	29	33	37	42	46	51	55	60	64	69	73
16	--	--	2	5	9	13	18	22	27	31	36	41	45	50	55	60	65	70	74	79
17	--	--	2	6	10	15	19	24	29	34	39	44	49	54	60	65	70	75	81	86
18	--	--	2	6	11	16	21	26	31	37	42	47	53	58	64	70	75	81	87	92
19	--	0	3	7	12	17	22	28	33	39	45	51	56	63	69	74	81	87	93	99
20	--	0	3	8	13	18	24	30	36	42	48	54	60	67	73	79	86	92	99	105

(6) U VALUES FOR THE .001 LEVEL OF CONFIDENCE

m \ n	1	2	3	4	5	6	7	8	9	10	11	12	13	14	15	16	17	18	19	20
1	--	--	--	--	--	--	--	--	--	--	--	--	--	--	--	--	--	--	--	--
2	--	--	--	--	--	--	--	--	--	--	--	--	--	--	--	--	--	--	--	--
3	--	--	--	--	--	--	--	--	--	--	--	--	--	--	--	--	0	0	0	0
4	--	--	--	--	--	--	--	--	0	0	0	1	1	1	2	2	3	3	3	3
5	--	--	--	--	--	--	--	0	1	1	2	2	3	3	4	5	5	6	7	7
6	--	--	--	--	--	--	0	1	2	3	4	4	5	6	7	8	9	10	11	12
7	--	--	--	--	--	0	1	2	3	5	6	7	8	9	10	11	13	14	15	16
8	--	--	--	--	0	1	2	4	5	6	8	9	11	12	14	15	17	18	20	21
9	--	--	--	--	1	2	3	5	7	8	10	12	14	15	17	19	21	23	25	26
10	--	--	--	0	1	3	5	6	8	10	12	14	17	19	21	23	25	27	29	32
11	--	--	--	0	2	4	6	8	10	12	15	17	20	22	24	27	29	32	34	37
12	--	--	--	0	2	4	7	9	12	14	17	20	23	25	28	31	34	37	40	42
13	--	--	--	1	3	5	8	11	14	17	20	23	26	29	32	35	38	42	45	48
14	--	--	--	1	3	6	9	12	15	19	22	25	29	32	36	39	43	46	50	54
15	--	--	--	1	4	7	10	14	17	21	24	28	32	36	40	43	47	51	55	59
16	--	--	--	2	5	8	11	15	19	23	27	31	35	39	43	48	52	56	60	65
17	--	--	0	2	5	9	13	17	21	25	29	34	38	43	47	52	57	61	66	70
18	--	--	0	3	6	10	14	18	23	27	32	37	42	46	51	56	61	66	71	76
19	--	--	0	3	7	11	15	20	25	29	34	40	45	50	55	60	66	71	77	82
20	--	--	0	3	7	12	16	21	26	32	37	42	48	54	59	65	70	76	82	88

TABLE X. CRITICAL VALUES OF T IN THE WILCOXON TEST FOR PAIRED DATA

N	α 0.05	0.02	0.01
6	0	—	—
7	2	0	—
8	4	2	0
9	6	3	2
10	8	5	3
11	11	7	5
12	14	10	7
13	17	13	10
14	21	16	13
15	25	20	16
16	30	24	20
17	35	28	23
18	40	33	28
19	46	38	32
20	52	43	38
21	59	49	43
22	66	56	49
23	73	62	55
24	81	69	61
25	89	77	68

Table X is abridged from Table II of Some Rapid Approximate Statistical Procedures by Frank Wilcoxon, American Cyanamid Company, New York, published by permission of the author and publisher.

TABLE XI. CRITICAL VALUES OF H (for three samples) FOR THE KRUSKAL-WALLIS TEST

The probabilities shown are the probabilities under the null hypothesis that H will equal or exceed the values in the column headed "H".

n_1	n_2	n_3	H	True Probability
2	1	1	2.7000	0.500
2	2	1	3.6000	0.200
2	2	2	4.5714	0.067
			3.7143	.200
3	1	1	3.2000	0.300
3	2	1	4.2857	0.100
			3.8571	.133
3	2	2	5.3572	0.029
			4.7143	.048
			4.5000	.067
			4.4643	.105
3	3	1	5.1429	0.043
			4.5714	.100
			4.0000	.129
3	3	2	6.2500	0.011
			5.3611	.032
			5.1389	.061
			4.5556	.100
			4.2500	.121
3	3	3	7.2000	0.004
			6.4889	.011
			5.6889	.029
			5.6000	.050
			5.0667	.086
			4.6222	.100
4	1	1	3.5714	0.200
4	2	1	4.8214	0.057
			4.5000	.076
			4.0179	.114
4	2	2	6.0000	0.014
			5.3333	.033
			5.1250	.052
			4.4583	.100
			4.1667	.105
4	3	1	5.8333	0.021
			5.2083	.050
			5.0000	.057
			4.0556	.093
			3.8889	.129
4	3	2	6.4444	0.008
			6.3000	.011
			5.4444	.046
			5.4000	.051
			4.5111	.098
			4.4444	.102
4	3	3	6.7455	0.010
			6.7091	.013
			5.7909	.046
			5.7273	.050
			4.7091	.092
			4.7000	.101
4	4	1	6.6667	0.010
			6.1667	.022
			4.9667	.048
			4.8667	.054
			4.1667	.082
			4.0667	.102
4	4	2	7.0364	0.006
			6.8727	.011
			5.4545	.046
			5.2364	.052
			4.5545	.098
			4.4455	.103
4	4	3	7.1439	0.010
			7.1364	.011
			5.5985	.049
			5.5758	.051
			5.4545	.099
			4.4773	.102
4	4	4	7.6538	0.008
			7.5385	.011
			5.6923	.049
			5.6538	.054
			4.6539	.097
			4.5001	.104
5	1	1	3.8571	0.143
5	2	1	5.2500	0.036
			5.0000	.048
			4.4500	.071
			4.2000	.095
			4.0500	.119
5	2	2	6.5333	0.008
			6.1333	.013
			5.1600	.034
			5.0400	.056
			4.3733	.090
			4.2933	.122
5	3	1	6.4000	0.012
			4.9600	.048
			4.8711	.052
			4.0178	.095
			3.8400	.123
5	3	2	6.9091	0.009
			6.8218	.010
			5.2509	.049
			5.1055	.052
			4.6509	.091
			4.4945	.101
5	3	3	7.0788	0.009
			6.9818	.011
			5.6485	.049
			5.5152	.051
			5.3333	.097
			4.4121	.109
5	4	1	6.9545	0.008
			6.8400	.011
			4.9855	.044
			4.8600	.056
			3.9873	.098
			3.9600	.102
5	4	2	7.2045	0.009
			7.1182	.010
			5.2727	.049
			5.2682	.050
			4.5409	.098
			4.5182	.101
5	4	3	7.4449	0.010
			7.3949	.011
			5.6564	.049
			5.6308	.050
			4.5487	.099
			4.5231	.103
5	4	4	7.7604	0.009
			7.7440	.011
			5.6571	.049
			5.6176	.050
			4.6187	.100
			4.5527	.102
5	5	1	7.3091	0.009
			6.8364	.011
			5.1273	.046
			4.9091	.053
			4.1091	.086
			4.0364	.105
5	5	2	7.3385	0.010
			7.2692	.010
			5.3385	.047
			5.2462	.051
			4.6231	.097
			4.5077	.100
5	5	3	7.5780	0.010
			7.5429	.010
			5.7055	.046
			5.6264	.051
			4.5451	.100
			4.5363	.102
5	5	4	7.8229	0.010
			7.7914	.010
			5.6657	.049
			5.6429	.050
			4.5229	.099
			4.5200	.101
5	5	5	8.0000	0.009
			7.9800	.010
			5.7800	.049
			5.6600	.051
			4.5600	.100
			4.5000	.102

Table XI is abridged from W. H. Kruskal and W. W. Wallis, "Use of Ranks in One-criterion Variance Analysis," Journal of the American Statistical Association, 47:584–621 (December, 1952) and "Errata," Journal of the American Statistical Association, 48:907–911 (December, 1953), by permission of the authors and publisher.

TABLE XIIa. VALUES OF Σd^2 FOR SPEARMAN RANK CORRELATION

The probability that $\Sigma d^2 \geq S$ for $S \geq \Sigma m$, or that $\Sigma d^2 \leq S$ for $S \leq \Sigma m$
(where Σm represents mean value of sum of squares)

	N = 2	3	4	5	6	7	8	9	10
s \ Σm	1	4	10	20	35	56	84	120	165
0	0.5000	0.1667	0.0417	0.0083	0.0014	0.0002	0.0003	0.0001	0.0000
2	.5000	.5000	.1667	.0417	.0083	.0014	.0006	.0002	.0001
4		.5000	.2083	.0667	.0167	.0034	.0011	.0003	.0001
6		.5000	.3750	.1167	.0292	.0062	.0018	.0005	.0001
8		.1667	.4583	.1750	.0514	.0119	.0028	.0007	.0002
10			0.5417	0.2250	0.0681	0.0171	0.0042	0.0010	0.0003
12			.4583	.2583	.0875	.0240	.0059	.0015	.0004
14			.3750	.3417	.1208	.0331	.0081	.0020	.0005
16			.2083	.3917	.1486	.0440	.0108	.0027	.0007
18			.1667	.4750	.1778	.0548	.0141	.0035	.0009
20			0.0417	0.5250	0.2097	0.0694	0.0179	0.0045	0.0011
22				.4750	.2486	.0833	.0224	.0057	.0014
24				.3917	.2819	.1000	.0275	.0071	.0018
26				.3417	.3292	.1179	.0331	.0087	.0022
28				.2583	.3569	.1333	.0396	.0106	.0027
30				0.2250	0.4014	0.1512	0.0469	0.0127	0.0032
32				.1750	.4597	.1768	.0550	.0152	.0039
34				.1167	.5000	.1978	.0639	.0179	.0046
36				.0667	.5000	.2222	.0736	.0210	.0054
38				.0417	.4597	.2488	.0841	.0244	.0064
40				0.0083	0.4014	0.2780	0.0956	0.0281	0.0075
42					.3569	.2974	.1078	.0323	.0086
44					.3292	.3308	.1207	.0368	.0100
46					.2819	.3565	.1345	.0417	.0114
48					.2486	.3913	.1491	.0470	.0130
50					0.2097	0.4198	0.1645	0.0528	0.0148
52					.1778	.4532	.1806	.0589	.0168
54					.1486	.4817	.1974	.0656	.0189
56					.1208	.5183	.2150	.0726	.0212
58					.0875	.4817	.2332	.0802	.0237
60					0.0681	0.4532	0.2520	0.0882	0.0264
62					.0514	.4198	.2715	.0966	.0293
64					.0292	.3913	.2915	.1056	.0324
66					.0167	.3565	.3120	.1149	.0358
68					.0083	.3308	.3330	.1248	.0394
70					0.0014	0.2974	0.3544	0.1351	0.0432
72						.2780	.3761	.1459	.0472
74						.2488	.3982	.1571	.0515
76						.2222	.4205	.1688	.0561
78						.1978	.4431	.1809	.0609

Tables XIIa is abridged from E. G. Olds, "Distributions of Sums of Squares of Rank Differences for Small Numbers of Individuals," Annals of Mathematical Statistics, 9:133-148 (1938), and E. G. Olds, "The 5% Significance Levels for Sums of Squares of Rank Differences and a Correction," Annals of Mathematical Statistics, 20:117-118 (1949), by permission of the author and publisher.

TABLE XIIa. VALUES OF Σd^2 FOR SPEARMAN RANK CORRELATION
(Continued)

The probability that $\Sigma d^2 \geq S$ for $S \geq \Sigma m$, or that $\Sigma d^2 \leq S$ for $S \leq \Sigma m$
(where Σm represents mean value of sum of squares)

	N = 2	3	4	5	6	7	8	9	10
Σm $\backslash$ s	1	4	10	20	35	56	84	120	165
80						0.1768	0.4657	0.1935	0.0659
82						.1512	.4885	.2065	.0713
84						.1333	.5113	.2198	.0769
86						.1179	.4885	.2336	.0828
88						.1000	.4657	.2477	.0889
90						0.0833	0.4431	0.2622	0.0954
92						.0694	.4205	.2770	.1021
94						.0548	.3982	.2922	.1091
96						.0440	.3761	.3077	.1164
98						.0331	.3544	.3234	.1239
100						0.0240	0.3330	0.3394	0.1318
102						.0171	.3120	.3557	.1399
104						.0119	.2915	.3721	.1483
106						.0062	.2715	.3888	.1570
108						.0034	.2520	.4056	.1659
110						0.0014	0.2332	0.4226	0.1751
112						.0002	.2150	.4397	.1846
114							.1974	.4568	.1944
116							.1806	.4741	.2044
118							.1645	.4914	.2146
120							0.1491	0.5086	0.2251
122							.1345	.4914	.2358
124							.1207	.4741	.2468
126							.1078	.4568	.2580
128							.0956	.4397	.2694
130							0.0841	0.4226	0.2810
132							.0736	.4056	.2928
134							.0639	.3888	.3048
136							.0550	.3721	.3169
138							.0469	.3557	.3293
140							0.0396	0.3394	0.3418
142							.0331	.3234	.3545
144							.0275	.3077	.3673
146							.0224	.2922	.3802
148							.0179	.2770	.3932
150							0.0141	0.2622	0.4063
152							.0108	.2477	.4196
154							.0081	.2336	.4328
156							.0059	.2198	.4462
158							.0042	.2065	.4596
160							0.0028	0.1935	0.4731
162							.0018	.1809	.4865
164							.0011	.1688	.5000
166							.0006	.1571	.5000
168							.0003	.1459	.4865

(Tables for cases of n=9 and n=10 can be completed by symmetry)

TABLE XIIb. CRITICAL VALUES FOR THE SPEARMAN RANK COEFFICIENT, R

N \ α	0.10	0.05	0.025	0.02	0.01	0.005
11	0.405	0.520	0.620	0.650	0.735	0.815
12	.376	.485	.591	.609	.712	.766
13	.370	.475	.566	.593	.671	.744
14	.355	.456	.544	.570	.645	.714
15	.342	.440	.524	.549	.622	.688
16	.331	.425	.506	.530	.601	.665
17	.320	.411	.490	.514	.582	.644
18	.311	.399	.475	.498	.564	.625
19	.302	.388	.462	.484	.548	.607
20	.294	.377	.450	.471	.534	.591
21	.287	.368	.438	.459	.520	.576
22	.280	.359	.428	.448	.508	.562
23	.273	.351	.418	.438	.496	.549
24	.267	.343	.409	.428	.485	.537
25	.262	.336	.400	.419	.475	.526
26	.256	.329	.392	.411	.465	.515
27	.251	.323	.384	.403	.456	.505
28	.247	.317	.377	.395	.448	.496
29	.242	.311	.370	.388	.440	.487
30	.238	.305	.364	.381	.432	.478

Table XIIb. is abridged from E. G. Olds, "Distributions of Sums of Squares of Rank Differences for Small Numbers of Individuals," Annals of Mathematical Statistics, 9:133-148 (1938), and E. G. Olds, "The 5% Significance Levels for Sums of Squares of Rank Differences and a Correction," Annals of Mathematical Statistics, 20:117-118 (1949), by permission of the author and publisher.

TABLE XIII. SQUARES, SQUARE ROOTS, AND RECIPROCALS

n	n^2	$\sqrt{n}$	$\sqrt{10n}$	$1/n$
1	1	1.000 000	3.162 278	1.000 000
2	4	1.414 214	4.472 136	0.500 000 0
3	9	1.732 051	5.477 226	.333 333 3
4	16	2.000 000	6.324 555	.250 000 0
5	25	2.236 068	7.071 068	0.200 000 0
6	36	2.449 490	7.745 967	.166 666 7
7	49	2.645 751	8.366 600	.142 857 1
8	64	2.828 427	8.944 272	.125 000 0
9	81	3.000 000	9.486 833	.111 111 1
10	100	3.162 278	10.000 00	0.100 000 0
11	121	3.316 625	10.488 09	.090 909 09
12	144	3.464 102	10.954 45	.083 333 33
13	169	3.605 551	11.401 75	.076 923 08
14	196	3.741 657	11.832 16	.071 428 57
15	225	3.872 983	12.247 45	0.066 666 67
16	256	4.000 000	12.649 11	.062 500 00
17	289	4.123 106	13.038 40	.058 823 53
18	324	4.242 641	13.416 41	.055 555 56
19	361	4.358 899	13.784 05	.052 631 58
20	400	4.472 136	14.142 14	0.050 000 00
21	441	4.582 576	14.491 38	.047 619 05
22	484	4.690 416	14.832 40	.045 454 55
23	529	4.795 832	15.165 75	.043 478 26
24	576	4.898 979	15.491 93	.041 666 67
25	625	5.000 000	15.811 39	0.040 000 00
26	676	5.099 020	16.124 52	.038 461 54
27	729	5.196 152	16.431 68	.037 037 04
28	784	5.291 503	16.733 20	.035 714 29
29	841	5.385 165	17.029 39	.034 482 76
30	900	5.477 226	17.320 51	0.033 333 33
31	961	5.567 764	17.606 82	.032 258 06
32	1 024	5.656 854	17.888 54	.031 250 00
33	1 089	5.744 563	18.165 90	.030 303 03
34	1 156	5.830 952	18.439 09	.029 411 76
35	1 225	5.916 080	18.708 29	0.028 571 43
36	1 296	6.000 000	18.973 67	.027 777 78
37	1 369	6.082 763	19.235 38	.027 027 03
38	1 444	6.164 414	19.493 59	.026 315 79
39	1 521	6.244 998	19.748 42	.025 641 03
40	1 600	6.324 555	20.000 00	0.025 000 00
41	1 681	6.403 124	20.248 46	.024 390 24
42	1 764	6.480 741	20.493 90	.023 809 52
43	1 849	6.557 439	20.736 44	.023 255 81
44	1 936	6.633 250	20.976 18	.022 727 27
45	2 025	6.708 204	21.213 20	0.022 222 22
46	2 116	6.782 330	21.447 61	.021 739 13
47	2 209	6.855 655	21.679 48	.021 276 60
48	2 304	6.928 203	21.908 90	.020 833 33
49	2 401	7.000 000	22.135 94	.020 408 16

Table XIII is abridged from Table 9, "Values of Reciprocals, Squares, Cubes, and Square Roots of Natural Numbers," Smithsonian Physical Tables, Ninth Edition, published by the Smithsonian Institution, Washington, D.C., by permission of Paul H. Oehser, Chief, Editorial and Publications Division.

TABLE XIII. SQUARES, SQUARE ROOTS, AND RECIPROCALS
(Continued)

n	n^2	$\sqrt{n}$	$\sqrt{10n}$	$1/n$
50	2 500	7.071 068	22.360 68	0.020 000 00
51	2 601	7.141 428	22.583 18	.019 607 84
52	2 704	7.211 103	22.803 51	.019 230 77
53	2 809	7.280 110	23.021 73	.018 867 92
54	2 916	7.348 469	23.237 90	.018 518 52
55	3 025	7.416 198	23.452 08	0.018 181 82
56	3 136	7.483 351	23.664 32	.017 857 14
57	3 249	7.549 834	23.874 67	.017 543 86
58	3 364	7.615 773	24.083 19	.017 241 38
59	3 481	7.681 146	24.289 92	.016 949 15
60	3 600	7.745 967	24.494 90	0.016 666 67
61	3 721	7.810 250	24.698 18	.016 393 44
62	3 844	7.874 008	24.899 80	.016 129 03
63	3 969	7.937 254	25.099 80	.015 873 02
64	4 096	8.000 000	25.298 22	.015 625 00
65	4 225	8.062 258	25.495 10	0.015 384 62
66	4 356	8.124 038	25.690 47	.015 151 52
67	4 489	8.185 353	25.884 36	.014 925 37
68	4 624	8.246 211	26.076 81	.014 705 88
69	4 761	8.306 624	26.267 85	.014 492 75
70	4 900	8.366 600	26.457 51	0.014 285 71
71	5 041	8.426 150	26.645 83	.014 084 51
72	5 184	8.485 281	26.832 82	.013 888 89
73	5 329	8.544 004	27.018 51	.013 698 63
74	5 476	8.602 325	27.202 94	.013 513 51
75	5 625	8.660 254	27.386 13	0.013 333 33
76	5 776	8.717 798	27.568 10	.013 157 89
77	5 929	8.774 964	27.748 87	.012 987 01
78	6 084	8.831 761	27.928 48	.012 820 51
79	6 241	8.888 194	28.106 94	.012 658 23
80	6 400	8.944 272	28.284 27	0.012 500 00
81	6 561	9.000 000	28.460 50	.012 345 68
82	6 724	9.055 385	28.635 64	.012 195 12
83	6 889	9.110 434	28.809 72	.012 048 19
84	7 056	9.165 151	28.982 75	.011 904 76
85	7 225	9.219 544	29.154 76	0.011 764 71
86	7 396	9.273 618	29.325 76	.011 627 91
87	7 569	9.327 379	29.495 76	.011 494 25
88	7 744	9.380 832	29.664 79	.011 363 64
89	7 921	9.433 981	29.832 87	.011 235 96
90	8 100	9.486 833	30.000 00	0.011 111 11
91	8 281	9.539 392	30.166 21	.010 989 01
92	8 464	9.591 663	30.331 50	.010 869 57
93	8 649	9.643 651	30.495 90	.010 752 69
94	8 836	9.695 360	30.659 42	.010 638 30
95	9 025	9.746 794	30.822 07	0.010 526 32
96	9 216	9.797 959	30.983 87	.010 416 67
97	9 409	9.848 858	31.144 82	.010 309 28
98	9 604	9.899 495	31.304 95	.010 204 08
99	9 801	9.949 874	31.464 27	.010 101 01
100	10 000	10.000 00	31.622 78	0.010 000 000
101	10 201	10.049 88	31.780 50	.009 900 990
102	10 404	10.099 50	31.937 44	.009 803 922
103	10 609	10.148 89	32.093 61	.009 708 738
104	10 816	10.198 04	32.249 03	.009 615 385
105	11 025	10.246 95	32.403 70	0.009 523 810
106	11 236	10.295 63	32.557 64	.009 433 962
107	11 449	10.344 08	32.710 85	.009 345 794
108	11 664	10.392 30	32.863 35	.009 259 259
109	11 881	10.440 31	33.015 15	.009 174 312

TABLE XIII. SQUARES, SQUARE ROOTS, AND RECIPROCALS
(Continued)

n	n^2	$\sqrt{n}$	$\sqrt{10n}$	$1/n$
110	12 100	10.488 09	33.166 25	0.009 090 909
111	12 321	10.535 65	33.316 66	.009 009 009
112	12 544	10.583 01	33.466 40	.008 928 571
113	12 769	10.630 15	33.615 47	.008 849 558
114	12 996	10.677 08	33.763 89	.008 771 930
115	13 225	10.723 81	33.911 65	0.008 695 652
116	13 456	10.770 33	34.058 77	.008 620 690
117	13 689	10.816 65	34.205 26	.008 547 009
118	13 924	10.826 78	34.351 13	.008 474 576
119	14 161	10.908 71	34.496 38	.008 403 361
120	14 400	10.954 45	34.641 02	0.008 333 333
121	14 641	11.000 00	34.785 05	.008 264 463
122	14 884	11.045 36	34.928 50	.008 196 721
123	15 129	11.090 54	35.071 36	.008 130 081
124	15 376	11.135 53	35.213 63	.008 064 516
125	15 625	11.180 34	35.355 34	0.008 000 000
126	15 876	11.224 97	35.496 48	.007 936 508
127	16 129	11.269 43	35.637 06	.007 874 016
128	16 384	11.313 71	35.777 09	.007 812 500
129	16 641	11.357 82	35.916 57	.007 751 938
130	16 900	11.401 75	36.055 51	0.007 692 308
131	17 161	11.445 52	36.193 92	.007 633 588
132	17 424	11.489 13	36.331 80	.007 575 758
133	17 689	11.532 56	36.469 17	.007 518 797
134	17 956	11.575 84	36.606 01	.007 462 687
135	18 225	11.618 95	36.742 35	0.007 407 407
136	18 496	11.661 90	36.878 18	.007 352 941
137	18 769	11.704 70	37.013 51	.007 299 270
138	19 044	11.747 34	37.148 35	.007 246 377
139	19 321	11.789 83	37.282 70	.007 194 245
140	19 600	11.832 16	37.416 57	0.007 142 857
141	19 881	11.874 34	37.549 97	.007 092 199
142	20 164	11.916 38	37.682 89	.007 042 254
143	20 449	11.958 26	37.815 34	.006 993 007
144	20 736	12.000 00	37.947 33	.006 944 444
145	21 025	12.041 59	38.078 87	0.006 896 552
146	21 316	12.083 05	38.209 95	.006 849 315
147	21 609	12.124 36	38.340 58	.006 802 721
148	21 904	12.165 53	38.470 77	.006 756 757
149	22 201	12.206 56	38.600 52	.006 711 409
150	22 500	12.247 45	38.729 83	0.006 666 667
151	22 801	12.288 21	38.858 72	.006 622 517
152	23 104	12.328 83	38.987 18	.006 578 947
153	23 409	12.369 32	39.115 21	.006 535 948
154	23 716	12.409 67	39.242 83	.006 493 506
155	24 025	12.449 90	39.370 04	0.006 451 613
156	24 336	12.490 00	39.496 84	.006 410 256
157	24 649	12.529 96	39.623 23	.006 369 427
158	24 964	12.569 81	39.749 21	.006 329 114
159	25 281	12.609 52	39.874 80	.006 289 308
160	25 600	12.649 11	40.000 00	0.006 250 000
161	25 921	12.688 58	40.124 81	.006 211 180
162	26 244	12.727 92	40.249 22	.006 172 840
163	26 569	12.767 15	40.373 26	.006 134 969
164	26 896	12.806 25	40.496 91	.006 097 561
165	27 225	12.845 23	40.620 19	0.006 060 606
166	27 556	12.884 10	40.743 10	.006 024 096
167	27 889	12.922 85	40.865 63	.005 988 024
168	28 224	12.961 48	40.987 80	.005 952 381
169	28 561	13.000 00	41.109 61	.005 917 160

TABLE XIII. SQUARES, SQUARE ROOTS, AND RECIPROCALS
(Continued)

n	n^2	$\sqrt{n}$	$\sqrt{10n}$	$1/n$
170	28 900	13.038 40	41.231 06	0.005 882 353
171	29 241	13.076 70	41.352 15	.005 847 953
172	29 584	13.114 88	41.472 88	.005 813 953
173	29 929	13.152 95	41.593 27	.005 780 347
174	30 276	13.190 91	41.713 31	.005 747 126
175	30 625	13.228 76	41.833 00	0.005 714 286
176	30 976	13.266 50	41.952 35	.005 681 818
177	31 329	13.304 13	42.071 37	.005 649 718
178	31 684	13.341 66	42.190 05	.005 617 978
179	32 041	13.379 09	42.308 39	.005 586 592
180	32 400	13.416 41	42.426 41	0.005 555 556
181	32 761	13.453 62	42.544 09	.005 524 862
182	33 124	13.490 74	42.661 46	.005 494 505
183	33 489	13.527 75	42.778 50	.005 464 481
184	33 856	13.564 66	42.895 22	.005 434 783
185	34 225	13.601 47	43.011 63	0.005 405 405
186	34 596	13.638 18	43.127 72	.005 376 344
187	34 969	13.674 79	43.243 50	.005 347 594
188	35 344	13.711 31	43.358 97	.005 319 149
189	35 721	13.747 73	43.474 13	.005 291 005
190	36 100	13.784 05	43.588 99	0.005 263 158
191	36 481	13.820 27	43.703 55	.005 235 602
192	36 864	13.856 41	43.817 80	.005 208 333
193	37 249	13.892 44	43.931 77	.005 181 347
194	37 636	13.928 39	44.045 43	.005 154 639
195	38 025	13.964 24	44.158 80	0.005 128 205
196	38 416	14.000 00	44.271 89	.005 102 041
197	38 809	14.035 67	44.384 68	.005 076 142
198	39 204	14.071 25	44.497 19	.005 050 505
199	39 601	14.106 74	44.609 42	.005 025 126
200	40 000	14.142 14	44.721 36	0.005 000 000
201	40 401	14.177 45	44.833 02	.004 975 124
202	40 804	14.212 67	44.944 41	.004 950 495
203	41 209	14.247 81	45.055 52	.004 926 108
204	41 616	14.282 86	45.166 36	.004 901 961
205	42 025	14.317 82	45.276 93	0.004 878 049
206	42 436	14.352 70	45.387 22	.004 854 369
207	42 849	14.387 49	45.497 25	.004 830 918
208	43 264	14.422 21	45.607 02	.004 807 692
209	43 681	14.456 83	45.716 52	.004 784 689
210	44 100	14.491 38	45.825 76	0.004 761 905
211	44 521	14.525 84	45.934 74	.004 739 336
212	44 944	14.560 22	46.043 46	.004 716 981
213	45 369	14.594 52	46.151 92	.004 694 836
214	45 796	14.628 74	46.260 13	.004 672 897
215	46 225	14.662 88	46.368 09	0.004 651 163
216	46 656	14.696 94	46.475 80	.004 629 630
217	47 089	14.730 92	46.583 26	.004 608 295
218	47 524	14.764 82	46.690 47	.004 587 156
219	47 961	14.798 65	46.797 44	.004 566 210
220	48 400	14.832 40	46.904 16	0.004 545 455
221	48 841	14.866 07	47.010 64	.004 524 887
222	49 284	14.899 66	47.116 88	.004 504 505
223	49 729	14.933 18	47.222 88	.004 484 305
224	50 176	14.966 63	47.328 64	.004 464 286
225	50 625	15.000 00	47.434 16	0.004 444 444
226	51 076	15.033 30	47.539 46	.004 424 779
227	51 529	15.066 52	47.644 52	.004 405 286
228	51.984	15.099 67	47.749 35	.004 385 965
229	52 441	15.132 75	47.853 94	.004 366 812

TABLE XIII. SQUARES, SQUARE ROOTS, AND RECIPROCALS

(Continued)

n	n^2	$\sqrt{n}$	$\sqrt{10n}$	$1/n$
230	52 900	15.165 75	47.958 32	0.004 347 826
231	53 361	15.198 68	48.062 46	.004 329 004
232	53 824	15.231 55	48.166 38	.004 310 345
233	54 289	15.264 34	48.270 07	.004 291 845
234	54 756	15.297 06	48.373 55	.004 273 504
235	55 225	15.329 71	48.476 80	0.004 255 319
236	55 696	15.362 29	48.579 83	.004 237 288
237	56 169	15.394 80	48.682 65	.004 219 409
238	56 644	15.427 25	48.785 24	.004 201 681
239	57 121	15.459 62	48.887 63	.004 184 100
240	57 600	15.491 93	48.989 79	0.004 166 667
241	58 081	15.524 17	49.091 75	.004 149 378
242	58 564	15.556 35	49.193 50	.004 132 231
243	59 049	15.588 46	49.295 03	.004 115 226
244	59 536	15.620 50	49.396 36	.004 098 361
245	60 025	15.652 48	49.497 47	0.004 081 633
246	60 516	15.684 39	49.598 39	.004 065 041
247	61 009	15.716 23	49.699 09	.004 048 583
248	61 504	15.748 02	49.799 60	.004 032 258
249	62 001	15.779 73	49.899 90	.004 016 064
250	62 500	15.811 39	50.000 00	0.004 000 000
251	63 001	15.842 98	50.099 90	.003 984 064
252	63 504	15.874 51	50.199 60	.003 968 254
253	64 009	15.905 97	50.299 11	.003 952 569
254	64 516	15.937 38	50.398 41	.003 937 008
255	65 025	15.968 72	50.497 52	0.003 921 569
256	65 536	16.000 00	50.596 44	.003 906 250
257	66 049	16.031 22	50.695 17	.003 891 051
258	66 564	16.062 38	50.793 70	.003 875 969
259	67 081	16.093 48	50.892 04	.003 861 004
260	67 600	16.124 52	50.990 20	0.003 846 154
261	68 121	16.155 49	51.088 16	.003 831 418
262	68 644	16.186 41	51.185 94	.003 816 794
263	69 169	16.217 27	51.283 53	.003 802 281
264	69 696	16.248 08	51.380 93	.003 787 879
265	70 225	16.278 82	51.478 15	0.003 773 585
266	70 756	16.309 51	51.575 19	.003 759 398
267	71 289	16.340 13	51.672 04	.003 745 318
268	71 824	16.370 71	51.766 72	.003 731 343
269	72 361	16.401 22	51.865 21	.003 717 472
270	72 900	16.431 68	51.961 52	0.003 703 704
271	73 441	16.462 08	52.057 66	.003 690 037
272	73 984	16.492 42	52.153 62	.003 676 471
273	74 529	16.522 71	52.249 40	.003 663 004
274	75 076	16.552 95	52.345 01	.003 649 635
275	75 625	16.583 12	52.440 44	0.003 636 364
276	76 176	16.613 25	52.535 70	.003 623 188
277	76 729	16.643 32	52.630 79	.003 610 108
278	77 284	16.673 33	52.725 71	.003 597 122
279	77 841	16.703 29	52.820 45	.003 584 229
280	78 400	16.733 20	52.915 03	0.003 571 429
281	78 961	16.763 05	53.009 43	.003 558 719
282	79 524	16.792 86	53.103 67	.003 546 099
283	80 089	16.822 60	53.197 74	.003 533 569
284	80 656	16.852 30	53.291 65	.003 521 127
285	81 225	16.881 94	53.385 39	0.003 508 772
286	81 796	16.911 53	53.478 97	.003 496 503
287	82 369	16.941 07	53.572 38	.003 484 321
288	82 944	16.970 56	53.665 63	.003 472 222
289	83 521	17.000 00	53.758 72	.003 460 208

TABLE XIII. SQUARES, SQUARE ROOTS, AND RECIPROCALS
(Continued)

n	n^2	$\sqrt{n}$	$\sqrt{10n}$	$1/n$
290	84 100	17.029 39	53.851 65	0.003 448 276
291	84 681	17.058 72	53.944 42	.003 436 426
292	85 264	17.088 01	54.037 02	.003 424 658
293	85 849	17.117 24	54.129 47	.003 412 969
294	86 436	17.146 43	54.221 77	.003 401 361
295	87 025	17.175 56	54.313 90	0.003 389 831
296	87 616	17.204 65	54.405 88	.003 378 378
297	88 209	17.233 69	54.497 71	.003 367 003
298	88 804	17.262 68	54.589 38	.003 355 705
299	89 401	17.291 62	54.680 89	.003 344 482
300	90 000	17.320 51	54.772 26	0.003 333 333
301	90 601	17.349 35	54.863 47	.003 322 259
302	91 204	17.378 15	54.954 53	.003 311 258
303	91 809	17.406 90	55.045 44	.003 300 330
304	92 416	17.435 60	55.136 20	.003 289 474
305	93 025	17.464 25	55.226 81	0.003 278 689
306	93 636	17.492 86	55.317 27	.003 267 974
307	94 249	17.521 42	55.407 58	.003 257 329
308	94 864	17.549 93	55.497 75	.003 246 753
309	95 481	17.578 40	55.587 77	.003 236 246
310	96 100	17.606 82	55.677 64	0.003 225 806
311	96 721	17.635 19	55.767 37	.003 215 434
312	97 344	17.663 52	55.856 96	.003 205 128
313	97 969	17.691 81	55.946 40	.003 194 888
314	98 596	17.720 05	56.035 70	.003 184 713
315	99 225	17.748 24	56.124 86	0.003 174 603
316	99 856	17.776 39	56.213 88	.003 164 557
317	100 489	17.804 49	56.302 75	.003 154 574
318	101 124	17.832 55	56.391 49	.003 144 654
319	101 761	17.860 57	56.480 08	.003 134 796
320	102 400	17.888 54	56.568 54	0.003 125 000
321	103 041	17.916 47	56.656 86	.003 115 265
322	103 684	17.944 36	56.745 04	.003 105 590
323	104 329	17.972 20	56.833 09	.003 095 975
324	104 976	18.000 00	56.921 00	.003 086 420
325	105 625	18.027 76	57.008 77	0.003 076 923
326	106 276	18.055 47	57.096 41	.003 067 485
327	106 929	18.083 14	57.183 91	.003 058 104
328	107 584	18.110 77	57.271 28	.003 048 780
329	108 241	18.138 36	57.358 52	.003 039 514
330	108 900	18.165 90	57.445 63	0.003 030 303
331	109 561	18.193 41	57.532 60	.003 021 148
332	110 224	18.220 87	57.619 44	.003 012 048
333	110 889	18.248 29	57.706 15	.003 003 003
334	111 556	18.275 67	57.792 73	.002 994 012
335	112 225	18.303 01	57.879 18	0.002 985 075
336	112 896	18.330 30	57.965 51	.002 976 190
337	113 569	18.357 56	58.051 70	.002 967 359
338	114 244	18.384 78	58.137 77	.002 958 580
339	114 921	18.411 95	58.223 71	.002 949 853
340	115 600	18.439 09	58.309 52	0.002 941 176
341	116 281	18.466 19	58.395 21	.002 932 551
342	116 964	18.493 24	58.480 77	.002 923 977
343	117 649	18.520 26	58.566 20	.002 915 452
344	118 336	18.547 24	58.651 51	.002 906 977
345	119 025	18.574 18	58.736 70	0.002 898 551
346	119 716	18.601 08	58.821 76	.002 890 173
347	120 409	18.627 94	58.906 71	.002 881 844
348	121 104	18.654 76	58.991 52	.002 873 563
349	121 801	18.681 54	59.076 22	.002 865 330

TABLE XIII. SQUARES, SQUARE ROOTS, AND RECIPROCALS
(Continued)

n	n^2	$\sqrt{n}$	$\sqrt{10n}$	$1/n$
350	122 500	18.708 29	59.160 80	0.002 857 143
351	123 201	18.734 99	59.245 25	.002 849 003
352	123 904	18.761 66	59.329 59	.002 840 909
353	124 609	18.788 29	59.413 80	.002 832 861
354	125 316	18.814 89	59.497 90	.002 824 859
355	126 025	18.841 44	59.581 88	0.002 816 901
356	126 736	18.867 96	59.665 74	.002 808 989
357	127 449	18.894 44	59.749 48	.002 801 120
358	128 164	18.920 89	59.833 10	.002 793 296
359	128 881	18.947 30	59.916 61	.002 785 515
360	129 600	18.973 67	60.000 00	0.002 777 778
361	130 321	19.000 00	60.083 28	.002 770 083
362	131 044	19.026 30	60.166 44	.002 762 431
363	131 769	19.052 56	60.249 48	.002 754 821
364	132 496	19.078 78	60.332 41	.002 747 253
365	133 225	19.104 97	60.415 23	0.002 739 726
366	133 956	19.131 13	60.497 93	.002 732 240
367	134 689	19.157 24	60.580 52	.002 724 796
368	135 424	19.183 33	60.663 00	.002 717 391
369	136 161	19.209 37	60.745 37	.002 710 027
370	136 900	19.235 38	60.827 63	0.002 702 703
371	137 641	19.261 36	60.909 77	.002 695 418
372	138 384	19.287 30	60.991 80	.002 688 172
373	139 129	19.313 21	61.073 73	.002 680 965
374	139 876	19.339 08	61.155 54	.002 673 797
375	140 625	19.364 92	61.237 24	0.002 666 667
376	141 376	19.390 72	61.318 84	.002 659 574
377	142 129	19.416 49	61.400 33	.002 652 520
378	142 884	19.442 22	61.481 70	.002 645 503
379	143 641	19.467 92	61.562 98	.002 638 522
380	144 400	19.493 59	61.644 14	0.002 631 579
381	145 161	19.519 22	61.725 20	.002 624 672
382	145 924	19.544 82	61.806 15	.002 617 801
383	146 689	19.570 39	61.886 99	.002 610 966
384	147 456	19.595 92	61.967 73	.002 604 167
385	148 225	19.621 42	62.048 37	0.002 597 403
386	148 996	19.646 88	62.128 90	.002 590 674
387	149 769	19.672 32	62.209 32	.002 583 979
388	150 544	19.697 72	62.289 65	.002 577 320
389	151 321	19.723 08	62.369 86	.002 570 694
390	152 100	19.748 42	62.449 98	0.002 564 103
391	152 881	19.773 72	62.529 99	.002 557 545
392	153 664	19.798 99	62.609 90	.002 551 020
393	154 449	19.824 23	62.689 71	.002 544 529
394	155 236	19.849 43	62.769 42	.002 538 071
395	156 025	19.874 61	62.849 03	0.002 531 646
396	156 816	19.899 75	62.928 53	.002 525 253
397	157 609	19.924 86	63.007 94	.002 518 892
398	158 404	19.949 94	63.087 24	.002 512 563
399	159 201	19.974 98	63.166 45	.002 506 266
400	160 000	20.000 00	63.245 55	0.002 500 000
401	160 801	20.024 98	63.324 56	.002 493 766
402	161 604	20.049 94	63.403 47	.002 487 562
403	162 409	20.074 86	63.482 28	.002 481 390
404	163 216	20.099 75	63.560 99	.002 475 248
405	164 025	20.124 61	63.639 61	0.002 469 136
406	164 836	20.149 44	63.718 13	.002 463 054
407	165 649	20.174 24	63.796 55	.002 457 002
408	166 464	20.199 01	63.874 88	.002 450 980
409	167 281	20.223 75	63.953 11	.002 444 988

TABLE XIII. SQUARES, SQUARE ROOTS, AND RECIPROCALS
(Continued)

n	n^2	$\sqrt{n}$	$\sqrt{10n}$	$1/n$
410	168 100	20.248 46	64.031 24	0.002 439 024
411	168 921	20.273 13	64.109 28	.002 433 090
412	169 744	20.297 78	64.187 23	.002 427 184
413	170 569	20.322 40	64.265 08	.002 421 308
414	171 396	20.346 99	64.342 83	.002 415 459
415	172 225	20.371 55	64.420 49	0.002 409 639
416	173 056	20.396 08	64.498 06	.002 403 846
417	173 889	20.420 58	64.575 54	.002 398 082
418	174 724	20.445 05	64.652 92	.002 392 344
419	175 561	20.469 49	64.730 21	.002 386 635
420	176 400	20.493 90	64.807 41	0.002 380 952
421	177 241	20.518 28	64.884 51	.002 375 297
422	178 084	20.542 64	64.961 53	.002 369 668
423	178 929	20.566 96	65.038 45	.002 364 066
424	179 776	20.591 26	65.115 28	.002 358 491
425	180 625	20.615 53	65.192 02	0.002 352 941
426	181 476	20.639 77	65.268 68	.002 347 418
427	182 329	20.663 98	65.345 24	.002 341 920
428	183 184	20.688 16	65.421 71	.002 336 449
429	184 041	20.712 32	65.498 09	.002 331 002
430	184 900	20.736 44	65.574 39	0.002 325 581
431	185 761	20.760 54	65.650 59	.002 320 186
432	186 624	20.784 61	65.726 71	.002 314 815
433	187 489	20.808 65	65.802 74	.002 309 469
434	188 356	20.832 67	65.878 68	.002 304 147
435	189 225	20.856 65	65.954 53	0.002 298 851
436	190 096	20.880 61	66.030 30	.002 293 578
437	190 969	20.904 54	66.105 98	.002 288 330
438	191 844	20.928 45	66.181 57	.002 283 105
439	192 721	20.952 33	66.257 08	.002 277 904
440	193 600	20.976 18	66.332 50	0.002 272 727
441	194 481	21.000 00	66.407 83	.002 267 574
442	195 364	21.023 80	66.483 08	.002 262 443
443	196 249	21.047 57	66.558 25	.002 257 336
444	197 136	21.071 31	66.633 32	.002 252 252
445	198 025	21.095 02	66.708 32	0.002 247 191
446	198 916	21.118 71	66.783 23	.002 242 152
447	199 809	21.142 37	66.858 06	.002 237 136
448	200 704	21.166 01	66.932 80	.002 232 143
449	201 601	21.189 62	67.007 46	.002 227 171
450	202 500	21.213 20	67.082 04	0.002 222 222
451	203 401	21.236 76	67.156 53	.002 217 295
452	204 304	21.260 29	67.230 95	.002 212 389
453	205 209	21.283 80	67.305 27	.002 207 506
454	206 116	21.307 28	67.379 52	.002 202 643
455	207 025	21.330 73	67.453 69	0.002 197 802
456	207 936	21.354 16	67.527 77	.002 192 982
457	208 849	21.377 56	67.601 78	.002 188 184
458	209 764	21.400 93	67.675 70	.002 183 406
459	210 681	21.424 29	67.749 54	.002 178 649
460	211 600	21.447 61	67.823 30	0.002 173 913
461	212 521	21.470 91	67.896 98	.002 169 197
462	213 444	21.494 19	67.970 58	.002 164 502
463	214 369	21.517 43	68.044 10	.002 159 827
464	215 296	21.540 66	68.117 55	.002 155 172
465	216 225	21.563 86	68.190 91	0.002 150 538
466	217 156	21.587 03	68.264 19	.002 145 923
467	218 089	21.610 18	68.337 40	.002 141 328
468	219 024	21.633 31	68.410 53	.002 136 752
469	219 961	21.656 41	68.483 57	.002 132 196

TABLE XIII. SQUARES, SQUARE ROOTS, AND RECIPROCALS
(Continued)

n	n^2	$\sqrt{n}$	$\sqrt{10n}$	$1/n$
470	220 900	21.679 48	68.556 55	0.002 127 660
471	221 841	21.702 53	68.629 44	.002 123 142
472	222 784	21.725 56	68.702 26	.002 118 644
473	223 729	21.748 56	68.775 00	.002 114 165
474	224 676	21.771 54	68.847 66	.002 109 705
475	225 625	21.794 49	68.920 24	0.002 105 263
476	226 576	21.817 42	68.992 75	.002 100 840
477	227 529	21.840 33	69.065 19	.002 096 436
478	228 484	21.863 21	69.137 54	.002 092 050
479	229 441	21.886 07	69.209 83	.002 087 683
480	230 400	21.908 90	69.282 03	0.002 083 333
481	231 361	21.931 71	69.354 16	.002 079 002
482	232 324	21.954 50	69.426 22	.002 074 689
483	233 289	21.977 26	69.498 20	.002 070 393
484	234 256	22.000 00	69.570 11	.002 066 116
485	235 225	22.022 72	69.641 94	0.002 061 856
486	236 196	22.045 41	69.713 70	.002 057 613
487	237 169	22.068 08	69.785 39	.002 053 388
488	238 144	22.090 72	69.857 00	.002 049 180
489	239 121	22.113 34	69.928 53	.002 044 990
490	240 100	22.135 94	70.000 00	0.002 040 816
491	241 081	22.158 52	70.071 39	.002 036 660
492	242 064	22.181 07	70.142 71	.002 032 520
493	243 049	22.203 60	70.213 96	.002 028 398
494	244 036	22.226 11	70.285 13	.002 024 291
495	245 025	22.248 60	70.356 24	0.002 020 202
496	246 016	22.271 06	70.427 27	.002 016 129
497	247 009	22.293 50	70.498 23	.002 012 072
498	248 004	22.315 91	70.569 12	.002 008 032
499	249 001	22.338 31	70.639 93	.002 004 008
500	250 000	22.360 68	70.710 68	0.002 000 000
501	251 001	22.383 03	70.781 35	.001 996 008
502	252 004	22.405 36	70.851 96	.001 992 032
503	253 009	22.427 66	70.922 49	.001 988 072
504	254 016	22.449 94	70.992 96	.001 984 127
505	255 025	22.472 21	71.063 35	0.001 980 198
506	256 036	22.494 44	71.133 68	.001 976 285
507	257 049	22.516 66	71.203 93	.001 972 387
508	258 064	22.538 86	71.274 12	.001 968 504
509	259 081	22.561 03	71.344 24	.001 964 637
510	260 100	22.583 18	71.414 28	0.001 960 784
511	261 121	22.605 31	71.484 26	.001 956 947
512	262 144	22.627 42	71.554 18	.001 953 125
513	263 169	22.649 50	71.624 02	.001 949 318
514	264 196	22.671 57	71.693 79	.001 945 525
515	265 225	22.693 61	71.763 50	0.001 941 748
516	266 256	22.715 63	71.833 14	.001 937 984
517	267 289	22.737 63	71.902 71	.001 934 236
518	268 324	22.759 61	71.972 22	.001 930 502
519	269 361	22.781 57	72.041 65	.001 926 782
520	270 400	22.803 51	72.111 03	0.001 923 077
521	271 441	22.825 42	72.180 33	.001 919 386
522	272 484	22.847 32	72.249 57	.001 915 709
523	273 529	22.869 19	72.318 74	.001 912 046
524	274 576	22.891 05	72.387 84	.001 908 397
525	275 625	22.912 88	72.456 88	0.001 904 762
526	276 676	22.934 69	72.525 86	.001 901 141
527	277 729	22.956 48	72.594 77	.001 897 533
528	278 784	22.978 25	72.663 61	.001 893 939
529	279 841	23.000 00	72.732 39	.001 890 359

TABLE XIII. SQUARES, SQUARE ROOTS, AND RECIPROCALS
(Continued)

n	n^2	$\sqrt{n}$	$\sqrt{10n}$	$1/n$
530	280 900	23.021 73	72.801 10	0.001 886 792
531	281 961	23.043 44	72.869 75	.001 883 239
532	283 024	23.065 13	72.938 33	.001 879 699
533	284 089	23.086 79	73.006 85	.001 876 173
534	285 156	23.108 44	73.075 30	.001 872 659
535	286 225	23.130 70	73.143 69	0.001 869 159
536	287 296	23.151 67	73.212 02	.001 865 672
537	288 369	23.173 26	73.280 28	.001 862 197
538	289 444	23.194 83	73.348 48	.001 858 736
539	290 521	23.216 37	73.416 62	.001 855 288
540	291 600	23.237 90	73.484 69	0.001 851 852
541	292 681	23.259 41	73.552 70	.001 848 429
542	293 764	23.280 89	73.620 65	.001 845 018
543	294 849	23.302 36	73.688 53	.001 841 621
544	295 936	23.323 81	73.756 36	.001 838 235
545	297 025	23.345 24	73.824 12	0.001 834 862
546	298 116	23.366 64	73.891 81	.001 831 502
547	299 209	23.388 03	73.959 45	.001 828 154
548	300 304	23.409 40	74.027 02	.001 824 818
549	301 401	23.430 75	74.094 53	.001 821 494
550	302 500	23.452 08	74.161 98	0.001 818 182
551	303 601	23.473 39	74.229 37	.001 814 882
552	304 704	23.494 68	74.296 70	.001 811 594
553	305 809	23.515 95	74.363 97	.001 808 318
554	306 916	23.537 20	74.431 18	.001 805 054
555	308 025	23.558 44	74.498 32	0.001 801 802
556	309 136	23.579 65	74.565 41	.001 798 561
557	310 249	23.600 85	74.632 43	.001 795 332
558	311 364	23.622 02	74.699 40	.001 792 115
559	312 481	23.643 18	74.766 30	.001 788 909
560	313 600	23.664 32	74.833 15	0.001 785 714
561	314 721	23.685 44	74.899 93	.001 782 531
562	315 844	23.706 54	74.966 66	.001 779 359
563	316 969	23.727 62	75.033 33	.001 776 199
564	318 096	23.748 68	75.099 93	.001 773 050
565	319 225	23.769 73	75.166 48	0.001 769 912
566	320 356	23.790 75	75.232 97	.001 766 784
567	321 489	23.811 76	75.299 40	.001 763 668
568	322 624	23.832 75	75.365 77	.001 760 563
569	323 761	23.853 72	75.432 09	.001 757 469
570	324 900	23.874 67	75.498 34	0.001 754 386
571	326 041	23.895 61	75.564 54	.001 751 313
572	327 184	23.916 52	75.630 68	.001 748 252
573	328 329	23.937 42	75.696 76	.001 745 201
574	329 476	23.958 30	75.762 79	.001 742 160
575	330 625	23.979 16	75.828 75	0.001 739 130
576	331 776	24.000 00	75.894 66	.001 736 111
577	332 929	24.020 82	75.960 52	.001 733 102
578	334 084	24.041 63	76.026 31	.001 730 104
579	335 241	24.062 42	76.092 05	.001 727 116
580	336 400	24.083 19	76.157 73	0.001 724 138
581	337 561	24.103 94	76.223 36	.001 721 170
582	338 724	24.124 68	76.288 92	.001 718 213
583	339 889	24.145 39	76.354 44	.001 715 266
584	341 056	24.166 09	76.419 89	.001 712 329
585	342 225	24.186 77	76.485 29	0.001 709 402
586	343 396	24.207 44	76.550 64	.001 706 485
587	344 569	24.228 08	76.615 93	.001 703 578
588	345 744	24.248 71	76.681 16	.001 700 680
589	346 921	24.269 32	76.746 34	.001 697 793

TABLE XIII. SQUARES, SQUARE ROOTS, AND RECIPROCALS
(Continued)

n	n^2	$\sqrt{n}$	$\sqrt{10n}$	$1/n$
590	348 100	24.289 92	76.811 46	0.001 694 915
591	349 281	24.310 49	76.876 52	.001 692 047
592	350 464	24.331 05	76.941 54	.001 689 189
593	351 649	24.351 59	77.006 49	.001 686 341
594	352 836	24.372 12	77.071 40	.001 683 502
595	354 025	24.392 62	77.136 24	0.001 680 672
596	355 216	24.413 11	77.201 04	.001 677 852
597	356 409	24.433 58	77.265 78	.001 675 042
598	357 604	24.454 04	77.330 46	.001 672 241
599	358 801	24.474 48	77.395 09	.001 669 449
600	360 000	24.494 90	77.459 67	0.001 666 667
601	361 201	24.515 30	77.524 19	.001 663 894
602	362 404	24.535 69	77.588 66	.001 661 130
603	363 609	24.556 06	77.653 07	.001 658 375
604	364 816	24.576 41	77.717 44	.001 655 629
605	366 025	24.596 75	77.781 75	0.001 652 893
606	367 236	24.617 07	77.846 00	.001 650 165
607	368 449	24.637 37	77.910 20	.001 647 446
608	369 664	24.657 66	77.974 35	.001 644 737
609	370 881	24.677 93	78.038 45	.001 642 036
610	372 100	24.698 18	78.102 50	0.001 639 344
611	373 321	24.718 41	78.166 49	.001 636 661
612	374 544	24.738 63	78.230 43	.001 633 987
613	375 769	24.758 84	78.294 32	.001 631 321
614	376 996	24.779 02	78.358 15	.001 628 664
615	378 225	24.799 19	78.421 94	0.001 626 016
616	379 456	24.819 35	78.485 67	.001 623 377
617	380 689	24.839 48	78.549 35	.001 620 746
618	381 924	24.859 61	78.612 98	.001 618 123
619	383 161	24.879 71	78.676 55	.001 615 509
620	384 400	24.899 80	78.740 08	0.001 612 903
621	385 641	24.919 87	78.803 55	.001 610 306
622	386 884	24.939 93	78.866 98	.001 607 717
623	388 129	24.959 97	78.930 35	.001 605 136
624	389 376	24.979 99	78.993 67	.001 602 564
625	390 625	25.000 00	79.056 94	0.001 600 000
626	391 876	25.019 99	79.120 16	.001 597 444
627	393 129	25.039 97	79.183 33	.001 594 896
628	394 384	25.059 93	79.246 45	.001 592 357
629	395 641	25.079 87	79.309 52	.001 589 825
630	396 900	25.099 80	79.372 54	0.001 587 302
631	398 161	25.119 71	79.435 51	.001 584 786
632	399 424	25.139 61	79.498 43	.001 582 278
633	400 689	25.159 49	79.561 30	.001 579 779
634	401 956	25.179 36	79.624 12	.001 577 287
635	403 225	25.199 21	79.686 89	0.001 574 803
636	404 496	25.219 04	79.749 61	.001 572 327
637	405 769	25.238 86	79.812 28	.001 569 859
638	407 044	25.258 66	79.874 90	.001 567 398
639	408 321	25.278 45	79.937 48	.001 564 945
640	409 600	25.298 22	80.000 00	0.001 562 500
641	410 881	25.317 98	80.062 48	.001 560 062
642	412 164	25.337 72	80.124 90	.001 557 632
643	413 449	25.357 44	80.187 28	.001 555 210
644	414 736	25.377 16	80.249 61	.001 552 795
645	416 025	25.396 85	80.311 89	0.001 550 388
646	417 316	25.416 53	80.374 13	.001 547 988
647	418 609	25.436 19	80.436 31	.001 545 595
648	419 904	25.455 84	80.498 45	.001 543 210
649	421 201	25.475 48	80.560 54	.001 540 832

TABLE XIII. SQUARES, SQUARE ROOTS, AND RECIPROCALS
(Continued)

n	n^2	$\sqrt{n}$	$\sqrt{10n}$	$1/n$
650	422 500	25.495 10	80.622 58	0.001 538 462
651	423 801	25.514 70	80.684 57	.001 536 098
652	425 104	25.534 29	80.746 52	.001 533 742
653	426 409	25.553 86	80.808 42	.001 531 394
654	427 716	25.573 42	80.870 27	.001 529 052
655	429 025	25.592 97	80.932 07	0.001 526 718
656	430 336	25.612 50	80.993 83	.001 524 390
657	431 649	25.632 01	81.055 54	.001 522 070
658	432 964	25.651 51	81.117 20	.001 519 757
659	434 281	25.671 00	81.178 81	.001 517 451
660	435 600	25.690 47	81.240 38	0.001 515 152
661	436 921	25.709 92	81.301 91	.001 512 859
662	438 244	25.729 36	81.363 38	.001 510 574
663	439 569	25.748 79	81.424 81	.001 508 296
664	440 896	25.768 20	81.486 20	.001 506 024
665	442 225	25.787 59	81.547 53	0.001 503 759
666	443 556	25.806 98	81.608 82	.001 501 502
667	444 889	25.826 34	81.670 07	.001 499 250
668	446 224	25.845 70	81.731 27	.001 497 006
669	447 561	25.865 03	81.792 42	.001 494 768
670	448 900	25.884 36	81.853 53	0.001 492 537
671	450 241	25.903 67	81.914 59	.001 490 313
672	451 584	25.922 96	81.975 61	.001 488 095
673	452 929	25.942 24	82.036 58	.001 485 884
674	454 276	25.961 51	82.097 50	.001 483 680
675	455 625	25.980 76	82.158 38	0.001 481 481
676	456 976	26.000 00	82.219 22	.001 479 290
677	458 329	26.019 22	82.280 01	.001 477 105
678	459 684	26.038 43	82.340 76	.001 474 926
679	461 041	26.057 63	82.401 46	.001 472 754
680	462 400	26.076 81	82.462 11	0.001 470 588
681	463 761	26.095 98	82.522 72	.001 468 429
682	465 124	26.115 13	82.583 29	.001 466 276
683	466 489	26.134 27	82.643 81	.001 464 129
684	467 856	26.153 39	82.704 29	.001 461 988
685	469 225	26.172 50	82.764 73	0.001 459 854
686	470 596	26.191 60	82.825 12	.001 457 726
687	471 969	26.210 68	82.885 46	.001 455 604
688	473 344	26.229 75	82.945 77	.001 453 488
689	474 721	26.248 81	83.006 02	.001 451 379
690	476 100	26.267 85	83.066 24	0.001 449 275
691	477 481	26.286 88	83.126 41	.001 447 178
692	478 864	26.305 89	83.186 54	.001 445 087
693	480 249	26.324 89	83.246 62	.001 443 001
694	481 636	26.343 88	83.306 66	.001 440 922
695	483 025	26.362 85	83.366 66	0.001 438 849
696	484 416	26.381 81	83.426 61	.001 436 782
697	485 809	26.400 76	83.486 53	.001 434 720
698	487 204	26.419 69	83.546 39	.001 432 665
699	488 601	26.438 61	83.606 22	.001 430 615
700	490 000	26.457 51	83.666 00	0.001 428 571
701	491 401	26.476 40	83.725 74	.001 426 534
702	492 804	26.495 28	83.785 44	.001 424 501
703	494 209	26.514 15	83.845 10	.001 422 475
704	495 616	26.533 00	83.904 71	.001 420 455
705	497 025	26.551 84	83.964 28	0.001 418 440
706	498 436	26.570 66	84.023 81	.001 416 431
707	499 849	26.589 47	84.083 29	.001 414 427
708	501 264	26.608 27	84.142 74	.001 412 429
709	502 681	26.627 05	84.202 14	.001 410 437

TABLE XIII. SQUARES, SQUARE ROOTS, AND RECIPROCALS
(Continued)

n	n^2	$\sqrt{n}$	$\sqrt{10n}$	$1/n$
710	504 100	26.645 83	84.261 50	0.001 408 451
711	505 521	26.664 58	84.320 82	.001 406 470
712	506 944	26.683 33	84.380 09	.001 404 494
713	508 369	26.702 06	84.439 33	.001 402 525
714	509 796	26.720 78	84.498 52	.001 400 560
715	511 225	26.739 48	84.557 67	0.001 398 601
716	512 656	26.758 18	84.616 78	.001 396 648
717	514 089	26.776 86	84.675 85	.001 394 700
718	515 524	26.795 52	84.734 88	.001 392 758
719	516 961	26.814 18	84.793 87	.001 390 821
720	518 400	26.832 82	84.852 81	0.001 388 889
721	519 841	26.851 44	84.911 72	.001 386 963
722	521 284	26.870 06	84.970 58	.001 385 042
723	522 729	26.888 66	85.029 41	.001 383 126
724	524 176	26.907 25	85.088 19	.001 381 215
725	525 625	26.925 82	85.146 93	0.001 379 310
726	527 076	26.944 39	85.205 63	.001 377 410
727	528 529	26.962 94	85.264 29	.001 375 516
728	529 984	26.981 48	85.322 92	.001 373 626
729	531 441	27.000 00	85.381 50	.001 371 742
730	532 900	27.018 51	85.440 04	0.001 369 863
731	534 361	27.037 01	85.498 54	.001 367 989
732	535 824	27.055 50	85.557 00	.001 366 120
733	537 289	27.073 97	85.615 42	.001 364 256
734	538 756	27.092 43	85.673 80	.001 362 398
735	540 225	27.110 88	85.732 14	0.001 360 544
736	541 696	27.129 32	85.790 44	.001 358 696
737	543 169	27.147 74	85.848 70	.001 356 852
738	544 644	27.166 16	85.906 93	.001 355 014
739	546 121	27.184 55	85.965 11	.001 353 180
740	547 600	27.202 94	86.023 25	0.001 351 351
741	549 081	27.221 32	86.081 36	.001 349 528
742	550 564	27.239 68	86.139 42	.001 347 709
743	552 049	27.258 03	86.197 45	.001 345 895
744	553 536	27.276 36	86.255 43	.001 344 086
745	555 025	27.294 69	86.313 38	0.001 342 282
746	556 516	27.313 00	86.371 29	.001 340 483
747	558 009	27.331 30	86.429 16	.001 338 688
748	559 504	27.349 59	86.486 99	.001 336 898
749	561 001	27.367 86	86.544 79	.001 335 113
750	562 500	27.386 13	86.602 54	0.001 333 333
751	564 001	27.404 38	86.660 26	.001 331 558
752	565 504	27.422 62	86.717 93	.001 329 787
753	567 009	27.440 85	86.775 57	.001 328 021
754	568 516	27.459 06	86.833 17	.001 326 260
755	570 025	27.477 26	86.890 74	0.001 324 503
756	571 536	27.495 45	86.948 26	.001 322 751
757	573 049	27.513 63	87.005 75	.001 321 004
758	574 564	27.531 80	87.063 20	.001 319 261
759	576 081	27.549 95	87.120 61	.001 317 523
760	577 600	27.568 10	87.177 98	0.001 315 789
761	579 121	27.586 23	87.235 31	.001 314 060
762	580 644	27.604 35	87.292 61	.001 312 336
763	582 169	27.622 45	87.349 87	.001 310 616
764	583 696	27.640 55	87.407 09	.001 308 901
765	585 225	27.658 63	87.464 28	0.001 307 190
766	586 756	27.676 71	87.521 43	.001 305 483
767	588 289	27.694 76	87.578 54	.001 303 781
768	589 824	27.712 81	87.635 61	.001 302 083
769	591 361	27.730 85	87.692 65	.001 300 390

TABLE XIII. SQUARES, SQUARE ROOTS, AND RECIPROCALS
(Continued)

n	n^2	$\sqrt{n}$	$\sqrt{10n}$	$1/n$
770	592 900	27.748 87	87.749 64	0.001 298 701
771	594 441	27.766 89	87.806 61	.001 297 017
772	595 984	27.784 89	87.863 53	.001 295 337
773	597 529	27.802 88	87.920 42	.001 293 661
774	599 076	27.820 86	87.977 27	.001 291 990
775	600 625	27.838 82	88.034 08	0.001 290 323
776	602 176	27.856 78	88.090 86	.001 288 660
777	603 729	27.874 72	88.147 60	.001 287 001
778	605 284	27.892 65	88.204 31	.001 285 347
779	606 841	27.910 57	88.260 98	.001 283 697
780	608 400	27.928 48	88.317 61	0.001 282 051
781	609 961	27.946 38	88.374 20	.001 280 410
782	611 524	27.964 26	88.430 76	.001 278 772
783	613 089	27.982 14	88.487 29	.001 277 139
784	614 656	28.000 00	88.543 77	.001 275 510
785	616 225	28.017 85	88.600 23	0.001 273 885
786	617 796	28.035 69	88.656 64	.001 272 265
787	619 369	28.053 52	88.713 02	.001 270 648
788	620 944	28.071 34	88.769 36	.001 269 036
789	622 521	28.089 14	88.825 67	.001 267 427
790	624 100	28.106 94	88.881 94	0.001 265 823
791	625 681	28.124 72	88.938 18	.001 264 223
792	627 264	28.142 49	88.994 38	.001 262 626
793	628 849	28.160 26	89.050 55	.001 261 034
794	630 436	28.178 01	89.106 68	.001 259 446
795	632 025	28.195 74	89.162 77	0.001 257 862
796	633 616	28.213 47	89.218 83	.001 256 281
797	635 209	28.231 19	89.274 86	.001 254 705
798	636 804	28.248 89	89.330 85	.001 253 133
799	638 401	28.266 59	89.386 80	.001 251 564
800	640 000	28.284 27	89.442 72	0.001 250 000
801	641 601	28.301 94	89.498 60	.001 248 439
802	643 204	28.319 60	89.554 45	.001 246 883
803	644 809	28.337 25	89.610 27	.001 245 330
804	646 416	28.354 89	89.666 05	.001 243 781
805	648 025	28.372 52	89.721 79	0.001 242 236
806	649 636	28.390 14	89.777 50	.001 240 695
807	651 249	28.407 75	89.833 18	.001 239 157
808	652 864	28.425 34	89.888 82	.001 237 624
809	654 481	28.442 93	89.944 43	.001 236 094
810	656 100	28.460 50	90.000 00	0.001 234 568
811	657 721	28.478 06	90.055 54	.001 233 046
812	659 344	28.495 61	90.111 04	.001 231 527
813	660 969	28.513 15	90.166 51	.001 230 012
814	662 596	28.530 69	90.221 95	.001 228 501
815	664 225	28.548 20	90.227 35	0.001 226 994
816	665 856	28.565 71	90.332 72	.001 225 490
817	667 489	28.583 21	90.388 05	.001 223 990
818	669 124	28.600 70	90.443 35	.001 222 494
819	670 761	28.618 18	90.498 62	.001 221 001
820	672 400	28.635 64	90.553 85	0.001 219 512
821	674 041	28.653 10	90.609 05	.001 218 027
822	675 684	28.670 54	90.664 22	.001 216 545
823	677 329	28.687 98	90.719 35	.001 215 067
824	678 976	28.705 40	90.774 45	.001 213 592
825	680 625	28.722 81	90.829 51	0.001 212 121
826	682 276	28.740 22	90.884 54	.001 210 654
827	683 929	28.757 61	90.939 54	.001 209 190
828	685 584	28.774 99	90.994 51	.001 207 729
829	687 241	28.792 36	91.049 44	.001 206 273

TABLE XIII. SQUARES, SQUARE ROOTS, AND RECIPROCALS
(Continued)

n	n^2	$\sqrt{n}$	$\sqrt{10n}$	$1/n$
830	688 900	28.809 72	91.104 34	0.001 204 819
831	690 561	28.827 07	91.159 20	.001 203 369
832	692 224	28.844 41	91.214 03	.001 201 923
833	693 889	28.861 74	91.268 83	.001 200 480
834	695 556	28.879 06	91.323 60	.001 199 041
835	697 225	28.896 37	91.378 33	0.001 197 605
836	698 896	28.913 66	91.433 04	.001 196 172
837	700 569	28.930 95	91.487 70	.001 194 743
838	702 244	28.948 23	91.542 34	.001 193 317
839	703 921	28.965 50	91.596 94	.001 191 895
840	705 600	28.982 75	91.651 51	0.001 190 476
841	707 281	29.000 00	91.706 05	.001 189 061
842	708 964	29.017 24	91.760 56	.001 187 648
843	710 649	29.034 46	91.815 03	.001 186 240
844	712 336	29.051 68	91.869 47	.001 184 834
845	714 025	29.068 88	91.923 88	0.001 183 432
846	715 716	29.086 08	91.978 26	.001 182 033
847	717 409	29.103 26	92.032 60	.001 180 638
848	719 104	29.120 44	92.086 92	.001 179 245
849	720 801	29.137 60	92.141 20	.001 177 856
850	722 500	29.154 76	92.195 44	0.001 176 471
851	724 201	29.171 90	92.249 66	.001 175 088
852	725 904	29.189 04	92.303 85	.001 173 709
853	727 609	29.206 16	92.358 00	.001 172 333
854	729 316	29.223 28	92.412 12	.001 170 960
855	731 025	29.240 38	92.466 21	0.001 169 591
856	732 736	29.257 48	92.520 27	.001 168 224
857	734 449	29.274 56	92.574 29	.001 166 861
858	736 164	29.291 64	92.628 29	.001 165 501
859	737 881	29.308 70	92.682 25	.001 164 144
860	739 600	29.325 76	92.736 18	0.001 162 791
861	741 321	29.342 80	92.790 09	.001 161 440
862	743 044	29.359 84	92.843 96	.001 160 093
863	744 769	29.376 86	92.897 79	.001 158 749
864	746 496	29.393 88	92.951 60	.001 157 407
865	748 225	29.410 88	93.005 38	0.001 156 069
866	749 956	29.427 88	93.059 12	.001 154 734
867	751 689	29.444 86	93.112 83	.001 153 403
868	753 424	29.461 84	93.166 52	.001 152 074
869	755 161	29.478 81	93.220 17	.001 150 748
870	756 900	29.495 76	93.273 79	0.001 149 425
871	758 641	29.512 71	93.327 38	.001 148 106
872	760 384	29.529 65	93.380 94	.001 146 789
873	762 129	29.546 57	93.434 47	.001 145 475
874	763 876	29.563 49	93.487 97	.001 144 165
875	765 625	29.580 40	93.541 43	0.001 142 857
876	767 376	29.597 30	93.594 87	.001 141 553
877	769 129	29.614 19	93.648 28	.001 140 251
878	770 884	29.631 06	93.701 65	.001 138 952
879	772 641	29.647 93	93.755 00	.001 137 656
880	774 400	29.664 79	93.808 32	0.001 136 364
881	776 161	29.681 64	93.861 60	.001 135 074
882	777 924	29.698 48	93.914 86	.001 133 787
883	779 689	29.715 32	93.968 08	.001 132 503
884	781 456	29.732 14	94.021 27	.001 131 222
885	783 225	29.748 95	94.074 44	0.001 129 944
886	784 996	29.765 75	94.127 57	.001 128 668
887	786 769	29.782 55	94.180 68	.001 127 396
888	788 544	29.799 33	94.233 75	.001 126 126
889	790 321	29.816 10	94.286 80	.001 124 859

TABLE XIII. SQUARES, SQUARE ROOTS, AND RECIPROCALS
(Continued)

n	n^2	$\sqrt{n}$	$\sqrt{10n}$	$1/n$
890	792 100	29.832 87	94.339 81	0.001 123 596
891	793 881	29.849 62	94.392 80	.001 122 334
892	795 664	29.866 37	94.445 75	.001 121 076
893	797 449	29.883 11	94.498 68	.001 119 821
894	799 236	29.899 83	94.551 57	.001 118 568
895	801 025	29.916 55	94.604 44	0.001 117 318
896	802 816	29.933 26	94.657 28	.001 116 071
897	804 609	29.949 96	94.710 08	.001 114 827
898	806 404	29.966 65	94.762 86	.001 113 586
899	808 201	29.983 33	94.815 61	.001 112 347
900	810 000	30.000 00	94.868 33	0.001 111 111
901	811 801	30.016 66	94.921 02	.001 109 878
902	813 604	30.033 31	94.973 68	.001 108 647
903	815 409	30.049 96	95.026 31	.001 107 420
904	817 216	30.066 59	95.078 91	.001 106 195
905	819 025	30.083 22	95.131 49	0.001 104 972
906	820 836	30.099 83	95.184 03	.001 103 753
907	822 649	30.116 44	95.236 55	.001 102 536
908	824 464	30.133 04	95.289 03	.001 101 322
909	826 281	30.149 63	95.341 49	.001 100 110
910	828 100	30.166 21	95.393 92	0.001 098 901
911	829 921	30.182 78	95.446 32	.001 097 695
912	831 744	30.199 34	95.498 69	.001 096 491
913	833 569	30.215 89	95.551 03	.001 095 290
914	835 396	30.232 43	95.603 35	.001 094 092
915	837 225	30.248 97	95.655 63	0.001 092 896
916	839 056	30.265 49	95.707 89	.001 091 703
917	840 889	30.282 01	95.760 12	.001 090 513
918	842 724	30.298 51	95.812 32	.001 089 325
919	844 561	30.315 01	95.864 49	.001 088 139
920	846 400	30.331 50	95.916 63	0.001 086 957
921	848 241	30.347 98	95.968 74	.001 085 776
922	850 084	30.364 45	96.020 83	.001 084 599
923	851 929	30.380 92	96.072 89	.001 083 494
924	853 776	30.397 37	96.124 92	.001 082 251
925	855 625	30.413 81	96.176 92	0.001 081 081
926	857 476	30.430 25	96.228 89	.001 079 914
927	859 329	30.446 67	96.280 84	.001 078 749
928	861 184	30.463 09	96.332 76	.001 077 586
929	863 041	30.479 50	96.384 65	.001 076 426
930	864 900	30.495 90	96.436 51	0.001 075 269
931	866 761	30.512 29	96.488 34	.001 074 114
932	868 624	30.528 68	96.540 15	.001 072 961
933	870 489	30.545 05	96.591 93	.001 071 811
934	872 356	30.561 41	96.643 68	.001 070 664
935	874 225	30.577 77	96.695 40	0.001 069 519
936	876 096	30.594 12	96.747 09	.001 068 376
937	877 969	30.610 46	96.798 76	.001 067 236
938	879 844	30.626 79	96.850 40	.001 066 098
939	881 721	30.643 11	96.902 01	.001 064 963
940	883 600	30.659 42	96.953 60	0.001 063 830
941	885 481	30.675 72	97.005 15	.001 062 699
942	887 364	30.692 02	97.056 68	.001 061 571
943	889 249	30.708 31	97.108 19	.001 060 445
944	891 136	30.724 58	97.159 66	.001 059 322
945	893 025	30.740 85	97.211 11	0.001 058 201
946	894 916	30.757 11	97.262 53	.001 057 082
947	896 809	30.773 37	97.313 93	.001 055 966
948	898 704	30.789 61	97.365 29	.001 054 852
949	900 601	30.805 84	97.416 63	.001 053 741

TABLE XIII. SQUARES, SQUARE ROOTS, AND RECIPROCALS
(Continued)

n	n^2	$\sqrt{n}$	$\sqrt{10n}$	$1/n$
950	902 500	30.822 07	97.467 94	0.001 052 632
951	904 401	30.838 29	97.519 23	.001 051 525
952	906 304	30.854 50	97.570 49	.001 050 420
953	908 209	30.870 70	97.621 72	.001 049 318
954	910 116	30.886 89	97.672 92	.001 048 218
955	912 025	30.903 07	97.724 10	0.001 047 120
956	913 936	30.919 25	97.775 25	.001 046 025
957	915 849	30.935 42	97.826 38	.001 044 932
958	917 764	30.951 58	97.877 47	.001 043 841
959	919 681	30.967 73	97.928 55	.001 042 753
960	921 600	30.983 87	97.979 59	0.001 041 667
961	923 521	31.000 00	98.030 61	.001 040 583
962	925 444	31.016 12	98.081 60	.001 039 501
963	927 369	31.032 24	98.132 56	.001 038 422
964	929 296	31.048 35	98.183 50	.001 037 344
965	931 225	31.064 45	98.234 41	0.001 036 269
966	933 156	31.080 54	98.285 30	.001 035 197
967	935 089	31.096 62	98.336 16	.001 034 126
968	937 024	31.112 70	98.386 99	.001 033 058
969	938 961	31.128 76	98.437 80	.001 031 992
970	940 900	31.144 82	98.488 58	0.001 030 928
971	942 841	31.160 87	98.539 33	.001 029 866
972	944 784	31.176 91	98.590 06	.001 028 807
973	946 729	31.192 95	98.640 76	.001 027 749
974	948 676	31.208 97	98.691 44	.001 026 694
975	950 625	31.224 99	98.742 09	0.001 025 641
976	952 576	31.241 00	98.792 71	.001 024 590
977	954 529	31.257 00	98.843 31	.001 023 541
978	956 484	31.272 99	98.893 88	.001 022 495
979	958 441	31.288 98	98.944 43	.001 021 450
980	960 400	31.304 95	98.994 95	0.001 020 408
981	962 361	31.320 92	99.045 44	.001 019 368
982	964 324	31.336 88	99.095 91	.001 018 330
983	966 289	31.352 83	99.146 36	.001 017 294
984	968 256	31.368 77	99.196 77	.001 016 260
985	970 225	31.384 71	99.247 17	0.001 015 228
986	972 196	31.400 64	99.297 53	.001 014 199
987	974 169	31.416 56	99.347 87	.001 013 171
988	976 144	31.432 47	99.398 19	.001 012 146
989	978 121	31.448 37	99.448 48	.001 011 122
990	980 100	31.464 27	99.498 74	0.001 010 101
991	982 081	31.480 15	99.548 98	.001 009 082
992	984 064	31.496 03	99.599 20	.001 008 065
993	986 049	31.511 90	99.649 39	.001 007 049
994	988 036	31.527 77	99.699 55	.001 006 036
995	990 025	31.543 62	99.749 69	0.001 005 025
996	992 016	31.559 47	99.799 80	.001 004 016
997	994 009	31.575 31	99.849 89	.001 003 009
998	996 004	31.591 14	99.899 95	.001 002 004
999	998 001	31.606 96	99.949 99	.001 001 001

TABLE XIV. VALUES OF THE EXPONENTIAL e^{-x}

x	e^{-x}	x	e^{-x}	x	e^{-x}	x	e^{-x}
0.00	1.000000	0.50	0.606531	1.00	0.367879	1.50	0.223130
.01	0.990050	.51	.600496	.01	.364219	.51	.220910
.02	.980199	.52	.594521	.02	.360595	.52	.218712
.03	.970446	.53	.588605	.03	.357007	.53	.216536
.04	.960789	.54	.582748	.04	.353455	.54	.214381
0.05	0.951229	0.55	0.576950	1.05	0.349938	1.55	0.212248
.06	.941765	.56	.571209	.06	.346456	.56	.210136
.07	.932394	.57	.565525	.07	.343009	.57	.208045
.08	.923116	.58	.559898	.08	.339596	.58	.205975
.09	.913931	.59	.554327	.09	.336216	.59	.203926
0.10	0.904837	0.60	0.548812	1.10	0.332871	1.60	0.201897
.11	.895834	.61	.543351	.11	.329559	.61	.199888
.12	.886920	.62	.537944	.12	.326280	.62	.197899
.13	.878095	.63	.532592	.13	.323033	.63	.195930
.14	.869358	.64	.527292	.14	.319819	.64	.193980
0.15	0.860708	0.65	0.522046	1.15	0.316637	1.65	0.192050
.16	.852144	.66	.516851	.16	.313486	.66	.190139
.17	.843665	.67	.511709	.17	.310367	.67	.188247
.18	.835270	.68	.506617	.18	.307279	.68	.186374
.19	.826959	.69	.501576	.19	.304221	.69	.184520
0.20	0.818731	0.70	0.496585	1.20	0.301194	1.70	0.182684
.21	.810584	.71	.491644	.21	.298197	.71	.180866
.22	.802519	.72	.486752	.22	.295230	.72	.179066
.23	.794534	.73	.481909	.23	.292293	.73	.177284
.24	.786628	.74	.477114	.24	.289384	.74	.175520
0.25	0.778801	0.75	0.472367	1.25	0.286505	1.75	0.173774
.26	.771052	.76	.467666	.26	.283654	.76	.172045
.27	.763379	.77	.463013	.27	.280832	.77	.170333
.28	.755784	.78	.458406	.28	.278037	.78	.168638
.29	.748264	.79	.453845	.29	.275271	.79	.166960
0.30	0.740818	0.80	0.449329	1.30	0.272532	1.80	0.165299
.31	.733447	.81	.444858	.31	.269820	.81	.163654
.32	.726149	.82	.440432	.32	.267135	.82	.162026
.33	.718924	.83	.436049	.33	.264477	.83	.160414
.34	.711770	.84	.431711	.34	.261846	.84	.158817
0.35	0.704688	0.85	0.427415	1.35	0.259240	1.85	0.157237
.36	.697676	.86	.423162	.36	.256661	.86	.155673
.37	.690734	.87	.418952	.37	.254107	.87	.154124
.38	.683861	.88	.414783	.38	.251579	.88	.152590
.39	.677057	.89	.410650	.39	.249075	.89	.151072
0.40	0.670320	0.90	0.406570	1.40	0.246597	1.90	0.149569
.41	.663650	.91	.402524	.41	.244143	.91	.148080
.42	.657047	.92	.398519	.42	.241714	.92	.146607
.43	.650509	.93	.394554	.43	.239309	.93	.145148
.44	.644036	.94	.390628	.44	.236928	.94	.143704
0.45	0.637628	0.95	0.386741	1.45	0.234570	1.95	0.142274
.46	.631284	.96	.382893	.46	.232236	.96	.140858
.47	.625002	.97	.379083	.47	.229925	.97	.139457
.48	.618783	.98	.375311	.48	.227638	.98	.138069
.49	.612626	.99	.371577	.49	.225373	.99	.136695
0.50	0.606531	1.00	0.367879	1.50	0.223130	2.00	0.135335

Table XIV is adapted from Table 19, "Exponential Functions," of Smithsonian Physical Tables, Ninth Edition, published by the Smithsonian Institution, Washington, D.C., by permission of Paul H. Oehser, Chief, Editorial and Publications Division.

TABLE XIV. VALUES OF THE EXPONENTIAL e^{-x}
(Continued)

x	e^{-x}	x	e^{-x}	x	e^{-x}	x	e^{-x}
2.00	0.135335	2.50	0.082085	3.00	0.049787	3.50	0.030197
.01	.133989	.51	.081268	.01	.049292	.51	.029897
.02	.132655	.52	.080460	.02	.048801	.52	.029599
.03	.131336	.53	.079659	.03	.048316	.53	.029305
.04	.130029	.54	.078866	.04	.047835	.54	.029013
2.05	0.128735	2.55	0.078082	3.05	0.047359	3.55	0.028725
.06	.127454	.56	.077305	.06	.046888	.56	.028439
.07	.126186	.57	.076536	.07	.046421	.57	.028156
.08	.124930	.58	.075774	.08	.045959	.58	.027876
.09	.123687	.59	.075020	.09	.045502	.59	.027598
2.10	0.122456	2.60	0.074274	3.10	0.045049	3.60	0.027324
.11	.121238	.61	.073535	.11	.044601	.61	.027052
.12	.120032	.62	.072803	.12	.044157	.62	.026783
.13	.118837	.63	.072078	.13	.043718	.63	.026516
.14	.117655	.64	.071361	.14	.043283	.64	.026252
2.15	0.116484	2.65	0.070651	3.15	0.042852	3.65	0.025991
.16	.115325	.66	.069948	.16	.042426	.66	.025733
.17	.114178	.67	.069252	.17	.042004	.67	.025476
.18	.113042	.68	.068563	.18	.041586	.68	.025223
.19	.111917	.69	.067881	.19	.041172	.69	.024972
2.20	0.110803	2.70	0.067206	3.20	0.040762	3.70	0.024724
.21	.109701	.71	.066537	.21	.040357	.71	.024478
.22	.108609	.72	.065875	.22	.039955	.72	.024234
.23	.107528	.73	.065219	.23	.039557	.73	.023993
.24	.106459	.74	.064570	.24	.039164	.74	.023754
2.25	0.105399	2.75	0.063928	3.25	0.038774	3.75	0.023518
.26	.104350	.76	.063292	.26	.038388	.76	.023284
.27	.103312	.77	.062662	.27	.038006	.77	.023052
.28	.102284	.78	.062039	.28	.037628	.78	.022823
.29	.101266	.79	.061421	.29	.037254	.79	.022596
2.30	0.100259	2.80	0.060810	3.30	0.036883	3.80	0.022371
.31	.099261	.81	.060205	.31	.036516	.81	.022148
.32	.098274	.82	.059606	.32	.036153	.82	.021928
.33	.097296	.83	.059013	.33	.035793	.83	.021710
.34	.096328	.84	.058426	.34	.035437	.84	.021494
2.35	0.095369	2.85	0.057844	3.35	0.035084	3.85	0.021280
.36	.094420	.86	.057269	.36	.034735	.86	.021068
.37	.093481	.87	.056699	.37	.034390	.87	.020858
.38	.092551	.88	.056135	.38	.034047	.88	.020651
.39	.091630	.89	.055576	.39	.033709	.89	.020445
2.40	0.090718	2.90	0.055023	3.40	0.033373	3.90	0.020242
.41	.089815	.91	.054476	.41	.033041	.91	.020041
.42	.088922	.92	.053934	.42	.032712	.92	.019841
.43	.088037	.93	.053397	.43	.032387	.93	.019644
.44	.087161	.94	.052866	.44	.032065	.94	.019448
2.45	0.086294	2.95	0.052340	3.45	0.031746	3.95	0.019255
.46	.085435	.96	.051819	.46	.031430	.96	.019063
.47	.084585	.97	.051303	.47	.031117	.97	.018873
.48	.083743	.98	.050793	.48	.030807	.98	.018686
.49	.082910	.99	.050287	.49	.030501	.99	.018500
2.50	0.082085	3.00	0.049787	3.50	0.030197	4.00	0.018316

TABLE XIV. VALUES OF THE EXPONENTIAL e^{-x}
(Continued)

x	e^{-x}	x	e^{-x}	x	e^{-x}	x	e^{-x}
4.00	0.018316	4.50	0.011109	5.00	0.006738	5.0	0.006738
.01	.018133	.51	.010998	.01	.006671	.1	.006097
.02	.017953	.52	.010889	.02	.006605	.2	.005517
.03	.017774	.53	.010781	.03	.006539	.3	.004992
.04	.017597	.54	.010673	.04	.006474	.4	.004517
4.05	0.017422	4.55	0.010567	5.05	0.006409	5.5	0.004087
.06	.017249	.56	.010462	.06	.006346	.6	.003698
.07	.017077	.57	.010358	.07	.006282	.7	.003346
.08	.016907	.58	.010255	.08	.006220	.8	.003028
.09	.016739	.59	.010153	.09	.006158	.9	.002739
4.10	0.016573	4.60	0.010052	5.10	0.006097	6.0	0.002479
.11	.016408	.61	.009952	.11	.006036	.1	.002243
.12	.016245	.62	.009853	.12	.005976	.2	.002029
.13	.016083	.63	.009755	.13	.005917	.3	.001836
.14	.015923	.64	.009658	.14	.005858	.4	.001662
4.15	0.015764	4.65	0.009562	5.15	0.005799	6.5	0.001503
.16	.015608	.66	.009466	.16	.005742	.6	.001360
.17	.015452	.67	.009372	.17	.005685	.7	.001231
.18	.015299	.68	.009279	.18	.005628	.8	.001114
.19	.015146	.69	.009187	.19	.005572	.9	.001008
4.20	0.014996	4.70	0.009095	5.20	0.005517	7.0	0.000912
.21	.014846	.71	.009005	.21	.005462	.1	.000825
.22	.014699	.72	.008915	.22	.005407	.2	.000747
.23	.014552	.73	.008826	.23	.005354	.3	.000676
.24	.014408	.74	.008739	.24	.005300	.4	.000611
4.25	0.014264	4.75	0.008652	5.25	0.005248	7.5	0.000553
.26	.014122	.76	.008566	.26	.005195	.6	.000500
.27	.013982	.77	.008480	.27	.005144	.7	.000453
.28	.013843	.78	.008396	.28	.005092	.8	.000410
.29	.013705	.79	.008312	.29	.005042	.9	.000371
4.30	0.013569	4.80	0.008230	5.30	0.004992	8.0	0.000335
.31	.013434	.81	.008148	.31	.004942	.1	.000304
.32	.013300	.82	.008067	.32	.004893	.2	.000275
.33	.013168	.83	.007987	.33	.004844	.3	.000249
.34	.013037	.84	.007907	.34	.004796	.4	.000225
4.35	0.012907	4.85	0.007828	5.35	0.004748	8.5	0.000203
.36	.012778	.86	.007750	.36	.004701	.6	.000184
.37	.012651	.87	.007673	.37	.004654	.7	.000167
.38	.012525	.88	.007597	.38	.004608	.8	.000151
.39	.012401	.89	.007521	.39	.004562	.9	.000136
4.40	0.012277	4.90	0.007447	5.40	0.004517	9.0	0.000123
.41	.012155	.91	.007372	.41	.004472	.1	.000112
.42	.012034	.92	.007299	.42	.004427	.2	.000101
.43	.011914	.93	.007227	.43	.004383	.3	.000091
.44	.011796	.94	.007155	.44	.004339	.4	.000083
4.45	0.011679	4.95	0.007083	5.45	0.004296	9.5	0.000075
.46	.011562	.96	.007013	.46	.004254	.6	.000068
.47	.011447	.97	.006943	.47	.004211	.7	.000061
.48	.011333	.98	.006874	.48	.004169	.8	.000055
.49	.011221	.99	.006806	.49	.004128	.9	.000050
4.50	0.011109	5.00	0.006738	5.50	0.004087	10.0	0.000045

TABLE XV

COMMON LOGARITHMS OF NUMBERS
FROM
1 TO 10009
TO
FIVE DECIMAL PLACES

1–100

N	Log	N	Log	N	Log	N	Log	N	Log
0	—	20	1.30 103	40	1.60 206	60	1.77 815	80	1.90 309
1	0.00 000	21	1.32 222	41	1.61 278	61	1.78 533	81	1.90 849
2	0.30 103	22	1.34 242	42	1.62 325	62	1.79 239	82	1.91 381
3	0.47 712	23	1.36 173	43	1.63 347	63	1.79 934	83	1.91 908
4	0.60 206	24	1.38 021	44	1.64 345	64	1.80 618	84	1.92 428
5	0.69 897	25	1.39 794	45	1.65 321	65	1.81 291	85	1.92 942
6	0.77 815	26	1.41 497	46	1.66 276	66	1.81 954	86	1.93 450
7	0.84 510	27	1.43 136	47	1.67 210	67	1.82 607	87	1.93 952
8	0.90 309	28	1.44 716	48	1.68 124	68	1.83 251	88	1.94 448
9	0.95 424	29	1.46 240	49	1.69 020	69	1.83 885	89	1.94 939
10	1.00 000	30	1.47 712	50	1.69 897	70	1.84 510	90	1.95 424
11	1.04 139	31	1.49 136	51	1.70 757	71	1.85 126	91	1.95 904
12	1.07 918	32	1.50 515	52	1.71 600	72	1.85 733	92	1.96 379
13	1.11 394	33	1.51 851	53	1.72 428	73	1.86 332	93	1.96 848
14	1.14 613	34	1.53 148	54	1.73 239	74	1.86 923	94	1.97 313
15	1.17 609	35	1.54 407	55	1.74 036	75	1.87 506	95	1.97 772
16	1.20 412	36	1.55 630	56	1.74 819	76	1.88 081	96	1.98 227
17	1.23 045	37	1.56 820	57	1.75 587	77	1.88 649	97	1.98 677
18	1.25 527	38	1.57 978	58	1.76 343	78	1.89 209	98	1.99 123
19	1.27 875	39	1.59 106	59	1.77 085	79	1.89 763	99	1.99 564
20	1.30 103	40	1.60 206	60	1.77 815	80	1.90 309	100	2.00 000

N	0	1	2	3	4	5	6	7	8	9	Prop. Pts.
100	00 000	043	087	130	173	217	260	303	346	389	
101	432	475	518	561	604	647	689	732	775	817	
102	860	903	945	988	*030	*072	*115	*157	*199	*242	
103	01 284	326	368	410	452	494	536	578	620	662	
104	703	745	787	828	870	912	953	995	*036	*078	
105	02 119	160	202	243	284	325	366	407	449	490	
106	531	572	612	653	694	735	776	816	857	898	
107	938	979	*019	*060	*100	*141	*181	*222	*262	*302	
108	03 342	383	423	463	503	543	583	623	663	703	
109	743	782	822	862	902	941	981	*021	*060	*100	
110	04 139	179	218	258	297	336	376	415	454	493	
111	532	571	610	650	689	727	766	805	844	883	
112	922	961	999	*038	*077	*115	*154	*192	*231	*269	
113	05 308	346	385	423	461	500	538	576	614	652	
114	690	729	767	805	843	881	918	956	994	*032	
115	06 070	108	145	183	221	258	296	333	371	408	
116	446	483	521	558	595	633	670	707	744	781	
117	819	856	893	930	967	*004	*041	*078	*115	*151	
118	07 188	225	262	298	335	372	408	445	482	518	
119	555	591	628	664	700	737	773	809	846	882	
120	918	954	990	*027	*063	*099	*135	*171	*207	*243	
121	08 279	314	350	386	422	458	493	529	565	600	
122	636	672	707	743	778	814	849	884	920	955	
123	991	*026	*061	*096	*132	*167	*202	*237	*272	*307	
124	09 342	377	412	447	482	517	552	587	621	656	
125	691	726	760	795	830	864	899	934	968	*003	
126	10 037	072	106	140	175	209	243	278	312	346	
127	380	415	449	483	517	551	585	619	653	687	
128	721	755	789	823	857	890	924	958	992	*025	
129	11 059	093	126	160	193	227	261	294	327	361	
130	394	428	461	494	528	561	594	628	661	694	
131	727	760	793	826	860	893	926	959	992	*024	
132	12 057	090	123	156	189	222	254	287	320	352	
133	385	418	450	483	516	548	581	613	646	678	
134	710	743	775	808	840	872	905	937	969	*001	
135	13 033	066	098	130	162	194	226	258	290	322	
136	354	386	418	450	481	513	545	577	609	640	
137	672	704	735	767	799	830	862	893	925	956	
138	988	*019	*051	*082	*114	*145	*176	*208	*239	*270	
139	14 301	333	364	395	426	457	489	520	551	582	
140	613	644	675	706	737	768	799	829	860	891	
141	922	953	983	*014	*045	*076	*106	*137	*168	*198	
142	15 229	259	290	320	351	381	412	442	473	503	
143	534	564	594	625	655	685	715	746	776	806	
144	836	866	897	927	957	987	*017	*047	*077	*107	
145	16 137	167	197	227	256	286	316	346	376	406	
146	435	465	495	524	554	584	613	643	673	702	
147	732	761	791	820	850	879	909	938	967	997	
148	17 026	056	085	114	143	173	202	231	260	289	
149	319	348	377	406	435	464	493	522	551	580	
150	609	638	667	696	725	754	782	811	840	869	
N	0	1	2	3	4	5	6	7	8	9	Prop. Pts.

Prop. Pts.

	44	43	42
1	4.4	4.3	4.2
2	8.8	8.6	8.4
3	13.2	12.9	12.6
4	17.6	17.2	16.8
5	22.0	21.5	21.0
6	26.4	25.8	25.2
7	30.8	30.1	29.4
8	35.2	34.4	33.6
9	39.6	38.7	37.8

	41	40	39
1	4.1	4.0	3.9
2	8.2	8.0	7.8
3	12.3	12.0	11.7
4	16.4	16.0	15.6
5	20.5	20.0	19.5
6	24.6	24.0	23.4
7	28.7	28.0	27.3
8	32.8	32.0	31.2
9	36.9	36.0	35.1

	38	37	36
1	3.8	3.7	3.6
2	7.6	7.4	7.2
3	11.4	11.1	10.8
4	15.2	14.8	14.4
5	19.0	18.5	18.0
6	22.8	22.2	21.6
7	26.6	25.9	25.2
8	30.4	29.6	28.8
9	34.2	33.3	32.4

	35	34	33
1	3.5	3.4	3.3
2	7.0	6.8	6.6
3	10.5	10.2	9.9
4	14.0	13.6	13.2
5	17.5	17.0	16.5
6	21.0	20.4	19.8
7	24.5	23.8	23.1
8	28.0	27.2	26.4
9	31.5	30.6	29.7

	32	31	30
1	3.2	3.1	3.0
2	6.4	6.2	6.0
3	9.6	9.3	9.0
4	12.8	12.4	12.0
5	16.0	15.5	15.0
6	19.2	18.6	18.0
7	22.4	21.7	21.0
8	25.6	24.8	24.0
9	28.8	27.9	27.0

N	0	1	2	3	4	5	6	7	8	9	Prop. Pts.
150	17 609	638	667	696	725	754	782	811	840	869	
151	898	926	955	984	*013	*041	*070	*099	*127	*156	
152	18 184	213	241	270	298	327	355	384	412	441	
153	469	498	526	554	583	611	639	667	696	724	
154	752	780	808	837	865	893	921	949	977	*005	
155	19 033	061	089	117	145	173	201	229	257	285	
156	312	340	368	396	424	451	479	507	535	562	
157	590	618	645	673	700	728	756	783	811	838	
158	866	893	921	948	976	*003	*030	*058	*085	*112	
159	20 140	167	194	222	249	276	303	330	358	385	
160	412	439	466	493	520	548	575	602	629	656	
161	683	710	737	763	790	817	844	871	898	925	
162	952	978	*005	*032	*059	*085	*112	*139	*165	*192	
163	21 219	245	272	299	325	352	378	405	431	458	
164	484	511	537	564	590	617	643	669	696	722	
165	748	775	801	827	854	880	906	932	958	985	
166	22 011	037	063	089	115	141	167	194	220	246	
167	272	298	324	350	376	401	427	453	479	505	
168	531	557	583	608	634	660	686	712	737	763	
169	789	814	840	866	891	917	943	968	994	*019	
170	23 045	070	096	121	147	172	198	223	249	274	
171	300	325	350	376	401	426	452	477	502	528	
172	553	578	603	629	654	679	704	729	754	779	
173	805	830	855	880	905	930	955	980	*005	*030	
174	24 055	080	105	130	155	180	204	229	254	279	
175	304	329	353	378	403	428	452	477	502	527	
176	551	576	601	625	650	674	699	724	748	773	
177	797	822	846	871	895	920	944	969	993	*018	
178	25 042	066	091	115	139	164	188	212	237	261	
179	285	310	334	358	382	406	431	455	479	503	
180	527	551	575	600	624	648	672	696	720	744	
181	768	792	816	840	864	888	912	935	959	983	
182	26 007	031	055	079	102	126	150	174	198	221	
183	245	269	293	316	340	364	387	411	435	458	
184	482	505	529	553	576	600	623	647	670	694	
185	717	741	764	788	811	834	858	881	905	928	
186	951	975	998	*021	*045	*068	*091	*114	*138	*161	
187	27 184	207	231	254	277	300	323	346	370	393	
188	416	439	462	485	508	531	554	577	600	623	
189	646	669	692	715	738	761	784	807	830	852	
190	875	898	921	944	967	989	*012	*035	*058	*081	
191	28 103	126	149	171	194	217	240	262	285	307	
192	330	353	375	398	421	443	466	488	511	533	
193	556	578	601	623	646	668	691	713	735	758	
194	780	803	825	847	870	892	914	937	959	981	
195	29 003	026	048	070	092	115	137	159	181	203	
196	226	248	270	292	314	336	358	380	403	425	
197	447	469	491	513	535	557	579	601	623	645	
198	667	688	710	732	754	776	798	820	842	863	
199	885	907	929	951	973	994	*016	*038	*060	*081	
200	30 103	125	146	168	190	211	233	255	276	298	
N	0	1	2	3	4	5	6	7	8	9	Prop. Pts.

Prop. Pts.

	29	28
1	2.9	2.8
2	5.8	5.6
3	8.7	8.4
4	11.6	11.2
5	14.5	14.0
6	17.4	16.8
7	20.3	19.6
8	23.2	22.4
9	26.1	25.2

	27	26
1	2.7	2.6
2	5.4	5.2
3	8.1	7.8
4	10.8	10.4
5	13.5	13.0
6	16.2	15.6
7	18.9	18.2
8	21.6	20.8
9	24.3	23.4

	25
1	2.5
2	5.0
3	7.5
4	10.0
5	12.5
6	15.0
7	17.5
8	20.0
9	22.5

	24	23
1	2.4	2.3
2	4.8	4.6
3	7.2	6.9
4	9.6	9.2
5	12.0	11.5
6	14.4	13.8
7	16.8	16.1
8	19.2	18.4
9	21.6	20.7

	22	21
1	2.2	2.1
2	4.4	4.2
3	6.6	6.3
4	8.8	8.4
5	11.0	10.5
6	13.2	12.6
7	15.4	14.7
8	17.6	16.8
9	19.8	18.9

N	0	1	2	3	4	5	6	7	8	9	Prop. Pts.
300	47 712	727	741	756	770	784	799	813	828	842	
301	857	871	885	900	914	929	943	958	972	986	
302	48 001	015	029	044	058	073	087	101	116	130	
303	144	159	173	187	202	216	230	244	259	273	
304	287	302	316	330	344	359	373	387	401	416	
305	430	444	458	473	487	501	515	530	544	558	
306	572	586	601	615	629	643	657	671	686	700	
307	714	728	742	756	770	785	799	813	827	841	
308	855	869	883	897	911	926	940	954	968	982	
309	996	*010	*024	*038	*052	*066	*080	*094	*108	*122	
310	49 136	150	164	178	192	206	220	234	248	262	
311	276	290	304	318	332	346	360	374	388	402	
312	415	429	443	457	471	485	499	513	527	541	
313	554	568	582	596	610	624	638	651	665	679	
314	693	707	721	734	748	762	776	790	803	817	
315	831	845	859	872	886	900	914	927	941	955	
316	969	982	996	*010	*024	*037	*051	*065	*079	*092	
317	50 106	120	133	147	161	174	188	202	215	229	
318	243	256	270	284	297	311	325	338	352	365	
319	379	393	406	420	433	447	461	474	488	501	
320	515	529	542	556	569	583	596	610	623	637	
321	651	664	678	691	705	718	732	745	759	772	
322	786	799	813	826	840	853	866	880	893	907	
323	920	934	947	961	974	987	*001	*014	*028	*041	
324	51 055	068	081	095	108	121	135	148	162	175	
325	188	202	215	228	242	255	268	282	295	308	
326	322	335	348	362	375	388	402	415	428	441	
327	455	468	481	495	508	521	534	548	561	574	
328	587	601	614	627	640	654	667	680	693	706	
329	720	733	746	759	772	786	799	812	825	838	
330	851	865	878	891	904	917	930	943	957	970	
331	983	996	*009	*022	*035	*048	*061	*075	*088	*101	
332	52 114	127	140	153	166	179	192	205	218	231	
333	244	257	270	284	297	310	323	336	349	362	
334	375	388	401	414	427	440	453	466	479	492	
335	504	517	530	543	556	569	582	595	608	621	
336	634	647	660	673	686	699	711	724	737	750	
337	763	776	789	802	815	827	840	853	866	879	
338	892	905	917	930	943	956	969	982	994	*007	
339	53 020	033	046	058	071	084	097	110	122	135	
340	148	161	173	186	199	212	224	237	250	263	
341	275	288	301	314	326	339	352	364	377	390	
342	403	415	428	441	453	466	479	491	504	517	
343	529	542	555	567	580	593	605	618	631	643	
344	656	668	681	694	706	719	732	744	757	769	
345	782	794	807	820	832	845	857	870	882	895	
346	908	920	933	945	958	970	983	995	*008	*020	
347	54 033	045	058	070	083	095	108	120	133	145	
348	158	170	183	195	208	220	233	245	258	270	
349	283	295	307	320	332	345	357	370	382	394	
350	407	419	432	444	456	469	481	494	506	518	
N	0	1	2	3	4	5	6	7	8	9	Prop. Pts.

Prop. Pts.

15
1 1.5
2 3.0
3 4.5
4 6.0
5 7.5
6 9.0
7 10.5
8 12.0
9 13.5

14
1 1.4
2 2.8
3 4.2
4 5.6
5 7.0
6 8.4
7 9.8
8 11.2
9 12.6

13
1 1.3
2 2.6
3 3.9
4 5.2
5 6.5
6 7.8
7 9.1
8 10.4
9 11.7

12
1 1.2
2 2.4
3 3.6
4 4.8
5 6.0
6 7.2
7 8.4
8 9.6
9 10.8

$\log \pi = 0.49715$

N	0	1	2	3	4	5	6	7	8	9
350	54 407	419	432	444	456	469	481	494	506	518
351	531	543	555	568	580	593	605	617	630	642
352	654	667	679	691	704	716	728	741	753	765
353	777	790	802	814	827	839	851	864	876	888
354	900	913	925	937	949	962	974	986	998	*011
355	55 023	035	047	060	072	084	096	108	121	133
356	145	157	169	182	194	206	218	230	242	255
357	267	279	291	303	315	328	340	352	364	376
358	388	400	413	425	437	449	461	473	485	497
359	509	522	534	546	558	570	582	594	606	618
360	630	642	654	666	678	691	703	715	727	739
361	751	763	775	787	799	811	823	835	847	859
362	871	883	895	907	919	931	943	955	967	979
363	991	*003	*015	*027	*038	*050	*062	*074	*086	*098
364	56 110	122	134	146	158	170	182	194	205	217
365	229	241	253	265	277	289	301	312	324	336
366	348	360	372	384	396	407	419	431	443	455
367	467	478	490	502	514	526	538	549	561	573
368	585	597	608	620	632	644	656	667	679	691
369	703	714	726	738	750	761	773	785	797	808
370	820	832	844	855	867	879	891	902	914	926
371	937	949	961	972	984	996	*008	*019	*031	*043
372	57 054	066	078	089	101	113	124	136	148	159
373	171	183	194	206	217	229	241	252	264	276
374	287	299	310	322	334	345	357	368	380	392
375	403	415	426	438	449	461	473	484	496	507
376	519	530	542	553	565	576	588	600	611	623
377	634	646	657	669	680	692	703	715	726	738
378	749	761	772	784	795	807	818	830	841	852
379	864	875	887	898	910	921	933	944	955	967
380	978	990	*001	*013	*024	*035	*047	*058	*070	*081
381	58 092	104	115	127	138	149	161	172	184	195
382	206	218	229	240	252	263	274	286	297	309
383	320	331	343	354	365	377	388	399	410	422
384	433	444	456	467	478	490	501	512	524	535
385	546	557	569	580	591	602	614	625	636	647
386	659	670	681	692	704	715	726	737	749	760
387	771	782	794	805	816	827	838	850	861	872
388	883	894	906	917	928	939	950	961	973	984
389	995	*006	*017	*028	*040	*051	*062	*073	*084	*095
390	59 106	118	129	140	151	162	173	184	195	207
391	218	229	240	251	262	273	284	295	306	318
392	329	340	351	362	373	384	395	406	417	428
393	439	450	461	472	483	494	506	517	528	539
394	550	561	572	583	594	605	616	627	638	649
395	660	671	682	693	704	715	726	737	748	759
396	770	780	791	802	813	824	835	846	857	868
397	879	890	901	912	923	934	945	956	966	977
398	988	999	*010	*021	*032	*043	*054	*065	*076	*086
399	60 097	108	119	130	141	152	163	173	184	195
400	206	217	228	239	249	260	271	282	293	304
N	0	1	2	3	4	5	6	7	8	9

Prop. Pts.

	13
1	1.3
2	2.6
3	3.9
4	5.2
5	6.5
6	7.8
7	9.1
8	10.4
9	11.7

	12
1	1.2
2	2.4
3	3.6
4	4.8
5	6.0
6	7.2
7	8.4
8	9.6
9	10.8

	11
1	1.1
2	2.2
3	3.3
4	4.4
5	5.5
6	6.6
7	7.7
8	8.8
9	9.9

	10
1	1.0
2	2.0
3	3.0
4	4.0
5	5.0
6	6.0
7	7.0
8	8.0
9	9.0

N	0	1	2	3	4	5	6	7	8	9	Prop. Pts.	
400	60 206	217	228	239	249	260	271	282	293	304		
401	314	325	336	347	358	369	379	390	401	412		
402	423	433	444	455	466	477	487	498	509	520		
403	531	541	552	563	574	584	595	606	617	627		
404	638	649	660	670	681	692	703	713	724	735		
405	746	756	767	778	788	799	810	821	831	842		
406	853	863	874	885	895	906	917	927	938	949		
407	959	970	981	991	*013	*002	*023	*034	*045	*055		
408	61 066	077	087	098	109	119	130	140	151	162		
409	172	183	194	204	215	225	236	247	257	268		
												11
410	278	289	300	'310	321	331	342	352	363	374	1	1.1
411	384	395	405	416	426	437	448	458	469	479	2	2.2
412	490	500	511	521	532	542	553	563	574	584	3	3.3
413	595	606	616	627	637	648	658	669	679	690	4	4.4
414	700	711	721	731	742	752	763	773	784	794	5	5.5
											6	6.6
415	805	815	826	836	847	857	868	878	888	899	7	7.7
416	909	920	930	941	951	962	972	982	993	*003	8	8.8
417	62 014	024	034	045	055	066	076	086	097	107	9	9.9
418	118	128	138	149	159	170	180	190	201	211		
419	221	232	242	252	263	273	284	294	304	315		
420	325	335	346	356	366	377	387	397	408	418		10
421	428	439	449	459	469	480	490	500	511	521		
422	531	542	552	562	572	583	593	603	613	624	1	1.0
423	634	644	655	665	675	685	696	706	716	726	2	2.0
424	737	747	757	767	778	788	798	808	818	829	3	3.0
											4	4.0
425	839	849	859	870	880	890	900	910	921	931	5	5.0
426	941	951	961	972	982	992	*002	*012	*022	*033	6	6.0
427	63 043	053	063	073	083	094	104	114	124	134	7	7.0
428	144	155	165	175	185	195	205	215	225	236	8	8.0
429	246	256	266	276	286	296	306	317	327	337	9	9.0
430	347	357	367	377	387	397	407	417	428	438		
431	448	458	468	478	488	498	508	518	528	538		
432	548	558	568	579	589	599	609	619	629	639		9
433	649	659	669	679	689	699	709	719	729	739		
434	749	759	769	779	789	799	809	819	829	839	1	0.9
											2	1.8
435	849	859	869	879	889	899	909	919	929	939	3	2.7
436	949	959	969	979	988	998	*008	*018	*028	*038	4	3.6
437	64 048	058	068	078	088	098	108	118	128	137	5	4.5
438	147	157	167	177	187	197	207	217	227	237	6	5.4
439	246	256	266	276	286	296	306	316	326	335	7	6.3
											8	7.2
440	345	355	365	375	385	395	404	414	424	434	9	8.1
441	444	454	464	473	483	493	503	513	523	532		
442	542	552	562	572	582	591	601	611	621	631		
443	640	650	660	670	680	689	699	709	719	729		
444	738	748	758	768	777	787	797	807	816	826		
445	836	846	856	865	875	885	895	904	914	924		
446	933	943	953	963	972	982	992	*002	*011	*021		
447	65 031	040	050	060	070	079	089	099	108	118		
448	128	137	147	157	167	176	186	196	205	215		
449	225	234	244	254	263	273	283	292	302	312		
450	321	331	341	350	360	369	379	389	398	408		
N	0	1	2	3	4	5	6	7	8	9	Prop. Pts.	

N	0	1	2	3	4	5	6	7	8	9	Prop. Pts.
450	65 321	331	341	350	360	369	379	389	398	408	
451	418	427	437	447	456	466	475	485	495	504	
452	514	523	533	543	552	562	571	581	591	600	
453	610	619	629	639	648	658	667	677	686	696	
454	706	715	725	734	744	753	763	772	782	792	
455	801	811	820	830	839	849	858	868	877	887	
456	896	906	916	925	935	944	954	963	973	982	
457	992	*001	*011	*020	*030	*039	*049	*058	*068	*077	
458	66 087	096	106	115	124	134	143	153	162	172	
459	181	191	200	210	219	229	238	247	257	266	
460	276	285	295	304	314	323	332	342	351	361	**10**
461	370	380	389	398	408	417	427	436	445	455	1 1.0
462	464	474	483	492	502	511	521	530	539	549	2 2.0
463	558	567	577	586	596	605	614	624	633	642	3 3.0
464	652	661	671	680	689	699	708	717	727	736	4 4.0
465	745	755	764	773	783	792	801	811	820	829	5 5.0
466	839	848	857	867	876	885	894	904	913	922	6 6.0
467	932	941	950	960	969	978	987	997	*006	*015	7 7.0
468	67 025	034	043	052	062	071	080	089	099	108	8 8.0
469	117	127	136	145	154	164	173	182	191	201	9 9.0
470	210	219	228	237	247	256	265	274	284	293	**9**
471	302	311	321	330	339	348	357	367	376	385	
472	394	403	413	422	431	440	449	459	468	477	1 0.9
473	486	495	504	514	523	532	541	550	560	569	2 1.8
474	578	587	596	605	614	624	633	642	651	660	3 2.7
475	669	679	688	697	706	715	724	733	742	752	4 3.6
476	761	770	779	788	797	806	815	825	834	843	5 4.5
477	852	861	870	879	888	897	906	916	925	934	6 5.4
478	943	952	961	970	979	988	997	*006	*015	*024	7 6.3
479	68 034	043	052	061	070	079	088	097	106	115	8 7.2
480	124	133	142	151	160	169	178	187	196	205	9 8.1
481	215	224	233	242	251	260	269	278	287	296	
482	305	314	323	332	341	350	359	368	377	386	**8**
483	395	404	413	422	431	440	449	458	467	476	1 0.8
484	485	494	502	511	520	529	538	547	556	565	2 1.6
485	574	583	592	601	610	619	628	637	646	655	3 2.4
486	664	673	681	690	699	708	717	726	735	744	4 3.2
487	753	762	771	780	789	797	806	815	824	833	5 4.0
488	842	851	860	869	878	886	895	904	913	922	6 4.8
489	931	940	949	958	966	975	984	993	*002	*011	7 5.6
490	69 020	028	037	046	055	064	073	082	090	099	8 6.4
491	108	117	126	135	144	152	161	170	179	188	9 7.2
492	197	205	214	223	232	241	249	258	267	276	
493	285	294	302	311	320	329	338	346	355	364	
494	373	381	390	399	408	417	425	434	443	452	
495	461	469	478	487	496	504	513	522	531	539	
496	548	557	566	574	583	592	601	609	618	627	
497	636	644	653	662	671	679	688	697	705	714	
498	723	732	740	749	758	767	775	784	793	801	
499	810	819	827	836	845	854	862	871	880	888	
500	897	906	914	923	932	940	949	958	966	975	
N	0	1	2	3	4	5	6	7	8	9	Prop. Pts.

N	0	1	2	3	4	5	6	7	8	9	Prop. Pts.	
500	69 897	906	914	923	932	940	949	958	966	975		
501	984	992	*001	*010	*018	*027	*036	*044	*053	*062		
502	70 070	079	088	096	105	114	122	131	140	148		
503	157	165	174	183	191	200	209	217	226	234		
504	243	252	260	269	278	286	295	303	312	321		
505	329	338	346	355	364	372	381	389	398	406		
506	415	424	432	441	449	458	467	475	484	492		
507	501	509	518	526	535	544	552	561	569	578		
508	586	595	603	612	621	629	638	646	655	663		
509	672	680	689	697	706	714	723	731	740	749		
510	757	766	774	783	791	800	808	817	825	834		9
511	842	851	859	868	876	885	893	902	910	919	1	0.9
512	927	935	944	952	961	969	978	986	995	*003	2	1.8
513	71 012	020	029	037	046	054	063	071	079	088	3	2.7
514	096	105	113	122	130	139	147	155	164	172	4	3.6
											5	4.5
515	181	189	198	206	214	223	231	240	248	257	6	5.4
516	265	273	282	290	299	307	315	324	332	341	7	6.3
517	349	357	366	374	383	391	399	408	416	425	8	7.2
518	433	441	450	458	466	475	483	492	500	508	9	8.1
519	517	525	533	542	550	559	567	575	584	592		
520	600	609	617	625	634	642	650	659	667	675		
521	684	692	700	709	717	725	734	742	750	759		8
522	767	775	784	792	800	809	817	825	834	842	1	0.8
523	850	858	867	875	883	892	900	908	917	925	2	1.6
524	933	941	950	958	966	975	983	991	999	*008	3	2.4
											4	3.2
525	72 016	024	032	041	049	057	066	074	082	090	5	4.0
526	099	107	115	123	132	140	148	156	165	173	6	4.8
527	181	189	198	206	214	222	230	239	247	255	7	5.6
528	263	272	280	288	296	304	313	321	329	337	8	6.4
529	346	354	362	370	378	387	395	403	411	419	9	7.2
530	428	436	444	452	460	469	477	485	493	501		
531	509	518	526	534	542	550	558	567	575	583		
532	591	599	607	616	624	632	640	648	656	665		7
533	673	681	689	697	705	713	722	730	738	746	1	0.7
534	754	762	770	779	787	795	803	811	819	827	2	1.4
											3	2.1
535	835	843	852	860	868	876	884	892	900	908	4	2.8
536	916	925	933	941	949	957	965	973	981	989	5	3.5
537	997	*006	*014	*022	*030	*038	*046	*054	*062	*070	6	4.2
538	73 078	086	094	102	111	119	127	135	143	151	7	4.9
539	159	167	175	183	191	199	207	215	223	231	8	5.6
											9	6.3
540	239	247	255	263	272	280	288	296	304	312		
541	320	328	336	344	352	360	368	376	384	392		
542	400	408	416	424	432	440	448	456	464	472		
543	480	488	496	504	512	520	528	536	544	552		
544	560	568	576	584	592	600	608	616	624	632		
545	640	648	656	664	672	679	687	695	703	711		
546	719	727	735	743	751	759	767	775	783	791		
547	799	807	815	823	830	838	846	854	862	870		
548	878	886	894	902	910	918	926	933	941	949		
549	957	965	973	981	989	997	*005	*013	*020	*028		
550	74 036	044	052	060	068	076	084	092	099	107		
N	0	1	2	3	4	5	6	7	8	9	Prop. Pts.	

N	0	1	2	3	4	5	6	7	8	9	Prop. Pts.
550	74 036	044	052	060	068	076	084	092	099	107	
551	115	123	131	139	147	155	162	170	178	186	
552	194	202	210	218	225	233	241	249	257	265	
553	273	280	288	296	304	312	320	327	335	343	
554	351	359	367	374	382	390	398	406	414	421	
555	429	437	445	453	461	468	476	484	492	500	
556	507	515	523	531	539	547	554	562	570	578	
557	586	593	601	609	617	624	632	640	648	656	
558	663	671	679	687	695	702	710	718	726	733	
559	741	749	757	764	772	780	788	796	803	811	
560	819	827	834	842	850	858	865	873	881	889	
561	896	904	912	920	927	935	943	950	958	966	
562	974	981	989	997	*005	*012	*020	*028	*035	*043	
563	75 051	059	066	074	082	089	097	105	113	120	
564	128	136	143	151	159	166	174	182	189	197	
565	205	213	220	228	236	243	251	259	266	274	8
566	282	289	297	305	312	320	328	335	343	351	1 0.8
567	358	366	374	381	389	397	404	412	420	427	2 1.6
568	435	442	450	458	465	473	481	488	496	504	3 2.4
569	511	519	526	534	542	549	557	565	572	580	4 3.2 / 5 4.0
570	587	595	603	610	618	626	633	641	648	656	6 4.8
571	664	671	679	686	694	702	709	717	724	732	7 5.6
572	740	747	755	762	770	778	785	793	800	808	8 6.4
573	815	823	831	838	846	853	861	868	876	884	9 7.2
574	891	899	906	914	921	929	937	944	952	959	
575	967	974	982	989	997	*005	*012	*020	*027	*035	
576	76 042	050	057	065	072	080	087	095	103	110	7
577	118	125	133	140	148	155	163	170	178	185	
578	193	200	208	215	223	230	238	245	253	260	1 0.7
579	268	275	283	290	298	305	313	320	328	335	2 1.4 / 3 2.1
580	343	350	358	365	373	380	388	395	403	410	4 2.8
581	418	425	433	440	448	455	462	470	477	485	5 3.5
582	492	500	507	515	522	530	537	545	552	559	6 4.2
583	567	574	582	589	597	604	612	619	626	634	7 4.9
584	641	649	656	664	671	678	686	693	701	708	8 5.6 / 9 6.3
585	716	723	730	738	745	753	760	768	775	782	
586	790	797	805	812	819	827	834	842	849	856	
587	864	871	879	886	893	901	908	916	923	930	
588	938	945	953	960	967	975	982	989	997	*004	
589	77 012	019	026	034	041	048	056	063	070	078	
590	085	093	100	107	115	122	129	137	144	151	
591	159	166	173	181	188	195	203	210	217	225	
592	232	240	247	254	262	269	276	283	291	298	
593	305	313	320	327	335	342	349	357	364	371	
594	379	386	393	401	408	415	422	430	437	444	
595	452	459	466	474	481	488	495	503	510	517	
596	525	532	539	546	554	561	568	576	583	590	
597	597	605	612	619	627	634	641	648	656	663	
598	670	677	685	692	699	706	714	721	728	735	
599	743	750	757	764	772	779	786	793	801	808	
600	815	822	830	837	844	851	859	866	873	880	
N	0	1	2	3	4	5	6	7	8	9	Prop. Pts.

N	0	1	2	3	4	5	6	7	8	9	Prop. Pts.	
600	77 815	822	830	837	844	851	859	866	873	880		
601	887	895	902	909	916	924	931	938	945	952		
602	960	967	974	981	988	996	*003	*010	*017	*025		
603	78 032	039	046	053	061	068	075	082	089	097		
604	104	111	118	125	132	140	147	154	161	168		
605	176	183	190	197	204	211	219	226	233	240		
606	247	254	262	269	276	283	290	297	305	312		
607	319	326	333	340	347	355	362	369	376	383		
608	390	398	405	412	419	426	433	440	447	455		
609	462	469	476	483	490	497	504	512	519	526		
												8
610	533	540	547	554	561	569	576	583	590	597	1	0.8
611	604	611	618	625	633	640	647	654	661	668	2	1.6
612	675	682	689	696	704	711	718	725	732	739	3	2.4
613	746	753	760	767	774	781	789	796	803	810	4	3.2
614	817	824	831	838	845	852	859	866	873	880	5	4.0
											6	4.8
615	888	895	902	909	916	923	930	937	944	951	7	5.6
616	958	965	972	979	986	993	*000	*007	*014	*021	8	6.4
617	79 029	036	043	050	057	064	071	078	085	092	9	7.2
618	099	106	113	120	127	134	141	148	155	162		
619	169	176	183	190	197	204	211	218	225	232		
620	239	246	253	260	267	274	281	288	295	302		
621	309	316	323	330	337	344	351	358	365	372		7
622	379	386	393	400	407	414	421	428	435	442	1	0.7
623	449	456	463	470	477	484	491	498	505	511	2	1.4
624	518	525	532	539	546	553	560	567	574	581	3	2.1
											4	2.8
625	588	595	602	609	616	623	630	637	644	650	5	3.5
626	657	664	671	678	685	692	699	706	713	720	6	4.2
627	727	734	741	748	754	761	768	775	782	789	7	4.9
628	796	803	810	817	824	831	837	844	851	858	8	5.6
629	865	872	879	886	893	900	906	913	920	927	9	6.3
630	934	941	948	955	962	969	975	982	989	996		
631	80 003	010	017	024	030	037	044	051	058	065		
632	072	079	085	092	099	106	113	120	127	134		6
633	140	147	154	161	168	175	182	188	195	202	1	0.6
634	209	216	223	229	236	243	250	257	264	271	2	1.2
											3	1.8
635	277	284	291	298	305	312	318	325	332	339	4	2.4
636	346	353	359	366	373	380	387	393	400	407	5	3.0
637	414	421	428	434	441	448	455	462	468	475	6	3.6
638	482	489	496	502	509	516	523	530	536	543	7	4.2
639	550	557	564	570	577	584	591	598	604	611	8	4.8
											9	5.4
640	618	625	632	638	645	652	659	665	672	679		
641	686	693	699	706	713	720	726	733	740	747		
642	754	760	767	774	781	787	794	801	808	814		
643	821	828	835	841	848	855	862	868	875	882		
644	889	895	902	909	916	922	929	936	943	949		
645	956	963	969	976	983	990	996	*003	*010	*017		
646	81 023	030	037	043	050	057	064	070	077	084		
647	090	097	104	111	117	124	131	137	144	151		
648	158	164	171	178	184	191	198	204	211	218		
649	224	231	238	245	251	258	265	271	278	285		
650	291	298	305	311	318	325	331	338	345	351		
N	0	1	2	3	4	5	6	7	8	9	Prop. Pts.	

N	0	1	2	3	4	5	6	7	8	9	Prop. Pts.
650	81 291	298	305	311	318	325	331	338	345	351	
651	358	365	371	378	385	391	398	405	411	418	
652	425	431	438	445	451	458	465	471	478	485	
653	491	498	505	511	518	525	531	538	544	551	
654	558	564	571	578	584	591	598	604	611	617	
655	624	631	637	644	651	657	664	671	677	684	
656	690	697	704	710	717	723	730	737	743	750	
657	757	763	770	776	783	790	796	803	809	816	
658	823	829	836	842	849	856	862	869	875	882	
659	889	895	902	908	915	921	928	935	941	948	
660	954	961	968	974	981	987	994	*000	*007	*014	
661	82 020	027	033	040	046	053	060	066	073	079	
662	086	092	099	105	112	119	125	132	138	145	
663	151	158	164	171	178	184	191	197	204	210	
664	217	223	230	236	243	249	256	263	269	276	
665	282	289	295	302	308	315	321	328	334	341	
666	347	354	360	367	373	380	387	393	400	406	
667	413	419	426	432	439	445	452	458	465	471	
668	478	484	491	497	504	510	517	523	530	536	
669	543	549	556	562	569	575	582	588	595	601	
670	607	614	620	627	633	640	646	653	659	666	
671	672	679	685	692	698	705	711	718	724	730	
672	737	743	750	756	763	769	776	782	789	795	
673	802	808	814	821	827	834	840	847	853	860	
674	866	872	879	885	892	898	905	911	918	924	
675	930	937	943	950	956	963	969	975	982	988	
676	995	*001	*008	*014	*020	*027	*033	*040	*046	*052	
677	83 059	065	072	078	085	091	097	104	110	117	
678	123	129	136	142	149	155	161	168	174	181	
679	187	193	200	206	213	219	225	232	238	245	
680	251	257	264	270	276	283	289	296	302	308	
681	315	321	327	334	340	347	353	359	366	372	
682	378	385	391	398	404	410	417	423	429	436	
683	442	448	455	461	467	474	480	487	493	499	
684	506	512	518	525	531	537	544	550	556	563	
685	569	575	582	588	594	601	607	613	620	626	
686	632	639	645	651	658	664	670	677	683	689	
687	696	702	708	715	721	727	734	740	746	753	
688	759	765	771	778	784	790	797	803	809	816	
689	822	828	835	841	847	853	860	866	872	879	
690	885	891	897	904	910	916	923	929	935	942	
691	948	954	960	967	973	979	985	992	998	*004	
692	84 011	017	023	029	036	042	048	055	061	067	
693	073	080	086	092	098	105	111	117	123	130	
694	136	142	148	155	161	167	173	180	186	192	
695	198	205	211	217	223	230	236	242	248	255	
696	261	267	273	280	286	292	298	305	311	317	
697	323	330	336	342	348	354	361	367	373	379	
698	386	392	398	404	410	417	423	429	435	442	
699	448	454	460	466	473	479	485	491	497	504	
700	510	516	522	528	535	541	547	553	559	566	
N	0	1	2	3	4	5	6	7	8	9	Prop. Pts.

Prop. Pts.

7
1 0.7
2 1.4
3 2.1
4 2.8
5 3.5
6 4.2
7 4.9
8 5.6
9 6.3

6
1 0.6
2 1.2
3 1.8
4 2.4
5 3.0
6 3.6
7 4.2
8 4.8
9 5.4

N	0	1	2	3	4	5	6	7	8	9	Prop. Pts.	
700	84 510	516	522	528	535	541	547	553	559	566		
701	572	578	584	590	597	603	609	615	621	628		
702	634	640	646	652	658	665	671	677	683	689		
703	696	702	708	714	720	726	733	739	745	751		
704	757	763	770	776	782	788	794	800	807	813		
705	819	825	831	837	844	850	856	862	868	874		
706	880	887	893	899	905	911	917	924	930	936		
707	942	948	954	960	967	973	979	985	991	997		
708	85 003	009	016	022	028	034	040	046	052	058		
709	065	071	077	083	089	095	101	107	114	120		7
710	126	132	138	144	150	156	163	169	175	181	1	0.7
711	187	193	199	205	211	217	224	230	236	242	2	1.4
712	248	254	260	266	272	278	285	291	297	303	3	2.1
713	309	315	321	327	333	339	345	352	358	364	4	2.8
714	370	376	382	388	394	400	406	412	418	425	5	3.5
											6	4.2
715	431	437	443	449	455	461	467	473	479	485	7	4.9
716	491	497	503	509	516	522	528	534	540	546	8	5.6
717	552	558	564	570	576	582	588	594	600	606	9	6.3
718	612	618	625	631	637	643	649	655	661	667		
719	673	679	685	691	697	703	709	715	721	727		
720	733	739	745	751	757	763	769	775	781	788		6
721	794	800	806	812	818	824	830	836	842	848		
722	854	860	866	872	878	884	890	896	902	908	1	0.6
723	914	920	926	932	938	944	950	956	962	968	2	1.2
724	974	980	986	992	998	*004	*010	*016	*022	*028	3	1.8
											4	2.4
725	86 034	040	046	052	058	064	070	076	082	088	5	3.0
726	094	100	106	112	118	124	130	136	141	147	6	3.6
727	153	159	165	171	177	183	189	195	201	207	7	4.2
728	213	219	225	231	237	243	249	255	261	267	8	4.8
729	273	279	285	291	297	303	308	314	320	326	9	5.4
730	332	338	344	350	356	362	368	374	380	386		
731	392	398	404	410	415	421	427	433	439	445		
732	451	457	463	469	475	481	487	493	499	504		5
733	510	516	522	528	534	540	546	552	558	564	1	0.5
734	570	576	581	587	593	599	605	611	617	623	2	1.0
											3	1.5
735	629	635	641	646	652	658	664	670	676	682	4	2.0
736	688	694	700	705	711	717	723	729	735	741	5	2.5
737	747	753	759	764	770	776	782	788	794	800	6	3.0
738	806	812	817	823	829	835	841	847	853	859	7	3.5
739	864	870	876	882	888	894	900	906	911	917	8	4.0
											9	4.5
740	923	929	935	941	947	953	958	964	970	976		
741	982	988	994	999	*005	*011	*017	*023	*029	*035		
742	87 040	046	052	058	064	070	075	081	087	093		
743	099	105	111	116	122	128	134	140	146	151		
744	157	163	169	175	181	186	192	198	204	210		
745	216	221	227	233	239	245	251	256	262	268		
746	274	280	286	291	297	303	309	315	320	326		
747	332	338	344	349	355	361	367	373	379	384		
748	390	396	402	408	413	419	425	431	437	442		
749	448	454	460	466	471	477	483	489	495	500		
750	506	512	518	523	529	535	541	547	552	558		
N	0	1	2	3	4	5	6	7	8	9	Prop. Pts.	

N	0	1	2	3	4	5	6	7	8	9	Prop. Pts.	
750	87 506	512	518	523	529	535	541	547	552	558		
751	564	570	576	581	587	593	599	604	610	616		
752	622	628	633	639	645	651	656	662	668	674		
753	679	685	691	697	703	708	714	720	726	731		
754	737	743	749	754	760	766	772	777	783	789		
755	795	800	806	812	818	823	829	835	841	846		
756	852	858	864	869	875	881	887	892	898	904		
757	910	915	921	927	933	938	944	950	955	961		
758	967	973	978	984	990	996	*001	*007	*013	*018		
759	88 024	030	036	041	047	053	058	064	070	076		
760	081	087	093	098	104	110	116	121	127	133		
761	138	144	150	156	161	167	173	178	184	190		
762	195	201	207	213	218	224	230	235	241	247		
763	252	258	264	270	275	281	287	292	298	304		
764	309	315	321	326	332	338	343	349	355	360		
												6
765	366	372	377	383	389	395	400	406	412	417	1	0.6
766	423	429	434	440	446	451	457	463	468	474	2	1.2
767	480	485	491	497	502	508	513	519	525	530	3	1.8
768	536	542	547	553	559	564	570	576	581	587	4	2.4
769	593	598	604	610	615	621	627	632	638	643	5	3.0
											6	3.6
770	649	655	660	666	672	677	683	689	694	700	7	4.2
771	705	711	717	722	728	734	739	745	750	756	8	4.8
772	762	767	773	779	784	790	795	801	807	812	9	5.4
773	818	824	829	835	840	846	852	857	863	868		
774	874	880	885	891	897	902	908	913	919	925		
775	930	936	941	947	953	958	964	969	975	981		
776	986	992	997	*003	*009	*014	*020	*025	*031	*037		6
777	89 042	048	053	059	064	070	076	081	087	092	1	0.5
778	098	104	109	115	120	126	131	137	143	148	2	1.0
779	154	159	165	170	176	182	187	193	198	204	3	1.5
780	209	215	221	226	232	237	243	248	254	260	4	2.0
781	265	271	276	282	287	293	298	304	310	315	5	2.5
782	321	326	332	337	343	348	354	360	365	371	6	3.0
783	376	382	387	393	398	404	409	415	421	426	7	3.5
784	432	437	443	448	454	459	465	470	476	481	8	4.0
											9	4.5
785	487	492	498	504	509	515	520	526	531	537		
786	542	548	553	559	564	570	575	581	586	592		
787	597	603	609	614	620	625	631	636	642	647		
788	653	658	664	669	675	680	686	691	697	702		
789	708	713	719	724	730	735	741	746	752	757		
790	763	768	774	779	785	790	796	801	807	812		
791	818	823	829	834	840	845	851	856	862	867		
792	873	878	883	889	894	900	905	911	916	922		
793	927	933	938	944	949	955	960	966	971	977		
794	982	988	993	998	*004	*009	*015	*020	*026	*031		
795	90 037	042	048	053	059	064	069	075	080	086		
796	091	097	102	108	113	119	124	129	135	140		
797	146	151	157	162	168	173	179	184	189	195		
798	200	206	211	217	222	227	233	238	244	249		
799	255	260	266	271	276	282	287	293	298	304		
800	309	314	320	325	331	336	342	347	352	358		
N	0	1	2	3	4	5	6	7	8	9	Prop. Pts.	

N	0	1	2	3	4	5	6	7	8	9	Prop. Pts.
800	90 309	314	320	325	331	336	342	347	352	358	
801	363	369	374	380	385	390	396	401	407	412	
802	417	423	428	434	439	445	450	455	461	466	
803	472	477	482	488	493	499	504	509	515	520	
804	526	531	536	542	547	553	558	563	569	574	
805	580	585	590	596	601	607	612	617	623	628	
806	634	639	644	650	655	660	666	671	677	682	
807	687	693	698	703	709	714	720	725	730	736	
808	741	747	752	757	763	768	773	779	784	789	
809	795	800	806	811	816	822	827	832	838	843	
810	849	854	859	865	870	875	881	886	891	897	
811	902	907	913	918	924	929	934	940	945	950	
812	956	961	966	972	977	982	988	993	998	*004	
813	91 009	014	020	025	030	036	041	046	052	057	
814	062	068	073	078	084	089	094	100	105	110	
815	116	121	126	132	137	142	148	153	158	164	
816	169	174	180	185	190	196	201	206	212	217	
817	222	228	233	238	243	249	254	259	265	270	
818	275	281	286	291	297	302	307	312	318	323	
819	328	334	339	344	350	355	360	365	371	376	
820	381	387	392	397	403	408	413	418	424	429	
821	434	440	445	450	455	461	466	471	477	482	
822	487	492	498	503	508	514	519	524	529	535	
823	540	545	551	556	561	566	572	577	582	587	
824	593	598	603	609	614	619	624	630	635	640	
825	645	651	656	661	666	672	677	682	687	693	
826	698	703	709	714	719	724	730	735	740	745	
827	751	756	761	766	772	777	782	787	793	798	
828	803	808	814	819	824	829	834	840	845	850	
829	855	861	866	871	876	882	887	892	897	903	
830	908	913	918	924	929	934	939	944	950	955	
831	960	965	971	976	981	986	991	997	*002	*007	
832	92 012	018	023	028	033	038	044	049	054	059	
833	065	070	075	080	085	091	096	101	106	111	
834	117	122	127	132	137	143	148	153	158	163	
835	169	174	179	184	189	195	200	205	210	215	
836	221	226	231	236	241	247	252	257	262	267	
837	273	278	283	288	293	298	304	309	314	319	
838	324	330	335	340	345	350	355	361	366	371	
839	376	381	387	392	397	402	407	412	418	423	
840	428	433	438	443	449	454	459	464	469	474	
841	480	485	490	495	500	505	511	516	521	526	
842	531	536	542	547	552	557	562	567	572	578	
843	583	588	593	598	603	609	614	619	624	629	
844	634	639	645	650	655	660	665	670	675	681	
845	686	691	696	701	706	711	716	722	727	732	
846	737	742	747	752	758	763	768	773	778	783	
847	788	793	799	804	809	814	819	824	829	834	
848	840	845	850	855	860	865	870	875	881	886	
849	891	896	901	906	911	916	921	927	932	937	
850	942	947	952	957	962	967	973	978	983	988	
N	0	1	2	3	4	5	6	7	8	9	Prop. Pts.

Prop. Pts.

	6
1	0.6
2	1.2
3	1.8
4	2.4
5	3.0
6	3.6
7	4.2
8	4.8
9	5.4

	5
1	0.5
2	1.0
3	1.5
4	2.0
5	2.5
6	3.0
7	3.5
8	4.0
9	4.5

N	0	1	2	3	4	5	6	7	8	9	Prop. Pts.
850	92 942	947	952	957	962	967	973	978	983	988	
851	993	998	*003	*008	*013	*018	*024	*029	*034	*039	
852	93 044	049	054	059	064	069	075	080	085	090	
853	095	100	105	110	115	120	125	131	136	141	
854	146	151	156	161	166	171	176	181	186	192	
855	197	202	207	212	217	222	227	232	237	242	
856	247	252	258	263	268	273	278	283	288	293	
857	298	303	308	313	318	323	328	334	339	344	
858	349	354	359	364	369	374	379	384	389	394	
859	399	404	409	414	420	425	430	435	440	445	
860	450	455	460	465	470	475	480	485	490	495	6
861	500	505	510	515	520	526	531	536	541	546	1 0.6
862	551	556	561	566	571	576	581	586	591	596	2 1.2
863	601	606	611	616	621	626	631	636	641	646	3 1.8
864	651	656	661	666	671	676	682	687	692	697	4 2.4
865	702	707	712	717	722	727	732	737	742	747	5 3.0
866	752	757	762	767	772	777	782	787	792	797	6 3.6
867	802	807	812	817	822	827	832	837	842	847	7 4.2
868	852	857	862	867	872	877	882	887	892	897	8 4.8
869	902	907	912	917	922	927	932	937	942	947	9 5.4
870	952	957	962	967	972	977	982	987	992	997	
871	94 002	007	012	017	022	027	032	037	042	047	5
872	052	057	062	067	072	077	082	086	091	096	1 0.5
873	101	106	111	116	121	126	131	136	141	146	2 1.0
874	151	156	161	166	171	176	181	186	191	196	3 1.5
											4 2.0
875	201	206	211	216	221	226	231	236	240	245	5 2.5
876	250	255	260	265	270	275	280	285	290	295	6 3.0
877	300	305	310	315	320	325	330	335	340	345	7 3.5
878	349	354	359	364	369	374	379	384	389	394	8 4.0
879	399	404	409	414	419	424	429	433	438	443	9 4.5
880	448	453	458	463	468	473	478	483	488	493	
881	498	503	507	512	517	522	527	532	537	542	
882	547	552	557	562	567	571	576	581	586	591	4
883	596	601	606	611	616	621	626	630	635	640	1 0.4
884	645	650	655	660	665	670	675	680	685	689	2 0.8
											3 1.2
885	694	699	704	709	714	719	724	729	734	738	4 1.6
886	743	748	753	758	763	768	773	778	783	787	5 2.0
887	792	797	802	807	812	817	822	827	832	836	6 2.4
888	841	846	851	856	861	866	871	876	880	885	7 2.8
889	890	895	900	905	910	915	919	924	929	934	8 3.2
											9 3.6
890	939	944	949	954	959	963	968	973	978	983	
891	988	993	998	*002	*007	*012	*017	*022	*027	*032	
892	95 036	041	046	051	056	061	066	071	075	080	
893	085	090	095	100	105	109	114	119	124	129	
894	134	139	143	148	153	158	163	168	173	177	
895	182	187	192	197	202	207	211	216	221	226	
896	231	236	240	245	250	255	260	265	270	274	
897	279	284	289	294	299	303	308	313	318	323	
898	328	332	337	342	347	352	357	361	366	371	
899	376	381	386	390	395	400	405	410	415	419	
900	424	429	434	439	444	448	453	458	463	468	
N	0	1	2	3	4	5	6	7	8	9	Prop. Pts.

N	0	1	2	3	4	5	6	7	8	9	Prop. Pts.
900	95 424	429	434	439	444	448	453	458	463	468	
901	472	477	482	487	492	497	501	506	511	516	
902	521	525	530	535	540	545	550	554	559	564	
903	569	574	578	583	588	593	598	602	607	612	
904	617	622	626	631	636	641	646	650	655	660	
905	665	670	674	679	684	689	694	698	703	708	
906	713	718	722	727	732	737	742	746	751	756	
907	761	766	770	775	780	785	789	794	799	804	
908	809	813	818	823	828	832	837	842	847	852	
909	856	861	866	871	875	880	885	890	895	899	
910	904	909	914	918	923	928	933	938	942	947	
911	952	957	961	966	971	976	980	985	990	995	
912	999	*004	*009	*014	*019	*023	*028	*033	*038	*042	
913	96 047	052	057	061	066	071	076	080	085	090	
914	095	099	104	109	114	118	123	128	133	137	
915	142	147	152	156	161	166	171	175	180	185	
916	190	194	199	204	209	213	218	223	227	232	
917	237	242	246	251	256	261	265	270	275	280	
918	284	289	294	298	303	308	313	317	322	327	
919	332	336	341	346	350	355	360	365	369	374	
920	379	384	388	393	398	402	407	412	417	421	
921	426	431	435	440	445	450	454	459	464	468	
922	473	478	483	487	492	497	501	506	511	515	
923	520	525	530	534	539	544	548	553	558	562	
924	567	572	577	581	586	591	595	600	605	609	
925	614	619	624	628	633	638	642	647	652	656	
926	661	666	670	675	680	685	689	694	699	703	
927	708	713	717	722	727	731	736	741	745	750	
928	755	759	764	769	774	778	783	788	792	797	
929	802	806	811	816	820	825	830	834	839	844	
930	848	853	858	862	867	872	876	881	886	890	
931	895	900	904	909	914	918	923	928	932	937	
932	942	946	951	956	960	965	970	974	979	984	
933	988	993	997	*002	*007	*011	*016	*021	*025	*030	
934	97 035	039	044	049	053	058	063	067	072	077	
935	081	086	090	095	100	104	109	114	118	123	
936	128	132	137	142	146	151	155	160	165	169	
937	174	179	183	188	192	197	202	206	211	216	
938	220	225	230	234	239	243	248	253	257	262	
939	267	271	276	280	285	290	294	299	304	308	
940	313	317	322	327	331	336	340	345	350	354	
941	359	364	368	373	377	382	387	391	396	400	
942	405	410	414	419	424	428	433	437	442	447	
943	451	456	460	465	470	474	479	483	488	493	
944	497	502	506	511	516	520	525	529	534	539	
945	543	548	552	557	562	566	571	575	580	585	
946	589	594	598	603	607	612	617	621	626	630	
947	635	640	644	649	653	658	663	667	672	676	
948	681	685	690	695	699	704	708	713	717	722	
949	727	731	736	740	745	749	754	759	763	768	
950	772	777	782	786	791	795	800	804	809	813	
N	0	1	2	3	4	5	6	7	8	9	Prop. Pts.

Prop. Pts.

	5
1	0.5
2	1.0
3	1.5
4	2.0
5	2.5
6	3.0
7	3.5
8	4.0
9	4.5

	4
1	0.4
2	0.8
3	1.2
4	1.6
5	2.0
6	2.4
7	2.8
8	3.2
9	3.6

N	0	1	2	3	4	5	6	7	8	9	Prop. Pts.	
950	97 772	777	782	786	791	795	800	804	809	813		
951	818	823	827	832	836	841	845	850	855	859		
952	864	868	873	877	882	886	891	896	900	905		
953	909	914	918	923	928	932	937	941	946	950		
954	955	959	964	968	973	978	982	987	991	996		
955	98 000	005	009	014	019	023	028	032	037	041		
956	046	050	055	059	064	068	073	078	082	087		
957	091	096	100	105	109	114	118	123	127	132		
958	137	141	146	150	155	159	164	168	173	177		
959	182	186	191	195	200	204	209	214	218	223		
960	227	232	236	241	245	250	254	259	263	268		
961	272	277	281	286	290	295	299	304	308	313		
962	318	322	327	331	336	340	345	349	354	358		
963	363	367	372	376	381	385	390	394	399	403		
964	408	412	417	421	426	430	435	439	444	448		
												5
965	453	457	462	466	471	475	480	484	489	493	1	0.5
966	498	502	507	511	516	520	525	529	534	538	2	1.0
967	543	547	552	556	561	565	570	574	579	583	3	1.5
968	588	592	597	601	605	610	614	619	623	628	4	2.0
969	632	637	641	646	650	655	659	664	668	673	5	2.5
											6	3.0
970	677	682	686	691	695	700	704	709	713	717	7	3.5
971	722	726	731	735	740	744	749	753	758	762	8	4.0
972	767	771	776	780	784	789	793	798	802	807	9	4.5
973	811	816	820	825	829	834	838	843	847	851		
974	856	860	865	869	874	878	883	887	892	896		
975	900	905	909	914	918	923	927	932	936	941		
976	945	949	954	958	963	967	972	976	981	985		**4**
977	989	994	998	*003	*007	*012	*016	*021	*025	*029		
978	99 034	038	043	047	052	056	061	065	069	074	1	0.4
979	078	083	087	092	096	100	105	109	114	118	2	0.8
											3	1.2
980	123	127	131	136	140	145	149	154	158	162	4	1.6
981	167	171	176	180	185	189	193	198	202	207	5	2.0
982	211	216	220	224	229	233	238	242	247	251	6	2.4
983	255	260	264	269	273	277	282	286	291	295	7	2.8
984	300	304	308	313	317	322	326	330	335	339	8	3.2
											9	3.6
985	344	348	352	357	361	366	370	374	379	383		
986	388	392	396	401	405	410	414	419	423	427		
987	432	436	441	445	449	454	458	463	467	471		
988	476	480	484	489	493	498	502	506	511	515		
989	520	524	528	533	537	542	546	550	555	559		
990	564	568	572	577	581	585	590	594	599	603		
991	607	612	616	621	625	629	634	638	642	647		
992	651	656	660	664	669	673	677	682	686	691		
993	695	699	704	708	712	717	721	726	730	734		
994	739	743	747	752	756	760	765	769	774	778		
995	782	787	791	795	800	804	808	813	817	822		
996	826	830	835	839	843	848	852	856	861	865		
997	870	874	878	883	887	891	896	900	904	909		
998	913	917	922	926	930	935	939	944	948	952		
999	957	961	965	970	974	978	983	987	991	996		
1000	00 000	004	009	013	017	022	026	030	035	039		
N	0	1	2	3	4	5	6	7	8	9	Prop. Pts.	

TABLE XVI
NATURAL LOGARITHMS OF NUMBERS
BASE e = 2.71828 . . .

NOTE. $\log_e 10N = \log_e N + \log_e 10$ $\log_e \frac{N}{10} = \log_e N - \log_e 10$.

$\log_e 10 = 2.30259$.

Examples: $\log_e 27 = \log_e 2.7 + \log_e 10 = 0.99325 + 2.30259 = 3.29584$.
$\log_e .27 = \log_e 2.7 - \log_e 10 = 0.99325 - 2.30259 = 8.69066 - 10$.

N	0	1	2	3	4	5	6	7	8	9
1.0	0.0 0000	0995	1980	2956	3922	4879	5827	6766	7696	8618
1.1	9531	*0436	*1333	*2222	*3103	*3976	*4842	*5700	*6551	*7395
1.2	0.1 8232	9062	9885	*0701	*1511	*2314	*3111	*3902	*4686	*5464
1.3	0.2 6236	7003	7763	8518	9267	*0010	*0748	*1481	*2208	*2930
1.4	0.3 3647	4359	5066	5767	6464	7156	7844	8526	9204	9878
1.5	0.4 0547	1211	1871	2527	3178	3825	4469	5108	5742	6373
1.6	7000	7623	8243	8858	9470	*0078	*0682	*1282	*1879	*2473
1.7	0.5 3063	3649	4232	4812	5389	5962	6531	7098	7661	8222
1.8	8779	9333	9884	*0432	*0977	*1519	*2058	*2594	*3127	*3658
1.9	0.6 4185	4710	5233	5752	6269	6783	7294	7803	8310	8813
2.0	9315	9813	*0310	*0804	*1295	*1784	*2271	*2755	*3237	*3716
2.1	0.7 4194	4669	5142	5612	6081	6547	7011	7473	7932	8390
2.2	8846	9299	9751	*0200	*0648	*1093	*1536	*1978	*2418	*2855
2.3	0.8 3291	3725	4157	4587	5015	5442	5866	6289	6710	7129
2.4	7547	7963	8377	8789	9200	9609	*0016	*0422	*0826	*1228
2.5	0.9 1629	2028	2426	2822	3216	3609	4001	4391	4779	5166
2.6	5551	5935	6317	6698	7078	7456	7833	8208	8582	8954
2.7	9325	9695	*0063	*0430	*0796	*1160	*1523	*1885	*2245	*2604
2.8	1.0 2962	3318	3674	4028	4380	4732	5082	5431	5779	6126
2.9	6471	6815	7158	7500	7841	8181	8519	8856	9192	9527
3.0	9861	*0194	*0526	*0856	*1186	*1514	*1841	*2168	*2493	*2817
3.1	1.1 3140	3462	3783	4103	4422	4740	5057	5373	5688	6002
3.2	6315	6627	6938	7248	7557	7865	8173	8479	8784	9089
3.3	9392	9695	9996	*0297	*0597	*0896	*1194	*1491	*1788	*2083
3.4	1.2 2378	2671	2964	3256	3547	3837	4127	4415	4703	4990
3.5	5276	5562	5846	6130	6413	6695	6976	7257	7536	7815
3.6	8093	8371	8647	8923	9198	9473	9746	*0019	*0291	*0563
3.7	1.3 0833	1103	1372	1641	1909	2176	2442	2708	2972	3237
3.8	3500	3763	4025	4286	4547	4807	5067	5325	5584	5841
3.9	6098	6354	6609	6864	7118	7372	7624	7877	8128	8379
4.0	8629	8879	9128	9377	9624	9872	*0118	*0364	*0610	*0854
4.1	1.4 1099	1342	1585	1828	2070	2311	2552	2792	3031	3270
4.2	3508	3746	3984	4220	4456	4692	4927	5161	5395	5629
4.3	5862	6094	6326	6557	6787	7018	7247	7476	7705	7933
4.4	8160	8387	8614	8840	9065	9290	9515	9739	9962	*0185
4.5	1.5 0408	0630	0851	1072	1293	1513	1732	1951	2170	2388
4.6	2606	2823	3039	3256	3471	3687	3902	4116	4330	4543
4.7	4756	4969	5181	5393	5604	5814	6025	6235	6444	6653
4.8	6862	7070	7277	7485	7691	7898	8104	8309	8515	8719
4.9	8924	9127	9331	9534	9737	9939	*0141	*0342	*0543	*0744
5.0	1.6 0944	1144	1343	1542	1741	1939	2137	2334	2531	2728
N	0	1	2	3	4	5	6	7	8	9

N	0	1	2	3	4	5	6	7	8	9
5.0	1.6 0944	1144	1343	1542	1741	1939	2137	2334	2531	2728
5.1	2924	3120	3315	3511	3705	3900	4094	4287	4481	4673
5.2	4866	5058	5250	5441	5632	5823	6013	6203	6393	6582
5.3	6771	6959	7147	7335	7523	7710	7896	8083	8269	8455
5.4	8640	8825	9010	9194	9378	9562	9745	9928	*0111	*0293
5.5	1.7 0475	0656	0838	1019	1199	1380	1560	1740	1919	2098
5.6	2277	2455	2633	2811	2988	3166	3342	3519	3695	3871
5.7	4047	4222	4397	4572	4746	4920	5094	5267	5440	5613
5.8	5786	5958	6130	6302	6473	6644	6815	6985	7156	7326
5.9	7495	7665	7834	8002	8171	8339	8507	8675	8842	9009
6.0	9176	9342	9509	9675	9840	*0006	*0171	*0336	*0500	*0665
6.1	1.8 0829	0993	1156	1319	1482	1645	1808	1970	2132	2294
6.2	2455	2616	2777	2938	3098	3258	3418	3578	3737	3896
6.3	4055	4214	4372	4530	4688	4845	5003	5160	5317	5473
6.4	5630	5786	5942	6097	6253	6408	6563	6718	6872	7026
6.5	7180	7334	7487	7641	7794	7947	8099	8251	8403	8555
6.6	8707	8858	9010	9160	9311	9462	9612	9762	9912	*0061
6.7	1.9 0211	0360	0509	0658	0806	0954	1102	1250	1398	1545
6.8	1692	1839	1986	2132	2279	2425	2571	2716	2862	3007
6.9	3152	3297	3442	3586	3730	3874	4018	4162	4305	4448
7.0	4591	4734	4876	5019	5161	5303	5445	5586	5727	5869
7.1	6009	6150	6291	6431	6571	6711	6851	6991	7130	7269
7.2	7408	7547	7685	7824	7962	8100	8238	8376	8513	8650
7.3	8787	8924	9061	9198	9334	9470	9606	9742	9877	*0013
7.4	2.0 0148	0283	0418	0553	0687	0821	0956	1089	1223	1357
7.5	1490	1624	1757	1890	2022	2155	2287	2419	2551	2683
7.6	2815	2946	3078	3209	3340	3471	3601	3732	3862	3992
7.7	4122	4252	4381	4511	4640	4769	4898	5027	5156	5284
7.8	5412	5540	5668	5796	5924	6051	6179	6306	6433	6560
7.9	6686	6813	6939	7065	7191	7317	7443	7568	7694	7819
8.0	7944	8069	8194	8318	8443	8567	8691	8815	8939	9063
8.1	9186	9310	9433	9556	9679	9802	9924	*0047	*0169	*0291
8.2	2.1 0413	0535	0657	0779	0900	1021	1142	1263	1384	1505
8.3	1626	1746	1866	1986	2106	2226	2346	2465	2585	2704
8.4	2823	2942	3061	3180	3298	3417	3535	3653	3771	3889
8.5	4007	4124	4242	4359	4476	4593	4710	4827	4943	5060
8.6	5176	5292	5409	5524	5640	5756	5871	5987	6102	6217
8.7	6332	6447	6562	6677	6791	6905	7020	7134	7248	7361
8.8	7475	7589	7702	7816	7929	8042	8155	8267	8380	8493
8.9	8605	8717	8830	8942	9054	9165	9277	9389	9500	9611
9.0	9722	9834	9944	*0055	*0166	*0276	*0387	*0497	*0607	*0717
9.1	2.2 0827	0937	1047	1157	1266	1375	1485	1594	1703	1812
9.2	1920	2029	2138	2246	2354	2462	2570	2678	2786	2894
9.3	3001	3109	3216	3324	3431	3538	3645	3751	3858	3965
9.4	4071	4177	4284	4390	4496	4601	4707	4813	4918	5024
9.5	5129	5234	5339	5444	5549	5654	5759	5863	5968	6072
9.6	6176	6280	6384	6488	6592	6696	6799	6903	7006	7109
9.7	7213	7316	7419	7521	7624	7727	7829	7932	8034	8136
9.8	8238	8340	8442	8544	8646	8747	8849	8950	9051	9152
9.9	9253	9354	9455	9556	9657	9757	9858	9958	*0058	*0158
10.0	2.3 0259	0358	0458	0558	0658	0757	0857	0956	1055	1154
N	0	1	2	3	4	5	6	7	8	9

TABLE XVII. TEN THOUSAND RANDOMLY ASSORTED DIGITS

	00–04	05–09	10–14	15–19	20–24	25–29	30–34	35–39	40–44	45–49
00	54463	22662	65905	70639	79365	67382	29085	69831	47058	08186
01	15389	85205	18850	39226	42249	90669	96325	23248	60933	26927
02	85941	40756	82414	02015	13858	78030	16269	65978	01385	15345
03	61149	69440	11286	88218	58925	03638	52862	62733	33451	77455
04	05219	81619	10651	67079	92511	59888	84502	72095	83463	75577
05	41417	98326	87719	92294	46614	50948	64886	20002	97365	30976
06	28357	94070	20652	35774	16249	75019	21145	05217	47286	76305
07	17783	00015	10806	83091	91530	36466	39981	62481	49177	75779
08	40950	84820	29881	85966	62800	70326	84740	62660	77379	90279
09	82995	64157	66164	41180	10089	41757	78258	96488	88629	37231
10	96754	17676	55659	44105	47361	34833	86679	23930	53249	27083
11	34357	88040	53364	71726	45690	66334	60332	22554	90600	71113
12	06318	37403	49927	57715	50423	67372	63116	48888	21505	80182
13	62111	52820	07243	79931	89292	84767	85693	73947	22278	11551
14	47534	09243	67879	00544	23410	12740	02540	54440	32949	13491
15	98614	75993	84460	62846	59844	14922	48730	73443	48167	34770
16	24856	03648	44898	09351	98795	18644	39765	71058	90368	44104
17	96887	12479	80621	66223	86085	78285	02432	53342	42846	94771
18	90801	21472	42815	77408	37390	76766	52615	32141	30268	18106
19	55165	77312	83666	36028	28420	70219	81369	41943	47366	41067
20	75884	12952	84318	95108	72305	64620	91318	89872	45375	85436
21	16777	37116	58550	42958	21460	43910	01175	87894	81378	10620
22	46230	43877	80207	88877	89380	32992	91380	03164	98656	59337
23	42902	66892	46134	01432	94710	23474	20423	60137	60609	13119
24	81007	00333	39693	28039	10154	95425	39220	19774	31782	49037
25	68089	01122	51111	72373	06902	74373	96199	97017	41273	21546
26	20411	67081	89950	16944	93054	87687	96693	87236	77054	33848
27	58212	13160	06468	15718	82627	76999	05999	58680	96739	63700
28	70577	42866	24969	61210	76046	67699	42054	12696	93758	03283
29	94522	74358	71659	62038	79643	79169	44741	05437	39038	13163
30	42626	86819	85651	88678	17401	03252	99547	32404	17918	62880
31	16051	33763	57194	16752	54450	19031	58580	47629	54132	60631
32	08244	27647	33851	44705	94211	46716	11738	55784	95374	72655
33	59497	04392	09419	89964	51211	04894	72882	17805	21896	83864
34	97155	13428	40293	09985	58434	01412	69124	82171	59058	82859
35	98409	66162	95763	47420	20792	61527	20441	39435	11859	41567
36	45476	84882	65109	96597	25930	66790	65706	61203	53634	22557
37	89300	69700	50741	30329	11658	23166	05400	66669	48708	03887
38	50051	95137	91631	66315	91428	12275	24816	68091	71710	33258
39	31753	85178	31310	89642	98364	02306	24617	09609	83942	22716
40	79152	53829	77250	20190	56535	18760	69942	77448	33278	48805
41	44560	38750	83635	56540	64900	42912	13953	79149	18710	68618
42	68328	83378	63369	71381	39564	05615	42451	64559	97501	65747
43	46939	38689	58625	08342	30459	85863	20781	09284	26333	91777
44	83544	86141	15707	96256	23068	13782	08467	89469	93842	55349
45	91621	00881	04900	54224	46177	55309	17852	27491	89415	23466
46	91896	67126	04151	03795	59077	11848	12630	98375	52068	60142
47	55751	62515	21108	80830	02263	29303	37204	96926	30506	09808
48	85156	87689	95493	88842	00664	55017	55539	17771	69448	87530
49	07521	56898	12236	60277	39102	62315	12239	07105	11844	01117

Table XVII is reproduced from Table 1.5.1, "Ten Thousand Randomly Assorted Digits," of G. W. Snedecor, Statistical Methods Applied to Experiments in Agriculture and Biology, published by the Iowa State University Press, Ames, Iowa, by permission of the author and publisher.

TABLE XVII. TEN THOUSAND RANDOMLY ASSORTED DIGITS
(Continued)

	50-54	55-59	60-64	65-69	70-74	75-79	80-84	85-89	90-94	95-99
00	59391	58030	52098	82718	87024	82848	04190	96574	90464	29065
01	99567	76364	77204	04615	27062	96621	43918	01896	83991	51141
02	10363	97518	51400	25670	98342	61891	27101	37855	06235	33316
03	86859	19558	64432	16706	99612	59798	32803	67708	15297	28612
04	11258	24591	36863	55368	31721	94335	34936	02566	80972	08188
05	95068	88628	35911	14530	33020	80428	39936	31855	34334	64865
06	54463	47237	73800	91017	36239	71824	83671	39892	60518	37092
07	16874	62677	57412	13215	31389	62233	80827	73917	82802	84420
08	92494	63157	76593	91316	03505	72389	96363	52887	01087	66091
09	15669	56689	35682	40844	53256	81872	35213	09840	34471	74441
10	99116	75486	84989	23476	52967	67104	39495	39100	17217	74073
11	15696	10703	65178	90637	63110	17622	53988	71087	84148	11670
12	97720	15369	51269	69620	03388	13699	33423	67453	43269	56720
13	11666	13841	71681	98000	35979	39719	81899	07449	47985	46967
14	71628	73130	78783	75691	41632	09847	61547	18707	85489	69944
15	40501	51089	99943	91843	41995	88931	73631	69361	05375	15417
16	22518	55576	98215	82068	10798	86211	36584	67466	69373	40054
17	75112	30485	62173	02132	14878	92879	22281	16783	86352	00077
18	80327	02671	98191	84342	90813	49268	95441	15496	20168	09271
19	60251	45548	02146	05597	48228	81366	34598	72856	66762	17002
20	57430	82270	10421	05540	43648	75888	66049	21511	47676	33444
21	73528	39559	34434	88596	54086	71693	43132	14414	79949	85193
22	25991	65959	70769	64721	86413	33475	42740	06175	82758	66248
23	78388	16638	09134	59880	63806	48472	39318	35434	24057	74739
24	12477	09965	96657	57994	59439	76330	24596	77515	09577	91871
25	83266	32883	42451	15579	38155	29793	40914	65990	16255	17777
26	76970	80876	10237	39515	79152	74798	39357	09054	73579	92359
27	37074	65198	44785	68624	98336	84481	97610	78735	46703	98265
28	83712	06514	30101	78295	54656	85417	43189	60048	72781	72606
29	20287	56862	69727	94443	64936	08366	27227	05158	50326	59566
30	74261	32592	86538	27041	65172	85532	07571	80609	39285	65340
31	64081	49863	08478	96001	18888	14810	70545	89755	59064	07210
32	05617	75818	47750	67814	29575	10526	66192	44464	27058	40467
33	26793	74951	95466	74307	13330	42664	85515	20632	05497	33625
34	65988	72850	48737	54719	52056	01596	03845	35067	03134	70322
35	27366	42271	44300	73399	21105	03280	73457	43093	05192	48657
36	56760	10909	98147	34736	33863	95256	12731	66598	50771	83665
37	72880	43338	93643	58904	59543	23943	11231	83268	65938	81581
38	77888	38100	03062	58103	47961	83841	25878	23746	55903	44115
39	28440	07819	21580	51459	47971	29882	13990	29226	23608	15873
40	63525	94441	77033	12147	51054	49955	58312	76923	96071	05813
41	47606	93410	16359	89033	89696	47231	64498	31776	05383	39902
42	52669	45030	96279	14709	52372	87832	02735	50803	72744	88208
43	16738	60159	07425	62369	07515	82721	37875	71153	21315	00132
44	59348	11695	45751	15865	74739	05572	32688	20271	65128	14551
45	12900	71775	29845	60774	94924	21810	38636	33717	67598	82521
46	75086	23537	49939	33595	13484	97588	28617	17979	70749	35234
47	99495	51434	29181	09993	38190	42553	68922	52125	91077	40197
48	26075	31671	45386	36583	93459	48599	52022	41330	60651	91321
49	13636	93596	23377	51133	95126	61496	42474	45141	46660	42338

TABLE XVII. TEN THOUSAND RANDOMLY ASSORTED DIGITS
(Continued)

	00–04	05–09	10–14	15–19	20–24	25–29	30–34	35–39	40–44	45–49
50	64249	63664	39652	40646	97306	31741	07294	84149	46797	82487
51	26538	44249	04050	48174	65570	44072	40192	51153	11397	58212
52	05845	00512	78630	55328	18116	69296	91705	86224	29503	57071
53	74897	68373	67359	51014	33510	83048	17056	72506	82949	54600
54	20872	54570	35017	88132	25730	22626	86723	91691	13191	77212
55	31432	96156	89177	75541	81355	24480	77243	76690	42507	84362
56	66890	61505	01240	00660	05873	13568	76082	79172	57913	93448
57	48194	57790	79970	33106	86904	48119	52503	24130	72824	21627
58	11303	87118	81471	52936	08555	28420	49416	44448	04269	27029
59	54374	57325	16947	45356	78371	10563	97191	53798	12693	27928
60	64852	34421	61046	90849	13966	39810	42699	21753	76192	10508
61	16309	20384	09491	91588	97720	89846	30376	76970	23063	35894
62	42587	37065	24526	72602	57589	98131	37292	05967	26002	51945
63	40177	98590	97161	41682	84533	67588	62036	49967	01990	72308
64	82309	76128	93965	26743	24141	04838	40254	26065	07938	76236
65	79788	68243	59732	04257	27084	14743	17520	95401	55811	76099
66	40538	79000	89559	25026	42274	23489	34502	75508	06059	86682
67	64016	73598	18609	73150	62463	33102	45205	87440	96767	67042
68	49767	12691	17903	93871	99721	79109	09425	26904	07419	76013
69	76974	55108	29795	08404	82684	00497	51126	79935	57450	55671
70	23854	08480	85983	96025	50117	64610	99425	62291	86943	21541
71	68973	70551	25098	78033	98573	79848	31778	29555	61446	23037
72	36444	93600	65350	14971	25325	00427	52073	64280	18847	24768
73	03003	87800	07391	11594	21196	00781	32550	57158	58887	73041
74	17540	26188	36647	78386	04558	61463	57842	90382	77019	24210
75	38916	55809	47982	41968	69760	79422	80154	91486	19180	15100
76	64288	19843	69122	42502	48508	28820	59933	72998	99942	10515
77	86809	51564	38040	39418	49915	19000	58050	16899	79952	57849
78	99800	99566	14742	05028	30033	94889	53381	23656	75787	59223
79	92345	31890	95712	08279	91794	94068	49337	88674	35355	12267
80	90363	65162	32245	82279	79256	80834	06088	99462	56705	06118
81	64437	32242	48431	04835	29070	59702	31508	60935	22390	52246
82	91714	53662	28373	34333	55791	74758	51144	18827	10704	76803
83	20902	17646	31391	31459	33315	03444	55743	74701	58851	27427
84	12217	86007	70371	52281	14510	76094	96579	54853	78339	20839
85	45177	02863	42307	53571	22532	74921	17735	42201	80540	54721
86	28325	90814	08804	52746	47913	54577	47525	77705	95330	21866
87	29019	28776	56116	54791	64604	08815	46049	71186	34650	14994
88	84979	81353	56219	67062	26146	82567	33122	14124	46240	92973
89	50371	26347	48513	63915	11158	25563	91915	18431	92978	11591
90	53422	06825	69711	67950	64716	18003	49581	45378	99878	61130
91	67453	35651	89316	41620	32048	70225	47597	33137	31443	51445
92	07294	85353	74819	23445	68237	07202	99515	62282	53809	26685
93	79544	00302	45338	16015	66613	88968	14595	63836	77716	79596
94	64144	85442	82060	46471	24162	39500	87351	36637	42833	71875
95	90919	11883	58318	00042	52402	28210	34075	33272	00840	73268
96	06670	57353	86275	92276	77591	46924	60839	55437	03183	13191
97	36634	93976	52062	83678	41256	60948	18685	48992	19462	96062
98	75101	72891	85745	67106	26010	62107	60885	37503	55461	71213
99	05112	71222	72654	51583	05228	62056	57390	42746	39272	96659

TABLE XVII. TEN THOUSAND RANDOMLY ASSORTED DIGITS

	50–54	55–59	60–64	65–69	70–74	75–79	80–84	85–89	90–94	95–99
50	32847	31282	03345	89593	69214	70381	78285	20054	91018	16742
51	16916	00041	30236	55023	14253	76582	12092	86533	92426	37655
52	66176	34047	21005	27137	03191	48970	64625	22394	39622	79085
53	46299	13335	12180	16861	38043	59292	62675	63631	37020	78195
54	22847	47839	45385	23289	47526	54098	45683	55849	51575	64689
55	41851	54160	92320	69936	34803	92479	33399	71160	64777	83378
56	28444	59497	91586	95917	68553	28639	06455	34174	11130	91994
57	47520	62378	98855	83174	13088	16561	68559	26679	06238	51254
58	34978	63271	13142	82681	05271	08822	06490	44984	49307	62717
59	37404	80416	69035	92980	49486	74378	75610	74976	70056	15478
60	32400	65482	52099	53676	74648	94148	65095	69597	52771	71551
61	89262	86332	51718	70663	11623	29834	79820	73002	84886	03591
62	86866	09127	98021	03871	27789	58444	44832	36505	40672	30180
63	90814	14833	08759	74645	05046	94056	99094	65091	32663	73040
64	19192	82756	20553	58446	55376	88914	75096	26119	83898	43816
65	77585	52593	56612	95766	10019	29531	73064	20953	53523	58136
66	23757	16364	05096	03192	62386	45389	85332	18877	55710	96459
67	45989	96257	23850	26216	23309	21526	07425	50254	19455	29315
68	92970	94243	07316	41467	64837	52406	25225	51553	31220	14032
69	74346	59596	40088	98176	17896	86900	20249	77753	19099	48885
70	87646	41309	27636	45153	29988	94770	07255	70908	05340	99751
71	50099	71038	45146	06146	55211	99429	43169	66259	97786	59180
72	10127	46900	64984	75348	04115	33624	68774	60013	35515	62556
73	67995	81977	18984	64091	02785	27762	42529	97144	80407	64524
74	26304	80217	84934	82657	69291	35397	98714	35104	08187	48109
75	81994	41070	56642	64091	31229	02595	13513	45148	78722	30144
76	59537	34662	79631	89403	65212	09975	06118	86197	58208	16162
77	51228	10937	62396	81460	47331	91403	95007	06047	16846	64809
78	31089	37995	29577	07828	42272	54016	21950	86192	99046	84864
79	38207	97938	93459	75174	79460	55436	57206	87644	21296	43395
80	88666	31142	09474	89712	63153	62333	42212	06140	42594	43671
81	53365	56134	67582	92557	89520	33452	05134	70628	27612	33738
82	89807	74530	38004	90102	11693	90257	05500	79920	62700	43325
83	18682	81038	85662	90915	91631	22223	91588	80774	07716	12548
84	63571	32579	63942	25371	09234	94592	98475	76884	37635	33608
85	68927	56492	67799	95398	77642	54913	91853	08424	81450	76229
86	56401	63186	39389	88798	31356	89235	97036	32341	33292	73757
87	24333	95603	02359	72942	46287	95382	08452	62862	97869	71775
88	17025	84202	95199	62272	06366	16175	97577	99304	41587	03686
89	02804	08253	52133	20224	68034	50865	57868	22343	55111	03607
90	08298	03879	20995	19850	73090	13191	18963	82244	78479	99121
91	59883	01785	82403	96062	03785	03488	12970	64896	38336	30030
92	46982	06682	62864	91837	74021	89094	39952	64158	79614	78235
93	31121	47266	07661	02051	67599	24471	69843	83696	71402	76287
94	97867	56641	63416	17577	30161	87320	37752	73276	48969	41915
95	57364	86746	08415	14621	49430	22311	15836	72492	49372	44103
96	09559	26263	69511	28064	75999	44540	13337	10918	79846	54809
97	53873	55571	00608	42661	91332	63956	74087	59008	47493	99581
98	35531	19162	86406	05299	77511	24311	57257	22826	77555	05941
99	28229	88629	25695	94932	30721	16197	78742	34974	97528	45447

TABLE XVIII. FACTORIALS

Part 1. Numerical

n	$\dfrac{1}{n!}$					$n! = 1\cdot2\cdot3\cdot4\cdots\cdots n$				n
1	1.								1	1
2	0.5								2	2
3	.16666	66666	66666	66666	66667				6	3
4	.04166	66666	66666	66666	66667				24	4
5	.00833	33333	33333	33333	33333				120	5
6	0.00138	88888	88888	88888	88889				720	6
7	.00019	84126	98412	69841	26984				5040	7
8	.00002	48015	87301	58730	15873				40320	8
9	.00000	27557	31922	39858	90653			3	62880	9
10	.00000	02755	73192	23985	89065			36	28800	10
11	0.00000	00250	52108	38544	17188			399	16800	11
12	.00000	00020	87675	69878	68099			4790	01600	12
13	.00000	00001	60590	43836	82161			62270	20800	13
14	.00000	00000	11470	74559	77297		8	71782	91200	14
15	.00000	00000	00764	71637	31820		130	76743	68000	15
16	0.00000	00000	00047	79477	33239		2092	27898	88000	16
17	.00000	00000	00002	81145	72543		35568	74280	96000	17
18	.00000	00000	00000	15619	20697	6	40237	37057	28000	18
19	.00000	00000	00000	00822	06352	121	64510	04088	32000	19
20	.00000	00000	00000	00041	10318	2432	90200	81766	40000	20

Part 2. Logarithmic

Logarithms of the products $1\cdot2\cdot3\cdots\cdots n$, n from 1 to 100.

n	$\log(n!)$	n	$\log(n!)$	n	$\log(n!)$	n	$\log(n!)$
1	0.000000	26	26.605619	51	66.190645	76	111.275425
2	0.301030	27	28.036983	52	67.906648	77	113.161916
3	0.778151	28	29.484141	53	69.630924	78	115.054011
4	1.380211	29	30.946539	54	71.363318	79	116.951638
5	2.079181	30	32.423660	55	73.103681	80	118.854728
6	2.857332	31	33.915022	56	74.851869	81	120.763213
7	3.702431	32	35.420172	57	76.607744	82	122.677027
8	4.605521	33	36.938686	58	78.371172	83	124.596105
9	5.559763	34	38.470165	59	80.142024	84	126.520384
10	6.559763	35	40.014233	60	81.920175	85	128.449803
11	7.601156	36	41.570535	61	83.705505	86	130.384301
12	8.680337	37	43.138737	62	85.497896	87	132.323821
13	9.794280	38	44.718520	63	87.297237	88	134.268303
14	10.940408	39	46.309585	64	89.103417	89	136.217693
15	12.116500	40	47.911645	65	90.916330	90	138.171936
16	13.320620	41	49.524429	66	92.735874	91	140.130977
17	14.551069	42	51.147678	67	94.561949	92	142.094765
18	15.806341	43	52.781147	68	96.394458	93	144.063248
19	17.085095	44	54.424599	69	98.233307	94	146.036376
20	18.386125	45	56.077812	70	100.078405	95	148.014099
21	19.708344	46	57.740570	71	101.929663	96	149.996371
22	21.050767	47	59.412668	72	103.786996	97	151.983142
23	22.412494	48	61.093909	73	105.650319	98	153.974368
24	23.792706	49	62.784105	74	107.519550	99	155.970004
25	25.190646	50	64.483075	75	109.394612	100	157.970004

Table XVIII is adapted from Table 12, "Factorials," of <u>Smithsonian Physical Tables</u>, Ninth Edition, Washington, D.C.; by permission of Paul H. Oehser, Chief, Editorial and Publications Division.

TABLE XIX. LOGARITHMS OF THE BINOMIAL COEFFICIENTS

x	N = 1	N = 2	N = 3	N = 4	N = 5	N = 6	N = 7	N = 8	N = 9	N = 10
1	.0000	.3010	.4771	.6021	.6990	.7782	.8451	.9031	.9542	1.0000
2			.4771	.7782	1.0000	1.1761	1.3222	1.4472	1.5563	1.6532
3					1.0000	1.3010	1.5441	1.7482	1.9243	2.0792
4							1.5441	1.8451	2.1004	2.3222
5									2.1004	2.4014

x	N = 11	N = 12	N = 13	N = 14	N = 15	N = 16	N = 17	N = 18	N = 19	N = 20
1	1.0414	1.0792	1.1139	1.1461	1.1761	1.2041	1.2304	1.2553	1.2788	1.3010
2	1.7404	1.8195	1.8921	1.9590	2.0212	2.0792	2.1335	2.1847	2.2330	2.2788
3	2.2175	2.3424	2.4564	2.5611	2.6580	2.7482	2.8325	2.9117	2.9863	3.0569
4	2.5185	2.6946	2.8543	3.0004	3.1351	3.2601	3.3766	3.4857	3.5884	3.6853
5	2.6646	2.8987	3.1096	3.3015	3.4776	3.6403	3.7916	3.9329	4.0655	4.1904
6	2.6646	2.9657	3.2345	3.4776	3.6994	3.9035	4.0926	4.2687	4.4335	4.5884
7			3.2345	3.5355	3.8085	4.0584	4.2889	4.5028	4.7023	4.8894
8					3.8085	4.1096	4.3858	4.6411	4.8784	5.1003
9							4.3858	4.6868	4.9656	5.2252
10									4.9656	5.2666

x	N = 21	N = 22	N = 23	N = 24	N = 25	N = 26	N = 27	N = 28	N = 29	N = 30
1	1.3222	1.3424	1.3617	1.3802	1.3979	1.4150	1.4314	1.4472	1.4624	1.4771
2	2.3222	2.3636	2.4031	2.4409	2.4771	2.5119	2.5453	2.5775	2.6085	2.6385
3	3.1239	3.1875	3.2482	3.3062	3.3617	3.4150	3.4661	3.5153	3.5628	3.6085
4	3.7771	3.8642	3.9472	4.0264	4.1021	4.1746	4.2443	4.3112	4.3757	4.4378
5	4.3085	4.4205	4.5270	4.6284	4.7253	4.8181	4.9070	4.9925	5.0747	5.1538
6	4.7345	4.8728	5.0041	5.1290	5.2482	5.3622	5.4713	5.5760	5.6767	5.7736
7	5.0655	5.2318	5.3894	5.5392	5.6819	5.8181	5.9484	6.0734	6.1933	6.3087
8	5.3085	5.5048	5.6905	5.8666	6.0341	6.1938	6.3464	6.4925	6.6327	6.7674
9	5.4682	5.6967	5.9123	6.1164	6.3103	6.4948	6.6709	6.8393	7.0007	7.1556
10	5.5474	5.8107	6.0585	6.2925	6.5144	6.7252	6.9262	7.1180	7.3017	7.4778
11	5.5474	5.8485	6.1310	6.3973	6.6491	6.8880	7.1152	7.3319	7.5390	7.7374
12			6.1310	6.4320	6.7160	6.9849	7.2401	7.4832	7.7151	7.9370
13					6.7160	7.0171	7.3023	7.5734	7.8316	8.0783
14							7.3023	7.6033	7.8896	8.1626
15									7.8896	8.1907

TABLE XIX. LOGARITHMS OF THE BINOMIAL COEFFICIENTS

(Continued)

x	N = 31	N = 32	N = 33	N = 34	N = 35	N = 36	N = 37	N = 38	N = 39	N = 40
1	1.4914	1.5052	1.5185	1.5315	1.5441	1.5563	1.5682	1.5798	1.5911	1.6021
2	2.6675	2.6955	2.7226	2.7490	2.7745	2.7993	2.8235	2.8470	2.8698	2.8921
3	3.6527	3.6955	3.7369	3.7770	3.8159	3.8537	3.8904	3.9261	3.9609	3.9948
4	4.4978	4.5558	4.6119	4.6663	4.7190	4.7702	4.8198	4.8681	4.9151	4.9609
5	5.2302	5.3040	5.3754	5.4444	5.5114	5.5763	5.6394	5.7007	5.7602	5.8182
6	5.8670	5.9572	6.0444	6.1287	6.2104	6.2895	6.3664	6.4410	6.5136	6.5841
7	6.4199	6.5271	6.6306	6.7308	6.8277	6.9216	7.0126	7.1011	7.1870	7.2705
8	6.8970	7.0219	7.1425	7.2590	7.3717	7.4809	7.5867	7.6893	7.7890	7.8860
9	7.3045	7.4479	7.5862	7.7198	7.8489	7.9738	8.0948	8.2122	8.3262	8.4369
10	7.6469	7.8096	7.9664	8.1177	8.2638	8.4052	8.5420	8.6746	8.8033	8.9282
11	7.9277	8.1107	8.2868	8.4565	8.6204	8.7787	8.9320	9.0804	9.2243	9.3640
12	8.1496	8.3537	8.5500	8.7391	8.9214	9.0975	9.2678	9.4326	9.5923	9.7472
13	8.3144	8.5408	8.7583	8.9675	9.1692	9.3638	9.5518	9.7336	9.9097	10.0804
14	8.4235	8.6734	8.9132	9.1436	9.3655	9.5794	9.7858	9.9854	10.1785	10.3656
15	8.4779	8.7526	9.0158	9.2686	9.5116	9.7457	9.9715	10.1895	10.4004	10.6045
16	8.4779	8.7789	9.0670	9.3432	9.6085	9.8638	10.1098	10.3471	10.5765	10.7983
17			9.0670	9.3680	9.6568	9.9344	10.2015	10.4591	10.7078	10.9481
18					9.6568	9.9579	10.2473	10.5261	10.7949	11.0545
19							10.2473	10.5483	10.8384	11.1182
20									10.8384	11.1394

x	N = 41	N = 42	N = 43	N = 44	N = 45	N = 46	N = 47	N = 48	N = 49	N = 50
1	1.6128	1.6232	1.6335	1.6435	1.6532	1.6628	1.6721	1.6812	1.6902	1.6990
2	2.9138	2.9350	2.9557	2.9759	2.9956	3.0149	3.0338	3.0523	3.0704	3.0881
3	4.0278	4.0599	4.0914	4.1220	4.1520	4.1813	4.2099	4.2379	4.2654	4.2923
4	5.0055	5.0489	5.0914	5.1327	5.1732	5.2127	5.2513	5.2891	5.3261	5.3623
5	5.8747	5.9298	5.9834	6.0358	6.0870	6.1370	6.1858	6.2336	6.2803	6.3261
6	6.6529	6.7198	6.7851	6.8487	6.9109	6.9716	7.0309	7.0889	7.1456	7.2011
7	7.3518	7.4310	7.5082	7.5834	7.6569	7.7286	7.7986	7.8670	7.9340	7.9995
8	7.9802	8.0720	8.1614	8.2485	8.3336	8.4165	8.4976	8.5767	8.6542	8.7299
9	8.5445	8.6492	8.7512	8.8506	8.9475	9.0421	9.1344	9.2246	9.3127	9.3989
10	9.0496	9.1677	9.2827	9.3947	9.5038	9.6103	9.7142	9.8156	9.9148	10.0117
11	9.4996	9.6315	9.7598	9.8848	10.0065	10.1252	10.2410	10.3540	10.4644	10.5723
12	9.8976	10.0437	10.1858	10.3241	10.4588	10.5901	10.7181	10.8430	10.9650	11.0842
13	10.2460	10.4069	10.5632	10.7153	10.8634	11.0076	11.1482	11.2854	11.4193	11.5501
14	10.5470	10.7231	10.8942	11.0605	11.2224	11.3800	11.5336	11.6833	11.8295	11.9721
15	10.8023	10.9942	11.1805	11.3616	11.5377	11.7090	11.8760	12.0387	12.1974	12.3523
16	11.0132	11.2214	11.4235	11.6198	11.8107	11.9963	12.1770	12.3531	12.5248	12.6923
17	11.1807	11.4060	11.6245	11.8365	12.0426	12.2430	12.4379	12.6278	12.8129	12.9933
18	11.3056	11.5486	11.7842	12.0126	12.2345	12.4501	12.6598	12.8639	13.0627	13.2566
19	11.3886	11.6501	11.9033	12.1489	12.3871	12.6185	12.8434	13.0623	13.2754	13.4830
20	11.4300	11.7108	11.9825	12.2458	12.5010	12.7488	12.9896	13.2236	13.4514	13.6733
21	11.4300	11.7310	12.0220	12.3038	12.5768	12.8416	13.0987	13.3486	13.5916	13.8282
22			12.0220	12.3231	12.6146	12.8971	13.1713	13.4375	13.6964	13.9482
23					12.6146	12.9156	13.2075	13.4908	13.7660	14.0336
24							13.2075	13.5085	13.8008	14.0848
25									13.8008	14.1018

TABLE XIX. LOGARITHMS OF THE BINOMIAL COEFFICIENTS
(Continued)

x	N = 51	N = 52	N = 53	N = 54	N = 55	N = 56	N = 57	N = 58	N = 59	N = 60
1	1.7076	1.7160	1.7243	1.7324	1.7404	1.7482	1.7559	1.7634	1.7709	1.7782
2	3.1055	3.1225	3.1392	3.1556	3.1717	3.1875	3.2030	3.2183	3.2333	3.2480
3	4.3186	4.3444	4.3697	4.3945	4.4189	4.4428	4.4663	4.4893	4.5120	4.5343
4	5.3978	5.4325	5.4666	5.5000	5.5328	5.5650	5.5966	5.6276	5.6581	5.6881
5	6.3709	6.4148	6.4578	6.5000	6.5414	6.5820	6.6219	6.6611	6.6995	6.7373
6	7.2555	7.3087	7.3609	7.4121	7.4622	7.5115	7.5598	7.6072	7.6538	7.6995
7	8.0636	8.1264	8.1879	8.2482	8.3073	8.3653	8.4222	8.4781	8.5329	8.5868
8	8.8040	8.8765	8.9476	9.0172	9.0855	9.1524	9.2181	9.2826	9.3459	9.4080
9	9.4832	9.5657	9.6466	9.7257	9.8033	9.8794	9.9541	10.0273	10.0992	10.1698
10	10.1065	10.1992	10.2900	10.3790	10.4661	10.5515	10.6353	10.7175	10.7982	10.8773
11	10.6778	10.7811	10.8821	10.9810	11.0779	11.1729	11.2660	11.3573	11.4470	11.5349
12	11.2007	11.3147	11.4262	11.5353	11.6422	11.7469	11.8496	11.9503	12.0490	12.1459
13	11.6778	11.8028	11.9250	12.0446	12.1617	12.2764	12.3889	12.4991	12.6072	12.7132
14	12.1115	12.2477	12.3809	12.5113	12.6388	12.7638	12.8862	13.0062	13.1238	13.2392
15	12.5036	12.6514	12.7959	12.9372	13.0755	13.2109	13.3436	13.4735	13.6009	13.7259
16	12.8558	13.0155	13.1716	13.3242	13.4735	13.6196	13.7627	13.9029	14.0403	14.1750
17	13.1694	13.3413	13.5093	13.6735	13.8341	13.9912	14.1450	14.2957	14.4433	14.5880
18	13.4456	13.6301	13.8104	13.9864	14.1586	14.3270	14.4918	14.6532	14.8113	14.9662
19	13.6854	13.8829	14.0757	14.2640	14.4481	14.6280	14.8041	14.9765	15.1453	15.3107
20	13.8895	14.1004	14.3061	14.5070	14.7033	14.8952	15.0829	15.2665	15.4463	15.6224
21	14.0586	14.2833	14.5024	14.7163	14.9252	15.1293	15.3289	15.5241	15.7152	15.9022
22	14.1933	14.4322	14.6651	14.8924	15.1142	15.3309	15.5427	15.7499	15.9525	16.1509
23	14.2940	14.5476	14.7948	15.0358	15.2710	15.5007	15.7251	15.9444	16.1590	16.3689
24	14.3610	14.6298	14.8917	15.1470	15.3960	15.6390	15.8764	16.1083	16.3351	16.5569
25	14.3944	14.6790	14.9561	15.2261	15.4894	15.7462	15.9969	16.2418	16.4812	16.7153
26	14.3944	14.6954	14.9883	15.2736	15.5515	15.8226	16.0871	16.3454	16.5977	16.8444
27			14.9883	15.2894	15.5826	15.8683	16.1471	16.4192	16.6849	16.9445
28					15.5826	15.8836	16.1771	16.4634	16.7429	17.0159
29							16.1771	16.4781	16.7718	17.0586
30									16.7718	17.0729

x	N = 61	N = 62	N = 63	N = 64	N = 65	N = 66	N = 67	N = 68	N = 69	N = 70
1	1.7853	1.7924	1.7993	1.8062	1.8129	1.8195	1.8261	1.8325	1.8388	1.8451
2	3.2625	3.2767	3.2907	3.3045	3.3181	3.3314	3.3446	3.3576	3.3703	3.3829
3	4.5562	4.5777	4.5989	4.6198	4.6403	4.6605	4.6804	4.7000	4.7193	4.7383
4	5.7175	5.7465	5.7750	5.8030	5.8306	5.8578	5.8845	5.9108	5.9368	5.9623
5	6.7745	6.8110	6.8469	6.8822	6.9170	6.9512	6.9849	7.0180	7.0507	7.0829
6	7.7445	7.7887	7.8322	7.8749	7.9170	7.9584	7.9991	8.0392	8.0787	8.1177
7	8.6398	8.6918	8.7429	8.7932	8.8427	8.8914	8.9393	8.9865	9.0330	9.0787
8	9.4691	9.5291	9.5880	9.6460	9.7031	9.7592	9.8144	9.8688	9.9223	9.9750
9	10.2391	10.3072	10.3742	10.4400	10.5047	10.5684	10.6310	10.6927	10.7534	10.8131
10	10.9551	11.0315	11.1066	11.1803	11.2529	11.3242	11.3944	11.4635	11.5315	11.5985
11	11.6213	11.7061	11.7894	11.8713	11.9519	12.0310	12.1089	12.1856	12.2610	12.3352
12	12.2411	12.3345	12.4263	12.5164	12.6051	12.6922	12.7779	12.8623	12.9452	13.0269
13	12.8173	12.9195	13.0199	13.1185	13.2154	13.3107	13.4044	13.4965	13.5872	13.6764
14	13.3524	13.4636	13.5727	13.6799	13.7853	13.8888	13.9906	14.0907	14.1892	14.2861
15	13.8484	13.9687	14.0868	14.2028	14.3168	14.4287	14.5388	14.6470	14.7535	14.8582
16	14.3071	14.4367	14.5640	14.6889	14.8116	14.9322	15.0507	15.1672	15.2818	15.3945
17	14.7298	14.8690	15.0056	15.1397	15.2714	15.4007	15.5278	15.6527	15.7756	15.8964
18	15.1180	15.2670	15.4131	15.5565	15.6973	15.8356	15.9715	16.1050	16.2363	16.3654
19	15.4727	15.6317	15.7875	15.9405	16.0907	16.2381	16.3829	16.5253	16.6651	16.8027
20	15.7950	15.9641	16.1300	16.2927	16.4524	16.6092	16.7632	16.9144	17.0631	17.2092

TABLE XIX. LOGARITHMS OF THE BINOMIAL COEFFICIENTS
(Continued)

x	N = 61	N = 62	N = 63	N = 64	N = 65	N = 66	N = 67	N = 68	N = 69	N = 70
21	16.0855	16.2651	16.4412	16.6139	16.7834	16.9497	17.1130	17.2734	17.4311	17.5860
22	16.3452	16.5355	16.7220	16.9050	17.0844	17.2605	17.4334	17.6031	17.7699	17.9337
23	16.5745	16.7758	16.9731	17.1665	17.3562	17.5422	17.7249	17.9042	18.0802	18.2532
24	16.7741	16.9867	17.1949	17.3991	17.5992	17.7955	17.9881	18.1772	18.3628	18.5451
25	16.9443	17.1685	17.3881	17.6032	17.8140	18.0208	18.2236	18.4227	18.6181	18.8099
26	17.0857	17.3217	17.5529	17.7793	18.0011	18.2186	18.4319	18.6412	18.8465	19.0482
27	17.1984	17.4467	17.6897	17.9277	18.1608	18.3893	18.6133	18.8330	19.0486	19.2603
28	17.2827	17.5436	17.7989	18.0487	18.2935	18.5332	18.7682	18.9987	19.2247	19.4466
29	17.3388	17.6127	17.8805	18.1426	18.3993	18.6506	18.8969	19.1383	19.3751	19.6074
30	17.3668	17.6541	17.9349	18.2096	18.4784	18.7417	18.9996	19.2523	19.5001	19.7431
31	17.3668	17.6679	17.9620	18.2497	18.5311	18.8066	19.0764	19.3407	19.5998	19.8538
32			17.9620	18.2631	18.5575	18.8455	19.1275	19.4038	19.6744	19.9397
33					18.5575	18.8585	19.1531	19.4415	19.7241	20.0010
34							19.1531	19.4541	19.7489	20.0377
35									19.7489	20.0499

x	N = 71	N = 72	N = 73	N = 74	N = 75	N = 76	N = 77	N = 78	N = 79	N = 80
1	1.8513	1.8573	1.8633	1.8692	1.8751	1.8808	1.8865	1.8921	1.8976	1.9031
2	3.3953	3.4076	3.4196	3.4315	3.4433	3.4548	3.4663	3.4776	3.4887	3.4997
3	4.7571	4.7755	4.7938	4.8117	4.8295	4.8470	4.8642	4.8812	4.8981	4.9147
4	5.9875	6.0123	6.0368	6.0609	6.0847	6.1082	6.1314	6.1542	6.1768	6.1991
5	7.1146	7.1459	7.1767	7.2071	7.2370	7.2666	7.2957	7.3245	7.3529	7.3809
6	8.1560	8.1938	8.2310	8.2678	8.3040	8.3397	8.3749	8.4097	8.4440	8.4778
7	9.1238	9.1682	9.2120	9.2552	9.2977	9.3397	9.3811	9.4219	9.4622	9.5020
8	10.0269	10.0781	10.1285	10.1782	10.2271	10.2754	10.3231	10.3701	10.4165	10.4622
9	10.8720	10.9300	10.9871	11.0435	11.0990	11.1537	12.0402	11.2077	11.3135	11.3653
10	11.6644	11.7293	11.7933	11.8564	11.9185	11.9798	12.0402	12.0998	12.1586	12.2166
11	12.4083	12.4803	12.5513	12.6212	12.6900	12.7579	12.8249	12.8909	12.9560	13.0203
12	13.1073	13.1865	13.2645	13.3413	13.4170	13.4917	13.5652	13.6378	13.7094	13.7799
13	13.7642	13.8507	13.9359	14.0198	14.1024	14.1839	14.2642	14.3434	14.4215	14.4985
14	14.3815	14.4754	14.5679	14.6590	14.7487	14.8371	14.9243	15.0102	15.0949	15.1784
15	14.9613	15.0628	15.1626	15.2610	15.3579	15.4534	15.5475	15.6403	15.7317	15.8219
16	15.5054	15.6145	15.7220	15.8278	15.9320	16.0346	16.1358	16.2355	16.3338	16.4307
17	16.0153	16.1322	16.2474	16.3607	16.4724	16.5823	16.6907	16.7974	16.9027	17.0064
18	16.4924	16.6173	16.7403	16.8613	16.9805	17.0979	17.2136	17.3275	17.4398	17.5505
19	16.9379	17.0710	17.2019	17.3308	17.4576	17.5826	17.7057	17.8269	17.9464	18.0641
20	17.3529	17.4942	17.6333	17.7701	17.9048	18.0374	18.1680	18.2967	18.4235	18.5484
21	17.7382	17.8880	18.0353	18.1803	18.3230	18.4634	18.6017	18.7379	18.8721	19.0044
22	18.0948	18.2532	18.4089	18.5621	18.7129	18.8613	19.0075	19.1514	19.2931	19.4328
23	18.4233	18.5904	18.7547	18.9164	19.0755	19.2320	19.3861	19.5378	19.6873	19.8345
24	18.7243	18.9004	19.0735	19.2438	19.4113	19.5761	19.7383	19.8980	20.0553	20.2102
25	18.9984	19.1837	19.3658	19.5448	19.7209	19.8941	20.0646	20.2324	20.3977	20.5604
26	19.2462	19.4408	19.6320	19.8200	20.0049	20.1867	20.3657	20.5417	20.7151	20.8858
27	19.4681	19.6722	19.8728	20.0699	20.2637	20.4543	20.6419	20.8264	21.0080	21.1868
28	19.6644	19.8783	20.0884	20.2948	20.4978	20.6974	20.8937	21.0868	21.2769	21.4639
29	19.8354	20.0593	20.2792	20.4952	20.7075	20.9162	21.1215	21.3234	21.5220	21.7175
30	19.9816	20.2157	20.4455	20.6713	20.8931	21.1112	21.3256	21.5364	21.7439	21.9480
31	20.1030	20.3475	20.5876	20.8234	21.0550	21.2826	21.5063	21.7263	21.9427	22.1556
32	20.1999	20.4552	20.7057	20.9517	21.1933	21.4307	21.6639	21.8933	22.1188	22.3406
33	20.2725	20.5387	20.8000	21.0564	21.3082	21.5556	21.7986	22.0375	22.2724	22.5034
34	20.3208	20.5983	20.8706	21.1377	21.4000	21.6576	21.9106	22.1592	22.4037	22.6440
35	20.3449	20.6340	20.9176	21.1957	21.4687	21.7368	22.0000	22.2586	22.5128	22.7627

TABLE XIX. LOGARITHMS OF THE BINOMIAL COEFFICIENTS
(Continued)

x	N = 71	N = 72	N = 73	N = 74	N = 75	N = 76	N = 77	N = 78	N = 79	N = 80
36	20.3449	20.6459	20.9410	21.2305	21.5145	21.7932	22.0670	22.3358	22.6000	22.8596
37			20.9410	21.2421	21.5374	21.8271	22.1115	22.3908	22.6652	22.9348
38					21.5374	21.8384	22.1338	22.4238	22.7087	22.9885
39							22.1338	22.4348	22.7304	23.0207
40									22.7304	23.0314

x	N = 81	N = 82	N = 83	N = 84	N = 85	N = 86	N = 87	N = 88	N = 89	N = 90
1	1.9085	1.9138	1.9191	1.9243	1.9294	1.9345	1.9395	1.9445	1.9494	1.9542
2	3.5105	3.5213	3.5319	3.5423	3.5527	3.5629	3.5730	3.5830	3.5928	3.6026
3	4.9311	4.9472	4.9632	4.9790	4.9946	5.0100	5.0253	5.0403	5.0552	5.0700
4	6.2211	6.2428	6.2643	6.2854	6.3064	6.3271	6.3475	6.3677	6.3877	6.4074
5	7.4086	7.4359	7.4629	7.4896	7.5159	7.5419	7.5676	7.5930	7.6181	7.6430
6	8.5113	8.5443	8.5769	8.6090	8.6408	8.6722	8.7033	8.7339	8.7643	8.7942
7	9.5412	9.5800	9.6182	9.6560	9.6934	9.7302	9.7667	9.8027	9.8382	9.8734
8	10.5074	10.5520	10.5960	10.6394	10.6824	10.7248	10.7667	10.8081	10.8490	10.8894
9	11.4165	11.4669	11.5168	11.5660	11.6146	11.6626	11.7100	11.7569	11.8032	11.8490
10	12.2738	12.3303	12.3860	12.4411	12.4954	12.5491	12.6021	12.6545	12.7063	12.7574
11	13.0837	13.1462	13.2080	13.2689	13.3291	13.3885	13.4472	13.5052	13.5625	13.6191
12	13.8496	13.9183	13.9861	14.0531	14.1191	14.1844	14.2489	14.3125	14.3754	14.4376
13	14.5745	14.6494	14.7234	14.7964	14.8685	14.9397	15.0100	15.0794	15.1480	15.2157
14	15.2609	15.3422	15.4224	15.5016	15.5797	15.6569	15.7331	15.8083	15.8827	15.9561
15	15.9108	15.9986	16.0851	16.1706	16.2549	16.3381	16.4203	16.5015	16.5816	16.6608
16	16.5263	16.6205	16.7135	16.8053	16.8959	16.9853	17.0735	17.1607	17.2468	17.3318
17	17.1087	17.2096	17.3092	17.4074	17.5043	17.5999	17.6943	17.7876	17.8796	17.9705
18	17.6596	17.7673	17.8734	17.9782	18.0815	18.1835	18.2842	18.3836	18.4817	18.5786
19	18.1802	18.2947	18.4076	18.5190	18.6288	18.7373	18.8443	18.9499	19.0542	19.1572
20	18.6716	18.7930	18.9127	19.0308	19.1473	19.2623	19.3757	19.4877	19.5983	19.7074
21	19.1347	19.2632	19.3899	19.5148	19.6380	19.7596	19.8796	19.9980	20.1149	20.2303
22	19.5704	19.7061	19.8398	19.9717	20.1018	20.2301	20.3567	20.4817	20.6050	20.7267
23	19.9795	20.1225	20.2634	20.4024	20.5394	20.6746	20.8079	20.9395	21.0693	21.1975
24	20.3628	20.5131	20.6614	20.8075	20.9516	21.0937	21.2339	21.3722	21.5087	21.6434
25	20.7207	20.8786	21.0343	21.1877	21.3390	21.4882	21.6353	21.7804	21.9236	22.0650
26	21.0539	21.2195	21.3827	21.5436	21.7022	21.8585	22.0127	22.1648	22.3148	22.4629
27	21.3629	21.5364	21.7073	21.8757	22.0416	22.2053	22.3667	22.5258	22.6828	22.8377
28	21.6481	21.8296	22.0083	22.1844	22.3579	22.5290	22.6977	22.8640	23.0280	23.1899
29	21.9100	22.0996	22.2862	22.4702	22.6514	22.8300	23.0061	23.1797	23.3510	23.5199
30	22.1489	22.3467	22.5415	22.7334	22.9225	23.1088	23.2924	23.4735	23.6520	23.8281
31	22.3651	22.5714	22.7744	22.9744	23.1715	23.3656	23.5569	23.7455	23.9315	24.1149
32	22.5589	22.7738	22.9853	23.1936	23.3987	23.6008	23.8000	23.9963	24.1898	24.3806
33	22.7306	22.9542	23.1743	23.3911	23.6045	23.8147	24.0218	24.2259	24.4271	24.6255
34	22.8804	23.1130	23.3418	23.5671	23.7890	24.0075	24.2227	24.4348	24.6438	24.8499
35	23.0084	23.2501	23.4880	23.7220	23.9525	24.1794	24.4029	24.6231	24.8401	25.0540
36	23.1149	23.3659	23.6129	23.8559	24.0952	24.3307	24.5626	24.7911	25.0162	25.2381
37	23.1999	23.4605	23.7168	23.9690	24.2172	24.4615	24.7020	24.9389	25.1723	25.4023
38	23.2635	23.5339	23.7998	24.0613	24.3186	24.5719	24.8212	25.0667	25.3085	25.5468
39	23.3060	23.5863	23.8619	24.1330	24.3996	24.6620	24.9203	25.1746	25.4250	25.6717
40	23.3271	23.6177	23.9033	24.1841	24.4603	24.7321	24.9995	25.2627	25.5219	25.7772
41	23.3271	23.6282	23.9240	24.2148	24.5008	24.7821	25.0588	25.3312	25.5994	25.8634
42		23.6282	23.9240	24.2250	24.5210	24.8120	25.0983	25.3801	25.6573	25.9303
43					24.5210	24.8220	25.1181	25.4093	25.6960	25.9781
44							25.1181	25.4191	25.7153	26.0068
45									25.7153	26.0163

TABLE XIX. LOGARITHMS OF THE BINOMIAL COEFFICIENTS
(Continued)

x	N = 91	N = 92	N = 93	N = 94	N = 95	N = 96	N = 97	N = 98	N = 99	N = 100
1	1.9590	1.9638	1.9685	1.9731	1.9777	1.9823	1.9868	1.9912	1.9956	2.0000
2	3.6123	3.6218	3.6312	3.6406	3.6498	3.6590	3.6680	3.6770	3.6858	3.6946
3	5.0845	5.0989	5.1132	5.1272	5.1412	5.1550	5.1686	5.1821	5.1955	5.2087
4	6.4269	6.4463	6.4653	6.4842	6.5029	6.5214	6.5397	6.5578	6.5757	6.5934
5	7.6675	7.6918	7.7158	7.7395	7.7630	7.7862	7.8092	7.8319	7.8544	7.8767
6	8.8238	8.8531	8.8821	8.9107	8.9391	8.9671	8.9948	9.0223	9.0494	9.0763
7	9.9082	9.9425	9.9765	10.0101	10.0434	10.0762	10.1088	10.1410	10.1728	10.2043
8	10.9294	10.9689	11.0079	11.0466	11.0848	11.1225	11.1599	11.1969	11.2335	11.2697
9	11.8942	11.9389	11.9831	12.0268	12.0700	12.1128	12.1551	12.1969	12.2383	12.2793
10	12.8080	12.8580	12.9074	12.9562	13.0045	13.0523	13.0996	13.1463	13.1925	13.2383
11	13.6751	13.7304	13.7851	13.8391	13.8926	13.9454	13.9977	14.0494	14.1005	14.1512
12	14.4990	14.5597	14.6197	14.6790	14.7377	14.7956	14.8530	14.9097	14.9658	15.0214
13	15.2827	15.3488	15.4142	15.4789	15.5428	15.6060	15.6685	15.7303	15.7914	15.8519
14	16.0287	16.1003	16.1712	16.2412	16.3105	16.3789	16.4466	16.5136	16.5798	16.6453
15	16.7391	16.8163	16.8927	16.9682	17.0429	17.1167	17.1896	17.2618	17.3331	17.4037
16	17.4157	17.4987	17.5807	17.6617	17.7418	17.8210	17.8993	17.9767	18.0533	18.1290
17	18.0604	18.1491	18.2368	18.3234	18.4090	18.4937	18.5773	18.6601	18.7419	18.8228
18	18.6743	18.7689	18.8623	18.9546	19.0458	19.1360	19.2252	19.3133	19.4005	19.4866
19	19.2589	19.3594	19.4586	19.5567	19.6536	19.7494	19.8440	19.9376	20.0302	20.1217
20	19.8152	19.9216	20.0268	20.1307	20.2334	20.3348	20.4351	20.5342	20.6322	20.7292
21	20.3442	20.4568	20.5679	20.6777	20.7862	20.8934	20.9994	21.1041	21.2076	21.3100
22	20.8469	20.9656	21.0828	21.1986	21.3130	21.4261	21.5378	21.6482	21.7573	21.8652
23	21.3240	21.4490	21.5723	21.6942	21.8146	21.9336	22.0511	22.1673	22.2821	22.3956
24	21.7763	21.9076	22.0372	22.1653	22.2917	22.4167	22.5401	22.6621	22.7827	22.9019
25	22.2045	22.3422	22.4781	22.6124	22.7450	22.8761	23.0055	23.1334	23.2598	23.3847
26	22.6090	22.7533	22.8957	23.0363	23.1752	23.3123	23.4479	23.5818	23.7141	23.8448
27	22.9906	23.1415	23.2904	23.4374	23.5827	23.7261	23.8678	24.0077	24.1460	24.2827
28	23.3496	23.5072	23.6628	23.8164	23.9680	24.1178	24.2657	24.4118	24.5562	24.6989
29	23.6865	23.8510	24.0133	24.1735	24.3317	24.4879	24.6421	24.7945	24.9451	25.0938
30	24.0018	24.1732	24.3424	24.5093	24.6741	24.8368	24.9975	25.1563	25.3130	25.4679
31	24.2958	24.4742	24.6503	24.8241	24.9957	25.1650	25.3322	25.4974	25.6605	25.8217
32	24.5688	24.7544	24.9376	25.1183	25.2967	25.4728	25.6466	25.8183	25.9879	26.1554
33	24.8211	25.0141	25.2044	25.3922	25.5775	25.7604	25.9410	26.1194	26.2954	26.4694
34	25.0531	25.2534	25.4511	25.6460	25.8384	26.0283	26.2157	26.4008	26.5835	26.7640
35	25.2649	25.4728	25.6778	25.8801	26.0797	26.2766	26.4710	26.6629	26.8524	27.0394
36	25.4568	25.6724	25.8850	26.0947	26.3015	26.5057	26.7071	26.9059	27.1022	27.2961
37	25.6289	25.8523	26.0726	26.2899	26.5042	26.7156	26.9242	27.1301	27.3334	27.5340
38	25.7815	26.0129	26.2410	26.4660	26.6878	26.9067	27.1226	27.3357	27.5460	27.7536
39	25.9147	26.1543	26.3903	26.6231	26.8526	27.0790	27.3024	27.5228	27.7402	27.9549
40	26.0287	26.2765	26.5207	26.7614	26.9988	27.2329	27.4638	27.6916	27.9163	28.1382
41	26.1235	26.3797	26.6322	26.8810	27.1264	27.3683	27.6068	27.8422	28.0744	28.3036
42	26.1992	26.4640	26.7249	26.9820	27.2355	27.4854	27.7318	27.9748	28.2146	28.4512
43	26.2559	26.5295	26.7990	27.0646	27.3263	27.5843	27.8387	28.0895	28.3370	28.5811
44	26.2937	26.5763	26.8545	27.1287	27.3989	27.6651	27.9276	28.1865	28.4417	28.6935
45	26.3126	26.6043	26.8915	27.1745	27.4532	27.7279	27.9987	28.2656	28.5289	28.7885
46	26.3126	26.6136	26.9100	27.2019	27.4894	27.7727	28.0519	28.3272	28.5985	28.8661
47			26.9100	27.2110	27.5075	27.7996	28.0874	28.3711	28.6507	28.9264
48					27.5075	27.8086	28.1051	28.3974	28.6855	28.9694
49							28.1051	28.4062	28.7028	28.9953
50									28.7028	29.0039

APPENDIX B

School and College Ability Test Scores
Verbal (X) and Quantitative (Y)
For 995 College Freshmen

Student ID No.	X	Y	Student ID No.	X	Y	Student ID No.	X	Y
1	39	35	51	32	22	101	40	33
2	57	37	52	44	31	102	40	26
3	36	47	53	20	17	103	50	40
4	54	46	54	53	48	104	50	39
5	38	35	55	39	35	105	42	29
6	29	34	56	57	49	106	40	16
7	53	39	57	28	27	107	44	30
8	55	33	58	33	41	108	45	29
9	42	24	59	59	45	109	39	36
10	39	35	60	44	44	110	34	21
11	30	34	61	49	46	111	47	31
12	34	31	62	45	25	112	40	44
13	38	45	63	52	36	113	45	32
14	31	28	64	40	33	114	32	38
15	29	30	65	44	33	115	45	19
16	46	46	66	38	30	116	40	47
17	42	36	67	39	33	117	55	35
18	48	41	68	36	22	118	24	30
19	31	29	69	36	34	119	42	32
20	35	34	70	54	32	120	41	30
21	56	43	71	43	38	121	23	25
22	48	43	72	42	39	122	25	11
23	46	36	73	52	40	123	6	21
24	27	19	74	45	40	124	53	35
25	36	44	75	36	46	125	56	42
26	47	38	76	56	37	126	51	28
27	54	38	77	49	40	127	53	36
28	52	36	78	30	42	128	52	39
29	45	42	79	38	24	129	52	43
30	45	43	80	36	34	130	48	21
31	50	32	81	56	34	131	44	40
32	34	42	82	32	46	132	16	31
33	44	17	83	44	24	133	32	36
34	43	29	84	29	38	134	43	22
35	47	41	85	22	25	135	51	40
36	35	37	86	35	32	136	23	29
37	43	46	87	50	35	137	54	31
38	50	46	88	27	18	138	47	46
39	44	28	89	50	39	139	47	37
40	36	43	90	45	34	140	36	22
41	46	43	91	45	33	141	49	33
42	16	29	92	33	28	142	49	31
43	41	22	93	43	49	143	42	38
44	53	33	94	54	29	144	26	28
45	40	17	95	5	14	145	53	44
46	31	34	96	57	31	146	31	20
47	38	15	97	48	48	147	38	43
48	28	33	98	46	36	148	49	29
49	41	32	99	46	36	149	53	26
50	39	32	100	25	27	150	47	34

Student ID No.	X	Y	Student ID No.	X	Y	Student ID No.	X	Y
151	34	36	211	36	17	271	33	33
152	51	40	212	36	45	272	22	20
153	38	35	213	41	41	273	31	31
154	38	28	214	51	42	274	54	41
155	37	45	215	39	42	275	35	23
156	50	42	216	32	37	276	49	28
157	43	40	217	36	36	277	41	42
158	31	24	218	37	27	278	47	38
159	56	39	219	46	33	279	43	39
160	53	39	220	47	31	280	38	34
161	32	46	221	11	07	281	54	35
162	52	27	222	40	29	282	37	33
163	51	31	223	31	44	283	38	28
164	48	35	224	55	43	284	37	32
165	33	38	225	35	19	285	25	29
166	35	43	226	52	39	286	47	38
167	43	33	227	44	34	287	42	33
168	45	41	228	37	47	288	29	41
169	54	29	229	33	28	289	32	18
170	41	30	230	39	26	290	40	45
171	37	26	231	51	36	291	41	16
172	56	30	232	50	25	292	45	47
173	57	24	233	42	39	293	41	42
174	45	44	234	51	29	294	48	31
175	33	47	235	34	32	295	50	33
176	54	40	236	32	31	296	39	31
177	21	15	237	53	34	297	38	16
178	30	16	238	43	34	298	41	24
179	41	25	239	50	44	299	42	26
180	39	45	240	55	24	300	47	22
181	48	40	241	41	31	301	34	37
182	26	24	242	11	09	302	51	33
183	34	30	243	27	31	303	30	17
184	47	35	244	38	37	304	50	29
185	35	43	245	25	33	305	30	27
186	50	37	246	45	43	306	41	41
187	40	35	247	32	45	307	47	34
188	48	42	248	59	35	308	28	36
189	36	26	249	46	15	309	37	29
190	42	42	250	45	46	310	44	18
191	34	23	251	33	37	311	25	24
192	24	31	252	38	26	312	53	25
193	35	40	253	41	35	313	55	46
194	48	50	254	55	46	314	31	27
195	49	27	255	41	31	315	41	34
196	41	21	256	21	36	316	40	29
197	31	29	257	54	39	317	40	28
198	46	27	258	37	14	318	31	38
199	37	45	259	48	40	319	52	20
200	31	33	260	26	09	320	55	41
201	47	44	261	43	37	321	60	46
202	34	31	262	46	50	322	45	34
203	35	31	263	23	33	323	32	38
204	53	25	264	23	24	324	48	26
205	48	39	265	43	32	325	34	28
206	35	30	266	42	32	326	24	34
207	36	30	267	39	30	327	32	42
208	43	29	268	47	31	328	43	26
209	30	45	269	46	41	329	31	25
210	35	26	270	38	35	330	54	49

Student ID No.	X	Y	Student ID No.	X	Y	Student ID No.	X	Y
331	21	37	391	54	28	451	47	24
332	46	37	392	48	49	452	32	38
333	41	24	393	45	33	453	55	35
334	52	26	394	46	35	454	35	43
335	47	32	395	45	30	455	45	41
336	54	39	396	49	34	456	30	34
337	45	38	397	45	41	457	57	36
338	53	46	398	40	34	458	54	37
339	42	43	399	53	48	459	50	38
340	40	29	400	56	31	460	51	21
341	40	44	401	54	42	461	46	49
342	44	43	402	39	40	462	42	33
343	54	39	403	48	41	463	47	47
344	39	42	404	29	40	464	50	36
345	49	43	405	52	27	465	59	35
346	53	31	406	36	37	466	35	30
347	25	37	407	53	36	467	59	50
348	52	37	408	53	35	468	31	43
349	48	14	409	52	27	469	26	30
350	35	48	410	47	36	470	33	22
351	42	41	411	33	41	471	52	25
352	54	48	412	30	33	472	40	35
353	25	07	413	36	31	473	45	46
354	39	44	414	45	38	474	55	47
355	53	31	415	47	26	475	54	37
356	56	47	416	29	28	476	44	22
357	29	30	417	36	42	477	45	35
358	57	50	418	28	32	478	47	33
359	33	31	419	37	39	479	44	33
360	51	45	420	52	35	480	59	26
361	34	28	421	54	43	481	50	42
362	22	32	422	43	31	482	37	28
363	44	29	423	44	42	483	31	37
364	32	40	424	33	37	484	44	16
365	52	33	425	40	30	485	43	31
366	47	35	426	37	31	486	52	23
367	43	34	427	42	32	487	42	26
368	48	33	428	32	22	488	48	41
369	37	28	429	59	43	489	43	39
370	27	24	430	38	20	490	30	46
371	50	44	431	38	49	491	22	26
372	35	10	432	48	34	492	65	26
373	35	44	433	49	37	493	56	38
374	33	36	434	40	21	494	34	34
375	48	43	435	34	32	495	54	30
376	39	20	436	43	45	496	41	37
377	34	35	437	44	28	497	50	25
378	19	15	438	44	39	498	43	27
379	52	34	439	45	36	499	52	39
380	42	27	440	24	23	500	45	43
381	24	37	441	39	43	501	42	36
382	37	31	442	44	25	502	50	27
383	40	42	443	32	28	503	38	34
384	38	34	444	35	21	504	33	24
385	36	37	445	37	32	505	43	37
386	41	48	446	25	29	506	37	39
387	37	17	447	44	37	507	30	28
388	41	38	448	37	42	508	42	28
389	23	36	449	54	27	509	40	32
390	46	43	450	40	32	510	40	39

Student ID No.	X	Y	Student ID No.	X	Y	Student ID No.	X	Y
511	43	26	571	34	43	631	43	49
512	49	46	572	35	44	632	36	32
513	34	27	573	46	36	633	42	28
514	37	21	574	38	25	634	56	30
515	39	28	575	45	37	635	38	18
516	37	29	576	40	44	636	55	39
517	42	39	577	25	31	637	44	33
518	22	21	578	1	30	638	43	21
519	36	23	579	24	23	639	40	45
520	28	27	580	28	26	640	53	32
521	57	46	581	42	36	641	41	32
522	49	19	582	48	45	642	32	26
523	19	09	583	41	19	643	37	37
524	55	32	584	53	35	644	51	42
525	39	38	585	40	31	645	40	41
526	32	28	586	36	27	646	51	48
527	33	50	587	32	34	647	34	27
528	47	46	588	30	40	648	41	47
529	44	33	589	43	42	649	44	22
530	34	37	590	53	33	650	42	29
531	44	49	591	28	40	651	32	34
532	46	33	592	42	20	652	40	39
533	52	21	593	36	37	653	42	43
534	32	22	594	46	37	654	53	42
535	52	49	595	48	38	655	45	29
536	30	34	596	55	35	656	32	40
537	24	36	597	45	34	657	43	42
538	45	41	598	49	40	658	34	39
539	36	24	599	43	36	659	45	33
540	18	20	600	48	39	660	32	47
541	51	46	601	41	35	661	47	31
542	30	30	602	36	30	662	37	33
543	49	38	603	41	37	663	44	33
544	38	38	604	41	42	664	23	23
545	48	41	605	40	36	665	56	47
546	42	35	606	34	26	666	44	34
547	44	40	607	30	33	667	45	45
548	40	30	608	50	45	668	44	46
549	50	16	609	34	45	669	27	30
550	27	34	610	38	24	670	39	23
551	46	38	611	27	31	671	54	30
552	30	29	612	37	45	672	37	13
553	40	47	613	58	36	673	53	40
554	44	26	614	41	14	674	50	39
555	19	20	615	46	44	675	33	24
556	56	48	616	38	34	676	59	35
557	57	36	617	38	41	677	36	38
558	37	29	618	21	40	678	40	30
559	46	39	619	36	42	679	39	42
560	39	33	620	39	44	680	57	41
561	46	26	621	56	33	681	39	37
562	35	29	622	39	31	682	35	31
563	39	25	623	29	27	683	44	42
564	49	43	624	35	32	684	49	45
565	40	26	625	48	23	685	31	21
566	44	32	626	50	41	686	39	16
567	56	29	627	53	34	687	38	31
568	28	25	628	31	37	688	50	42
569	40	41	629	51	39	689	53	45
570	43	33	630	38	36	690	49	43

Student ID No.	X	Y	Student ID No.	X	Y	Student ID No.	X	Y
691	45	27	751	58	32	811	52	31
692	41	32	752	38	35	812	47	46
693	48	29	753	51	47	813	43	37
694	28	35	754	49	38	814	54	28
695	42	38	755	42	42	815	49	29
696	41	23	756	41	29	816	37	31
697	51	28	757	51	29	817	49	34
698	24	12	758	44	48	818	27	31
699	47	33	759	37	35	819	48	37
700	24	33	760	58	32	820	36	41
701	45	29	761	27	37	821	30	37
702	45	34	762	28	31	822	33	34
703	18	15	763	43	29	823	35	29
704	52	22	764	29	36	824	43	34
705	46	41	765	49	41	825	53	32
706	44	32	766	58	37	826	51	36
707	41	37	767	41	23	827	34	43
708	36	43	768	53	41	828	26	23
709	42	32	769	51	38	829	49	41
710	57	41	770	40	35	830	41	42
711	35	24	771	50	39	831	44	30
712	24	30	772	34	27	832	36	22
713	50	34	773	58	42	833	30	38
714	40	27	774	48	43	834	45	33
715	39	43	775	47	37	835	51	39
716	41	36	776	46	35	836	47	37
717	54	37	777	41	38	837	37	36
718	36	34	778	46	30	838	40	37
719	56	37	779	39	29	839	31	29
720	47	40	780	38	29	840	20	33
721	43	36	781	49	44	841	49	36
722	19	14	782	36	39	842	33	26
723	44	34	783	37	41	843	28	30
724	43	30	784	32	23	844	22	27
725	31	31	785	22	25	845	35	43
726	42	26	786	36	34	846	19	26
727	26	39	787	32	24	847	41	43
728	54	44	788	53	47	848	40	32
729	45	22	789	47	36	849	56	45
730	53	44	790	43	45	850	40	42
731	37	45	791	20	11	851	57	48
732	42	36	792	34	27	852	38	32
733	37	39	793	41	38	853	24	28
734	53	40	794	46	41	854	55	47
735	46	46	795	52	21	855	55	37
736	34	32	796	36	44	856	37	40
737	33	26	797	26	37	857	45	31
738	28	33	798	51	40	858	50	44
739	48	45	799	50	50	859	36	40
740	58	47	800	36	26	860	34	24
741	48	48	801	35	29	861	45	43
742	37	33	802	50	33	862	39	42
743	45	27	803	52	45	863	28	30
744	56	40	804	30	39	864	41	23
745	51	28	805	49	25	865	49	45
746	29	33	806	33	37	866	23	22
747	38	19	807	34	31	867	58	46
748	35	43	808	30	22	868	52	46
749	45	27	809	50	32	869	55	40
750	46	46	810	52	29	870	31	25

Student ID No.	X	Y	Student ID No.	X	Y	Student ID No.	X	Y
871	39	38	916	51	41	961	52	22
872	36	24	917	28	22	962	37	19
873	29	29	918	32	38	963	35	37
874	46	39	919	44	36	964	34	32
875	33	33	920	43	31	965	40	35
876	50	40	921	34	44	966	44	26
877	45	35	922	26	31	967	31	43
878	30	24	923	52	36	968	37	25
879	43	38	924	35	25	969	48	42
880	30	48	925	44	24	970	51	31
881	50	34	926	27	19	971	45	21
882	49	31	927	38	38	972	39	28
883	43	42	928	45	32	973	49	33
884	43	25	929	31	30	974	52	47
885	37	40	930	41	50	975	43	36
886	47	31	931	38	35	976	14	19
887	36	32	932	50	49	977	46	40
888	50	32	933	60	48	978	29	33
889	41	24	934	56	29	979	32	35
890	31	24	935	32	19	980	23	21
891	35	33	936	30	34	981	37	29
892	41	43	937	36	28	982	37	19
893	28	25	938	36	29	983	36	26
894	44	40	939	38	31	984	50	46
895	42	29	940	59	43	985	23	6
896	24	19	941	30	19	986	37	33
897	47	43	942	22	16	987	33	32
898	30	21	943	35	32	988	43	42
899	46	40	944	59	34	989	35	34
900	41	45	945	39	40	990	46	27
901	40	34	946	36	38	991	46	46
902	40	40	947	24	34	992	41	35
903	30	19	948	38	35	993	46	28
904	42	27	949	35	37	994	25	28
905	36	35	950	47	38	995	52	29
906	35	37	951	24	30			
907	42	16	952	28	29			
908	46	30	953	42	31			
909	52	41	954	49	29			
910	37	35	955	35	22			
911	36	33	956	34	37			
912	53	31	957	44	41			
913	44	42	958	38	26			
914	38	22	959	33	38			
915	40	17	960	55	42			

APPENDIX C

For all of the tests listed below, the following three assumptions or conditions must be satisfied before the tests may be applied:

(a) Randomness of sample
(b) Normality of distribution
   (Or the distribution must be either very nearly normal or such that it may be made normal by means of some type of transformation.)
(c) Independency of data

If these conditions cannot be met, some type of nonparametric statistic must be used; see *Nonparametric Statistics for the Behavioral Sciences*, by Sidney Siegel (New York: McGraw-Hill Book Company, Inc., 1956).

HYPOTHESIS TO BE TESTED	TEST TO USE	CONDITIONS WHICH MUST BE PRESENT
1. About the value of a single population mean	z-test	Must know *both* μ and σ
	t-test d.f. $= n - 1$	Only μ known
2. Equality of two population means a. When data are not paired or correlated	t-test for significance between means d.f. $= n_1 + n_2 - 2$	Common value of σ for both populations must be assumed, or else modification involving computation of d.f. must be used.
b. When data are paired or correlated	t-test for paired or correlated data d.f. $= n - 1$	Same as for 2a
3. Equality of more than two population means	Analysis of variance	Common variance
4. About the value of a single population proportion	z-test	Must know p', q', n

HYPOTHESIS TO BE TESTED	TEST TO USE	CONDITIONS WHICH MUST BE PRESENT
5. Equality of two population proportions a. Uncorrelated data	z-test for uncorrelated proportions or X^2 test for 2×2 contingency table	
b. Correlated proportions	z-test using modification of standard error	
6. Equality of more than two population proportions	X^2 test d.f. $= (r - 1)(c - 1)$	
7. About the value of a single population variance	X^2/d.f. test d.f. $= n - 1$	
8. Equality of two population variances	F-ratio d.f.: $f_1 = n_1 - 1$ $f_2 = n_2 - 1$	
9. Equality of more than two population variances	Bartlett's X^2 approximation d.f. $= k - 1$	
10. Significant relationship between two or more variables	Coefficient of correlation	For relationship between two variables, data must be linearly related if Pearson Product Moment method is to be used.
11. To develop a predictive equation of relationship between two or more variables	Regression equation	

ANSWERS TO PROBLEMS

Chapter 1   PAGE 8

1. 3360; 29400; 68600; 19.1
2. 40.1076; 42.23; 9.584
3. 3.14; 26.85; 125.82; 29.92; 26.00; 88.20
4. (a) 0.2; (b) 0.00019; (c) 5.5; (d) 7.33
5. (a) 0.013 mm.^{2}; (b) 3.69 in.^{2}; (c) 7.67 cm.^{2}
6. (a) 7.24; (b) 0.0572; (c) 27.2; (d) 0.20
7. (a) 35.00; (b) 0.130; (c) 18.600; (d) 7.82000; (e) 13.600; (f) 28.900; (g) 147.00; (h) 16.292; (i) 26.3

Chapter 2   PAGE 21

1. (a) $\overline{X} = 53$, Median $= 51$; (b) $\overline{X} = 25$, Median $= 25$; (c) $\overline{X} = 6$, Median $= 5$, Mode $= 2, 4, 8$; (d) $\overline{X} = 262$, Median $= 262.2$, Mode $= 262$; (e) $\overline{X} = 16.3$, Median $= 16.3$, Mode $= 16.5$; (f) $\overline{X} = 9.4$, Median $= 9.4$; (g) $\overline{X} = 1267$, Median $= 1268$, Mode $= 1268$
2. (a) 21; (b) 32; (c) 16; (d) 77
3. (a) $\sum_{i=1}^{3} X_i$; (b) $\sum_{i=1}^{4} 3X_i$
4. 80
6. (a) 4; (b) 15; when all members of the set are equal
7. $\overline{X} = 34.8$, Median $= 35.7$
10. 3.7

Chapter 3   PAGE 39

1. (a) $\overline{X} = 3$, $s^2 = 10.3$, $s = 3.21$; (b) $\overline{X} = 24$, $s^2 = 6.5$, $s = 2.6$; (c) $\overline{X} = 4.6$, $s^2 = 7.4$, $s = 2.7$
2. $\overline{X} = 51$, $s^2 = 1071.43$, $s = 32.73$
3. (a) $\overline{X} = 34.1$, $s = 7.08$
4. $\overline{X} = 16.1$, $s^2 = 0.075$, $s = 0.273$
5. $\overline{X} = 7$, $s = 2.2$
6. $[(X_1 - X_2 + X_3 - X_4)/2]^2 + [(X_1 - X_2 - X_3 + X_4)/2]^2 + [(X_1 + X_2 - X_3 - X_4)/2]^2$
7. 1.00, 1.50
8. 38.0, 50.0, 66.0, 54.0, 42.0
9.

	STUDENT		
TEST	A	B	C
1	69.3	75.3	41.6
2	50.0	38.3	65.6
3	50.0	55.4	75.4
4	41.2	37.9	26.9

10. $\overline{X} = 518.5$, $s = 67.83$

11. For $X_1, X_2, \ldots, X_N$ as X_i's and $z_1, z_2, \ldots, z_N$ as their standardized deviate equivalents where

$$z_i = \frac{X_i - \mu}{\sigma} \quad \text{and} \quad \sigma^2 = \frac{\sum(X - \mu)^2}{N}$$

$$\sum_{i=1}^{N} z_i^2 = \sum_{i=1}^{N}\left[\frac{X - \mu}{\sigma}\right]^2 = \sum_{i=1}^{N}\frac{(X - \mu)^2}{\sigma^2}$$

$$= \frac{\sum(X - \mu)^2}{\frac{\sum(X - \mu)^2}{N}} = [\sum(X - \mu)^2][N/\sum(X - \mu)^2]$$

$$= N$$

13. $\overline{X} = 99.997$, $s^2 = 0.000013$, $s = 0.004$

14. $\overline{X} = 0.9996$, $s^2 = 0.000002933 = 2.9 \times 10^{-6}$, $s = 0.00171 = 1.7 \times 10^{-3}$

15. $\overline{X} = 0.91360$, $s^2 = 26 \times 10^{-10}$, $s = 5.1 \times 10^{-5}$

Chapter 4 PAGE 56

1. (a) $\frac{1}{6}$; (b) $\frac{1}{52}$; (c) $\frac{12}{19}$

2. $\frac{4}{6}$ or $\frac{2}{3}$

3. $\frac{1}{16}$

4. $\frac{5}{36}$

5. $H_1H_2H_3$, $H_1H_2T_3$, $H_1T_2H_3$, $T_1H_2H_3$, $H_1T_2T_3$, $T_1H_2T_3$, $T_1T_2H_3$, $T_1T_2T_3$
plus a 1, 2, 3, 4, 5, or 6 on the die. As such the answers are
  (a) $\frac{1}{16}$ (b) $\frac{1}{3}$

6. $\frac{1}{128}$, $\frac{7}{128}$, $\frac{21}{128}$, $\frac{35}{128}$, $\frac{35}{128}$, $\frac{21}{128}$, $\frac{7}{128}$, $\frac{1}{128}$; $\frac{7}{8}$

7. $\frac{8}{19}$; $\frac{8}{19}$

8. $\frac{1250}{7776} = \frac{625}{3888}$

9. $\frac{7}{128}$

10. $1/230,300$

11. 150

12. (a) $\frac{8}{27}$; (b) $\frac{1}{27}$; (c) $\frac{12}{27}$; (d) $\frac{6}{27}$

13. $\frac{12}{25}$

14. $n! = 24$

15. $\frac{120}{1024} = \frac{15}{128}$

16. $\frac{41}{9765625}$

17. 0.1000

18. 0.60

19. $\frac{32}{243}$

20. $\frac{45}{1024}$; $\frac{144}{1024}$

21. (a) $\frac{30}{77}$; (b) $\frac{10}{77}$; (c) $\frac{40}{77}$

22. 0.0844

23. $\frac{1}{4}$

24. $\dfrac{1}{7!}; \dfrac{1}{3!}, \dfrac{1}{4!}, \dfrac{1}{5!}, \dfrac{1}{6!}$

25. (a) 0.000027216; (b) 1/10!

Chapter 5 PAGE 82

1. 0.30854; 0.066807; 0.40129; 0.61708; 0.54674; 0.0066807

2. 0.10565; 0.9946139; 0.060799; 0.9946139; $P[19.43 \le \overline{X} \le 22.57] = 0.95$; $P[18.75 \le \overline{X} \le 23.25] = 0.995$

3. Approximately $0.999; 1.8751 \times 10^{-6}; 0.20054; P[-8.0024 \le \overline{X} \le -3.9976] = 0.80$

4. $0.42074; 0.65542; 0.9999; P[0.0545 \le \overline{d} \le 3.9455] = 0.9999$

5. (a) $P[11.5 \le s^2 \le 30.3] = 0.90 \mid \sigma^2 = 20, n = 25$
$P[15.7 \le s^2 \le 25.1] = 0.90 \mid \sigma^2 = 20, n = 100$
$P[10.3 \le s^2 \le 32.9] = 0.95 \mid \sigma^2 = 20, n = 25$
$P[14.8 \le s^2 \le 25.9] = 0.95 \mid \sigma^2 = 20, n = 100$
$P[8.2 \le s^2 \le 36.8] = 0.99 \mid \sigma^2 = 20, n = 25$
$P[13.4 \le s^2 \le 28.1] = 0.99 \mid \sigma^2 = 20, n = 100$

(b) $P[16.8 \le \overline{X} \le 19.2] = 0.90 \mid \mu = 18, \sigma^2 = 20, n = 25$
$P[17.4 \le \overline{X} \le 18.6] = 0.90 \mid \mu = 18, \sigma^2 = 20, n = 100$
$P[16.2 \le \overline{X} \le 19.7] = 0.95 \mid \mu = 18, \sigma^2 = 20, n = 25$
$P[17.1 \le \overline{X} \le 18.9] = 0.95 \mid \mu = 18, \sigma^2 = 20, n = 100$
$P[15.7 \le \overline{X} \le 20.3] = 0.99 \mid \mu = 18, \sigma^2 = 20, n = 25$
$P[16.8 \le \overline{X} \le 19.2] = 0.99 \mid \mu = 18, \sigma^2 = 20, n = 100$

(c) $P[-1.42 \le (\overline{X}_1 - \overline{X}_2) \le 1.42] = 0.90 \mid \mu_1 = \mu_2, \sigma_1^2 = \sigma_2^2, s_1^2 = s_2^2 = 9, n_1 = n_2 = 25$
$P[-0.70 \le (\overline{X}_1 - \overline{X}_2) \le 0.70] = 0.90 \mid \mu_1 = \mu_2, \sigma_1^2 = \sigma_2^2, s_1^2 = s_2^2 = 9, n_1 = n_2 = 100$
$P[-1.70 \le (\overline{X}_1 - \overline{X}_2) \le 1.70] = 0.95 \mid \mu_1 = \mu_2, \sigma_1^2 = \sigma_2^2, s_1^2 = s_2^2 = 9, n_1 = n_2 = 25$
$P[-0.84 \le (\overline{X}_1 - \overline{X}_2) \le 0.84] = 0.95 \mid \mu_1 = \mu_2, \sigma_1^2 = \sigma_2^2, s_1^2 = s_2^2 = 9, n_1 = n_2 = 100$
$P[-2.28 \le (\overline{X}_1 - \overline{X}_2) \le 2.28] = 0.99 \mid \mu_1 = \mu_2, \sigma_1^2 = \sigma_2^2, s_1^2 = s_2^2 = 9, n_1 = n_2 = 25$
$P[-1.10 \le (\overline{X}_1 - \overline{X}_2) \le 1.10] = 0.99 \mid \mu_1 = \mu_2, \sigma_1^2 = \sigma_2^2, s_1^2 = s_2^2 = 9, n_1 = n_2 = 100$

(d) $P[0.83 \le \overline{d} \le 1.17] = 0.90 \mid \mu_d = 1, s_d = 0.5, n = 25 \text{ and } n = 100$
$P[0.79 \le \overline{d} \le 1.21] = 0.95 \mid \mu_d = 1, s_d = 0.5, n = 25$
$P[0.80 \le \overline{d} \le 1.20] = 0.95 \mid \mu_d = 1, s_d = 0.5, n = 100$
$P[0.72 \le \overline{d} \le 1.28] = 0.99 \mid \mu_d = 1, s_d = 0.5, n = 25$
$P[0.74 \le \overline{d} \le 1.26] = 0.99 \mid \mu_d = 1, s_d = 0.5, n = 100$

(e) $P[8.4 \leq X \leq 16.6] = 0.90 \mid p' = \frac{1}{2}, n = 25$
$P[41.8 \leq X \leq 58.2] = 0.90 \mid p' = \frac{1}{2}, n = 100$
$P[7.6 \leq X \leq 17.4] = 0.95 \mid p' = \frac{1}{2}, n = 25$
$P[40.2 \leq X \leq 59.8] = 0.95 \mid p' = \frac{1}{2}, n = 100$
$P[6.1 \leq X \leq 18.9] = 0.99 \mid p' = \frac{1}{2}, n = 25$
$P[37.1 \leq X \leq 62.9] = 0.99 \mid p' = \frac{1}{2}, n = 100$

6. (a) 0.040059; (b) 0.174255; (c) 0.060796

7. 0.12449

8. 0.0031474

9. 0.012224

10. 0.13030

11. 0.030742

12. 0.009409; 94.09

Chapter 6 PAGE 102

1. For $\alpha = 0.10$

TEST	96	97	98	99	100	101	102	103	104
a	0.0005	0.0027	0.0113	0.0375	0.1000	0.2177	0.3879	0.5871	0.7642
b	0.7642	0.5871	0.3897	0.2177	0.1000	0.0375	0.0113	0.0027	0.0005
c	0.6388	0.4432	0.2636	0.1421	0.1000	0.1421	0.2636	0.4432	0.6388

For $\alpha = 0.05$

a	0.0001	0.0008	0.0041	0.0160	0.0500	0.1261	0.2595	0.4424	0.6387
b	0.6387	0.4424	0.2595	0.1261	0.0500	0.0160	0.0041	0.0008	0.0001
c	0.5160	0.3230	0.1701	0.0791	0.0500	0.0791	0.1701	0.3230	0.5160

For $\alpha = 0.02$

a	0.0000	0.0002	0.0011	0.0052	0.0200	0.0600	0.1457	0.2894	0.4781
b	0.4781	0.2894	0.1457	0.0600	0.0200	0.0052	0.0011	0.0002	0.0000
c	0.3783	0.2048	0.0970	0.0364	0.0200	0.0364	0.0970	0.2048	0.3783

For $\alpha = 0.01$

a	0.0000	0.0001	0.0004	0.0024	0.0100	0.0340	0.0926	0.2047	0.3726
b	0.3726	0.2047	0.0926	0.0340	0.0100	0.0024	0.0004	0.0001	0.0000
c	0.2823	0.1410	0.0581	0.0200	0.0100	0.0200	0.0581	0.1410	0.2823

2. 180,314.54, use 180,315; 342,554.08, use 342,555; 630,732.04, use 630,733

3. (a) 0.000396885; (b) approximately 1.000; (c) 0.4305

4. (a) Approximately 1.000; (b) 0.0037; (c) 0.0000010686, approximately 1.000

5. 1082.41, use 1083

6. 657.41, use 658; 1686.7, use 1687; 2164.1, use 2165

7. The new $n = 3426.9316$, or use 3427. This would mean an increase of 2,345.

8.

		$1 - \alpha$		
		0.90	0.98	0.99
$1 - \beta$	0.80	$n = 1804.5504$ use 1,805	$n = 3354.7264$ use 3,355	$n = 4014.4896$ use 4,015
	0.95	$n = 3426.9316$ use 3,427	$n = 5473.0404$ use 5.474	$n = 6307.5364$ use 6,308
	0.98	$n = 4451.5584$ use 4,452	$n = 6750.2656$ use 6,751	$n = 7673.7600$ use 7,764

Chapter 7 PAGE 114

1. $z = -0.274$; do not reject the hypothesis.

2. $z = -1.125$; do not reject the hypothesis.
$P[47.7 \leq \overline{X} \leq 54.3] = 0.9842 \mid \mu = 51.5$;
574,335.40994064, use 574,336

3. $t = -1.799$; for test (c), do not reject H_o; for test (b), reject H_o.

4. $t = 0.318$; do not reject H_o.

5. (a) $P[-2.8 < (\mu_1 - \mu_2) < 2.0] = 0.90$; (b) $P[-3.5 < \mu_1 < 0.7] = 0.90$;
(c) $P[-5.4 < (\mu_1 - \mu_2) < -0.2] = 0.90$; (d) $P[7.6 < \mu_d < 8.5] = 0.90$

6. $t = 2.000$; reject H_o.

7. $z = -0.67$; do not reject H_o.

8. $z = -2.50$; reject H_o.

9. $t = -2.125$; do not reject H_o.

10. $z = -5.000$; reject H_o.

11. $t = -8.433$; reject H_o. Randomness of sample, normality of distribution, independence of data, homoscedasticity; $P[-7.42 < (\mu_1 - \mu_2) < -4.58] = 0.95$

Chapter 8 PAGE 126

1. $s^2/\sigma^2 = 0.485$; reject H_o in both cases.

2. $P[2.99 < \sigma^2 < 9.941] = 0.99$

3. $\chi^2 = 3.750$; do not reject H_o: $\sigma_1^2 = \sigma_2^2 = \sigma_3^2 = \sigma_4^2 = \sigma_5^2 = \sigma_0^2$; $P[24.5 < \sigma_0^2 < 46.7] = 0.95$

4. $F = 1.354$; do not reject H_o.

5. $s^2/\sigma^2 = 1.44$; do not reject H_o.

6. $s \leq 22.9$
7. Reject H_o if $F > F_{(24,24),\ 0.99} = 2.6591$.
8. $F = 2.40$; do not reject H_o.
9. $s^2/\sigma^2 = 1.15$; do not reject H_o.

Chapter 9 PAGE 141

1. $z = 0.577$; do not reject H_o.
2. $z = 3.340$; reject H_o.
3. $z = 0.305$; do not reject H_o.
4. $\chi^2 = 44.4$; reject H_o.
5. $\chi^2 = 3.361$; do not reject H_o.
6. $\chi^2 = 4.555$; do not reject H_o.
7. $\chi^2 = 42.42$; reject H_o.
8. Not significant
9. $\chi^2 = 10.8$; reject H_o.
10. $\chi^2 = 5.64$; reject H_o.

Chapter 10 PAGE 168

1.

SOURCE OF VARIABILITY	SSD	$d.f.$	MS	F
BETWEEN SAMPLES	945.88	5	189.176	1.071[a]
WITHIN SAMPLES	10936.30	54	202.524	
TOTAL	12828.06	59		

[a] Not significant at the 0.05 level; do not reject H_o.

2.

SOURCE OF VARIABILITY	SSD	$d.f.$	MS	F
BETWEEN DRUGS	268.593	2	134.296	1.084[a]
BETWEEN DISORDERS	179.148	2	89.574	1.625[a]
INTERACTION: DRUGS × DISORDERS	986.518	4	246.630	1.695[a]
WITHIN	6548.333	45	145.518	
TOTAL	7982.593	53		

[a] Not significant at the 0.05 level; do not reject H_o.

3.

SOURCE OF VARIABILITY	SSD	$d.f.$	MS	F
BETWEEN DRUGS	45.15	2	22.575	1.820[a]
BETWEEN DISORDERS	29.45	2	14.725	2.791[a]
WITHIN	164.42	4	41.105	
TOTAL	239.02	8		

[a] Not significant at the 0.05 level; do not reject H_o.

5.

SOURCE OF VARIABILITY	SSD	$d.f.$	MS	F
BETWEEN SEXES (S)	166.272	1	166.272	2.669[a]
BETWEEN METHODS (M)	222.411	2	111.206	3.990[a]
BETWEEN LEVELS (L)	1718.044	2	859.022	1.936[a]
INTERACTIONS:				
S × M	2210.211	2	1105.106	2.490[a]
S × L	818.312	2	409.156	1.085[a]
L × M	2053.956	4	513.489	1.157[a]
S × M × L	2596.155	4	649.039	1.462[a]
WITHIN	71891.500	162	443.775	
TOTAL	81676.861	179		

[a] Not significant at the 0.05 level; do not reject H_o.

Chapter 11   PAGE 191

1. (b) $\overline{X} = 88.5$, $\overline{Y} = 66.7$, $s_y = 9.98$, $s_x = 237.64$, $b_{y.x} = 0.5816$, $s_{y.x} = 4.53$, $b_{x.y} = 1.387$; $Y_c = 15.28 + 0.5816X$, $X_c = -4.09 + 1.387Y$

(c) Part 1. Test for Linearity

SOURCE OF VARIABILITY	SSD	$d.f.$	MS	F
BETWEEN GROUPS	2331.10	1		
ABOUT REGRESSION	558.77	19	29.41	1.181[a]
WITHIN	312.67	9	34.74	
TOTAL	2889.87	29		

[a] Not significant at the 0.05 level; do not reject H_o of linearity.

Part 2. Test for Independency of Data: $t = 10.65$; reject H_o.
Part 3. $P[13.60 < A_{y.x} < 16.98] = 0.95$
Part 4. $P[0.4699 < B_{y.x} < 0.6933] = 0.95$
Part 5. $P[12.9 < \sigma^2_{y.x} < 37.5] = 0.95$

2. Both regression equations intersect at $\overline{X}$ and Y.

3. $a = 44.89$, $b_{y.x} = -0.036$

4. Table (1): $Y_c = 38.43 + 4.00X$; $Y_c = 52.43$
   Table (2): $Y_c = 200X$; $Y_c = 700$
   Table (3): $Y_c = 89.07 - 1.812X$; $Y_c = 82.724$
   Table (4): $Y_c = 1630.34 - 172.04X$; $Y_c = 1028.27$

Chapter 12 PAGE 211

1. (a) $r_{xy} = 0.015$; (b) $t = 0.079$; accept H_o; (c) $P[-0.3666 < \rho_{xy} < 0.3876] = 0.95$

2. (a) Change 80 to 81 and 67 to 68 in Test 2; (b) before change, $r_{xy} = 0.9991$

4. (a–c)

X	x	Y	y	x^2	y^2	xy
4	−2.7	0	−6	7.29	36	16.2
5	−1.7	3	−3	2.89	9	5.1
6	−0.7	5	−1	0.49	1	0.7
7	0.4	6	0	0.16	0	0.0
8	1.3	7	1	1.69	1	1.3
10	3.3	15	9	10.89	81	29.7
$\sum$ 40	−0.1	36	0	23.41	128	53.0

   (d) $r_{xy} = 0.968$; (e) $s_x^2 = 28$, $s_x = 5.29$, $s_y^2 = 153.6$, $s_y = 12.39$

5. $t = 1.85$; do not reject H_o.

6. $z = -0.352$; do not reject H_o.

7. [8.1] (a) $Y_c = -0.34 + 0.466X$; (b) $r_{xy} = 0.924$ (c) $t = 4.84$; reject H_o.
   [8.2] (a) $Y_c = 5.37 + 2.143X$; (b) $r_{xy} = 0.985$; (c) $t = 11.41$; reject H_o.

8. (a) $Y_c = 70 + 0.60(X - 60)$; (b) $Y_c = 68.8$

Chapter 15 PAGE 263

1. $r = 21$; do not reject H_o.

2. $z = -4.501$; reject H_o (underestimated).

3. $z = 0.136$; do not reject H_o (B greater).

4. $\alpha = 0.047$, max $[2.5, 1] \nless 0$, min $[-5, -5] \ngtr 0$; do not reject H_o.

INDEX

Addition Rules, simple probability, 46
Alpha error, α, 88
Analysis of covariance, 230ff
  basic assumptions in, 230
  completely randomized design, 231
  Latin square design, 237
  randomized complete block design, 234
Analysis-of-data sheet, 369
Analysis of variance, 144ff
  basic assumptions in, 144ff
  single classification, 144
    computation table, 149
  three-way classification, 163
    computation table, 165
  two-way classification, single value, 150
    computation table, 155
  two-way classification with replications, 156
    computation table, 161
Approximate numbers, 4
Arithmetic mean, 16
Assumptions, basic
  in analysis of covariance, 230ff
  in analysis of variance, 144ff
  in correlation, 196
Average deviation, 26

Bartlett's test for homoscedasticity, 123
Beta error, β, 91
Binomial coefficients, $C_{n,r}$, 52
Binomial distribution, 47
  mean of, 53
  theoretical frequencies, 49
  variance of, 53

Central tendency, measures of, 14ff
Charlier checks, 34
Chi-square distribution, 74ff
Chi-square test, 128ff
  of goodness-of-fit, 140
  of independence, 138
  one-way classification, 137
  in two-by-two tables, 139
  two-way classification, 138

Class intervals, 11
Cochran Q test, 256
Coding, 19
Coefficient of correlation, 194
  confidence interval estimate for, 208
  rank-difference, 261
Combinations, 51
Completely randomized block design, 221
Completely randomized design, analysis of covariance, 231
Components of variance, three factor classification with replications, 220
Computational procedures
  arithmetic, rules for, 6
  coefficient of correlation
    from deviations from means, 204
    from grouped data, 199
    from raw scores, 205
  completely randomized block design, 223
    analysis of covariance, 233
  expected mean square, two-way classification, fixed, 220
  Latin square design, 225
    analysis of covariance, 238
  r_{xy}
    from deviations from means, 204
    from grouped data, 199
    from raw scores, 205
  randomized complete block design, analysis of covariance, 234
  single classification analysis of variance, 149
  single value, two-way classification analysis of variance, 155
  test for linearity of data, 186
  three-way classification analysis of variance, 165
  two-factor factorial design, 228
  two-factor randomized complete block design, analysis of covariance, 240
  two-way classification with replications analysis of variance, 161
Concept of least squares, 175
Conditional probability, 47

Confidence interval estimate
  correlation coefficient, 208
  differences between two population
      means
    sigmas known, 113
    sigmas unknown, correlated data,
        114
    sigmas unknown, uncorrelated
        data, 114
  difference between two proportions,
      uncorrelated data, 132
  of ρ, 208
  ratio of two population variances,
      123
  regression
    $A_{y.x}$, 189
    $B_{y.x}$, 189
    dependent value of Y, 190
    $\mu_{y.x}$, 190
    $\sigma_{y.x}^{2}$, 190
  regression coefficients, 189
  single population mean, 105
  single population variance, 119
  single proportion, 131
Contingency table, 135, 136
Continuous data, 3
Continuous sampling distributions, 60ff
Correction for continuity, 230
Correlation
  coefficient of, 194
  linear, 193ff
  negative, 195
  positive, 195
  Spearman's rank-difference, 261
Counting numbers, 3
Covariance, 180ff
Critical region, 88
Cumulative frequency, 11
Cumulative frequency polygon, 13
Cumulative percentage frequency, 15

Data
  continuous, 3
  dichotomous, 42
  discontinuous (discrete), 3
  transformation of, 81f, 207
Decision making, statistical, rules for,
    85ff

Degrees of freedom
  Chi-square distribution, 75
  χ^{2}/d.f. distribution, 78
  F distribution, 78
  t distribution, 72, 73
Dependent variable, 172
Deviation, average, 26
Dichotomous data, 42
Discontinuous data, 3
Discrete data, 3
Dispersion, 25
Distribution
  binomial, 47
  Chi-square, 74
  of difference between two sample
      means, paired data, 71
  of enumeration data, 75
  F, 78ff
  frequency, 10
  normal, 61ff
  rectangular, 60
  of sample means, 65
  of sample variances, 77ff
  t, 72
  χ^{2}/d.f., 74
Dot frequency diagrams, 25

Equation for straight line, 174
Error
  alpha, 88
  beta, 91
  statistical, 87
  type I, 88
  type II, 91
Estimate (*See also* Confidence interval
    estimate)
  of variance, 217
Exact numbers, 4
Expected frequency, 136
Expected mean square, 217
Expected mean square values, two-way
    classification, fixed factor model,
    218
Experimental design
  analysis of covariance, 231ff
  completely randomized, 221
    analysis of covariance, 231
  factorial, 226

fixed factor, 217
Latin square, 224
  analysis of covariance, 237
mixed factor, 217
random factor, 217
randomized complete block, analysis of covariance, 234
two-factor randomized complete block, analysis of covariance, 240

F distribution, 78
Factorial design, 226
Fisher's exact probability, 139
Fisher's ζ transformation, 207
Fixed factor model, 217
Formulas
  $a_{y.x}$, 176
  $b_{y.x}$, 176
  Bartlett's test for homoscedasticity, 123
  binomial distribution, 52, 128
  Chi-square, 77
  Chi-square statistic, contingency table, $m \times n$, 136
  Cochran Q statistic, 258
  combinations, 51
  confidence interval estimate
    of $A_{y.x}$, 189
    of $B_{y.x}$, 189
    difference, two population means, 113
    difference between two proportions, uncorrelated data, 132
    of $\mu_{y.x}$, 190
    of predicted value of Y, 190
    of $\sigma^2_{y.x}$, 190
    single population
      sigma known, 105
      sigma unknown, 106
    single population variance, 119
    single proportion, 131
  difference between two means
    sigma known, 108
    sigma unknown, 109
  difference between two population means
    paired data, 71

Formulas (cont.)
  sigma known, 68
  F statistic, 78, 120
  Kruskal-Wallis, 259
    corrected for ties, 259
  linear regression
    $a_{y.x}$, 176
    $b_{y.x}$, 176
    regression factor, 176
    Y-intercept, sample data, 176
  Mann-Whitney, standard error, 250
    corrected for ties, 250
  Mann-Whitney U, 248
  mean, 16
    binomial distribution, 53
    coded data, 19
    grouped data, 18
  median, 15
  normal approximation to binomial, 129
  normal distribution, 61
  permutations, 50
  pooled proportion estimate, two population proportions, uncorrelated data, 132
  pooled variance, 109
  probability
    addition rules, 46
    multiplication rule, 46
    simple, 44
  Q, 27
  r_{xy}
    deviations from mean, 204
    grouped data, 199
    raw scores, 205
  rectangular distribution, 60
  runs test, normal approximation, 246
    standard error, 246
  sample coefficient of correlation, 198
  sample size
    alpha considered, 94
    alpha and beta considered, 96
  sample variance, paired data, 112
  semi-quartile range, 27
  Spearman's rank-difference correlation, 262
    test of significance, 263

Formulas (cont.)
standard deviation, grouped coded
data, 33
standard error of estimate
difference of two population proportions, 131
difference between two correlated
proportions, 133
linear regression, 181
two correlation coefficients, 209
standard error
sample, two populations, pooled
variance estimator, 110
sample variances, population variances not equal, 111
standardized score, normal distribution, z, 62
t statistic, test for $\rho = 0.0$, 208
t test
difference between means, 111
paired data, 73
test for differences between two coefficients of correlation, 209
test for independence of regression
variables, 188
test for linearity of data, linear regression, 186
test about values of $A_{y.x}$, 189
variance
binomial distribution, 54
definition, 28
ungrouped data, 29
Wilcoxon signed rank test, normal
approximation, 253
z statistic
differences between two proportions, uncorrelated data, 132
enumeration data, binomial, 75
logarithmic transformed data, 81
single population proportion, 130
single population proportion, correction for continuity, 130
Frequency
cumulative, 11
expected, 136
relative, 43
Frequency distributions, 10
Frequency polygons, 12

Frequency tables, 10

Goodness-of-fit, 140
Grouped frequency table, 11

Histograms, 12
Homoscedasticity, 145
Hypotheses (*See also* Tests of hypotheses)
statistical, 85

Independence, test for, 138
Interquartile range, 27
Interval scale, 3

Kruskal-Wallis technique, 258
correction for ties, 259

Latin square design, 224
analysis of covariance, 237
computation table, 238
Least squares concept, 175
Level of significance, 88
Limits (*See* Confidence interval esti-
mate)
Line of best fit, 173
Linear correlation, 193ff
basic assumptions, 185
Linear equation, 174
Linear regression, 172ff
basic assumptions, 185
sum of products and covariance, 179
Linearity of regression, 185
Logarithmic transformation of data, 81

μ, 16
$\mu_{y.x}$, 190
Mann-Whitney U test, 248
correction for ties, 250
n greater than 20, 250
normal approximation, 250
Marginal probability, 135
Marginal proportions, 136
McNemar test, 251
Mean
arithmetic, 16
binomial distribution, 53

coded data, 19
  formula, 19
  formula, 16
  grouped data, 18
    formula, 18
  ungrouped data, 16
Measurement
  scales of, 3
  units of, 4
Measures
  of central tendency, 10ff
  of variability, 25ff
Median, 13
  formula, 15
Median test, 255
Mixed factor model, 217
Mode, 14

Nominal scale, 3
Non-parametric statistical techniques,
    244ff
  Cochran Q test, 256
  correlated data
    more than two populations, Coch-
      ran Q test, 256
    Wilcoxon signed rank test, 251
  Kruskal-Wallis technique, 258
  more than two populations, indepen-
    dent data, 258
  more than two samples, 256
  single sample technique, 244
  two sample techniques, 248ff
  two samples
    correlated data, 251
      Walsh test, 253
    median test, 255
    uncorrelated data, 248
Normal approximation
  Mann-Whitney technique, 250
  runs test, 246
  Wilcoxon signed rank test, 253
Normal distribution, 61ff
  differences between two means, in-
    dependent data, 68
  sample means, 65
Numbers
  approximate, 4
  counting, 3

exact, 4
rounding, rules for, 5

Ogive, 28
Ordinal scale, 3

p (*See* Proportions)
Parameter, 2
Pearson product moment coefficient of
    correlation, r, 200
Percentile, 14
Percentile rank, 15
Permutations, 50
Polygon
  cumulative frequency, 13
  frequency, 12
Pooled variance, 109
Population, 1
  defined, 1
  finite, 2
  infinite, 2
  mean, single, confidence interval
    estimate, 105
    sigma known, 105
    sigma unknown, 106
Power curves, 98
Power of test, 97
Probability
  addition rules, 46
  conditional, 47
  defined, 42
  elementary, 42ff
  empirical, 44
  marginal, 135
  multiplication rule, 46
  normal distribution, 62
  simple, formula, 44
Proportions, 128ff
  confidence interval estimate
    for difference between two
      populations, uncorrelated
      data, 132
    for single population, 131
  distribution of
    difference between two
      populations, 132
    more than two populations,
      134–136

Proportions (cont.)
  single populations, 130
  formulas
    confidence interval estimates, 131, 132
    standard error of estimate, 131, 133
    z statistic, 130, 132
  standard error of estimate, 131–133
  tests of hypotheses about
    differences between two populations, 131, 133
    more than two populations, 134–136
    single populations, 130

Q, formula, 27
Quartile, 27

r, methods of calculation of, 199
ρ, 197, 208
Random digits, table for, 7
Random factor model, 217
Randomized complete block design, analysis of covariance, 234
Range, 26
  interquartile, 27
  semi-quartile, 27
Ratio scale, 3
Rectangular distribution, 60
Reduction of data, 1
Regression, 172
  concept of, 181
  and correlation relationship, 205
  equation for population, 174
  of X on Y, 178
  of Y on X, 172
Relative frequency, 43
Rules for computation
  addition, 6
  division, 6
  multiplication, 6
  square root, 6
  subtraction, 6
Runs test, 244
  normal approximation, 246

Σ, 16
s (*See* Standard deviation)

s^2, 28
σ^2, 28
s_p^2, 109
$s_{y.x}^2$, 180
$\sigma_{y.x}^2$, 180
Sample, 1
  defined, 2
  random, 7
Sample size, effect on alpha and beta, 92
Sampling distributions, continuous, 60ff
Scale
  interval, 3
  nominal, 3
  ordinal, 3
  ratio, 3
Scattergram, 173
Score interval, 11
Scores
  normalized, 62
  standard, 62
  T, 36
  z, 62
Semi-quartile range, 27
Sign test, 244
Significant digits, 5
Spearman's rank-difference correlation, 261
Standard deviation, 30ff
  derivation of, 34
  from grouped data, 31
    by coding, 32
Standard scores, 35
Standard error of estimate
  differences between two coefficients of correlation, 209
  differences between two correlated proportions, 133
  differences between two proportions, 131
  linear regression, 180
  of the mean, 66
  population, 66
Stanine scale, 38
Statistic, 2
Statistical errors, 87
Statistical hypotheses, steps in testing, 100

Statistical inference, 85
Student's t-distribution, 72ff
Sum of products and covariance, 179
Summation, rules of, 17
Summation notation, 16

T-scores, 36
t test, paired data, 73
Tables, list of, xv, 269
Test for goodness-of-fit, 140
Tests of statistical hypotheses, 100ff
  binomial distribution, 128
  central tendency, 104ff
  Chi-square statistic, 2×2 contingency table, 139
  coefficient of correlation, 208
  correlated data, 112
  differences among more than two proportions, 134
    double classification, 138
    single classification, 137
  differences between two correlation coefficients, 209
  differences between two means, 106
    independent data, 106
    sigmas known, 108
    sigmas unknown, 108
  differences between two proportions, correlated data, 133
  equality of more than two means, 144ff
  goodness-of-fit, 140
  homogeneity of variances, 123
  homoscedasticity, 123
  independency of data, 138
  measures of dispersion, 117ff
  normal approximation to binomial, 128
  paired data, 112
  $\rho \neq 0.0$, 209
  randomness of data, 244
  regression
    independence of variables, 188
    linear, basic assumptions, 185
    linearity of data, 185
    about values of $A_{y.x}$, 189

Tests of statistical hypotheses (cont.)
  single population mean, 104
    sigma known, 104
  single population variance, 117
  single proportion, 130
  two population proportions, 131
    uncorrelated data, 131
  two variances, 120
    value of $\mu_{y.x}$, 190
  zero order coefficient of correlation, 208
Three-way classification, 163
Transformations
  data, 81
  Fisher's ζ, 207
  logarithmic, 81
Two-factor factorial randomized complete block design, analysis of covariance, 240
Two-way classification, fixed factor model, expected mean square, 218
Type I error, 88
Type II error, 91

Universe, defined, 2

Variance, 28ff
  binomial distribution, 53
  definition, 28
  definition formula, 28
  pooled, 109
  sample, paired data, 112

Walsh test, 253
Wilcoxon signed rank test, 251
  normal approximation, 253

$\chi^2/$d.f., 74

Yates' correction factor, 139

z, 62
z score, 62